Water and
Wastewater Engineering
Volume 1. Water Supply and
    Wastewater Removal

Water and Wastewater Engineering

Volume 2. *Water Purification and Wastewater Treatment*

By the same authors with the collaboration of

Abel Wolman
Professor of Sanitary Engineering Emeritus
The Johns Hopkins University

J. Carrell Morris
Gordon McKay Professor of Sanitary Chemistry
Harvard University

C. Fred Gurnham
Professor of Civil Engineering and Chemical Engineering
Illinois Institute of Technology

Werner Stumm
Gordon McKay Professor of Applied Chemistry
Harvard University

Charles M. Weiss
Professor of Environmental Biology
The University of North Carolina at Chapel Hill

Elements of Water Supply and Waste-Water Disposal
By Gordon M. Fair and John C. Geyer
John Wiley & Sons, New York, 1958

Sewage Treatment
By Karl Imhoff and Gordon M. Fair
Second Edition, John Wiley & Sons, New York, 1956

Water and Wastewater Engineering

Volume 1. Water Supply and Wastewater Removal

GORDON MASKEW FAIR
*Abbott and James Lawrence Professor of Engineering Emeritus
and Gordon McKay Professor of Sanitary Engineering Emeritus, Harvard University*

JOHN CHARLES GEYER
Professor of Sanitary Engineering, The Johns Hopkins University

DANIEL ALEXANDER OKUN
*Professor of Sanitary Engineering
The University of North Carolina at Chapel Hill*

*With chapters on Information Analysis and Optimization
Techniques by Myron Bernard Fiering, Assistant Professor
of Engineering and Applied Mathematics, Harvard University*

JOHN WILEY & SONS, INC.   *New York London Sydney*

Library of Congress Catalog Card Number: 66-16139
Printed in the United States of America

Preface

This treatise, entitled *Water and Wastewater Engineering*, is based upon *Water Supply and Wastewater Disposal*, written by Gordon M. Fair and John C. Geyer, and published by John Wiley and Sons in 1954. Like its forerunner, the present two-volume work is a textbook in the dictionary sense: a book presenting the principles of a subject as the basis of instruction. Needless to say, principles are more durable than practices. Like its forerunner, too, the new treatise is intended for students of civil and sanitary engineering, no matter whether they belong to the student body of a university or are already established in their profession. Accordingly, it is assumed that they possess reasonable competency in mathematics and the sciences—including the engineering sciences—and an acquaintance with the salient components of civil engineering. Yet it is realized that in some of the areas of enquiry of this book a refreshment of mind may promote fruitful rapport between author and reader. To bring this about, elements of information analysis, hydrology, and hydraulics are included in Volume 1, and discussions of pertinent physical, chemical, and biological properties of water in Volume 2. Because of this, moreover, both volumes should be important also to physical and investment planners of urban and regional developments. In this sense, too, the second volume should be of interest to chemists and biologists who are students of water and the water environment.

Like other fields of engineering, water and wastewater engineering has its science, its art, and its culture. To reach the audience to which this book is addressed, the *science* of water and wastewater engineering is given principal emphasis in both volumes. However, the *art* of water and wastewater engineering is not totally neglected. Enough is said about it to keep the reader aware of the constructions that place water at the service

v

of cities and towns, and of villages and homesteads. The *culture* of water and wastewater engineering, too, is given expression. It is exemplified in the introductory chapter of each volume and in statements and footnotes scattered through the text. The intention is to present to the reader a cultural perspective of concepts and their originators and the meaning of important scientific and engineering terms. A sense of history reinforces an understanding of the present through knowledge of the past. It prepares the mind to grasp the forces of change and to direct them to the advantage of the future.

This book has been written in a time of mounting urbanization and industrialization and resulting stress on water and wastewater systems. Clean and ample sources of water for municipal uses are becoming less easy to find and more expensive to develop. Quality management of receiving waters is becoming more difficult while public demand for clean lakes and streams is becoming more persuasive. As pressures on the water resource for multipurpose development build up, competition for water between governmental jurisdictions and special interests becomes more intense. The design, construction, and operation of larger systems and the reconciliation of more complex interactions await the attention of engineers and supporting scientists as well as economists, political scientists, and urban and regional planners in cooperative and imaginative enterprise.

The title of this book—*Water and Wastewater Engineering*—advertises its intent and purpose. It recognizes that design, construction, and operation of the works by which water is supplied to cities and removed from them in wastewater systems are primarily engineering responsibilities. Even though the engineer may seek the advice of geologists, geophysicists, hydrologists, chemists, biologists, or systems analysts, no decisions are thereby taken out of his hands. Neither do consultations with architects and members of the engineering profession in the special fields of soil mechanics, structures, and water power lessen his responsibility. Even though the authors, in like manner and for similar reasons, have invited a number of colleagues to take part in the preparation of certain chapters in this book, they, too, are not relieved of responsibility for the book as a whole.

The subtitles of the two volumes suggest their content: *Water Supply and Wastewater Removal* in Volume 1, and *Water Purification and Wastewater Treatment* in Volume 2. In specific reference to Volume 1, it should be said that J. C. Geyer made Chapter 9, *Groundwater Flow*, and Chapter 10, *Groundwater Supplies*, his principal concern; and that D. A. Okun did so for Chapter 18, *Engineering Projects*. Authorship of Chapter 4, *Information Analysis*, and Chapter 17, *Optimization Techniques*, by M. B. Fiering is specified on the title page. Preparation of the remaining chapters and general editorship were assumed by the senior author.

In writing this volume we have made free use of materials included in *Water Supply and Wastewater Disposal.* As members of university departments of sanitary engineering at Harvard, Hopkins, and Chapel Hill, furthermore, we cannot fail to be under heavy obligation to colleagues in these departments. Our colleagues have, indeed, shared the burden of producing this book. To the names of individuals who have written chapters of their own should be added those of Dr. H. A. Thomas, Jr. (at Harvard) and Dr. Robert S. Gemmell (now at Northwestern University). Search for information on the *History of Hydraulics* has led repeatedly to the authoritative book with this title by Hunter Rouse and Simon Ince, Iowa Institute of Hydraulics Research, Iowa City, 1957; search for information on the biography of scientists has brought us to the four-volume edition of *The Harper Encyclopedia of Science,* edited by James R. Newman, Harper and Row, New York and Evanston, 1963.

A book does not come off the press through the efforts of authors alone. Its preparation begins with the typescript and passes successively through editorial and production stages. To all who have guided our efforts along these ways, we are warmly grateful. To single out but one name might seem unfair, yet it would be wrong not to cite the name of Irja E. Hutchinson, who typed the manuscript for this book and for its forerunner.

A book is not written in long evenings and on holidays without the consent, encouragement, and cooperation of the writer's family. This, too, should be a matter of record.

Gordon M. Fair
John C. Geyer
Daniel A. Okun

March 1966

Contents

CHAPTER 1

Water in the Service of Cities

1-1 Social and Engineering Challenge

The planning, design, financing, construction, and operation of modern urban water and wastewater systems are complex undertakings. Although each water and wastewater scheme, by its very nature, must be uniquely conceived, its execution asks for public procedure, information, and decision, and for materials, equipment, and technological support that can be provided fully only within the framework of a highly developed governmental and social structure and a strong and diverse industrial community. In many of its aspects, therefore, the important factor is not so much one of engineering enterprise, unique as that may be, as of political, social, and industrial maturity.

Even in its most specific sense as an engineering enterprise, satisfactory development of water and wastewater schemes depends upon demographic, hydrologic, geodetic, and geologic information that can be made available only by decades of institutionalized, orderly observation, recording, and analysis. Furthermore, the competitive position of developments of urban water and wastewater, as but one of a number of essential uses of water, must be legally, hygienically, esthetically, and economically defined. To safeguard the public interest, there must be public control as well as public promotion of essential works through public-health authorities, water-resource commissions, public works or public-utility organizations, and quasi-public or self-regulatory agencies. Moreover, there must be support from teaching, research, and professional institutions deeply concerned with the advancement of the underlying sciences and technologies. Nor should one underestimate the contributions of imaginative planners and practitioners, of responsible manufacturers of water and wastewater equipment, and of superintendent managers who keep the water utilities running and their books in balance.

The opening chapter of this treatise will give emphasis to water-quality management, because a concern for the fitness of water and for its safety, attractiveness, and economic usefulness distinguishes water supply and wastewater removal from other hydraulic undertakings in the development of the water resource. An awareness of quality inheres in underlying hydrological studies, in hydraulic and structural designs giving form to necessary engineering works, and in the operation of completed systems. If water quality were not controlled in this sense, works supplying water and disposing of wastewaters would fail of their purpose. If quality control becomes a prime objective, it lends substance to Pindar's words,[1] "best of all things is water."

The planning, design, construction, and supervision of water and wastewater systems have long been the responsibility of civil engineers. Needed skills in water-resource development are possessed in largest measure by this oldest group of engineering practitioners.

That cholera, typhoid fever, and other enteric infections could be transmitted through drinking water and that sewage often contained the causative agents of disease were not discovered until the middle of the nineteenth century or scientifically confirmed until the end of that century. Eventually, too, the evolving physical and natural sciences suggested ways for preventing the transmission of common waterborne diseases and otherwise insuring the safety, palatability, and economic usefulness of water. At the same time, the behavior of wastewater flowing from communities and industries was explored, and it became possible to protect receiving bodies of water against contamination and pollution.[2]

Civil engineers with an understanding of water-quality management became known as *sanitary engineers*; but they were also called *public health* or *environmental health engineers*, especially when they were attached to departments of public health for the administration of engineering programs affecting the public health and well-being. Water control is such a program.

[1] *ariston men hudor*, from an ode written in 460 B.C.
[2] By convention, water contamination is considered to be the introduction or release into water of pathogenic organisms or toxic substances that render it unfit for human consumption or domestic use. In like sense, water pollution is held to be the introduction into water of substances that impair its usefulness or make it offensive to the senses of sight, taste, or smell. Contamination may and often does accompany pollution.

1-2   Community Water Supply and Disposal

Water is introduced into municipalities for many purposes: (1) for drinking and culinary uses; (2) for washing, bathing, and laundering; (3) for cleaning windows, walls, and floors; (4) for heating and air conditioning; (5) for watering lawns and gardens; (6) for sprinkling and cleaning streets; (7) for filling swimming and wading pools; (8) for display in fountains and cascades; (9) for producing hydraulic and steam power; (10) for employment in numerous and varied industrial processes; (11) for protecting life and property against fire; and (12) for removing offensive and potentially dangerous wastes from household (sewage) and industry (industrial wastewaters). To provide for these varying uses, which total about 100 gallons per capita per day (gpcd) in average North American *residential* communities and 150 gpcd or more in large *industrial* cities, the supply of water must be satisfactory in quality and adequate in quantity, readily available to the user, relatively cheap, and easily disposed of after it has served its many purposes. Necessary engineering works are water works, or water-supply systems, and wastewater works, or wastewater-disposal systems.[3]

Water works withdraw water from natural sources of supply, purify it if necessary, and deliver it to the consumer. Wastewater works collect the spent water of the community—about 70% of the water supplied—together with varying amounts of entering ground and surface waters. In many older places, for reasons explained later, sewage continues to be discharged to systems of drains intended also for removal of surface runoff from rainstorms and melting snow or ice. This is called *combined* sewerage. However, in most young places, sewage and runoff are each remanded to their own separate systems of sanitary sewers and storm drains in order to avoid pollution of water courses by occasional spills of sewage and stormwater mixtures. This is called *separate* sewerage. The collected wastewaters are treated and discharged, usually into a natural drainage channel; more rarely onto land. Often the receiving body of water continues to serve also as a source of important water supplies for many purposes. It is this multiple use of natural waters that creates the most impelling reasons for sound water-quality management.

The interdependence of water supply and wastewater disposal is the more pronounced the greater the regional urbanization and the farther advanced its general and sanitary economy. The connecting link between

---

[3] Strictly, the terms *sewage works* and *sewerage systems* are more limited in concept than the terms *wastewater works* and *wastewater-disposal systems*. Quite generally, however, they are employed to describe the collection and disposal of stormwater runoff as well as sewage and industrial wastewaters.

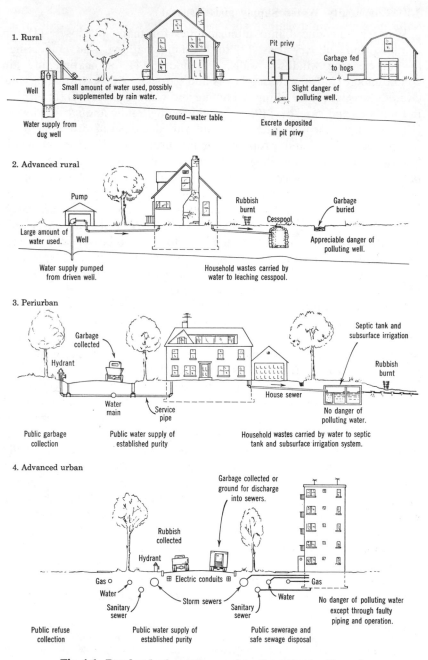

Fig. 1-1. Rural and urban water supply and wastewater disposal.

water supply and wastewater disposal is the system of water and waste-water piping within dwellings, commercial establishments, and industries. More often than not the collection of solid refuse is an independent undertaking. Exceptions are the grinding of garbage and its discharge into sewers and the operation of refuse incinerators in conjunction with sewage-treatment works. Figure 1-1 illustrates, from the householder's point of view, the progress from individualistic practices of rural populations to communal services of urban dwellers. Associated problems of water-quality management are indicated.

1-3 Historical Factors

As suggested, with felicity, by Reginald Reynolds:[4] "Sanitation has its history, its archeology, its literature, and its science. Most religions concern themselves with it, sociology includes it within its sphere, and its study is imperative to social ethics. Some knowledge of psychology is necessary to understand its development and retardation, an esthetic sense is required for its full appreciation, [and] economics determine, to a large degree, its growth and extent . . . . Whoever, indeed, would study this subject with a knowledge worthy of its magnitude must consider it from all angles and with a . . . wealth of learning."

The story of water supply and disposal begins with the growth of ancient capital cities, or religious and trade centers. Constructed as works of considerable magnitude and complexity, their remnants are monuments to sound, yet daring, feats of early engineers. Especially notable are the aqueducts and sewers of Rome and her colonial dependencies.[5]

However, purposeful quality control of water supply and wastewater disposal is quite recent in origin. It, too, begins with the growth of cities, in this instance factory towns emerging from the industrial revolution of the nineteenth century. The scientific discoveries and engineering inventions of the eighteenth and nineteenth centuries created centralized industries to which people flocked for employment. The standard of living of great numbers of men was thereby improved; but lack of community organization soon created slums through which the apocalyptic

[4] Reginald Reynolds, *Cleanliness and Godliness*, George Allen and Unwin, London, 1943, p. 4.
[5] Sextus Julius Frontinus, water commissioner of Rome, A.D. 97, reported the existence of nine aqueducts supplying water to Rome and varying in length from 10 to over 50 miles and in cross-section from 7 to over 50 sq ft. Clemens Herschel (1842–1930), inventive hydraulic engineer (Venturi meter) and translator of classical manuscripts (*Frontinus and the Water Supply of the City of Rome*, Longmans, Green and Co., New York, 1913), estimated the aggregate capacity of the aqueducts at 84 mgd. The great sewer, known as the *cloaca maxima* and constructed to drain the Roman Forum, is still in service.

horsemen of pestilence and death rode with rein unchecked. The community facilities of the mushrooming industrial cities were soon overtaxed. The need for abundant distribution of safe water and for effective disposal of human excrement and other wastes could not be met. Water was drawn from polluted rivers or shallow wells in crowded sections of the community and "distributed in courts by standpipes on intermittent days. The fatigue of fetching it was so great that they (the inhabitants of the courts) only used it for purposes which they deemed of absolute necessity, such as cooking; they rarely bestowed much of it on their clothes or persons."[6]

Although cities had for centuries been provided with drainage systems, they had been built to carry away the runoff from storms. Discharge of fecal and other wastes into them was forbidden well into the nineteenth century. Before that time the use of existing drains for waste disposal had been clandestine only.[7] Until sanitary sewerage became an accepted method of municipal cleansing, "many dwellings of the poor were arranged round narrow courts having no other opening to the main street than a narrow covered passage. In these courts there were several occupants, each of whom accumulated a heap. In some cases, each of these heaps was piled up separately in the court, with a general receptacle in the middle for drainage. In others a pit was dug in the middle of the court for the general use of all the occupants. In some the whole courts up to the very doors of the houses were covered with filth."[8] In the great cities of the world, all too many people lived in basements and cellars. "In very many cases the vaults and privies were situated on the same or a higher level, and their contents frequently oozed through walls into the occupied apartments beside them."[9] The privies themselves were often "too small in size and too few in number, and without ventilation or seat covers."[9]

The admission of human excrement to existing storm drains seemed to offer a cheap and ready way out of this hygienic and esthetic dilemma. Combined sewers, so called because they carried both stormwater and sewage, were the result, and the early drainage works of most metropolitan areas followed this scheme even when their drains were newly constructed. Justifiably, the original storm drains had been built to terminate in

[6] *First Report of the Metropolitan Sanitary Commission*, London, 1848.
[7] That storms helped to cleanse cities superficially can be judged from Jonathan Swift's description of a London shower of October 1710: "Now from all parts the swelling kennels flow, and bear their trophies with them as they go: Filth of all hues and odour, seem to tell what street they sail'd from, by their sight and smell."
[8] *Report from the Poor Law Commissioners on an Inquiry into the Sanitary Conditions of the Labouring Population of Great Britain*, 1842, *Local Reports*, p. 2. (In this quotation, the past tense replaces the present tense of the original.)
[9] *Report of the Council of Hygiene and Public Health of the Citizens' Association of New York upon the Sanitary Condition of the City*, 1865. (In this quotation, too, the past tense replaces the present tense of the original.)

nearby rivers, lakes, and tidal estuaries. However, when domestic wastes were also emptied into these bodies of water, their receiving capacity for organic matter was, more often than not, overtaxed. The nuisances, so happily removed from dwellings by water carriage of waste matters, were now transferred to the water courses of the region. First the smaller and then the larger bodies of water began to "seethe and ferment under a burning sun, in one vast open *cloaca*,"[10] and "large (surrounding) territories were at once, and frequently, enveloped in an atmosphere of stench so strong as to arouse the sleeping, terrify the weak, and nauseate and exasperate everybody."[11]

To remedy conditions of this kind, many of the smaller streams were covered and converted into sewers; but the larger bodies of water remained open to view and sensory disapprobation, until the discharge of waste matters into them was cut down, either by interception of the dry-weather flow and treatment of the collected wastewaters or by construction of separate systems of sanitary sewers and storm drains.

The men who prodded the social conscience and aroused the sanitary consciousness of the people and their representatives in government included doctors, lawyers, engineers, writers, and statesmen.[12] Notable among them was Sir Edwin Chadwick, by training a lawyer, by calling a crusader for health.[13] Communities are indebted to him for his general contributions to the advancement of public health; engineers for his specific interest in sanitary works, including advocacy of small tile sewers and separate systems of sewerage. Separation he epitomized in the slogan "the rain to the river and the sewage to the soil." Closely associated with Chadwick was Sir John Simon, first Medical Officer of Health of London.[14] In the United States the counterparts of Chadwick and Dr. Simon were played by Lemuel Shattuck of Boston and Dr. Stephen Smith of New York.[15]

[10] William Budd, *Typhoid Fever*, 1873, relative to the condition of the Thames River during the hot months of 1858 and 1859.

[11] E. C. Clark, *Report on the Main Drainage Works of the City of Boston*, 1885, quoting excerpts from one of the Annual Reports of the Board of Health.

[12] Among writers, Charles Dickens, in commenting upon the slums of London at a public meeting in 1850, said that he "knew of many places in London unsurpassed in the accumulated horrors of their neglect by the *dirtiest* old spots in the *dirtiest* old towns under the *worst* old governments in Europe."

[13] His was the chief voice in the *Report from the Poor Law Commissioners on an Inquiry into the Sanitary Conditions of the Labouring Population of Great Britain*, 1842.

[14] Author of *English Sanitary Institutions* (1860).

[15] Shattuck was the principal author of the *Report of the Sanitary Commission of Massachusetts* (1850), which led years later to the creation of the Massachusetts State Board of Health (1869). This Board established an engineering division in 1886 and assigned to it the task of protecting the purity of inland waters. Stephen Smith was responsible for the *Report of the Council of Hygiene and Public Safety of the Citizens' Association of New York upon the Sanitary Condition of the City* (1865). The revelations of this document forced the passage of the Metropolitan Health Law (1866).

The researches of two medical authorities grace this period, aptly called the Great Sanitary Awakening: those of Dr. John Snow who, in 1849, demonstrated to a world, not yet blessed by the discoveries of Louis Pasteur, the role of fecal pollution of drinking water in the epidemicity of cholera; and those of Dr. William Budd, who from 1857 onward investigated typhoid fever, its nature, mode of spreading, and prevention.

Among engineers, James Simpson,[16] in 1829, built sizable filters for the Chelsea Water Company to improve its supply from the Thames River: Sir Robert Rawlinson, Superintendent Inspector of the General Board of Health (1848), conducted engineering studies for sanitary works in industrial Britain; Sir John Bazalgette started the main drainage of London in 1850; and John Roe accepted Chadwick's suggestion to construct sewer lines of vitrified tile pipe. In similar functions in the United States, Julius W. Adams, in 1857, designed the first comprehensive system of sewerage for Brooklyn, N.Y.; James P. Kirkwood, in 1871, built the first sizable water filters at Poughkeepsie, N.Y.; and Hiram F. Mills, in 1886, as the engineer member of the Massachusetts State Board of Health, gave direction to its newly formed engineering division and caused its work to be supported and advanced by the sanitary researches of the Lawrence Experiment Station of the Board.

Other historical developments in water supply and wastewater disposal are touched upon later in this treatise in connection with individual subject matters.

1-4 Sanitation of Water Supplies

To meet modern quality requirements, water supplies must be wholesome and palatable, attributes that are intertwined. If water is not attractive to the senses of sight, taste, and smell—if it disgusts the consumer—people will shun it and either drink amounts insufficient to meet physiological needs or resort to waters pleasant to the senses, but possibly unsafe.

To be wholesome, water must be free from disease organisms, poisonous substances, and excessive amounts of mineral and organic matter. To be palatable, it must be significantly free from color, turbidity, taste, and odor, of moderate temperature in summer and winter, and well aerated. (See Vol. 2, Chap. 19, of this book.)

1-5 Water-Quality Control

Water-quality control enters into every phase of technical water-works management. It starts with the preparation, supervision, and maintenance

[16] The first water filter was actually constructed in 1804 by John Gibb at Paisley in Scotland.

of catchment areas or sources of supply; follows conduits through purification works into distribution systems; and terminates only at household fixtures and manufacturing equipment to which water is supplied. Each part of the works has its own problems of control; for all parts, eternal vigilance is the price of safety.

Source of Supply.   A naturally clean water comes only from a clean source or watershed. Water-works managers, therefore, should be thoroughly familiar with the catchment area of their supply or, if there are large streams and lakes as well as groundwater works, with reaches of the watershed within significant distances from the source. Watersheds should be visited at all seasons of the year and under all conditions of weather—during summer and winter and during drought and flood. Only in this way can fitful or obscure hazards to water quality be uncovered and removed. Much can be done by sanitation of the catchment area, drainage of swamps, prevention of soil erosion, reforestation and afforestation, proper farming practices (contour plowing), disciplined use of pesticides, suitable preparation of reservoir sites in advance of filling, control of water weeds and plankton (algae), and shifting depths of draft. Regulation and supervision of recreational activities—camping, picnicking, swimming, boating, and fishing—as well as lumbering and ice harvesting, are other facets of the problem. Protection of the source of supply during construction, additions, and repairs may be a large responsibility.

Purification.   Modern water-purification works can be elaborated in great variety to meet community needs and wants. Regardless of raw-water quality, effluents of desired safety, clarity, and chemical composition can be produced by suitable treatment methods. However, it may be well for engineers to remember that man is fundamentally attuned to water that has been distilled by the sun. So long as there are uncertainties in our understanding of possible adverse effects of pollutants, it would seem wise to search for naturally clean water whenever practicable and to keep it clean for human consumption. Economic considerations should remain secondary to hygienic and esthetic requirements.

All surface waters and many groundwaters should be disinfected even when they appear to be clean and presumably safe in their natural state or following treatment. However, this injunction does not imply delivering a dilute disinfectant to the consumer on the last tap of the distribution system.

Transmission and Distribution.   Masonry and metal structures conducting water to communities and consumers may be attacked by the water they convey and, in turn, change its quality. Accordingly, it should be within the responsibility and power of designers to adjust the materials employed to the quality of the water carried and within the responsibility and power of operators to adjust the quality of the water conveyed to the materials employed. Suitable treatment will hold in check the corrosion of metals and disintegration of cement and concrete.

No conduit should go into service, upon installation, or be returned to service, after repair or exposure to contamination by an unusual drop in system pressure, until it has been thoroughly disinfected. Of equal hygienic importance are (1) the control and elimination of cross-connections of the public supply with polluted or otherwise unsafe private supplies (Figs. 2-9 and 2-10) and (2) the prevention in plumbing systems of

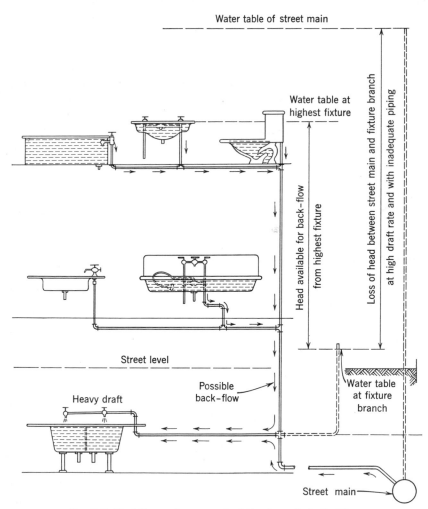

Fig. 1-2. Backflow and common backflow hazards in dwellings.

backflow or siphonage of polluted waters from fixtures and other portions of the drainage system into the pure-water piping of buildings (Fig. 1-2). To these purposes water purveyors should have the right to regulate and inspect water piping on private property or to cooperate with other duly constituted authorities in doing so.

In poorly proportioned or heavily corroded plumbing systems, pressures may drop so low that high-lying (upper-story) fixtures run dry when water is being drawn rapidly below. The resulting vacuum or negative pressure may then pull contaminated or polluted water into the system from fixtures not protected against backflow (see Fig. 1-2). Negative pressures (pressures below atmospheric) may be created also when street mains break or are emptied rapidly for inspection and repairs, or when water is pumped from hydrants at excessively high rates in the excitement of fire fighting. To prevent this kind of vacuum, which may collapse hot-water boilers, check valves are sometimes installed in distribution systems at or near the terminus of service pipes on the building side of water meters (Fig. 2-11).

Chlorine or ammonia-chlorine residuals keep down bacterial growths in distribution systems and so imply a clean bill of health, but it is quite improbable that normally used residuals can neutralize *slugs of pollution* discharged into systems from within. At best, such residuals serve as traveling sentinels of safety. Their disappearance should alert water authorities to possible dangers.

1-6 Sanitation of Wastewater Disposal

That water supply and wastewater disposal are interrelated community assets has been pointed out before. However, the safety and palatability of its water supply involve only the selfish concern of the community served; the sanitary disposal of its wastewaters is an exercise in mature altruism and solicitude for the safety and comfort of others. Because of this difference, it has generally been necessary to reinforce the sanitation of receiving bodies of water through judicial as well as legislative, advisory, and regulatory functions of government.

To fulfill the requirements of water-quality management, wastewater-disposal systems must perform two functions: (1) reliable and inoffensive collection of waste matters and (2) safe disposal of suitably treated waste-waters into receiving bodies of water or onto land. Otherwise, as happened in early drainage works, the collection system merely shifts hazards and nuisances longitudinally from the immediate premises of dwellings and industrial establishments to regional drainage channels. By contrast, runoff from rainstorms and from melting ice and snow creates relatively few sanitary hazards when it is collected in rigidly separate storm-drainage systems.

1-7 Objectionable Properties of Wastewaters

Much of our interest in wastewater disposal stems from the primitive warnings of our senses that decay means danger; and so it may for food. However, the odors of decomposing sewage matters and industrial wastes, once called sewer gases and supposedly inimical to man, do not, in fact, produce infection, even though some emanations from sewers and sewage tanks are toxic. Hydrogen sulfide, one of the many odoriferous products of anaerobic decomposition of sewage, is an example of a toxic gas. Because flammable as well as toxic gases, including illuminating gas from distribution mains, may seep into manholes, sewers, and appurtenant underground structures, workmen descending into them should include in their operating routine reasonable precautions against asphyxiation in the absence of needed oxygen and against poisoning and explosion.

It is probable that every category of infectious or parasitic agent of human disease has been introduced into sewage at one time or another. Whether the organisms issue from the intestinal or urinary tract, respiratory system, or outer surface of his body, the habits of civilized man are such that his excretions, secretions, and ablutions are committed to sewerage systems. Yet the number of diseases with widespread transmission through sewage is relatively small. Modes of transmission and routes of infection are ordinarily well defined, although often quite devious.

Although the unsightliness of sewage and industrial wastes is of no direct hygienic significance, it is objectionable and should be taken into account in the design and operation of wastewater-disposal systems. Unsightliness is particularly important when it interferes with the recreational or esthetic enjoyment of rivers, lakes, and estuaries because waste matters are emptied into them.

1-8 Control of Wastewater Quality

The sanitary management of wastewaters enters into every phase of technical wastewater disposal. It starts, where water supply ends, at fixtures or appurtenances through which wastewater is emptied into sewers, follows the collecting system through the treatment works, and terminates only after streams or other bodies of receiving water have been returned to wanted purity or lost themselves in the oceans.

In addition to the spreading of disease, the pollution of receiving waters may cause (1) physical, chemical, and biological deterioration of water supplies, bathing places, shellfish layings, and ice supplies; (2) conditions offensive to sight and smell; (3) destruction of food fish and other valuable aquatic life; (4) enrichment of the nutrient content of ponds and lakes (eutrophication) leading to the degradation and eventual death of such receiving bodies of water; and (5) other impairment of the enjoyment and usefulness of natural waters for recreation, agriculture, commerce, or industry.

Collection.   Within the system of branching drains that compose underground schemes for urban cleansing, waste matters should flow steadily and rapidly to the point of disposal. The system should be self-cleansing, self-ventilating, frost-resistant, and hydraulically tight. Within buildings of every kind, foul air and sewage liquids should not seep from the drains and stacks of plumbing systems. Neither should roaches and other vermin find shelter or convenient routes of travel through them.

Before the introduction of preformed joints, many tile and masonry sewers lost some liquid to surrounding soils and took in some groundwater. Both exchanges are undesirable. Their elimination or control is economically justifiable, especially when outward leakage endangers water supply or inward seepage surcharges sewers. Modern sewer-pipe materials and methods of laying ensure tightness in hazardous situations; and underdrains left in place after construction reduce seepage but may pollute water courses into which they empty.

In combined systems of sewerage, some sewage and industrial wastes are bound to escape with flood runoff through stormwater overflows. Although the amounts so released seldom exceed 5% of the annual flow of sewage and industrial wastes when intercepters are designed to carry the maximum dry-weather flow (close to twice the average dry-weather flow), the ensuing pollution and contamination of receiving waters and bathing beaches may be heavy. This is an important reason why public health authorities prefer separate to combined systems. Another reason is that catch basins often breed mosquitoes, some of them possible vectors of viral infections such as dengue and yellow fever and protozoal infections such as malaria and filariasis. Hydraulic and economic considerations also enter into the choice of system.

Treatment.   Although modern wastewater-treatment works can meet most any specified performance requirements, actual choice of processes and works is a matter of hygiene, esthetics, and economy. Basically, wastewater-treatment plants should be integrated into general plans for optimal exploitation of regional water resources. Under increasingly rarer conditions, treatment may be omitted; in more usual circumstances, treatment may aim for full protection of receiving waters against obvious impairment of their usefulness; almost never does treatment have to be so complete that the effluent approaches drinking water in quality.

Chadwick's advice that sewage be discharged to the soil implies putting its fertilizing constituents to use.[17] However, agricultural dispersal of sewage or end products of sewage treatment presents many sanitary hazards and few compensating benefits. Sewage is valuable principally as irrigation water, and especially valuable, therefore, in semiarid regions which cannot be supplied more cheaply from other sources. Nevertheless, the complete but safe use of community wastes is a continuing challenge and a problem that awaits a better solution than it has received so far.

Disposal. In the absence of full consumptive use by irrigation, wastewater will eventually reach regional drainage channels. Although the resulting fusion with natural waters is called disposal by dilution, it is more than mere physical dispersal of dissolved and suspended waste matters and living organisms in additional volumes of water. It is also the marshaling of important natural or self-purifying powers in receiving waters. These manifest themselves as biological degradation and stabilization of waste organic substances and as die-away of pathogenic organisms both within flowing waters and bottom deposits laid down by them. Given enough time and favorable conditions, even heavily polluted waters are returned to the standards of clean surface waters in nature.[18]

The pollutional loading of receiving waters is circumscribed in an engineering sense by their capacity for self-purification. In a balanced natural economy wastewater treatment and self-purification combine optimally to preserve the usefulness of receiving waters. Groundwaters, too, purify themselves. The forces at work, though similar in kind to those in surface waters, are of different intensity. Filtration through fine-textured but porous geological formations normally produces the most potent effects.

1-9 Engineering Accomplishment

How acceptable good water is to communities long without it is illustrated by the celebration on Boston Common when a new supply of water was brought in from Lake Cochituate in 1848. For the event, a

[17] Recommending the application of the sewage and night soil of Paris to farms along the Seine, Victor Hugo (in *Les Misérables*) puts a question and answers it: "Do you know what those piles of ordure are, heaped at the corners of streets, those carts of dung carried off at night from the streets, the frightful barrels of the night-soil man, and the fetid streams of subterranean sewage which the pavement hides from you? All this is a flowering field, it is green grass, it is mint, thyme, and sage; it is game, it is cattle, it is the satisfied lowing of well-fed kine; at night it is perfumed hay, it is golden wheat, it is bread on your table, it is warm blood in your veins, it is health, it is joy, it is life."
[18] Thereby answering the question put by Samuel Taylor Coleridge during a visit to Cologne near the end of the eighteenth century: "The river Rhine, it is well known, doth wash your city of Cologne; but tell me, nymphs, what power divine shall henceforth wash the river Rhine?"

a poem by James Russell Lowell began as follows: "My name is Water: I have sped through strange, dark ways, untried before, by pure desire of friendship led, Cochituate's ambassador; he sends four royal gifts by me, long life, health, peace, and purity."

In similar praise, Stobart[19] has said of house drainage: "There is no truer sign of civilization and culture than good sanitation. It goes with refined senses and orderly habits. A good drain implies as much as a beautiful statue. And let it be remembered that the world did not reach the Minoan[20] standard of cleanliness again until the great sanitary movement of the late nineteenth century."

Unfortunately, there is no ready measure of human comfort and well-being, whereas sickness and death are recordable in figures, even though the reporting of illness is seldom complete, and diagnoses, except in epidemics, are often uncertain. Morbidity (case) and mortality (death) rates are commonly expressed as the annual number of cases or deaths from a specific disease within a given region or community per 100,000 population. The ratio of deaths to cases is the case fatality. In water-quality management not only these annual rates but also the number of outbreaks of waterborne disease and their causes are of interest (Vol.2, Chap. 19).

1-10   Examples

The accomplishments of water-quality control are best exemplified for water supply, for which cause and effect are usually quite clear. For wastewater this is not so, because there can be no sewerage without water supply and the results of sewerage are masked by the results of water supply. For discernible effects, we must look, instead, at the record of enteric disease in rural and urban areas. To this purpose Leach and Maxcy[21] recorded the rates of typhoid fever per 100,000 population in communities of different sizes or types, shown in Table 1-1. These statistics they interpreted as showing relatively good sanitary protection (1) in rural areas because of lack of contact and (2) in larger communities because of good community sanitation, including both water supply and wastewater disposal.

An example of what can be accomplished by the introduction and intelligent management of public water supplies is offered by the Commonwealth of Massachusetts. In this state an engineering division was

---

[19] J. C. Stobart, *The Glory That Was Greece* (revised by F. N. Pryce), Appleton-Century Co., New York, 1935, p. 29.

[20] Named after King Minos of Crete. According to archeologists, his palace of Knossos contained bathrooms, a latrine flushed by rainwater, and tile drains.

[21] C. N. Leach and K. F. Maxcy, The Relative Incidence of Typhoid Fever in Cities, Towns, and Country Districts of a Southern State, *Public Health Rept.*, **41,** 705 (1926).

Table 1-1 Typhoid Fever and Size or Type of Community

Morbidity = cases per 100,000 population

Size or type	rural	500–1000	1000–2500	2500–5000
Morbidity	52	443	307	180
Size	5000–10,000	10,000–25,000		> 25,000
Morbidity	165	118		63

organized in 1886 (Sec. 1-3) "to protect the purity of inland waters." Among its accomplishments was an increase in public water supplies and with it the striking reduction in typhoid fever portrayed in Fig. 1-3.

An observation that should be made in the interest of developing countries is that the introduction of water supplies imposes a peculiarly heavy responsibility on water authorities for strict and effective supervision of water quality. Otherwise, drinking water may become the disseminator of enteric infections in large-scale epidemics such as occurred in North America during the second half of the nineteenth century.

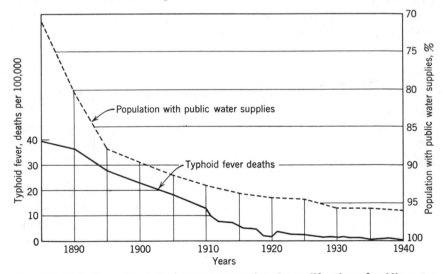

Fig. 1-3. Reduction of typhoid fever accompanying the proliferation of public water supplies in the Commonwealth of Massachusetts. (After *Whipple and Horwood*.)

Important, too, is the realization that epidemics of enteric infections like typhoid fever leave large numbers of chronic carriers in their wake. What we should deduce from American experience is that a rising tide of waterborne disease must have preceded the flood crest of typhoid fever and its subsequent reduction through the careful management of public water supplies during the first half of the twentieth century.

CHAPTER 2

Water Systems

2-1 General Features

Each section of this chapter offers, in a sense, a preview of matters discussed at length in later parts of this treatise. There they are dealt with as isolated topics to be mastered in detail. Here they appear in sequence as parts of the whole in order that their general purpose and significance in the scheme of things may be understood and may give reason for closer study.

Municipal water systems generally comprise (1) collection works, (2) purification works, (3) transmission works, and (4) distribution works. The relative functions and positions of these components in a surface-water supply are sketched in Fig. 2-1. Collection works either tap a source continuously adequate in volume for present and reasonable future demands or convert an intermittently insufficient source into a continuously adequate supply. To ensure adequacy, seasonal and, in high developments, even annual surpluses must be stored for use in times of insufficiency. When the quality of the water collected is not satisfactory, purification works are introduced to render it suitable for the purposes it must serve: contaminated water is disinfected; esthetically displeasing water made attractive and palatable; water containing iron or manganese deferrized or demanganized; corrosive water deactivated; and hard water softened. Transmission works convey the collected and purified supply to the community, where distribution works dispense it to consumers in wanted volume at adequate pressure. Ordinarily, the water delivered is metered so that an equable charge can be made for its use and often also, for its disposal after use.

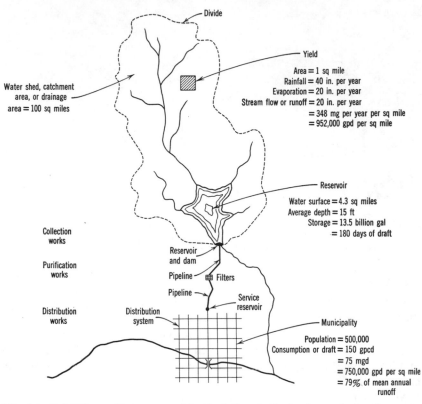

Fig. 2-1. Rainfall, runoff, storage, and draft relations in the development of surface-water supplies.

2-2   Required Capacity

Water-supply systems are designed to meet community needs for a reasonable number of years in the future. Rate of consumption is normally expressed as the mean annual use in gallons per capita daily (gpcd), and seasonal, monthly, daily, and hourly departures in rate are given in percentages of the mean. In North America the spread in consumption is large: from 35 to 500 gpcd, varying radically with industrial water demands. Average rates between 100 and 200 gpcd are common, and a generalized average of 150 gpcd is a useful guide to normal requirements.

The capacity of individual system components is set by what is expected of them. Distribution systems, for example, must be large enough to combat and control serious conflagrations without failing to supply maximum coincident domestic and industrial drafts. Fire demands vary with size and value of properties to be protected and are normally a function of the gross size of the community. The distribution system leading to the high-value district of an average American city of 100,000 people, for example, must have an excess of *fire stand-by* capacity equal in itself to the average rate of draft. For smaller or large American communities, the stand-by capacity falls or rises, within certain limits, more or less in proportion to the square root of the population.

2-3 Sources of Supply

The source of water commonly determines the nature of the collection, purification, transmission, and distribution works. Common sources of fresh water and their development are:

1. Rainwater.[1]
    (a) From roofs, stored in cisterns, for small individual supplies.
    (b) From larger, prepared watersheds, or *catches*, stored in reservoirs, for large communal supplies.
2. Surface water.
    (a) From streams, natural ponds, and lakes of sufficient size, by continuous draft.
    (b) From streams with adequate flood flows, by intermittent, seasonal, or selective draft of clean flood waters, and their storage in reservoirs adjacent to the streams, or otherwise readily accessible from them.
    (c) From streams with low dry-weather flows but sufficient annual discharge, by continuous draft through storage of necessary flows in excess of daily use in one or more reservoirs impounded by dams thrown across the stream valleys.
3. Groundwater.
    (a) From natural springs.
    (b) From wells.
    (c) From infiltration galleries, basins, or cribs.
    (d) From wells, galleries, and, possibly, springs, with flows augmented from some other source (1) spread on the surface of the gathering ground, (2) carried into charging basins or ditches, or (3) led into diffusion galleries or wells.
    (e) From wells or galleries with flows maintained by returning to the ground, water previously withdrawn from the same aquifer for cooling or similar purposes.

On board ship and in arid lands where fresh water is not immediately available, salt or brackish water may have to be supplied for all but drinking and culinary uses. Ships usually carry drinking water in tanks, but they often produce fresh water also by evaporation of seawater. Where there is no fresh water for community supply, it is either hauled in by road, rail, or water, or produced as a whole or in part by desalinizing

[1] Strictly speaking, rainwater is collected as surface runoff.

salt or brackish waters. Mildly saline waters are desalted most economically by electrodialysis; strongly saline waters by evaporation and condensation.

Municipal supplies may be derived from more than one source, the yields of available sources ordinarily being combined before distribution. Dual public water supplies of unequal quality are unusual in North America. However, they do exist; for example, as a high-grade supply for general municipal uses and a low-grade supply for specific industrial purposes or fire fighting. Unless the low-grade (nonpotable) supply is rigorously disinfected, its existence is frowned upon by health authorities because it may be cross-connected,[2] wittingly or unwittingly, with the high-grade (potable) supply.

2-4 Rainwater

Rain is rarely the immediate provenance of municipal water supplies.[3] Instead, the capture of rainwater is confined to farms and rural settlements usually in semiarid regions devoid of satisfactory ground or surface waters. On homesteads, rainwater running off roofs is led through gutters and down spouts to rain barrels or cisterns situated on or in the ground (Fig. 1-1). Storage transforms the intermittent rainfall into a continuous supply. For municipal service, sheds or catches on ground naturally impervious or made tight by grouting, cementing, paving, or similar means must usually be added.

The gross yield of rainwater is proportional to the receiving area and the amount of precipitation. However, some rain is blown off the roof, evaporated or lost in wetting the collecting surfaces and conduits and in filling depressions or improperly pitched gutters. Also, the first flush of water may have to be wasted because it contains dust, bird-droppings, and other unwanted washings. The combined loss may be high. A cutoff, switch, or deflector in the downspout permits selective diversion of unwanted water from the system. Sand filters will cleanse the water as it enters the cistern and prevent its deterioration by growths of undesirable organisms and consequent tastes, odors, and other changes in attractiveness and palatability.

The storage to be provided in cisterns depends upon the distribution of rainfall. It varies with the length of dry spells and commonly approximates one-third to one-half the annual consumption. There must be stand-by capacity in advance of filtration, if rainfalls of high intensity are

---

[2] A *cross-connection* is a junction between water supply systems through which water from doubtful or unsafe sources may enter an otherwise safe supply.
[3] A notable example is the water supplies of Bermuda, where there are no streams, and ground water in the coral formations is brackish.

to be captured. Because their area is small, roofs seldom yield much water. A careful analysis of storm rainfalls and seasonal variations in precipitation is, therefore, required.

Example 2-1.   Make a rough estimate of the gallons of water that can be caught by 3000 sq ft of horizontally projected roof area (the average area of American farm buildings) in a region where the mean annual rainfall is 15 in.

Gross yield = $3000 \times \frac{15}{12} \times 7.5 = 28,100$ gal annually = 77 gpd.

Net yield approximates two-thirds gross yield = 18,800 gal annually = 51 gpd.

About half the net yield, or 9400 gal = 1250 cu ft, must normally be stored to tide the supply over dry spells.

2-5   Surface Water

In North America by far the largest volumes of municipal water are collected from surface sources. The quantities that can be gathered vary directly with the size of the catchment area, or watershed, and with the difference between the amounts of water falling on it and the amounts lost by evapotranspiration.[4] The significance of these relations to water supply is illustrated in Fig. 2-1. Where surface-water and groundwater sheds do not coincide, some groundwater may enter from neighboring catchment areas or escape to them.

Continuous Draft.   Communities on or near streams, ponds, or lakes may take their supplies from them by continuous draft if stream flow and pond or lake capacity are high enough at all seasons of the year to furnish requisite water volumes.[5] Collecting works include ordinarily (1) an intake crib, gatehouse, or tower; (2) an intake conduit; and (3) in many places, a pumping station. On small streams serving communities of moderate size, an intake or diversion dam may create sufficient depth of water to submerge the intake pipe and protect it against ice. From intakes close to the community the water must generally be lifted to purification works and thence to the distribution system (Fig. 2-2).

Most large streams are polluted by wastes from upstream communities and industries. Purification of their waters is then a necessity. Cities on large lakes usually guard their supplies against their own and their

[4] This awkward term has been accepted into the vocabulary of hydrology as including all water lost to the atmosphere, whether by evaporation, transpiration, or other processes.

[5] Examples of continuous draft from streams are the water supplies of Montreal, P.Q., St. Lawrence River; Philadelphia, Pa., Delaware and Schuylkill rivers; Pittsburgh, Pa., Allegheny River; Cincinnati, O., and Louisville, Ky., Ohio River; Kansas City, Mo., Missouri River; Minneapolis and St. Paul, Minn., Mississippi River; St. Louis, Mo., Missouri and Mississippi rivers; and New Orleans, La., Mississippi River. Examples of continuous draft from lakes are furnished by Burlington, Vt., Lake Champlain Syracuse, N.Y., Lake Skaneateles; Toronto, Ont., Lake Ontario; Buffalo, N.Y., and Cleveland, O., Lake Erie; Detroit, Mich., Lake St. Clair; Chicago, Ill., and Milwaukee, Wis., Lake Michigan; and Duluth, Minn., Lake Superior.

neighbor's sewage and spent industrial-process waters by moving their intakes far away from shore and purifying both their water and wastewater. Diversion of sewage from lakes will retard their eutrophication (Sec. 1-8).

Selective Draft. Low stream flows are often left untouched. They may be wanted for other valley purposes, or they may be too highly polluted for reasonable use. Only clean flood waters are then diverted into reservoirs constructed in meadow lands adjacent to the stream or otherwise conveniently available.[6] The amount of water so stored must supply demands during seasons of unavailable stream flow. If draft is confined to

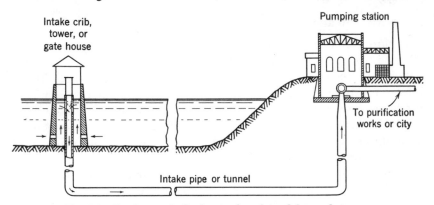

Fig. 2-2. Continuous draft of water from large lakes and streams.

a quarter year, for example, the reservoir must hold at least three-fourths of the annual supply. In spite of its selection and long storage, the water may have to be purified.

Impoundage. In their search for clean water and water that can be brought and distributed to the community by gravity, engineers have developed supplies from upland streams. Most of them are tapped near their source in high and sparsely settled regions. To be of use, their annual discharge must equal or exceed the demands of the community they serve for a reasonable number of years in the future. Because their dry-season flows generally fall short of concurrent municipal requirements, their floodwaters must usually be stored in sufficient volume to assure an adequate supply. Necessary reservoirs are impounded by throwing dams across the stream valley (Fig. 2-3). In this way, amounts up to the mean annual flow can be utilized. The area draining to impoundages is known

[6] London, England, meets parts of its water needs from the Thames River by storing relatively clean floodwaters in large basins surrounded by dikes in the Thames Valley. The Boston, Mass., Metropolitan Water Supply diverts the freshets of the Ware River through a tunnel either to the previously existing Wachusett Reservoir which impounds the waters of a branch of the Nashua River, or to the subsequently completed Quabbin Reservoir which impounds the Swift River.

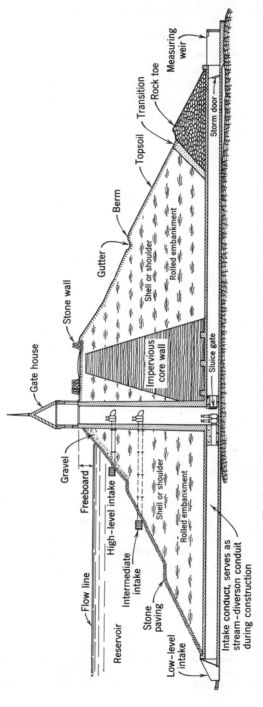

Fig. 2-3. Dam and intake tower for an impounded surface-water supply.

as the catchment area or watershed. Its economical development depends upon the value of water in the region, but it is a function, too, of runoff and its variation, accessibility of catchment areas, interference with existing water rights, and costs of construction. Allowances must be made for evaporation from new-water surfaces generated by the impoundage, and often, too, for release of agreed-upon flows to the valley below the dam (compensating water). Increased ground storage in the flooded area and the gradual diminution of reservoir volumes by siltation must also be considered.

Intake structures are incorporated in impounding dams or kept separate. Other important components of impounding reservoirs are (1) spillways safely passing floods in excess of reservoir capacity and (2) diversion conduits safely carrying the stream past the construction site until the reservoir has been completed and its spillway can go into action. Analysis of flood records enters into the design of these ancillary structures.

Some impounded supplies[7] are sufficiently safe, attractive, and palatable to be used without treatment other than protective disinfection. However, it may be necessary to remove high color imparted to the stored water by the decomposition of organic matter in swamps and on the flooded valley bottom; odors and tastes generated in the decomposition or growth of algae, especially during the first years after filling; and turbidity (finely divided clay or silt) carried into streams or reservoirs by surface wash, wave action, or bank erosion. Recreational uses of watersheds and reservoirs may call for treatment of the flows withdrawn from storage.

Much of the water in streams, ponds, lakes, and reservoirs in times of drought, or when precipitation is frozen, is seepage from the soil. Nevertheless, it is classified as surface runoff rather than groundwater. Water seeps *from* the ground when surface streams are low, and *to* the ground when surface streams are high. Release of water from ground storage or from accumulations of snow in high mountains is a determining factor in the yield of some catchment areas. Although surface waters are derived ultimately from precipitation, the relations between precipitation, runoff, infiltration, evaporation, and transpiration are so complex that engineers rightly prefer to base calculations of yield upon available stream gagings. For adequate information, gagings must extend over a considerable number of years.

---

[7] Examples of untreated, impounded, upland supplies are the Croton River, Catskill, and Delaware River supplies of New York, N.Y., and the Wachusett and Quabbin supplies of the Metropolitan District of Boston, Mass. Examples of treated impounded supplies are found at Baltimore, Md.; Providence, R.I.; Hartford, Conn.; Springfield, Mass.; and Springfield, Ill.

Example 2-2. Certain rough estimates of the yield of surface-water sheds and storage requirements are shown in Fig. 2-1. Rainfall is used as the point of departure, merely to identify the dimensions of possible rainfall-runoff relationships the following conversion factors and approximations being employed:

1. 1 in./sq mile = 17.378 mg. Hence 20 in./sq mile annually = 20 × 17.378 = 348 mg annually or 348/365 = 0.952 mgd.

2. A stream flow of about 1 mgd (1.547 cfs)/sq mile is a good average for the well-watered sections of North America. Not all of it can be adduced economically by storage. For 75% development (750,000 gpd per sq mile), about half a year's supply must generally be stored in regions of this kind. For a catchment area of 100 sq miles, therefore, the storage = 0.75 × 100 × 180 = 13.5 billion gal. In semiarid regions storage of three times the mean annual stream flow is not uncommon, i.e., water is held over from wet years to supply demands during dry years (overyear storage).

3. For an average consumption of 150 gpcd, the drainage area of 100 sq miles and impoundage of 13.5 billion gal will supply a population of 100 × 750,000/150 = 500,000.

4. For water supply by continuous draft, low-water flows rather than average annual yields govern. In well-watered sections of North America these approximate 0.1 cfs or 64,600 gpd per sq mile. A catchment area of 100 sq miles, therefore, can supply without storage 100 × 64,600/150 = 43,000 people against 500,000 people in the presence of proper storage.

2-6 Groundwater

Smaller in daily delivery, but many times more numerous than surface-water supplies, are the municipal and private groundwater supplies of North America. Groundwater is drawn from many different geological formations: (1) from the pores of alluvial (waterborne), glacial, or aeolian (windblown) deposits of granular, unconsolidated materials such as sand and gravel, and from consolidated materials such as sandstone; (2) from the solution passages, caverns, and cleavage planes of sedimentary rocks such as limestone, slate, and shale; (3) from the fractures and fissures of igneous rocks; and (4) from combinations of these unconsolidated and consolidated geological formations (Fig. 2-4). Groundwater sources, too, have an intake or catchment area, but the catch, or recharge, is by infiltration into soil openings rather than by runoff over its surface. The intake area may be nearby or a considerable distance away, especially when flow is confined within a water-bearing stratum or *aquifer*,[8] underlying an impervious stratum or *aquiclude*.[9]

The maximum yield of groundwater is directly proportional to the size of the intake area and to the difference between precipitation and the sum of evapotranspiration and storm runoff. Laterally, flow extends across

---

[8] The word *aquifer* comes from the Latin *aqua*, water, and *ferre*, to bear.

[9] The word *aquiclude* comes from the Latin *aqua*, water, and *cludere*, to shut or close (out). Although an aquiclude may contain water, it is incapable of transmitting it in significant amounts; clay is an example. An *aquifuge* (from *aqua*, water, and *fugere*, to drive away) neither contains nor transmits water; solid (unfissured) granite is an example.

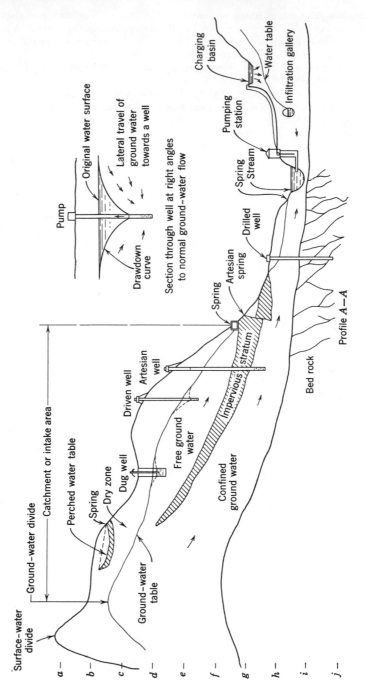

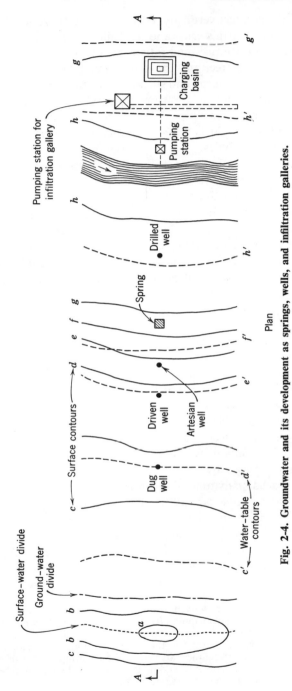

Fig. 2-4. Groundwater and its development as springs, wells, and infiltration galleries.

the width of the aquifer; vertically, it is as deep as the zone of open pores and passages in the earth's crust and as shallow as the *groundwater table*. When the water surface rises and falls with seasonal changes in recharge, flow is unconfined or free, and the groundwater table slopes downward more or less parallel to the ground surface. Flow then moves at right angles to the water-table contours. If a porous stratum dips beneath an impervious layer, flow is confined as in a pipe dropping below the hydraulic grade line. When this kind of aquifer is tapped, *artesian water*[10] rises from it under pressure; in some geological situations, even in free-flowing fountains. In other geological formations, water is perched on a lens of impervious material above the true groundwater table.

Groundwater reaches daylight through springs: (1) when the ground surface drops sharply below the normal groundwater table (depression springs); (2) when a geological obstruction impounds soil water behind it and forces it to the surface (contact springs); and (3) when a fault in an impervious stratum lets artesian water escape from confinement (also contact springs). A cut-off wall carried to bedrock will hold back subsurface as well as surface flows behind an impounding dam and so put the full capacity of the catchment area to use unless there is lateral leakage through the sides of the reservoir or around the abutments of the dam.

The rate of flow through the substantially vertical cross-section of ground at right angles to the direction of flow is not great. Owing to the high resistance of the normally narrow pores of the soil, the water moves forward only slowly, traveling about as far in a year as stream flow does in an hour. Natural rates of flow are seldom more than a few feet an hour; nor are they less than a few feet a day in aquifers delivering useful water supplies. However, if a well is sunk into the ground and the level of water in it is lowered by pumping, water is discharged into the well not only from the direction of natural flow but from all directions (Fig. 2-4). That is why wells can be spaced many times their own diameter apart and yet intercept most of the water once escaping through the intervening space.

Springs. Springs[11] are usually developed to capture the natural flow of an aquifer. In favorable circumstances their yield can be increased by driving collecting pipes or galleries, more or less horizontally, into the water-bearing formations that feed them. Pollution generally originates close to the point of capture. It is prevented (1) by excluding shallow

[10] The term *artesian water* is derived from *Artois*, the name of the northern-most province of France, where water supplies from *flowing wells* were brought in about 1750.
[11] Some of the drinking-water supply of Paris, France, is collected from springs. Part of the New River supply, developed for the City of London, England, by Sir Hugh Middleton in the seventeenth century, also comes from springs. In North America, the use of springs is ordinarily confined to communities of small size, a number of springs being harnessed by a common collecting conduit.

seepage waters through encircling the spring with a watertight chamber penetrating a safe distance into the aquifer and (2) by diverting surface run-off away from the immediate vicinity (Fig. 2-14). Some springs yield less than 1 gpm; a few yield more than 50 mgd. Some are perennial; others are periodically or seasonally intermittent.

Wells. Depending upon the geological formations through which they pass and upon their depth, wells are dug, driven, bored, or drilled into the ground. Dug and driven wells are usually confined to soft ground, sand, and gravel at depths normally less than 100 ft. Hard ground and rock generally call for bored and drilled wells sunk to depths of hundreds and even thousands of feet.[12] In well-watered regions successful wells of moderate depth and diameter yield 1 to 50 gpm[13] in hard rock and 50 to 500 gpm in coarse sand and gravel as well as coarse sandstone. Wells in deep aquifers may yield 100 gpm or more.

Except in hard rock, particularly limestone, without sand or gravel cover, wells are generally not polluted by lateral seepage but by vertical entrance of pollution at or near the ground surface. Pollution is excluded (1) by watertight casings or seals extending into the aquifer and at least 10 ft below the ground surface, together with (2) diversion of surface run-off from the well area and its protection against inundation by nearby streams.

Infiltration Galleries. Groundwater traveling towards streams or lakes from neighboring uplands can be intercepted by infiltration galleries laid more or less at right angles to the direction of flow and carrying entrant water to pumping stations.[14] Water is drawn into more or less horizontal conduits from both sides, or the river side is blanked off to exclude the often less satisfactory water seeping in from the river itself. Infiltration basins and trenches are similar in conception. They are, in essence, large, or long, shallow, open wells. Filter cribs built into alluvial deposits of streams intercept the underflow. Groundwater can be collected also from the driftways and stopes of mines, galleries driven into mountainsides specifically for this purpose, or abandoned mines. Some infiltration galleries yield as much as a million gallons of water daily from a thousand feet of gallery. They are particularly useful in tapping aquifers of shallow depth or where deep saline waters are to be excluded.

[12] Memphis, Tenn., is the largest municipality in the United States supplied with groundwater. There are about 30 wells 8 and 12 in. in diameter and 450 to 1400 ft deep. The groundwater table reaches within 15 to 50 ft of the surface when no water is being pumped.

[13] The yield of groundwater is commonly expressed in gallons per minute because pumps are conventionally rated in gallons per minute; 1 gpm = 1440 gpd.

[14] The water supplies of Des Moines, Ia., and Brussels, Belgium, are drawn from infiltration galleries.

Recharging Devices. As outlined in Sec. 2-3, the yield of ground-water works can be augmented or maintained at high level by water spreading or diffusion. The necessary structures are built close to the collecting works within the groundwater shed. Charging ditches or basins[15] are filled with river or lake water by gravity or pumping. In the flooding method, water diverted from streams by check dams is led onto a suitable area of pervious soils. The applied waters soak into the ground and increase its natural flows. The incentive is either augmentation of a dwindling or inadequate supply or taking advantage of natural filtration as a means of water purification. Gathering a more uniformly cool water is also a consideration. Badly polluted surface water may be partially purified before it is introduced into the charging structure.[16] Some diffusion galleries and wells return waters abstracted earlier from the ground for cooling and other purposes.

Groundwater collection works usually include pumps. To them water flows from all or much of the well field either by gravity through deep-lying conduits or under negative pressure through suction mains. Individual pumping units are often used instead, especially when the water table lies at considerable depths.

Most natural groundwaters are clean, palatable, and cool. However, passage through some soils may make them unpalatable, unattractive, corrosive, or hard (soap-consuming). Their treatment must be varied according to needs.

To determine the yield of groundwater areas, the engineer must know the geology as well as the hydrology of the region. He can learn much from existing supplies in nearby areas, but his ultimate judgment must generally rest on the behavior of test wells.

Example 2-3. Make a rough estimate of the yield of an aquifer 20 ft deep through which water moves at a rate of 3 ft a day (1) if all the groundwater laterally within 500 ft of the well comes fully within its influence and (2) if a gallery 1000 ft long collects water from both sides.

1. $20 \times 1000 \times 3 \times 7.5/1440 = 310$ gpm.
2. $20 \times 1000 \times 2 \times 3 \times 7.5/1,000,000 = 0.90$ mgd.

2-7 Purification Works

The quality of some waters from surface[17] or ground sources is naturally satisfactory for all common uses. Disinfection may be the only required safeguard. Other waters contain objectionable substances that must be

---

[15] The collecting works at Des Moines, Ia., include charging basins.
[16] Frankfort, Germany, at one time filtered the polluted Main River water before leading it into a charging gallery.
[17] As said before, rainwater is actually collected from a surface source.

removed, reduced to tolerable limits, destroyed, or otherwise altered in character before the water is sent to the consumer. Impurities are acquired in the passage of water through the atmosphere, over the earth's surface, or through the pores of the earth. They are associated in their pollutional aspects with man's activities, in particular, with his own use of water in household and industry and return of spent water to natural water courses. As has been said before, some of the heavy metals (lead, copper, zinc, and iron) come from the corrosion of metallic water pipes. Contamination of distribution systems through cross-connections with impure water supplies and through *backflow*[18] in plumbing systems is another hazard.

How to treat a given supply depends upon its inherent traits and upon accepted water quality standards. Municipal works must deliver water that is (1) hygienically safe, (2) esthetically attractive and palatable, and (3) economically satisfactory for its intended uses. The nature and sources of impurities have already been described. The most common classes of municipal water-purification works and their principal functions are:

1. Filtration plants[19] that remove objectionable color, turbidity, and bacteria as well as other potentially harmful organisms by filtration through sand or other granular substances after necessary preparation of the water by coagulation and sedimentation.

2. Deferrization and demanganization plants[19] that remove excessive amounts of iron and manganese by oxidizing the dissolved metals and converting them into insoluble flocs removable by sedimentation and filtration.

3. Softening plants[19] that remove excessive amounts of scale-forming, soap-consuming ingredients, chiefly calcium and magnesium ions (a) by the addition of lime and soda ash which precipitate calcium as a carbonate and magnesium as a hydrate, or (b) by passage of the water through cation-exchange media that substitute sodium for calcium and magnesium ions and are themselves regenerated by brine.

[18] *Backflow* permits water drawn into a fixture, tank, or similar device to flow back into the supply line by gravity or by siphonage.

[19] In North America many filtration plants, large and small, incorporate the treatment processes sketched in Fig. 2-5a. Among them are the filter plants of (1) Buffalo, N.Y., Cleveland, O., Detroit, Mich., and Milwaukee, Wis., on the Great Lakes; (2) Cincinnati, O., Louisville, Ky., Minneapolis and St. Paul, Minn., St. Louis, Mo., and New Orleans, La., in the drainage basin of the Mississippi River; and (3) Cambridge, Mass., Albany, N.Y., and Providence, R.I., which filter impounded upland supplies. Deferrization plants (Fig. 2-5b) are numerous in New England, among them the plants at Amesbury and Brookline, Mass., both of which treat groundwaters. Slow sand filters not employed in connection with deferrization and, therefore, without coke prefilters are in operation (1) at Springfield, Mass., and Hartford, Conn., for impounded upland waters, and (2) at Philadelphia and Pittsburgh, Pa., for the waters of large streams. Softening plants (Fig. 2-5c) are found at Columbus, O. (Scioto River); Springfield, Ill., (impounded supply); Kansas City, Mo. (Missouri River); Los Angeles, Cal. (Colorado River); and numerous smaller places.

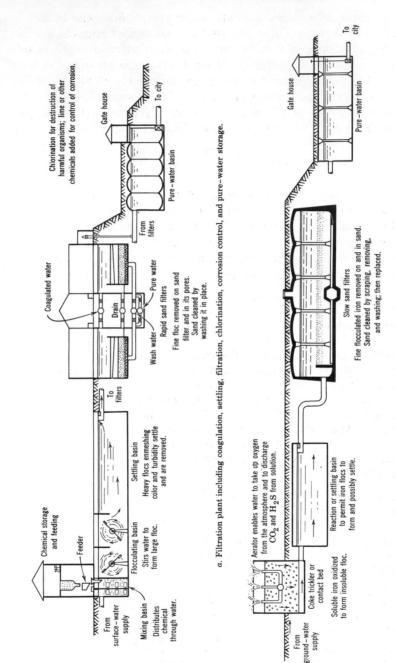

a. Filtration plant including coagulation, settling, filtration, chlorination, corrosion control, and pure-water storage.

b. Deferrization plant including aeration, contact treatment, filtration, and pure-water storage.

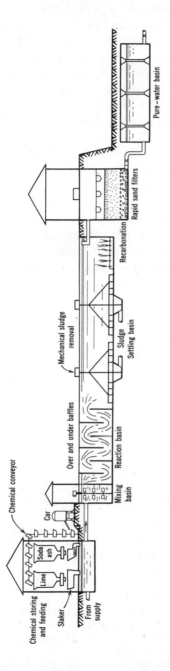

c. Softening plant including addition of softening chemicals, settling, recarbonation, filtration, and pure–water storage.

Fig. 2-5. Common types of water-purification plants.

Pictorial flow sheets of purification plants of this kind are developed in Fig. 2-5. Today most water supplies are chlorinated to assure their disinfection. Lime or other chemicals are often added to reduce the corrosiveness of water to iron and other metals and so to preserve water quality during distribution and ensure longer life to metallic pipes in particular. Odor- or taste-producing substances are adsorbed onto activated carbon, or destroyed by high doses of chlorine or chlorine dioxide. Numerous other treatment methods serve special needs.

The design of water-purification plants requires: (1) an understanding of unit operations that bring about removal or modification of objectionable substances (process design); (2) a knowledge of the flow of water through the structures composing water-purification plants—channels, pipes including perforated pipes, gates, measuring devices, basins, beds of sand and other granular materials, and pumps (hydraulic design); (3) a comprehension of the behavior of needed structures under load (structural design), and (4) an appreciation of treatment costs and associated benefits (economic design). The following normally applicable requirements give a concept of the sizing of principal structures:

1. Mixing basins hold a few minutes of flow.
2. Flocculating and reaction basins hold about half an hour's flow.
3. Sedimentation basins hold an hour or more of flow and are rated at about $\frac{1}{2}$ gpm per sq ft of water-surface area.
4. Slow sand filters pass water at rates of about 3 million gallons per acre daily (mgad) in surface-water filtration stepped up to about 10 mgad in groundwater deferrization and demanganization or when they are preceded by *roughing* filters.
5. Rapid filters operate at rates of 125 mgad or 2 gpm per sq ft, but rates run higher in modern works that include flocculating chambers.
6. Coke tricklers are rated at about 75 mgad, or 1.2 gpm per sq ft.

Example 2-4.   Estimate the capacity of the components of a rapid sand filtration plant (Fig. 2-5a) that is to deliver 10 mgd (6940 gpm) of water to a city of 67,000 people.
  1. Two mixing basins, 10 ft deep.
     (a)   Assumed detention period = 2 min.
     (b)   Volume = 2 × 6940/2 = 6940 gal = 928 cu ft each.
     (c)   Diameter = $\sqrt{92.8 \times 4/\pi}$ = 10.9 ft.
  2. Two flocculating basins, 10 ft deep.
     (a)   Assumed detention period = 30 min.
     (b)   Volume = 30 × 6940/2 = 104,000 gal = 13,900 cu ft.
     (c)   Surface area = 1390 sq ft (such as 20 ft by 70 ft).
  3. Two settling basins, 10 ft deep, but allow for 2 ft of sludge.
     (a)   Assumed detention period = 2 hr.
     (b)   Effective volume = 120 × 6940/2 = 416,000 gal = 55,700 cu ft.

(c) Surface area = 55,700/8 = 6960 sq ft (such as 35 ft by 200 ft).
(d) Surface rating = 6940/6960 = 1.0 gpm/sq ft.
4. Six rapid sand filters.
(a) Assumed rating = 3 gpm/sq ft.
(b) Area = 6940/(6 × 3) = 385 sq ft (such as 15 ft by 26 ft).

2-8   Transmission Works

Supply conduits, or aqueducts,[20] transport water from the source of supply to the community and so form the connecting link between collection works and distribution systems. Source location determines whether conduits are short or long, and whether transport is by gravity or pumping. Depending upon topography and available materials, conduits are designed for open-channel or pressure flow. They may follow the hydraulic grade line as canals dug through the ground, flumes elevated above the ground, grade aqueducts laid in balanced cut and cover at the ground surface, and grade tunnels penetrating hills; or they may depart from the hydraulic grade line as pressure aqueducts laid in balanced cut and cover at the ground surface, pressure tunnels dipping beneath valleys or hills, and pipelines of fabricated materials following the ground surface, if necessary over hill and through dale, sometimes even rising above the hydraulic grade line.[21] The profile and typical cross-sections of a supply conduit are shown in Fig. 2-6. Static heads and hydraulic grade lines are indicated for pressure conduits.

Size and shape of supply conduits are determined by hydraulic, structural, and economic considerations. Velocities of flow ordinarily lie between 3 and 5 fps. Requisite capacities depend upon the inclusion and size of supporting *service*, or *distributing*, reservoirs. If these store enough water to (1) care for hourly variations in water consumption in excess of inflow, (2) deliver water needed to fight serious fires, and (3) permit shutting down incoming lines for inspection and minor repairs, the supply conduits (Fig. 2-1) need operate only at the maximum daily rate, about 50% in excess of the average daily rate. Ordinarily, required storage approximates

[20] The word *aqueduct* comes from the Latin *aqua*, water, and *ducere*, to lead or conduct. It describes all artificial channels that transport water. Engineers often apply the word more specifically to covered masonry conduits built in place. Because they lacked pressure-resisting materials, the Romans constructed aqueducts tapping high-lying clean sources of water and conveyed it along the hydraulic grade line to the city, where it was distributed by gravity.
[21] The Colorado River Aqueduct of the Metropolitan Water District of Southern California is 242 miles long and includes 92 miles of grade tunnel, 63 miles of canal, 54 miles of grade aqueduct, 29 miles of inverted siphons, and 4 miles of force main. The Delaware Aqueduct of New York, N.Y., comprises 85 miles of pressure tunnel in three sections. Pressure tunnels 25 miles in length supply the metropolitan districts of Boston and San Francisco. The supply conduits of Springfield, Mass., are made of steel pipe and reinforced-concrete pipe; those of Albany, N.Y., of cast-iron pipe.

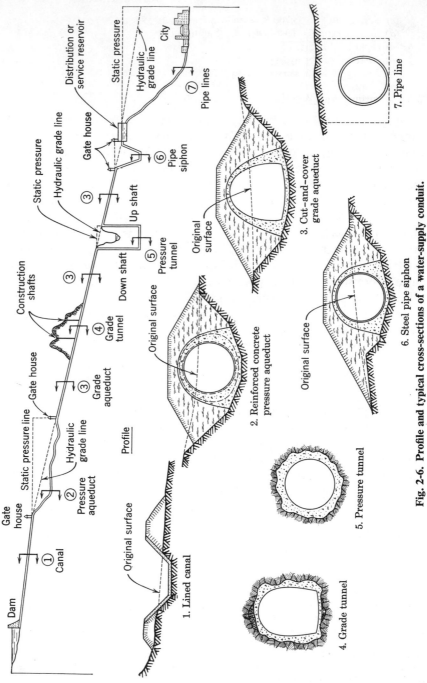

Fig. 2-6. Profile and typical cross-sections of a water-supply conduit.

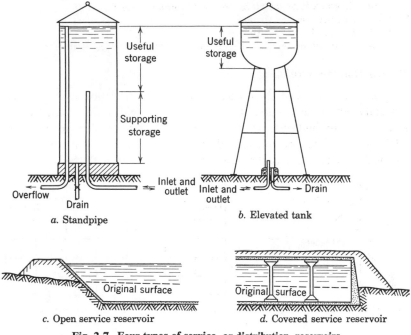

a. Standpipe

b. Elevated tank

c. Open service reservoir

d. Covered service reservoir

Fig. 2-7. Four types of service, or distribution, reservoirs.

a day's consumption. Distribution reservoirs are open or covered basins in balanced cut and fill, standpipes, or elevated tanks. Selection depends upon size and location in particular reference to available elevations above the area served (Fig. 2-7). More than one reservoir may be needed in large systems. Open reservoirs are troubled by soot and dust falls, by algal growths, and in seacoast cities by sea gulls. Today, covered reservoirs are preferred.

Example 2-5. Estimate roughly the size of a supply conduit leading to an adequate distributing reservoir serving (1) a relatively small residential community of 10,000 people, and (2) a relatively large industrial community of 400,000 people, and find its hydraulic gradient.
1. Average daily water consumption at (1) 100 gpcd and (2) 150 gpcd respectively:
   (a) $10,000 \times 100/1,000,000 = 1.0$ mgd.
   (b) $400,000 \times 150/1,000,000 = 60$ mgd.
2. Maximum daily use 50% greater than the average:
   (a) $1.0 \times 1.5 = 1.5$ mgd $= 2.32$ cfs.
   (b) $60 \times 1.5 = 90$ mgd $= 139$ cfs.
3. Diameter of circular conduit flowing at 4 fps:
   (a) Diameter $= 12\sqrt{2.32/\pi} = 10$ in.
   (b) Diameter $= 12\sqrt{139/\pi} = 80$ in.

4. Hydraulic gradient by the Hazen-Williams formula[22] for $C = 100$:
  (a) Loss of head = 10.8 ft/1000.
  (b) Loss of head = 0.85 ft/1000.
The higher loss of head in small conduits at equal velocities is understandable.

2-9 Distribution Works

Supply conduits feed their waters into the distribution system which eventually serves each individual property—household, mercantile establishment, public building, or factory (Fig. 2-1). Street plan, topography, and location of supply works and service storage establish the type of distribution system and its character of flow. In accord with the street plan,

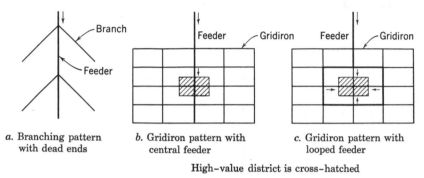

a. Branching pattern   b. Gridiron pattern with   c. Gridiron pattern with
   with dead ends   central feeder   looped feeder

High–value district is cross–hatched

Fig. 2-8. Patterns of water-distribution systems.

two distribution patterns emerge: (1) a branching pattern on the outskirts of the community, in which ribbon development follows the primary arteries of roads and streets (Fig. 2-8a), and (2) a gridiron pattern within the built-up portions of the community where streets criss-cross and water mains are interconnected (Figs. 2-8b and 2-8c). Hydraulically, the gridiron system has the advantage of delivering water to any spot from more than one direction and of avoiding dead ends. Gridiron systems are strengthened by substituting for a central feeder a loop or belt of feeders that supply water to the *congested*, or *high-value*, district from at least two directions. This more or less doubles the delivery of the grid (Fig. 2-8c). In large systems feeders are constructed as pressure tunnels, pressure aqueducts, steel pipes, or reinforced concrete pipes. In smaller communities the entire distribution system may consist of cast-iron pipes. Cast iron is, indeed, the most common material for water mains, but asbestos-cement, in general, and plastics, in the case of small supplies, are also important.

High and Low Services. Sections of the community too high to be supplied directly from the principal, or *low-service*, works are generally

[22] See Sec. 12-2.

incorporated into separate distribution systems with independent piping and service storage. The resulting *high services* are normally fed by pumps that take water from the main supply and boost its pressure as required. Areas varying widely in elevation may be formed into intermediate districts or zones. Gated connections between the different systems are opened by hand during emergencies or go into operation automatically through pressure-regulating valves (Fig. 13-14).

Fire Supplies. Before the days of high-capacity, high-pressure, motorized fire engines conflagrations in the congested central, or *high-value,*

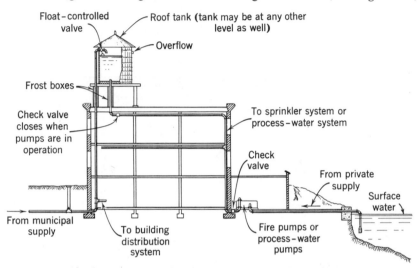

Fig. 2-9. Use of private water supply without cross-connection. (After *Minnesota State Board of Health.*)

district of some large cities were fought through independent high-pressure systems of pipes and hydrants. Taking water from the public supply and boosting its pressure by pumps in power stations whenever an alarm was rung in, these systems performed well.[23] For extreme emergencies, rigorously protected connections usually led to independent sources of water: rivers, lakes, or tidal estuaries. Large industrial establishments, with heavy investment in plant, equipment, raw materials, and finished products, concentrated in a small area, are generally equipped with high-pressure fire supplies and distribution networks of their own. Because such supplies may be drawn from sources of questionable quality, some regulatory agencies enforce rigid separation of private fire supplies and public systems. Others prescribe *protected cross-connections* regularly inspected for tightness (Figs. 2-9, 2-10). How the two sources can be divorced without losing

[23] Boston, Mass., still maintains a separate *fire supply.*

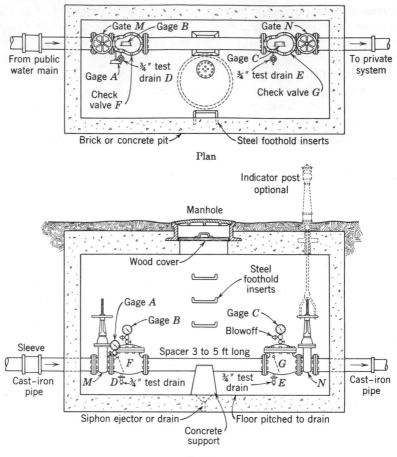

Fig. 2-10. Cross-connection between municipal water supply and private (industrial) water supply protected by double check-valve installation. To test installation : (1) close gates *M* and *N*; (2) open test drain *D*, and observe gages *A* and *B*; (3) open test drain *E*, and observe gage *C*. If check valves *F* and *G* are tight, gage *A* will drop to zero; gages *B* and *C* will drop slightly owing to compression of rubber gaskets on check valves *F* and *G*.

all the protective benefit of a dual supply is illustrated in Fig. 2-9. Ground-level storage and pumping are less advantageous.

A widely approved arrangement of double check valves in vaults accessible for inspection and for test by valves, gages, and bleeders is shown in Fig. 2-10. No waterborne disease has been traced to approved and properly supervised and protected cross-connections of this kind. Automatic chlorination of the auxiliary supply can introduce a further safeguard.

Pressures.   In normal municipal practice, pressures of 60 to 75 psig are maintained in business blocks and 40 psig in residential areas. Higher pressures (100 psig or more) delivering adequate amounts of water for fire fighting through hose attached directly to fire hydrants are no longer important. Instead, modern motor pumpers can discharge thousands of gallons per minute at even greater pressures. Moreover, low operating pressures make for low leakage from mains and reduce the amount of water *unaccounted for.* To supply their upper stories, tall buildings boost water to tanks at various elevations and on their roofs or in towers. In individual industrial complexes the water pressure may be raised during fires by fixed installations of fire pumps (Fig. 2-9).

Capacity.   The capacity of distribution systems is dictated by domestic, industrial, and other normal water uses and by the *stand-by* or *ready-to-serve* requirements for fire fighting. Pipes should be able to carry the maximum *coincident* draft at velocities that do not produce high pressure drops and water hammer. Velocities of 2 to 4 fps and minimum pipe diameters of 6 in. are common in North American municipalities.

Example 2-6.   Estimate the number of people who can be supplied with water from (*a*) a 12-in. and (*b*) a 24-in. main (1) in the absence of fire service for a maximum draft of 200 gpcd, (2) with a residential fire-flow requirement of 500 gpm and a coincident draft of 150 gpcd. Also find the hydraulic gradient.

A. Cross-sectional area of pipes: (*a*) 113 sq in. and (*b*) 425 sq in.

B. Capacity of pipes at velocity of 3 fps: (*a*) $113 \times 3/144 = 2.35$ cfs and (*b*) 9.42 cfs.

C. Flow available for domestic use:

(1) With no fire service: (*a*) $2.35 \times 646,000 = 1,520,000$ gpd and (*b*) $9.42 \times 646,000 = 6,080,000$ gpd.

(2) With fire service of 500 gpm $= 720,000$ gpd; (*a*) $(1,520,000 - 720,000) = 800,000$ gpd and (*b*) $(6,080,000 - 720,000) = 5,360,000$ gpd.

D. Population served:

(1) With no fire service and a rate of 200 gpcd: (*a*) $1,520,000/200 = 7600$ people and (*b*) $6,080,000/200 = 30,400$ people.

(2) With fire service of 500 gpm and a rate of 150 gpcd: (*a*) $800,000/150 = 5300$ people and (*b*) $5,360,000/150 = 36,000$ people.

E. At velocity of 3 fps and for $C = 100$ in Hazen-Williams formula,[22] loss of head per 1000 ft:

(*a*) 4.6 ft $= 2.0$ psi; (*b*) 2.0 ft $= 0.9$ psi.

Service to Premises.   Water reaches individual premises from the street main through one or more service pipes tapping the distribution system. The building supply between the public main and the take-offs to the various plumbing fixtures or other points of water use is illustrated in Fig. 2-11, the remainder of the system in Fig. 2-12. Small services are made of cement-lined iron or steel, brass of varying copper content, admiralty metal, copper, and plastics such as polyethylene (PE) or polyvinyl

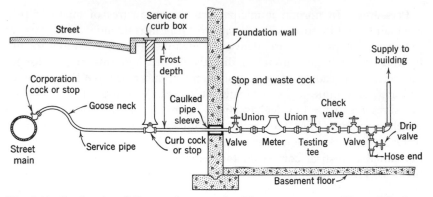

Fig. 2-11. Service pipe, fittings, and accessories. There are many possible modifications, both inside and outside the building. In moderate climates, the meter is conveniently placed in a vault outside the building.

chloride (PVC). Because lead and lead-lined pipes may corrode and release lead to the water, they are no longer installed afresh. For large services, coated or lined cast-iron pipe is often employed. For dwellings and similar buildings, the minimum desirable size of service is $\frac{3}{4}$ in. Pipe-tapping machines connect services to the main without shutting off the water. They also make larger connections within water-distribution systems.

2-10 Water Systems Management

Construction of water supplies from the ground up, or their improvement and extension, progresses from preliminary investigations or planning through financing, design, and construction to operation, maintenance, and repair (Chap. 18). Political and financial procedures are involved as well as engineering.

Municipal Supplies. The cost of public water supplies gives some concept of the magnitude of engineering activity and responsibility associated with their design and construction. Per capita investment in physical plant depends upon many factors: nature, proximity, and abundance of suitable water sources; need for water treatment; availability and price of labor and materials; size and construction conditions of the system; habits of the people; and characteristics of the areas served. Wide differences in these factors make for much variation in first cost.[24] For communities in excess of 10,000 population, replacement costs in North America lie in the vicinity of $300 per capita, with much of the investment in small communities chargeable to fire protection. Of the various system components, collection and transportation works cost about a fourth,

[24] For 1965 price levels. For other years multiply by the ratio of applicable *Engineering News-Record* indexes.

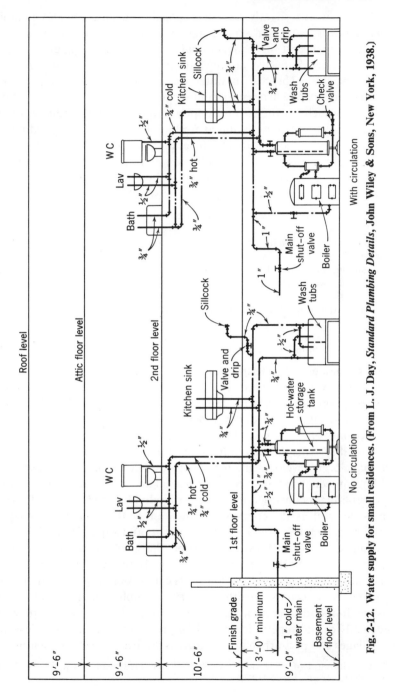

Fig. 2-12. Water supply for small residences. (From L. J. Day, *Standard Plumbing Details*, John Wiley & Sons, New York, 1938.)

distribution works slightly less than a half, purification and pumping works about a tenth, and service lines and meters nearly a sixth of the total. The first cost of conventional water-filtration plants is about $250,000 per mgd capacity, varying with plant size as the two-thirds power of the capacity.[25] The cost of water treatment, excluding fixed charges, lies in the vicinity of $70 per mg (million gallons), varying with plant output capacity inversely as the two-fifths power of the daily production.[25] Including interest and depreciation as well as charges against operation and maintenance, water costs $50 to $500 per mg and is charged for accordingly. As one of our most prized commodities, water is nevertheless remarkably cheap—as low as 2 cents a ton delivered to the premises of large consumers and as little as 4 cents a ton to the taps of small consumers.

Example 2-7. Roughly, what is the replacement cost of the water works of a city of 100,000 people?

1. Assuming a per capita cost of $250, the total first cost is $250 \times 100,000 = \$25,000,000$.

2. Assuming that 30% of this amount is invested in the collection works, 10% in the purification works, and 60% in the distribution works, the breakdown is as follows:

(*a*) Collection works $0.3 \times 25,000,000 = \$7,500,000$.

(*b*) Purification works $0.10 \times 25,000,000 = \$2,500,000$.

(*c*) Distribution works $0.60 \times 25,000,000 = \$15,000,000$.

(*d*) Assuming a water consumption of 150 gpcd, the total consumption is 15 mgd, and the cost of a filtration plant becomes $(15)^{2/3} \times 250,000 = \$1,500,000$.

Rural Supplies. The term *rural* is used in this book to describe those situations in which the needs and amenities of water supply and wastewater disposal are normally satisfied by relatively small and compact systems individually owned, developed, and operated, and kept within the property lines of the owner. Normally, this implies construction of wanted or required systems through individual rather than community effort. But there have been developments for villages and communities with scattered buildings in which local government has taken the initiative and assumed responsibility for construction and care of individualized systems. Property owners, as well as the community, then enjoy the benefits of adequate planning, design, construction, management, and supervision. Otherwise, unfortunately, necessary works are rarely designed by qualified engineers and, often, satisfy their purposes poorly, both in a sanitary and an economic sense. Reasonably good results can be obtained (1) if engineering departments of central health authorities publish manuals of design, construction, and operation that fit local conditions, and (2) if they give needed advice and supervision as well as provide for regulation. Nevertheless, villages and peri-urban or *fringe* areas are best served, in the long run,

[25] G. T. Orlob and M. R. Lindorf, Cost of Water Treatment in California, *J. Am. Water Works Assoc.*, **50**, 45 (1958).

by the extension of central water lines and sewers, or by incorporation of *water and sewer districts* comprising more than a single unit of local government.

2-11 Rural Water Systems

Because of the natural purifying capacity and protection of the soil, rural water supplies are generally drawn from springs, infiltration galleries, and wells. Where ground water is highly mineralized or unavailable, rainwater is next best in general safety and quality. Only in uninhabited and well-protected upland areas should ponds and streams be tapped without purifying the waters drawn.

Some of the safeguards for groundwater works are illustrated in Figs. 2-13 to 2-16. They share the following features in common: (1) diversion of

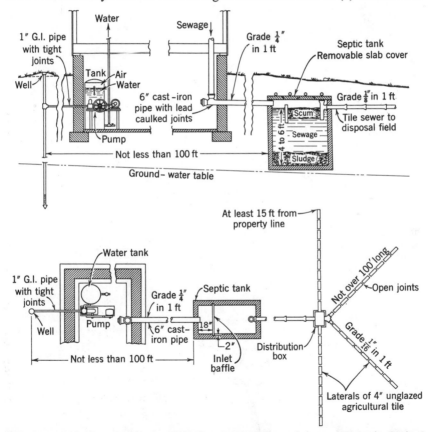

Fig. 2-13. Typical rural water-supply and wastewater-disposal system. Water is obtained from a driven well and distributed by pneumatic pressure. Wastewater is treated in a septic tank and discharged through a subsurface irrigation system.

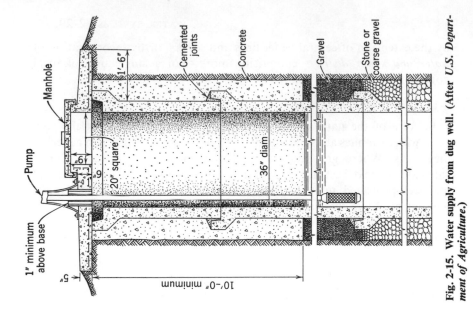

Fig. 2-15. Water supply from dug well. (After *U.S. Department of Agriculture.*)

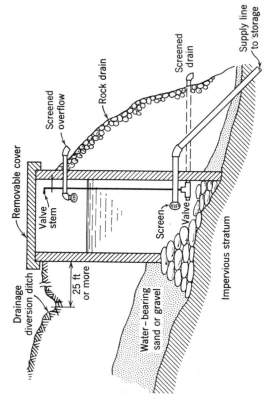

Fig. 2-14. Water supply from spring. (After *U.S. Public Health Service.*)

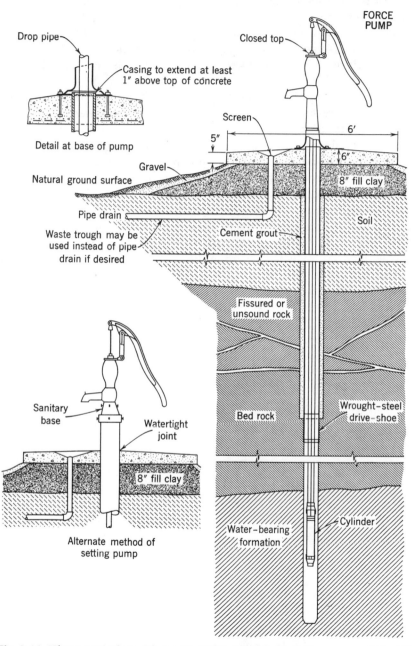

Fig. 2-16. Water supply from driven well. (After *Virginia State Department of Health*.)

surface water from intake structures; (2) drainage of overflow or spillage waters away from intake structures; (3) water tightness of intake works for at least 10 ft below the ground surface and, if necessary, until the aquifer is reached; and (4) prevention of backflow into intakes.

Where there is no electric power, water is pumped by hand, wind, water, or gasoline engines.

Rural water supplies are not without their purification problems (Vol. 2). Gravity and pressure filters are employed to improve waters of doubtful purity; zeolite softeners and other ion-exchange units for the removal of unwanted hardness. Iron-bearing groundwaters that issue from their source sparklingly clear but become rusty on exposure to air (by oxidation and precipitation of iron) are best treated in manganese-cation exchange units. Hexametaphosphates may keep iron from precipitating, but this requires skillful management. It may be advisable to seek an iron-free source instead. Some soft groundwaters containing much carbon dioxide are highly corrosive. Passage through marble or limestone chips takes calcium into solution and reduces the carbon dioxide proportionately. Hardness is increased, but corrosiveness is decreased. For the chlorination of polluted rural supplies, there are solution-feed dosing devices that proportion the amount of added chlorine to flow. Instead, the householder may prefer to boil his drinking and culinary water. Investment in an inherently safe and satisfactory supply, however, is usually wisest in the long run.

CHAPTER 3

Wastewater Systems

3-1 General Features

This companion chapter to Water Systems (Chap. 2) outlines the broad purpose and composition of wastewater systems into which water systems empty. With an understanding of the whys and wherefores of needed structures and operations as a whole, we can proceed more fruitfully to a rigorous consideration of details. The practitioner, too, does not move to detailed design until he has settled on a general plan.

Wastewater systems normally comprise: (1) collection works, (2) treatment works, and (3) outfall or disposal works. Together, their structures compose a *sewerage* or drainage system. Although individual systems are in a sense unique, they do conform to one of the types outlined in Fig. 3-4. As there shown, wastewaters from households and industries are either collected along with stormwater runoff in the *combined sewers*[1] of a *combined system* of sewerage or are led away by themselves through separate *sanitary sewers*, while stormwaters are emptied by themselves into the separate *storm sewers* of a *separate system* of sewerage. The water-carried wastes from households are *domestic sewage;* those from manufacturing establishments *industrial* or *trade wastes; municipal sewage* includes both. Combined sewerage systems are common to the older cities of the world,[2] where they evolved from existing systems of storm drains (Sec. 1-3).

[1] The word *sewer* is derived ultimately from the Latin *ex*, out, and *aqua*, water. In the eighteenth and early nineteenth centuries, the common form of the word was *shor*.
[2] The sewerage systems of London, England, Paris, France, New York, N.Y., and Boston, Mass., are examples of this evolution.

The converging conduits of wastewater-collection works remove sewage or stormwater in *free* flow as if it were traveling through branch or tributary streams into the trunk or main channel of an underground river system. The main collector of some combined systems is, in fact, a brook eventually covered over when pollution made its waters too unsightly, malodorous, and otherwise objectionable. To be gravitational, flow in sewers and drains proceeds continuously downhill, except where pumping stations and force mains are interpolated to lift flows through force mains into higher-lying conduits, thereby (1) avoiding the costly construction of deep conduits in flat country or bad ground and (2) transfering waste-waters from low-lying subareas to main drainage schemes. Sewers are not intended to flow under pressure. If they were, wastewaters would have to be forced into them through individual building services and property drains or their inverts would have to be placed far enough below cellar level to keep sewage from backing into basements and spilling out of fixtures. Both arrangements are now impractical. Hydraulically, sewers are designed as *open channels*, flowing partly full or, at most, just filled. Vitrified-clay pipes are the material of choice for small sewers; concrete or masonry pipes or conduits for large ones.

In well-watered regions of the earth the collected wastewaters are normally discharged into nearby water courses after suitable treatment. This is referred to as disposal by *dilution*, although natural purification as well as physical dilution is involved. In semiarid regions or otherwise useful circumstances, terminal discharge may be onto land by *irrigation*. Treatment before disposal removes unsightly and putrescible matters, stabilizes degradable substances, and removes or destroys disease-producing organisms in suitable degree. Economical conservation of water and land resources is the important consideration.

3-2 Sources of Wastewaters

Sanitary sewage is the spent water supply of the community; *domestic sewage* the wastewater from kitchen, bathroom, lavatory, toilet, and laundry. To the mineral and organic matter already in the water supplied to the community is added a burden of human excrement, paper, soap, dirt, food wastes (garbage), and other substances. Some of the waste matters remain in suspension, some go into solution, and others are, or become, so finely divided that they acquire the properties of colloidal (dispersed, ultramicroscopic) particles. Much of the waste substance is organic and useful to saprophytic microorganisms, i.e., organisms of decay. It follows that domestic sewage is unstable, bio-degradable, or putrescible, and may generate offensive odors. It must be presumed that enteric organisms are present in domestic sewage and make it dangerous.

Industrial wastewaters vary in composition with industrial operations. Some are relatively clean rinse waters; others are heavily laden with organic or mineral matter, or with corrosive, poisonous, flammable, or explosive substances. Some are so objectionable that they should not be admitted to the public sewerage system; others contain so little and such

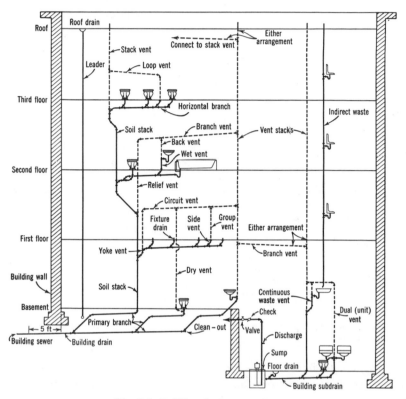

Fig. 3-1. Building drainage system.

unobjectionable waste matters that it is safe to discharge them into storm drains or directly to natural bodies of water. Fats, lime, hair, and fibers adhere to sewers and clog them; acids and hydrogen sulfide destroy cement, concrete, and metals; hot wastes crack tile and masonry conduits; poisonous chemicals disrupt biological treatment, kill useful aquatic life, and endanger water supplies; fertilizing elements add to the eutrophication of lakes; anthrax and other living organisms are infective to man; flammable or explosive liquors imperil the structures through which they flow; and toxic gases or vapors are hazardous to workmen and operators of sewage works, and occasionally also to householders.

Some groundwater enters sewer pipe through its many joints.[3] In combined systems and stormwater drains, runoff from rainfall and melting ice and snow adds the washings from streets, roofs, gardens, parks, and yards. Entering dirt, dust, sand, gravel, and other gritty substances are heavy and inert; leaves and organic debris are light and degradable. Water for

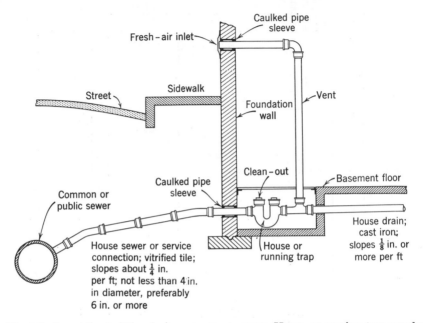

Fig. 3-2. Connecting building drainage system to sewer. House, or running, trap may be installed or omitted.

flushing streets, fighting fires, or scouring water mains through hydrants, as well as wastewater from fountains, wading and swimming pools, swell the tide.

To introduce the reader to the beginning of wastewater schemes, a drainage system of a building is outlined in Fig. 3-1 and its connection to the public sewer in Figs. 3-2 and 3-3. The three illustrations are self-explanatory. The service pipes are called *house* or *building drains* inside the building and *house* or *building sewers* outside. Stormwater from roofs and paved areas taken into a *property drain* is discharged into the street gutter or directly into the storm sewer. In combined systems, roofwater may be led into the house drain, water from yard areas into the house sewer.

[3] Vitrified-clay sewer pipe, 4 to 36 in. in diameter, is ordinarily 3 to 6 ft long. Unreinforced-concrete sewer pipe, 4 to 24 in. in diameter, is generally 2 to 4 ft long. Preformed joints made of resilient plastic materials increase the tightness of the system.

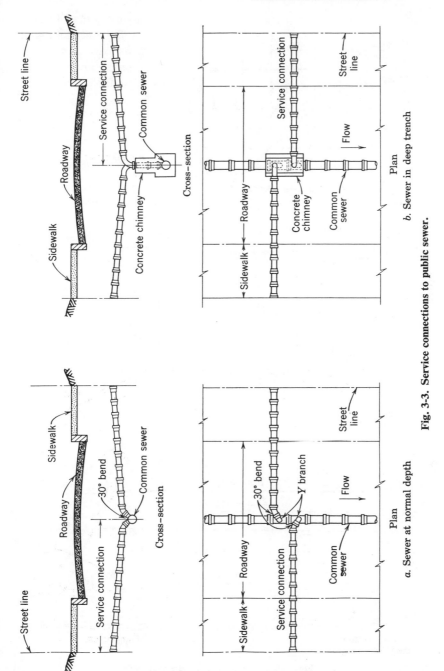

Fig. 3-3. Service connections to public sewer.

a. Sewer at normal depth

b. Sewer in deep trench

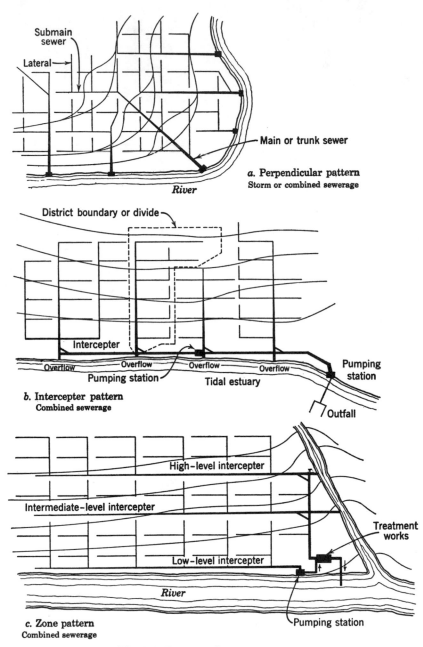

Submain sewer

Lateral →

— Main or trunk sewer

a. Perpendicular pattern
Storm or combined sewerage

River

District boundary or divide

Intercepter

Overflow Overflow Overflow Overflow

Pumping station Tidal estuary

Pumping station

b. Intercepter pattern
Combined sewerage

Outfall

High-level intercepter

Intermediate-level intercepter

Treatment works

Low-level intercepter

River

c. Zone pattern
Combined sewerage

Pumping station

Fig. 3-4. Patterns of sewerage systems.

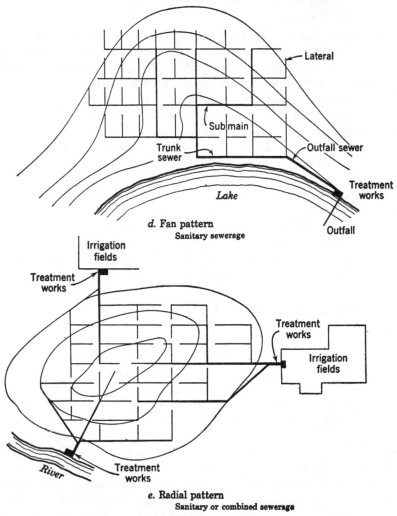

d. Fan pattern
Sanitary sewerage

e. Radial pattern
Sanitary or combined sewerage

Fig. 3-4 (continued)

Otherwise, storm runoff travels over the ground, reaches the street gutter, flows along it, enters a stormwater inlet or catch basin, and is piped to a manhole, whence it empties into the drainage system. In separate systems, connections to the wrong sewer, in violation of common regulations, carry some stormwater into sanitary sewers and some sewage into storm drains. The dry-weather flow of combined sewers is primarily sewage and groundwater; the wet-weather flow predominantly storm runoff. The first flush of stormwater scours away deposited solids, including much putrescent organic matter.

3-3 System Patterns

Among the factors determining the pattern of collecting systems are: (1) type of system (whether separate or combined); (2) street lines or rights of way; (3) topography, hydrology, and geology of the drainage area; (4) political boundaries; and (5) location and nature of treatment and disposal works. Five general patterns are sketched in Fig. 3-4.

Storm drains are naturally made to seek the shortest path to existing surface channels. This creates the *perpendicular pattern* of storm and combined sewerage shown in example *a* of Fig. 3-4.[4] Combined systems of this type have become rare. They pollute the waters washing the immediate shores of the community and make sewage treatment difficult. More often, their flows are intercepted before they can spill into waters to be protected. A resulting intercepter pattern is shown in example *b* of Fig. 3-4.[4] If the tributary area is at all large, the capacity of the intercepter should be held to some reasonable multiple of the average dry-weather flow or to the dry-weather flow plus the first flush of stormwater which, understandably, is most heavily polluted. Rainfall intensities and durations are deciding factors. In North America, rainfalls are so intense that the number of spills cannot be reduced appreciably by raising the capacity of intercepters even to as much as ten times the dry-weather flow. No more than the maximum dry-weather flow becomes the economically justifiable limit. Sewage in excess of this amount spills into the receiving water through outlets that antedate interception, or through stormwater overflows constructed for this purpose. Pumping, so commonly associated with water-front intercepters, pipe sizes, and difficulties of construction in low-lying and often bad ground, can sometimes be reduced by dividing the drainage area into a series of more or less parallel zones differing in elevation and lending themselves to separate interception. A *zone pattern* is formed as shown in example *c* of Fig. 3-4.[4] This pattern is often useful also for sanitary sewers. The *fan pattern* (*d* in Fig. 3-4[4]) concentrates flows inward from the outskirts of communities and makes for a single outfall. However, its largest sewers quite likely traverse the most congested districts, and it is difficult to increase the capacity of the system, for example, by building *relief sewers* when outlying suburbs grow and add their flows. In the *radial pattern* (*e* in Fig. 3-4[4]), on the contrary, sewage flows outward from the

---

[4] Lower Manhattan Island in the City of New York offers an example of the perpendicular pattern. Intercepter and zone patterns are found in London, England, Boston, Mass., Buffalo, N.Y., Cleveland, O., Chicago, Ill., Milwaukee, Wis., and many other places. The fan pattern is typified by the combined system of Vienna, Austria, where the Vienna River, covered in part to serve as a combined sewer, drains the side valley through which the city recedes from the banks of the Danube. The radial pattern is employed by Berlin, Germany, a radial city in flat country.

heart of the city, as along the spokes of a wheel. Lines are relatively small and short, but the number of treatment works may be multiplied.

3-4 Collection of Sewage

Because about 70% of the water brought into a community must be removed as *spent water*, the average flow in sanitary sewers is about 100 gpcd in North America. Variations in water use step up the maximum hourly rate about threefold. Illicit stormwater and groundwater magnify the required capacity still further, and a design value of 400 gpcd is not uncommon.

Sanitary sewers are fouled by the deposition of waste matters unless they impart self-cleaning velocities of 2 to 2.5 fps. Except in unusually flat country, sewer grades are made steep enough to generate these velocities when the sewers are running reasonably full.[5] Nevertheless, there will be deposition of solids. To find and remove them, sewers must be accessible for inspection and cleaning. Except in large sewers, manholes are built at all junctions with other sewers, and at all changes in direction or grade. Straight runs between manholes can then be rodded out effectively if intervening distances are not too great. Maxima of 300 or 400 ft for pipes less than 24 in. in diameter are generally specified, but effective cleaning is the essential criterion. For larger sewers, distances between manholes may be upped to as much as 600 ft. Sewers so large that workmen can enter them for inspection, cleaning, and repair are freed from these restrictions, and access manholes are placed quite far apart either above the center line or tangential to one side. Introduction of flexible cleaning devices has encouraged the construction of curved sewers of all sizes, especially in residential areas. A plan and profile of a sanitary sewer and its laterals are shown in Fig. 3-5, together with enlarged sections of sewer trenches and manholes. On short runs (<150 ft) and temporary stubs of sewer lines, terminal cleanouts are sometimes substituted for manholes. They slope to the street surface in a straight run from a Y in the sewer or in a gentle curve that can be rodded out. In very flat country and in other unusual circumstances sewers are laid on flat grades, in spite of greater operating difficulties, in order to keep depths reasonably small and pumping reasonably infrequent.

The smallest public sewers in North America are normally 8 in. in diameter. Smaller pipes clog quickly and are hard to clean. Vitrified clay is the material of choice for small sewers, prefabricated concrete for large sewers. To reduce infiltration of groundwater, sewers laid without preformed (factory-made) joints in wet ground must be underdrained or made

---

[5] Half full or more in circular sections, because the hydraulic radius of a semicircle equals that of a circle.

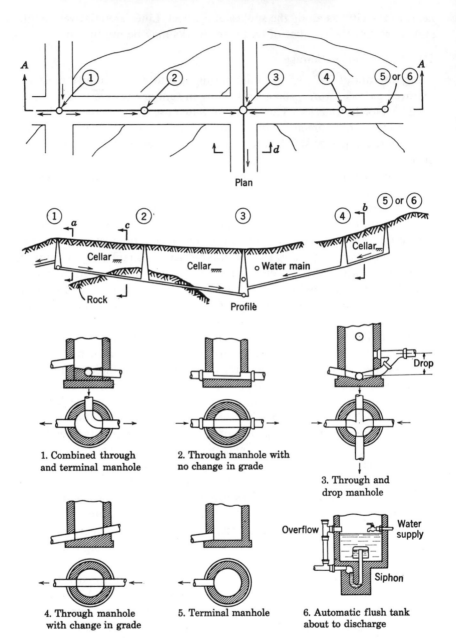

Fig. 3-5. Plan, profile, and constructional details of sanitary sewers.

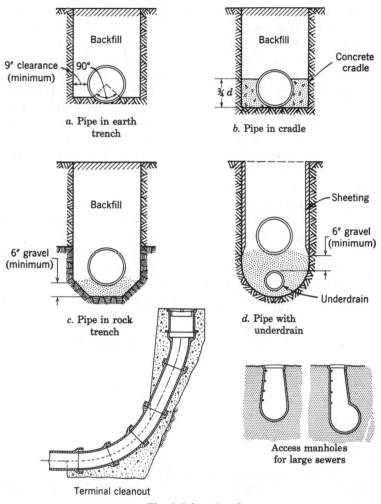

a. Pipe in earth trench

b. Pipe in cradle

c. Pipe in rock trench

d. Pipe with underdrain

Terminal cleanout

Access manholes for large sewers

Fig. 3-5 (*continued*)

of cast iron, asbestos cement, or other suitable materials. Cast-iron and asbestos-cement pipes are long and their joints are tight. Underdrainage is by porous pipes or clay pipes laid with open joints in a bed of gravel or broken stone beneath the sewer. Underdrains may serve during construction only or become permanent adjuncts to the system and discharge freely into natural water courses. Some sewage may eventually seep into permanent underdrains and thence into receiving waters. Grit or other abrading materials will wear the invert of concrete sewers unless velocities are held below 8 to 10 fps. Very large sewers are built in place, some by tunneling. Hydraulically and structurally, they share the properties of grade aqueducts (Fig. 2-6).

Sewers are laid deep enough (1) to protect them against breakage, by traffic shock, for example; (2) to keep them from freezing; and (3) to permit them to drain the lowest fixture in the premises served. Common figures are 3 ft below the basement floor, 11 ft below the top of building foundations (12 ft or more for basements in commercial districts), together with an allowance of $\frac{1}{4}$ in. per ft (2%) for the slope of the building sewer.[6] In the northern United States, cellar depths range from 6 to 8 ft and frost depths from 4 to 6 ft. A 2-ft earth cover will cushion most shocks. The deep basements of tall buildings are drained by ejectors or pumps.

As shown in Fig. 3-5, manholes are channeled to improve flow, and the entrance of high-lying laterals is eased by constructing drop manholes rather than lowering the last length of run, a wasteful arrangement. In their upper reaches, most sewers receive so little flow that they are not self-cleaning and must be flushed from time to time. This is done by (1) damming up the flow at a lower manhole and releasing the stored waters after the sewer has almost filled; (2) suddenly pouring a large amount of water into an upstream manhole; (3) providing at the uppermost end of the line a *flushing manhole* that can be filled with water through fire hose attached to a nearby hydrant before a flap valve, shear gate, or similar quick-opening device leading to the sewer is opened; and (4) installing an automatic flush tank that fills slowly and discharges suddenly. Apart from cost and difficulties of maintenance, the danger of backflow from the sewer into the water supply is a bad feature of automatic flush tanks.

Example 3-1. An 8-in. sewer is to flow full at a velocity of 2.5 fps. (1) What is its maximum capacity in cfs and gpd? (2) What is the minimum grade on which this sewer must be laid, if the coefficient of roughness is assumed to be 0.013? (3) How many people can it serve if the maximum per capita flow is 300 gpd? (4) How many acres will it drain if the population density is 50 per acre?

1. Capacity $= [(\pi \times 64)/(4 \times 144)] \times 2.5 = 0.87$ cfs; and $0.87 \times 646,000 = 560,000$ gpd.

2. By Manning's formula, minimum grade $= 5.20$ ft/1000 (Table 14-2, $V = 2.5$ fps).

3. People served $= 560,000/300 = 1870$.

4. Area drained $= 1870/50 = 37.4$ acres.

3-5 Collection of Stormwater

Much of the suspended load of solids entering storm drains is sand and gravel. Because fine sand is moved along at velocities of 1 fps or more and gravel at 2 fps or more, recommended minimum velocities are 2.5 to 3 fps, or about 0.5 fps more than for sanitary sewers. Factors determining the

---

[6] At this slope a 6-in. sewer flowing full will discharge about 300 gpm or 40 cfm at a velocity of 3.5 fps.

capacity of storm drains are: (1) intensity and duration of local rainstorms; (2) size and runoff characteristics of tributary areas; and (3) economy of design, determined largely by the opportunity for quick discharge of collected stormwaters into natural water courses. Rate of storm runoff is ordinarily the governing factor in the hydraulic design of storm drains. To prevent inundation of streets, walks, and yards and flooding of basements and other low-lying structures, together with attendant inconvenience, traffic disruption, and damage to property, storm sewers are made large enough to drain away, rapidly and without becoming surcharged, the runoff from storms shown by experience to be of such intensity and frequency as to be objectionable. The heavier the storm, the greater but less frequent is the potential inconvenience or damage; the higher the property values, the more sizable is the possible damage. In a well-balanced system of storm drains, these factors will have received proper recognition for the kind of areas served: residential, mercantile, industrial, and mixed. For example, in high-value mercantile districts with basement stores and stock rooms, storm drains may be made large enough to carry away surface runoff from all but unusual storms, estimated to occur only once in 5, 10, 20, 50, or even 100 years, whereas the drains in suburban residential districts are allowed to be surcharged by all but the 1- or 2-year storm.

Until there are storm drains in a given area and the area itself is developed to its ultimate use, runoff measurements are neither possible nor meaningful. Accordingly, the design of storm sewers is normally based not on analysis of recorded runoff but on (1) analysis of storm rainfalls—their intensity or rate of precipitation, duration, and frequency of occurrence—and (2) estimation of runoff resulting from these rainfalls in the planned development.

Storm sewers are occasionally surcharged and subjected to pressures, but usually no more than their depth below street level. Nevertheless, they are designed for open-channel flow and equipped with manholes in much the same way as sanitary sewers. In North American practice, the minimum size of storm sewers is 12 in. to prevent clogging by trash of one kind or another. Their minimum depth is set by structural requirements rather than basement elevations. Surface runoff enters from street gutters through *street inlets* or *catch basins* (Fig. 3-6) and *property drains*. Size, number, and placement of street inlets govern the degree of freedom from flooding of traffic ways and pedestrian crossings. To permit inspection and cleaning, it is preferable to discharge street inlets directly into manholes. Catch basins are, in a sense, enlarged and trapped street inlets in which debris and heavy solids are held back or settle out. Historically, they antedate street inlets and were devised to protect combined sewerage systems at a time

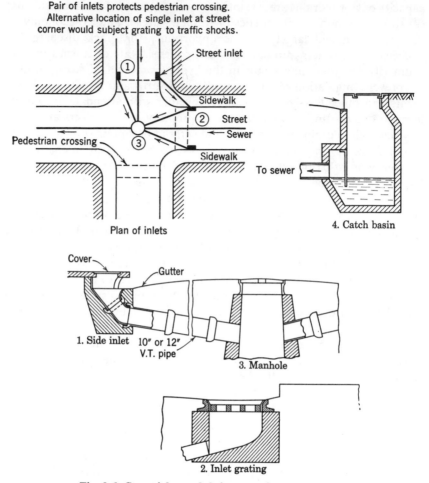

Pair of inlets protects pedestrian crossing.
Alternative location of single inlet at street
corner would subject grating to traffic shocks.

Plan of inlets

4. Catch basin

1. Side inlet   10″ or 12″
V.T. pipe

3. Manhole

2. Inlet grating

Fig. 3-6. Street inlets and their connection to a manhole.

when much sand and gravel were washed from unpaved streets. Historically, too, the air in sewers, called *sewer gas*, was once deemed dangerous
to health; this is why catch basins were given water-sealed traps. Catch
basins need much maintenance; they should be cleaned after every major
storm and may have to be oiled to prevent production of large crops of
mosquitoes. On the whole, there is little reason for continuing their use in
modern sewerage systems.

Example 3-2. A storm sewer is to drain an area of 37.4 acres (the area drained by
an 8-in. sanitary sewer in Example 3-1). How large must this drain be if it is to carry
away rain falling at a rate of 2 in. per hr during 30 min, the time needed for the entire

drainage area to become tributary to the sewer? The required velocity of flow is to be 3 fps, and the ratio of the peak rate of runoff to the rate of rainfall on the area is assumed to be 0.6.

1. 1 acre-in./hr = 1.0083 cfs = 1.0 cfs closely enough. This is a fact to remember.
2. Rate of runoff = $2 \times 0.6 \times 37.4 = 45$ cfs.
3. Cross-sectional area of drain = $45/3.0 = 15$ sq ft.
4. Diameter of drain = $12\sqrt{4 \times 15.0/\pi} = 53$ in.
5. Ratio of storm runoff to sanitary sewage (Example 3-1): 45.0:0.87 = 52:1; i.e., sanitary sewage, if admitted, would constitute less than 2% of the combined flow.
6. Per capita storm runoff for a population density of 50 per acre = $2 \times 0.6 \times 646,000/50 = 15,500$ gpcd, against sanitary sewage of 300 gpcd.

3-6 Collection of Combined Sewage

In combined sewerage systems, stormwaters often exceed sanitary sewage by 50 to 100 times (Example 3-2), and the accuracy with which rates of surface runoff can be estimated is generally less than the difference between rates of stormwater and combined-sewage flows. Accordingly, most combined sewers are designed to serve principally as storm drains. Understandably, however, they are placed as deep as sanitary sewers. Surcharge and overflow of combined sewers are obviously more objectionable than the backing-up of drains that carry nothing but stormwater. Moreover, they are given velocities up to 5.0 fps to keep them clean.

The wide range of flows in combined sewers requires the solution of certain special problems, among them choice of a cross-section that will ensure self-cleaning velocities for both storm and dry-weather flows; design of self-cleaning inverted siphons—also called sag pipes and depressed sewers—dipping beneath the hydraulic grade line as they carry sewage across a depression or under an obstruction; and provision of stormwater overflows in intercepting systems.

Cross-sections. Departures from circular cross-sections are prompted by hydraulic as well as structural and economic considerations. Examples are the *egg-shaped* sections and *cunettes* illustrated in Fig. 3-7. Two circular sewers, an underlying sanitary sewer, and an overlying storm drain are fused into a single egg-shaped section. The resulting hydraulic radius is nearly constant at all depths. Cunettes[7] form troughs dimensioned to the dry-weather flow, or sanitary sewage. *Rectangular sections* are easy to construct and make for economical trenching with low head-room requirements. *Horseshoe sections* are structurally very satisfactory; egg-shaped sections are not. Large outfall sewers have been built as pressure tunnels.

---

[7] The main drains of Paris, France, made famous by Victor Hugo's references to them in *Les Misérables*, were constructed from 1833 onward. They were made sufficiently large (6 ft high and at least 2 ft 6 in. wide) to permit laborers to work in comfort. Their conversion from 1880 onward into combined sewers necessitated the addition of *cunettes*.

Inverted Siphons. Flowing full and under pressure, the velocities of flow in siphons are relatively much more variable than in open-channel flow where depth and cross-section change simultaneously with flow. To keep velocities up and clogging by sediments down, two or more parallel pipes are thrown in and out of operation as flows rise and fall. The pipes

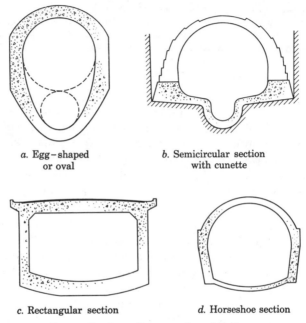

a. Egg–shaped or oval	*b.* Semicircular section with cunette
c. Rectangular section	*d.* Horseshoe section

Fig. 3-7. Sections of storm and combined sewers.

dispatch characteristic flows at self-cleaning velocities. Figure 3-8 shows a simple example: low dry-weather flows of sanitary sewage are passed through the central siphon; higher dry-weather flows and storm flows spill over weirs into lateral siphons to right and left. The three siphons combine to equal the capacity of the approach sewer. Weir heights are fixed at depths reached by characteristic flows in the approach sewer and inlet structure. Flows are reunited in a chamber in advance of the outlet sewer.

Example 3-3. A siphon is to carry a minimum dry-weather flow of 1.0 cfs, a maximum dry-weather flow of 3.0 cfs, and a storm flow of 45.0 cfs in three pipes. Select the proper diameters to assure velocities of 3.0 fps in all pipes.

1. For minimum dry-weather flow of 1.0 cfs, the nearest standard diameter of pipe is $12\sqrt{4 \times 1.0/(\pi \times 3.0)} = 8$ in.; actual capacity $= \pi \times (8)^2 \times 3/(4 \times 144) = 1.05$ cfs.

2. For maximum dry-weather flow in excess of the minimum, namely, $3.0 - 1.05 = 1.95$ cfs, the nearest standard diameter of pipe is $12\sqrt{4 \times 1.95/(\pi \times 3.0)} = 12$ in.; actual capacity $= \pi(\tfrac{1}{4}) \times 3 = 2.36$ cfs.

3. For storm flows in excess of maximum dry-weather flow, namely, $45 - (2.36 + 1.05) = 41.6$ cfs, the next lowest standard diameter of pipe is $12\sqrt{4 \times 41.6/(\pi \times 3.0)} = 48$ ins., which will have to flow at a velocity of $(41.6 \times 4)/(\pi \times 4^2) = 3.3$ fps.

Intercepters. Intercepting sewers are generally designed to carry away some multiple of the dry-weather flow in order to bleed off as much storm-water and included sewage as can be justified by hygienic, esthetic, and

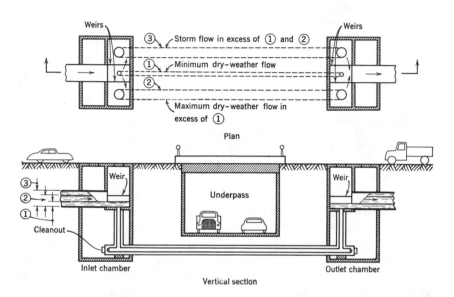

Fig. 3-8. Inverted siphon or suppressed sewer for combined sewage.

economic considerations. Where rainfalls are intense and sharp, as in most of North America, it is not possible to lead away much stormwater through reasonably proportioned intercepters. Consequently, they are designed to transport not much more than the maximum dry-weather flow, or approximately one and half to three times the average dry-weather flow of 250 to 600 gpcd. A more informative measure of intercepter capacity in excess of average dry-weather flow is the rate of rainfall or runoff they can accept without overflowing. Studies of rainfalls in the hydrological surroundings of the United States usually led to the conclusion that most precipitation in excess of 0.1 in. is spilled, that spills occur about half a dozen times a month, and that interception is not improved greatly by going even to ten times the dry-weather flow. However, where rains are gentle and long, as in the United Kingdom, six times the dry-weather flow comprises much of the runoff from rainfall and becomes a useful design factor.

Because the first flush of stormwater dislodges most of the deposits accumulating in sewers between storms, interception of primary flows is important. Otherwise, overflows would contain only their proportionate share of the sanitary sewage flowing in combined systems at the time of spill. However, even in these terms, the total yearly pollution reaching an intercepter-protected body of water is a significant fraction (3%) of the

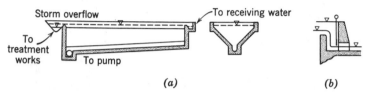

Storm overflow   To receiving water
To treatment works   To pump

(a)   (b)

Fig. 3-9. Stormwater detention tank and outlet weir: After *Innhoff and Fair*. (a) Longitudinal and transverse section of tank; (b) Two-level outlet weir; lower level for dryweather flow to treatment works, upper level for stormwater overflow to receiving water.

total annual volume of sanitary sewage. How much sewage of this kind goes overboard can be calculated from pertinent rainfall records; how much material is dislodged can be estimated only roughly.

Retarding Basins. Interception can be improved by introducing into combined systems retarding devices, for example, up-system detention basins or equalizing tanks. Constructed in advance of junctions between submains and intercepters, they store flows in excess of intercepter capacity until they are filled. After that, they continue to retard and equalize flows in lesser degree, but they do function as settling basins for the removal of gross and unsightly settleable matter (Fig. 3-9). Depending upon local conditions, detention periods as short as 15 minutes can be quite effective. Operating ranges extend from the dry-weather flowline of the intercepter to the crown of the conjoined combined sewer. After storms subside, the tank contents are flushed or lifted into the intercepter, and the accumulated solids eventually reach the treatment works. Where much stormwater is carried as far as the treatment plant—in the British Isles, for example—stormwater stand-by tanks become useful adjuncts to the works.

Overflows. The amounts of water entering interceptors at junctions with submains must be controlled. Only as much should be admitted as individual intercepter reaches can carry without being surcharged. Higher flows must be diverted into stormwater overflows. As shown in Fig. 3-10, admission and diversion can be regulated hydraulically or mechanically.

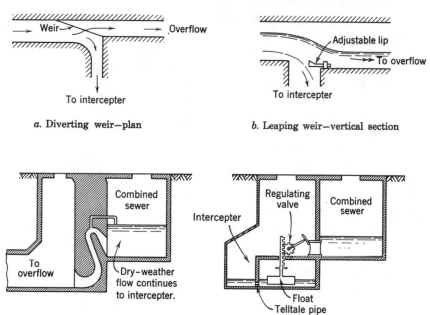

a. Diverting weir—plan

b. Leaping weir—vertical section

c. Siphon spillway—vertical section

d. Mechanical diverter, or regulator—vertical section; actual mechanisms are more complicated.

Fig. 3-10. Regulation of stormwater overflow.

Hydraulic separation of excess flows from dry-weather flows is accomplished by devices such as the following:

1. Diverting weirs in the form of side spillways leading to overflows. Crest level and length are chosen to spill excess flows that, figuratively speaking, override the dry-weather flows. Dry-weather flows follow their accustomed path to the intercepter (Fig. 3-10a).

2. Leaping weirs, essentially gaps in the floor of the channel. Excess flows jump the gap under their own momentum; dry-weather flows tumble through it into the intercepter (Fig. 1-30b).

3. Siphon spillways. Flows in excess of intercepter capacity are siphoned off into the overflow channel (Fig. 3-10c).

4. Mechanical devices. Diversion of storm-water flows is generally regulated by float-operated control valves activated by flow levels in the intercepter (Fig. 3-10d).

3-7 Choice of Collecting System

Apart from questions of economy, the combined system of sewerage is at best a compromise between two wholly different objectives: water

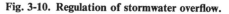

carriage of wastes and removal of flooding runoff. In the life of growing communities, initial economies are offset in the long run (1) by undesirable pollution of natural water courses through stormwater spills and consequent nuisance or, at least, debased esthetic and recreational values of receiving bodies of water; (2) by increased cost of treating and pumping intercepted sewage; and (3) by more obnoxious conditions when streets and basements are flooded by combined sewage instead of stormwater. In the past, small streams, around which parks and other recreational areas could have grown, have been forced into combined sewerage systems because pressing them into service as receiving waters had degraded them into open sewers. By contrast, a separate system of sewerage can exploit natural water courses hydraulically by discharging stormwater into them through short runs of storm drains while preserving their esthetic and recreational assets. However, they may have to be channelized if they are to perform well.

3-8 Disposal of Sewage

The water-carriage system of sewerage is a simple and economical means of removing unsightly, putrescible, and dangerous wastes from household and industry. However, it concentrates potential nuisances and dangers at the terminus of the collecting system. If rivers and canals, ponds and lakes, and tidal estuaries and coastal waters are not to become heavily polluted, the load imposed upon the transporting water must be *unloaded* prior to its disposal into the receiving bodies of water. As previously stated, but in somewhat different connotation, the unloading is assigned to sewage-treatment plants to prevent: (1) contamination of water supplies, bathing places, shellfish layings, and ice supplies; (2) pollution of receiving waters that will make them unsightly or malodorous and eutrophy ponds and lakes; (3) destruction of food fish and other valuable aquatic life; and (4) other impairment of the usefulness of natural waters for recreation, commerce, and industry. The required degree of treatment before disposal depends upon the nature and extent of the receiving water and upon the regional water economy.

In the treatment of sewage before disposal by irrigation, full recovery of the *water value* of sewage is intended together with as much recovery of *fertilizing value* as is consistent with: (1) avoiding the spread of disease by crops grown on sewage-irrigated lands or animals pastured on them; (2) preventing nuisances such as unsightliness and bad odors around disposal areas; and (3) optimizing, in an economic sense, sewage disposal costs and agricultural returns. The design of the irrigation areas themselves is based on the nature and size of available lands and the purposes they can serve in the regional agricultural economy.

As countries grow and their waters are used more widely and intensively, the discharge of raw or inadequately treated sewage into their streams, lakes, and tidal waters or onto their irrigation areas becomes intolerable. The daily load of solids imposed upon domestic sewage amounts to about half a pound per person. The resulting mixture of water and waste substances is very dilute—less than 0.1 % solid matter by weight when wastewater flows are 100 gpcd. Some industrial wastewaters are far more concentrated. Floating and other suspended solids render sewage and its receiving waters unsightly; settling solids build up sludge banks; organic solids cause sewage and its receiving waters to putrefy; pathogenic bacteria and other organisms make them dangerous.

Sewage-Treatment Processes.   Waste matters are removed from transporting water in a number of different ways. In municipal sewage-treatment works of fair size, the following processes and devices are common:

1. Bulky floating and suspended matter is strained out: *racks and screens*, producing rakings and screenings. Cutting racks and screens comminute the rakings and screenings in place and return them to the wastewater.

2. Oil and grease are skimmed off after rising during quiescence: *flotation tanks*, producing skimmings.

3. Heavy and coarse suspended matters are allowed to settle to the bottom of stilling chambers: *grit chambers, detritus tanks, settling tanks*, or *sedimentation basins*, producing grit, detritus, or sludge.

4. Non-settleable suspended matters and some dissolved solids are converted into settleable solids and become amenable to sedimentation by flocculation and precipitation with chemicals: *chemical flocculation* or *precipitation tanks*, producing sludge precipitates.

5. Colloidal and dissolved organic matter is metabolized and converted into settleable cell substance by biological growths or slimes. The hosts of living cells that populate the slimes utilize the waste matters for growth and energy. Their growth unfolds large interfaces at which adsorption, absorption, diffusion, and other interfacial forces or contact phenomena bring about exchanges between sewage and slimes. To remain active and aerobic, the biomasses are supplied with air. They are either supported on beds of granular material, such as broken stone over which the sewage trickles more or less continuously, or they are generated in the flowing sewage, returned to it in wanted amounts, and kept in suspension by agitating the mixed liquor with air or mechanically: *trickling filters* and *activated-sludge tanks*, producing trickling filter humus and excess activated sludge.

6. Some pathogenic bacteria and other organisms are removed from sewage along with the solids in which they are embedded or to which they cling. Others die because the imposed environment is too unfavorable. Fuller and more direct destruction is accomplished by disinfection: *chlorination units*.

How wastewaters from single dwellings and small communities are treated and disposed of is discussed in Sec. 3-11.

Sludge Disposal Processes. The solids separated from sewage in treatment works contain much water[8] and organic matter. This makes them bulky and putrescible. To simplify handling and disposal, sludge is dewatered and stabilized in varying degree. The following ways and devices are common:

1. Organic matter in sludge stored in tanks is metabolized and converted into relatively stable residues by bacteria and other saprophytic organisms. Continuing hosts of living things use the waste matters in the digesting sludge for growth and energy. There is liquefaction and gasification. Dissolved oxygen disappears, and the biomass becomes anaerobic: *sludge-digestion tanks* producing concentrated, stabilized, and rapidly dewatering sludges, sludge liquor, and gases of decomposition, primarily methane and carbon dioxide.

2. Water is removed from sludge (usually digested sludge) run into beds of sand or other granular materials by evaporation of moisture to the air and percolation of water into and through the beds: *sludge-drying beds* producing a spadable sludge cake.

3. Sludge is dewatered by passing it (usually after chemical coagulation) through a centrifuge or a filter medium such as cloth or coiled wires wound around a drum to which a vacuum is applied: *centrifuges* and *vacuum filters* producing a sludge cake or paste.

4. Sludge cake or paste (usually vacuum-filtered) is dried by heat: *flash driers* producing commercially (usually vacuum-dried) dry sludge granules.

5. Organic matter in partially dewatered or heat-dried sludge is burned as a fuel: *incinerators* producing ash.

6. Sludge is thickened in advance of digestion, drying or dewatering by stirring: *sludge thickeners* or *flocculators* producing a more concentrated sludge.

7. Organic matter in thickened sludge is destroyed by wet combustion: *sludge retorts* operating at high pressures and temperatures and producing readily dewatered, mineralized residues.

The marsh gas or methane released during digestion is a combustible gas of high fuel value and is put to good and varied uses in modern treatment works. After digestion, sewage solids are no longer recognizable as such. Their colloidal structure has been destroyed and they dry rapidly in the air. Heat-dried sludge is stable and essentially sterile. The final product of incineration is ash. Although all treatment methods reduce the number of possibly pathogenic organisms concentrated in sludge, only heat-drying makes it fully safe.

---

[8] Sludge settling from sewage by plain sedimentation contains about 95% water; activated sludge, 98% or more. If the daily flow of sewage is millions of gallons, the daily volume of sludge is thousands of gallons.

Methods of final disposal include the use of sewage sludges as fertilizers and soil builders; dumping sludge at sea; and filling low-lying lands. Only heat-treated sludge and sludge stored for many months should come into contact with food or forage crops.

Pictorial flow sheets of sewage-treatment plants are presented in Fig. 3-11. There are numerous other combinations of treatment processes.[9] The plants shown provide so-called primary and secondary treatment of both sewage and sludge. Partial treatment of either or both is often enough. However, more complete treatment may be needed at critical times of the year; for example, during low summer runoff and high recreational use of receiving waters. Tertiary treatment, also called water renovation, may be provided to remove residual, toxic, foaming, or otherwise objectionable substances.

The works illustrated will remove from 80 to 95% or more of the suspended solids, putrescible matter, and bacteria. Effluent chlorination can ensure 99% or higher destruction of bacteria. Partial treatment can achieve removal values between 40 and 70%.

Design of Sewage-Treatment Works. The design of sewage-treatment works is based upon an understanding of (1) treatment processes and devices (process design); (2) factors affecting the flow of sewage, sludge, and often air, through the structures employed (hydraulic and pneumatic design); (3) behavior of needed structures and mechanisms under load (structural and mechanical design), and (4) treatment costs relative to benefits received (economic design). The following facts (normally applicable to domestic sewage) give some concept of the size of principal structures:

1. Primary settling tanks hold sewage for about 2 hr and are rated at about 900 gpd per sq ft of water surface.

2. Secondary settling tanks, following biological treatment, have detention periods of about $1\frac{1}{2}$ hr and surface loadings up to 1800 gpd per sq ft.

3. Heated separate sludge-digestion tanks have a combined capacity of about 2 cu ft per capita in the northern United States when the digested sludge is to be air-dried. Agitation reduces required detention capacity, and favorable drying conditions as well as mechanical dewatering reduce required storage capacity.

[9] The combination of sedimentation and sludge digestion in a two-storied tank or in separate settling and digestion tanks, followed by biological treatment of the clarified sewage on a trickling filter (a and b in Fig. 3-11), has found wide favor in North America, particularly in cities of moderate size: Fitchburg and Worcester, Mass.; Reading, Pa.; Schenectady, N.Y.; Trenton, N.J.; and Atlanta, Ga. Plain sedimentation followed by activated-sludge treatment with or without separate sludge digestion has been employed, particularly, in large treatment works (c in Fig. 3-11): the Tallman's Island, Bowery Bay, and Jamaica Bay plants of New York, N.Y.; the North Side and Southwest Side plants of Chicago, Ill.; and the Easterly Works of Cleveland, O.

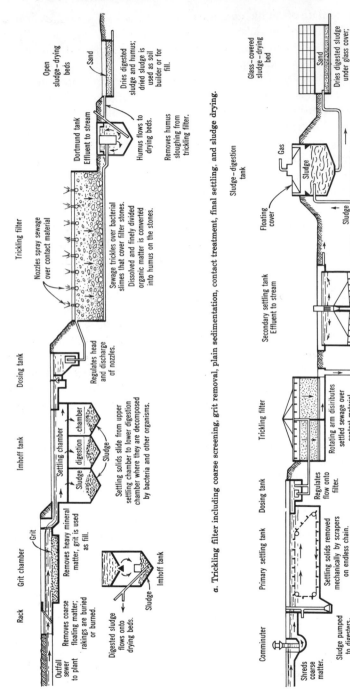

a. Trickling filter including coarse screening, grit removal, plain sedimentation, contact treatment, final settling, and sludge drying.

b. Trickling filter including comminution, plain sedimentation, contact treatment, final settling, and digestion and drying of sludge.

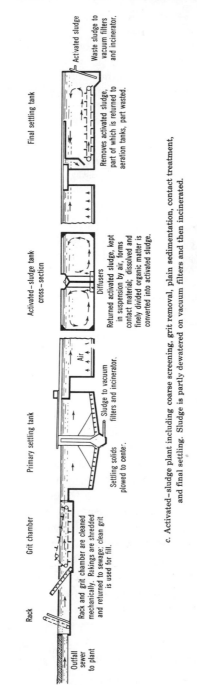

Rack

Grit chamber

Primary settling tank

Activated–sludge tank
cross–section

Final settling tank

Outfall sewer to plant

Rack and grit chamber are cleaned mechanically. Rakings are shredded and returned to sewage: clean grit is used for fill.

Settling solids plowed to center.

Sludge to vacuum filters and incinerator.

Air

Diffusers

Returned activated sludge, kept in suspension by air, forms contact material; dissolved and finely divided organic matter is converted into activated sludge.

Removes activated sludge, part of which is returned to aeration tanks, part wasted.

Activated sludge

Waste sludge to vacuum filters and incinerator.

c. Activated–sludge plant including coarse screening, grit removal, plain sedimentation, contact treatment, and final settling. Sludge is partly dewatered on vacuum filters and then incinerated.

Fig. 3-11. Common types of sewage-treatment plants.

4. Trickling filters are rated at about 3 mgad in conventional operation and at about 25 mgad in high-rate operation.

5. Activated-sludge tanks aerate the sewage and returned activated sludge, which equals about 25% of the volume of the sewage, for about 6 hr in conventional operation; both time of treatment and returned sludge volumes are modified in numerous variations on the conventional process.

6. Open drying beds for digested sludge provide an area of about 1 sq ft per capita in the northern United States. Glass covering and favorable climate lower the required area.

Example 3-4. Estimate the capacity of the components of a small trickling-filter plant (Fig. 3-11) treating 0.8 mgd of domestic sewage from 8000 people.
1. Settling compartments in 2 Imhoff tanks, averaging 10 ft in depth.
   (a) Assumed detention period = 2 hr.
   (b) Effective volume = 800,000 × (2/24)/2 = 33,300 gal = 4460 cu ft.
   (c) Surface area = 4460/10 = 446 sq ft (such as 20 ft by 23 ft).
   (d) Surface rating = (800,000/2)/446 = 900 gpd per sq ft.
2. Sludge digestion compartments in 2 Imhoff tanks:
   (a) Assumed storage requirement = 2 cu ft per capita.
   (b) Effective volume 2 × 8000/2 = 8000 cu ft.
   (c) Depth below settling compartment = 8000/446 = 18 ft (plus 2 ft to keep sludge clear of slots).
3. Sludge-drying beds, 4 in number.
   (a) Assumed area requirement = 1 sq ft per capita.
   (b) Effective area 1 × 8000/4 = 2000 sq ft (such as 20 ft by 100 ft).
4. Trickling filters, 1 in number.
   (a) Assumed loading = 3 mgad.
   (b) Effective area = 0.8/3 = 0.27 acre.

Disposal into Receiving Waters. Outfalls into receiving waters should terminate well below low-water mark. Sewage or effluent is dispersed effectively when a number of outlets, called *diffusers*, are (1) spaced sufficiently far apart to prevent interference and (2) situated at or near the bottom of the receiving water to keep the generally warmer and lighter[10] sewage from spreading over the receiving water in a persistent layer (Fig. 3-12). Density differences make themselves felt especially in marine outfalls. Strength, direction, and dimension of prevailing currents and the likelihood of their reaching water-works intakes, bathing places, shellfish layings, and other important spots are matters for study.

Whatever the relative dilution, the forces of natural purification, or self-purification, inherent in natural bodies of water can, in the course of time and distance, ultimately return the receiving water close to its original state of cleanliness. However, the enrichment of lakes, ponds, and impoundages with plant nutrients (eutrophication) and the resulting ecological changes in receiving waters of this kind are quite another thing.

[10] Especially when discharge is into seawater.

In a sense, natural purification is the prototype of biological treatment. Inherent metabolic activities remain aerobic so long as the rate of oxygen supply is not outbalanced by the rate of oxygen demand. The turbulence of streams usually keeps their running waters aerobic. However, their benthal environment may become anaerobic, because oxygen diffuses into bottom deposits only slowly. Anaerobic conditions are most likely to appear in

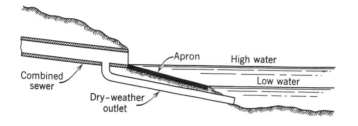

a. Outfall of combined sewer into a stream.

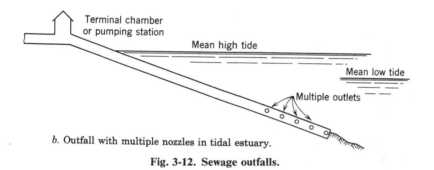

b. Outfall with multiple nozzles in tidal estuary.

Fig. 3-12. Sewage outfalls.

deep standing waters in which stratification makes for stagnation and consequently poor oxygen transport to the low water strata. Heavily polluted streams may become, for a time at least, black, unsightly, septic, and malodorous bodies of water in which the normal aerobic, clean-water flora and fauna have given way to a different, generally less acceptable, assemblage of living things.

A rule of thumb formulated by engineers for large American rivers and giving a rough estimate of the amount of dilution that would be required in the absence of treatment if combined sewage from 1000 persons was to be discharged without much nuisance is (1) for swift streams 2.5 cfs of diluting water; (2) for sluggish streams 10 cfs; and (3) for normal streams 6 cfs. For domestic sewage, treated sewage, and industrial wastes, *equivalent* populations should be substituted. Combined sewage averages about 40%

stronger than domestic sewage. Industrial waste waters may be weaker or stronger. Treated sewage is weaker in proportion to the amount of putrescible matter removed or destroyed. Where emphasis is on water supply, recreational enjoyment of water, and conservation of fish and other useful aquatic life, dilution or treatment becomes more urgent.

Example 3-5. The low-water flow of a normally rapid stream draining 2000 sq miles is 0.1 cfs per sq mile. Estimate the extent to which domestic sewage from a city of 80,000 people must be treated before discharge into this stream if nuisance is to be avoided; also the resulting dilution ratio of sewage to stream water. Assume a per capita flow of sewage of 100 gpd.

    1. Low-water flow = 0.1 × 2000 = 200 cfs.
    2. Required flow for disposal of domestic sewage if it is left untreated = 6 × 80/1.4 = 340 cfs.
    3. Per cent removal of pollutional load needed = 80(340 − 200)/340 = 33%.
    4. Dilution ratio = (80,000 × 100):(200 × 646,000) = 1:16.

Disposal onto Land. Objectives of terminal discharge of sewage onto land or into the soil are safe disposal and, possibly, croppage. In municipal practice, *disposal by irrigation* can seldom compete economically with discharge into receiving waters, unless the water resources of the region are poor and large tracts of suitable land can be acquired cheaply. Whether sewage should be treated before irrigation depends upon local and hygienic considerations. There is the obvious hazard of contaminating food raised on irrigated soil and infecting animals pastured on irrigated land. By contrast, the discharge of settled sewage into the ground through agricultural tile pipes in the disposal of sewage from isolated dwellings, known as subsurface irrigation, can be quite safe.

In one sense, shallow earth basins holding sewage for a number of days and called *sewage lagoons* or *stabilization ponds* are purposely inundated or waterlogged irrigation areas producing suspended (algal) rather than rooted crops. There is much evaporation from the ponds and some seepage. In another sense, the displacement of pond waters is often fast enough to approach the natural purification of sluggish receiving streams.

Under favorable climatic conditions, pond loadings may be as high as 500 persons per acre for raw domestic sewage.

Example 3-6. Estimate the daily volume of sewage that can be disposed of on an acre of land and the land area required to dispose of the domestic sewage from a community of 10,000 people by irrigation and through stabilization ponds 4 ft deep. Assume that the annual depth of water employed in the irrigation of crops is 10 in. and that the sewage flow is 80 gpcd.

    1. Rate of irrigation = [(10/12) × 7.5 × 43,560]/365 = 750 gpad.
    2. Irrigation area = 10,000 × 80/750 = 1100 acres = 1.7 sq miles.
    3. Stabilization-pond area = 10,000/500 = 20 acres.
    4. Detention period in ponds = 20 × 43,560 × 4 × 7.48/(10,000 × 80) = 33 days.

3-9 Disposal of Industrial Wastewaters

Most water-carried industrial wastes can safely be added to municipal sewage for treatment and disposal; but there are wastes so strong that they damage collection systems and interfere with or overload treatment facilities; pretreatment or separation from the collection system then becomes mandatory. The requisite degree of preparatory treatment or treatment in combination with municipal sewage depends upon the composition, concentration, and condition of the wastes, the nature and capacity of the treatment works, and the nature and capacity of the receiving waters. Shock loads, through sudden release of batches of wastes, are especially objectionable. Holding or storage basins will dampen shocks if they apportion waste discharge to available treatment-plant and receiving-water capacities.

Wastes rich in carbohydrates, proteins, and fats and not unlike domestic sewage in their degradability have a valid *population equivalent*. For example, the putrescible matter in the combined wastes from a distillery that processes 1000 bushels of grain a day is equivalent to the sewage from 3500 people. By contrast, other industrial wastes may persist in water without much change. Some may even interfere with sewage treatment and natural purification in receiving waters. Copper and other metal wastes are examples. At high concentrations, copper inhibits the anaerobic digestion of settled solids and destroys the biological masses in trickling filters and activated-sludge units. New synthetic organics may also be quite destructive. Yet it is possible to habituate biological slimes to many otherwise toxic organic chemicals, such as phenols and formaldehyde, which are degraded in treatment plants and receiving waters. When the chemicals contain the only available carbon, for example, a flora or succession of florae develops that is not only inured to the otherwise toxic substances but degrades them in the course of making use of the carbon they contain.

Guiding principles in the solution of industrial-wastes problems are, in order of preference: (1) recovery of useful materials; (2) improvement of manufacturing processes whereby waste matters and waste waters are reduced in amount; (3) recycling of process waters; and (4) development of economic methods of treatment. Recovery is most successful when the substances recovered are either very valuable or otherwise not so unlike the primary products of manufacture that a separate management organization must be developed. Improvement in manufacturing processes may permit discharge of remaining waste matters into public sewers.

There are satisfactory treatment processes for a wide variety of industrial wastes. Most of them are not unlike established sewage-treatment methods; but some chemical wastes require quite a different disposal approach. For example, cyanides from plating industries are most conveniently oxidized to cyanates; chromates from the same source are most conveniently reduced to chromic compounds; and acids and alkalis from many industries are most conveniently neutralized.

3-10 Systems Management

In keeping with water-works practice, the construction of wastewater systems from the ground up, or their improvement and extension, progresses from preliminary studies through financing, design, and construction to operation, maintenance, and repair. The per capita investment in sewerage systems varies with system type; topography, hydrology, and geology of communities served; nature, volume, and proximity of receiving waters; need for sewage treatment; availability and cost of labor and materials; and size and character of the community.

The first cost of sanitary sewers lies between \$30 and \$100 per capita in North America. The cost of storm drains and combined sewers, depending upon local conditions, is about three times as much. The first cost of sewage-treatment works varies with the degree of treatment provided. Depending upon plant size, which, for wastewater, is more clearly a function of the population load than the volume of water purified (Sec. 2-10), the per capita cost of wastewater treatment works is about as follows,[11] as of 1965: (1) works including (a) Imhoff tanks \$20, and (b) trickling filters as well as Imhoff tanks \$26, both a and b varying inversely with the population load approximately as the $\frac{1}{2}$ power of ($10^{-4} \times$ population), i.e., $1/(P \times 10^{-4})^{1/2}$; (2) for works including (a) mechanized settling and heated sludge-digestion tanks \$35, varying approximately as $1/(P \times 10^{-4})^{1/3}$, (b) activated-sludge units as well as primary treatment \$47, also varying approximately as $1/(P \times 10^{-4})$,$^{1/4}$ and (c) trickling filters as well as primary treatment \$45, varying approximately as $1/(P \times 10^{-4})^{2/5}$; and (3) for stabilization ponds \$0.90, varying approximately as $1/(P \times 10^{-4})^{1/4}$. For years other than 1965, construction costs must be adjusted by means of a suitable cost index.[12]

The annual per capita operating and maintenance cost for plants themselves, i.e., exclusive of central administrative expenses, is about as follows:[13]

---

[11] P. P. Rowan, K. L. Jenkins, and D. W. Butler, Sewage Treatment Construction Costs, *J. Water Poll. Control Fed.*, **32**, 594 (1960), after an analysis of the cost of more than 500 plants, suggested the equational relationship $C = a/P^b$ where C is the cost, P the population, and a and b are coefficients for different types of plants. Also see *Public Health Service Construction Cost Index*.

[12] The *Engineering News-Record Construction Cost Index*, for example.

[13] P. P. Rowan, K. L. Jenkins, and D. H. Howells, Estimating Sewage Treatment Operation and Maintenance Costs, *J. Water Poll. Control Fed.*, **33**, 111 (1961) in an analysis of more than 300 plants arrived at the equational relationship $\log (10C) = 1/[a + b \log (10^{-2}P)]$ with the same notation as in footnote 11.

(1) for primary plants, $2.7, 1.4, 0.91, and 0.67 for communities of 10^3, 10^4, 10^5, and 10^6 people respectively; (2) for activated-sludge plants similarly $9.2, 3.5, 1.9, 1.2 and 0.88; (3) for conventional trickling-filter plants $3.5, 1.3, and 0.75 (there being no value for 10^6 people); and (4) for high-rate trickling-filter plants $4.6, 1.4, and 0.73, in the same sense as for conventional plants. For years other than 1965, it is more difficult to find a suitable index of operating and maintenance costs than a construction cost index; prevailing wage rates are, perhaps, the best index, but the cost of light and power, heat and chemicals also enters into the problem.

Including interest and depreciation, as well as charges against operation and management, the removal of domestic sewage and its safe disposal cost from $50 to $100 per mg. In comparison with water purification plants, sewage treatment works are relatively twice as expensive; in comparison with water distribution systems, collection systems for domestic sewage about half as expensive. Sewer use charges, also called rentals, like charges for water, can place the cost of sewerage upon a *value received* basis. Use charges may cover part or all of the cost of the service rendered and are generally related to the water bill as a matter of equity.

Example 3-7. Roughly, how much money is invested in the sanitary sewerage system of a city of 100,000 people?
1. Assuming the per capita cost at $75, the total first cost is $75 × 100,000 = $7,500,000.
2. Assuming that the sewage is treated in an activated-sludge plant, the expected cost is $47 × 10^5/(10)^{1/4} = $2,600,000, or about a third of the total cost. The annual cost of operation and maintenance, incidentally, is about $120,000.

No general costs can be assigned to separate treatment of industrial wastewaters. When they are discharged into municipal sewerage systems, treatment costs can be assessed in terms of loads imposed on the municipal works as suspended solids, putrescible matter, or a combination of the two.

3-11 Rural Wastewater Systems

In the absence of public sewerage, wastewaters from rural dwellings and ancillary buildings are normally discharged into the ground. The absorptive capacity of the soil is then of controlling importance. It is greatly increased if settleable waste matters are first removed; for example, by sedimentation combined with digestion and consolidation of the deposited sludge and scum. Sedimentation and digestion are accomplished more often than not either in leaching cesspools or in septic tanks (or tight cesspools). Subsurface absorption fields or seepage pits follow.

A leaching-cesspool and seepage-pit installation is shown in Fig. 3-13; a septic tank and absorption field in Fig. 2-13.

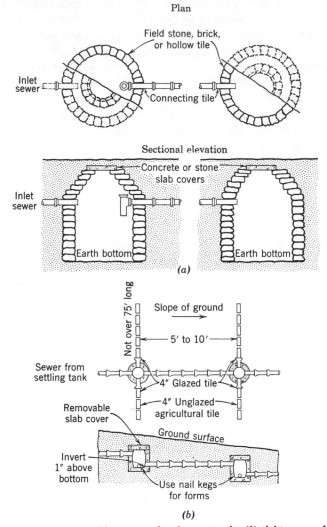

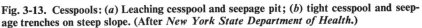

Fig. 3-13. Cesspools: (a) Leaching cesspool and seepage pit; (b) tight cesspool and seep-age trenches on steep slope. (After *New York State Department of Health.*)

When there is much wastewater, modification of conventional municipal plants are brought into operation. However, the required structures are generally covered or placed below ground. The line of separation between small and large facilities is often drawn at about 10,000 gpd.

CHAPTER 4

Information Analysis

4-1 Basic Concepts

Probability and statistics, often linked and sometimes mistakenly inter-changed, are distinct disciplines; yet they share a rigorous mathematical basis. Probability theory starts with certain axioms, generates theorems, and is developed in an orderly, deductive fashion. In contrast, statistics pos-sesses an inductive component; the statistician is concerned with decision making, selection among alternative hypotheses, and similar matters. Consider the commonplace problem of fitting a curve to pairs of obser-vations. The formalisms inherent in fitting a polynomial of degree $n - 1$ to n observed pairs or points lie within the province of mathematics or numerical analysis. Paradoxically, it is harder to fit a polynomial of degree $n - 2$ rather than $n - 1$ to the same n observations because, for example, only one parabola but an infinite number of straight lines can be fitted to three points; the task degenerates, clearly, when the points are colinear. However, a unique linear solution to the general case, the *best* fit, implies some criterion of *goodness of fit*. This dichotomy is analogous to the dis-tinction between problems in probability and statistics because the statis-tical solution requires an unequivocal statement of objective. Only then can one treat the statistical issues that identify the *best-fitting* linear function or, more fundamentally, that indicate whether a linear function can reasonably be expected to represent the data at all.

In this chapter the emphasis is on statistics rather than probability, particularly in reference to the analysis of hydrologic information but useful, too, in the generalization of other quantitative data: population

4-1

growth, water consumption and its corollary wastewater release, water goodness and badness, and water and wastewater treatment. The engineer can discern at once the close similarity between his normal tasks of design and the mechanism of statistical analysis because induction is inherent in both. Statistical techniques provide a formalism for decision making. Through their use, enormous amounts of quantitative information can often be reduced to a handful of parameters that convey, clearly and incisively, the underlying structure of the original or raw data. Appropriate manipulation of these parameters, combined with proper regard for their reliability, forms the framework of this chapter.

The meteorologic and hydrologic processes with which engineers must ordinarily cope are very old. Yet a long rainfall or streamflow record, say 50 or even 100 years, represents but a fraction of the geologic history of a particular process; but the vast portion of these data originates in early geological regimes no longer extant. Most geomorphological processes are so slow that a good historical record of important hydrological events can safely be assumed to represent the pertinent characteristics of specific phenomena. There are, of course, exceptions. Within the span of a few years the Mississippi River deposits great quantities of silt in its delta and changes the local topography; more spectacularly, landslides and volcanic eruptions can alter the earth's face within a few moments; and, last, the works of man encroach upon nature's domain and change her patterns· significantly over time.

In this chapter, however, only processes that are stationary by virtue of not exhibiting the effects of long-term trends and man-made perturbations will be treated. Nonetheless, the problem of statistical inference remains formidable even after sweeping aside the complications and inconsistencies of data collection. This is so because the engineer, in his hydrologic studies, must often manipulate a small sample to predict the behavior of an expensive system over the span of its useful (economic) life. For example, if the economic life of a proposed dam is 100 years, and if only 10 years of flow data are available,[1] substantial funds are ventured on the engineer's ability to generalize and interpret the meager information efficiently. Consequently the engineer must concentrate his efforts on alleviating the effect of the paucity of reliable records.

Implicit in the foregoing statement is the distinction between a sample and its parent population.[2] If the height of each student in a particular classroom is recorded and the arithmetic mean height[3] is computed, this

[1] Neglected here are the important considerations of the accuracy and precision of the data themselves.
[2] Meaning by *population* the sum total of collectable data on a specific matter.
[3] Commonly referred to as the average height.

single number, derived from a sample of size n, is certainly not representative of all students. A few of the many sample characteristics are age, sex, genetic (or family) traits, medical and nutritional history, racial background, and regional characteristics. Accordingly, the computed average would be more meaningful if the sample were limited to a random selection from 8-year-old white males from New England, with no evidence of malnutrition. If the sample is fully representative of the population, appreciable confidence could then be attached to the sample average as an estimate of the average height of this, but only this, population. Inferring the nature of the population from a few sample data is not a trivial matter.

Final introductory comments are directed to the schism between continuous and discrete values. Traditionally, the contrast centers about the word infinity; in some manner a discrete process is said to possess a finite number of states,[4] a continuous process an infinite number.[5] Two separate mathematical systems were developed, one applicable to each process. Modern theory tends to consolidate the two because it is conceptually simple to translate the arithmetic summation of the discrete case to the mathematical integration of the continuous case. Indeed, both cases can attain an infinity of states, but the discrete case is described by a denumerable infinity of states, the continuous case by a continuous infinity of states. Thus, if a pointer is spun on a dial, discrete theory admits of results such as 42.7583 degrees if the measurement is good to 0.0001 degree; continuous theory admits of irrational results such as $\pi/\sqrt{2}$ radians, a value without a terminating decimal.

To recapitulate, the statistical significance of arrays of quantitative data resulting from stationary processes will be studied, the uncertainties generated by sampling noted, and continuous and discrete notation freely interchanged as the material warrants. The purpose of this chapter is to develop a feeling for the statistical nature of the world of the sanitary engineer and for the shorthand and vocabulary used to describe it.

4-2 Characteristics of a Frequency Function

Consider a fair coin, where fair implies that the coin is equally likely to land *heads* as *tails*. An alternative assertion is that if the coin were tossed many times, say 10^6 times, approximately 5×10^5 heads would be expected. The *probability* of a head can be defined: P (heads) = number of heads observed/total tosses; and similarly, P (tails) = number of tails observed/total tosses, where the number of tosses is large and the ratios are stable. If it is agreed to eliminate rare results, such as landing on edge, heads and

[4] For example, throw a die and observe the result: it must be 1, 2, . . . , or 6.
[5] For example, spin a pointer on a dial and observe its angular deviation from true north.

tails are the only possible results. Then P (tails) $+ P$ (heads) $= 1$, and heads and tails, the two outcomes, are said to be mutually exclusive and collectively exhaustive: a head precluding a tail on the same trial and conversely (hence, mutual exclusiveness), and heads and tails together comprising the complete set of possible outcomes (hence, collective exhaustiveness). In general, if x_i specifies the ith possible outcome and $P(x_i)$ is its probability, and if there are n such mutually exclusive and collectively exhaustive outcomes, then

$$\sum_{i=1}^{n} P(x_i) = 1 \qquad\qquad (4\text{-}1)$$

Two definitions of probability are intertwined in the preceding paragraph. By referring to *equally likely*, it is tacitly assumed that P (heads) $= P$ (tails) $= 0.5$, wherefore the argument becomes circular because *equally likely* is used to define *probability*, which is, in turn, implicit in the definition of *equally likely*. The early theorists evolved the following (inadequate) definition, known as the classical definition of probability: if there are n equally likely outcomes of an experiment, the probability of any single outcome is $1/n$.

The second definition requires the execution of an experiment and some simple bookkeeping. In the coin example, it is a simple matter, at least conceptually, to perform the tossing experiment.[6] The essence of the experiment is that it is conceivable and its possible outcomes are denumerable, leading to the more recent, operational definition of probability: if an experiment is performed n times, and if outcome A is observed in m of the trials, the probability of event A is the ratio m/n as n approaches infinity.

Other new definitions of probability, based on information theory, will not be given here, because the operational definition is here adequate, although extrapolation beyond the limits of observation stands on less secure ground. For example, let a hydrologic record of n years' duration serve as an experiment with n trials. The probability that the flow lies in the range, say, of 1000 to 2000 cfs can be read from the record. However, if the engineer is asked to design a flood-control reservoir to contain the 500-year flood, or a flood so severe that the probability of its occurrence is $1/500$ or 2×10^{-3}, no experiment is capable of measuring the probability of the design flood, because n is much less than 500. Both the classical and the operational approaches fail to provide a meaningful definition for the 500-year flood, and, indeed, there is some basis for questioning whether the 500-year flood is at all significant from a rigorous mathematical point

---

[6] Practically speaking, the coin would be worn and its tosser exhausted long before completing the million tosses.

of view. An alternative approach to the study of extreme values—the use of *synthetic* or *operational records*—is offered later in this chapter.

Suppose that a coin is tossed 5 times, and the number of heads is recorded. There are 6 possible results, characterized by x, the number of heads recorded in the experiment. Only integral values of x in the range $0 \leq x \leq 5$ are meaningful. To continue with an experiment in which each of 1000 persons tosses a coin 5 times and reports the number of heads observed, the probability of any one person's tossing m heads in 5 trials is $P(m$ heads$) = $ number of persons who observed m heads/1000, and $\sum_{m=0}^{5} P(m$ heads$) = 1$. Typical results are shown in Table 4-1. The issue of fairness of the coin is

Table 4-1   Probability of m Heads in 5 Trials

Number of heads in 5 trials, m	0	1	2	3	4	5	Total
Number of persons	30	160	300	320	155	35	1000
Probability of one person tossing m heads in 5 trials, $P(m)$	0.030	0.160	0.300	0.320	0.155	0.035	1.000

nowhere raised. Individual coins are probably[7] worn, bent, smoothed at the edges, and elsewise rendered imperfectly balanced. However, this in no way affects the computation because operational probability is computed from experimental evidence without regard to *a priori*[8] bias.

Assume that the coin is fair.[9] Invoking the classical definition, assign equal *a priori* probabilities to the two possible outcomes of a single trial, and consider the probability of 0, 1, . . . , 5 heads in 5 trials.

The probability of exactly m successes (heads) in N trials is given by the equation

$$P(x = m) = \binom{N}{m} p^m q^{N-m} \tag{4-2}$$

where p is the probability of success in any trial, $q = 1 - p$ is the probability of failure in any trial, and $\binom{N}{m} = \dfrac{N!}{m!\,(N-m)!}$. The function

[7] Here is yet another definition of probability—quite outside our mathematical framework.
[8] Latin: *a* (*ab*) from, and *prior* former, meaning by reason alone.
[9] This assumption may be based on the dynamics of rigid bodies, observations of minting procedure, or other suitable empirical evidence.

$P(x = m)$ of the independent variable x is a probability function and is generally written $f(x)$. It is zero for $x < 0$, for $x > N$, and for all non-integral values of x. Because it drops to zero instantaneously when x is not integral, the function $f(x)$ is called a discrete function. Equation 4-2, the binomial distribution, plays a singular role in statistical theory, because the most commonly used distributions are approximations to the binomial distribution.

The binomial density function has two components, the exponential $[p^m q^{N-m}]$ and the combinatorial $\binom{N}{m}$. The exponential component represents the joint probability of m successes (each success arising with probability p) followed by $N - m$ failures (each arising with probability $q = 1 - p$). Their product denotes the probability of m successes and $N - m$ failures in any order, given that success and failure are independent events.[10] The combinatorial component, $\binom{N}{m}$, is the number of different ways m successes and $N - m$ failures can be ordered, assuming that any success (or failure) is indistinguishable from the others. For example, if there are 3 identical red balls ($R1, R2, R3$) and 2 identical white balls ($W1, W2$), the number of permutations is $\binom{5}{2} = \binom{5}{3} = \dfrac{5!}{2!\,3!} = 10$, because $R1$, $R2$, and $R3$ are indistinguishable and can be replaced by R, just as $W1$ and $W2$ can be replaced by W.

The term $p^m q^{N-m} \binom{N}{m}$ is the product of the number of ways an event can occur and the probability of each combination, which is tantamount to the probability of exactly m successes in N trials. The results of computations based on the binomial distribution (Eq. 4-2) for a fair coin ($p = 0.5$) and a biased coin ($p = 0.4$) are presented in Table 4-2 and Fig. 4-1.

The probabilities for $p = 0.5$ in Table 4-2 agree closely with the data in Table 4-1, indicating that the binomial model with $p = 0.5$ is a reasonable representation of the coin-tossing game summarized in that table. However, it is not at all obvious that the coin used in the game is unbiased. To decide this, some level of acceptance or tolerance must be specified, and this is the role of statistical inference. The two alternative hypotheses are: (1) the coin is fair and (2) the coin is biased. The statistician cannot select one or the other unless he is told what degree of deviation from the theoretical value or tolerance to accept.

---

[10] Statistically, independence implies that the probability of success or failure on any trial does not depend on what has occurred in any earlier trial.

Table 4-2 Probability and Cumulative Binomial Distributions for a Fair and a Biased Coin

Number of heads, m	0	1	2	3	4	5
Probability of heads in m trials, $P(x = m)$ for $p = 0.5$ (fair coin)	0.03125	0.15625	0.31250	0.31250	0.15625	0.03125
Cumulatively, $P(x \leq m)$	0.03125	0.18750	0.50000	0.81250	0.96875	1.00000
Probability of heads in m trials, $P(x = m)$ for $p = 0.4$ (biased coin)	0.07776	0.25920	0.34560	0.23040	0.07680	0.01024
Cumulatively, $P(x \leq m)$	0.07776	0.33696	0.68256	0.91296	0.98976	1.00000

Table 4-2 and Fig. 4-1 can be enlarged to include the probabilities that the number of heads is less than or equal to m or, symbolically,

$$P(x \leq m) = F(x) = \int_{-\infty}^{m} f(x)\, dx \quad \text{or} \quad P(x \leq m) = F(x_m) = \sum_{i=0}^{m} f(x_i)$$

$$(4\text{-}3)$$

For a function $f(x)$ to be an admissible probability function, it must satisfy three criteria: (1) the integral or sum of $f(x)$ over all possible values of x must be unity; (2) the function must be nowhere negative; and (3) the function must be single-valued. The first criterion is expressed symbolically

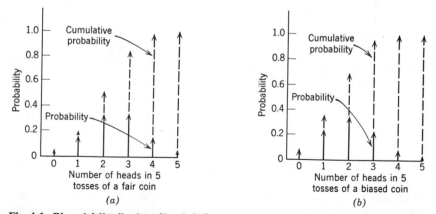

Fig. 4-1. Binomial distribution of heads in five tosses of a fair and a biased coin respectively; (a) Fair coin, $p = 0.5$; (b) Biased coin, $p = 0.4$.

by

$$\int_{-\infty}^{\infty} f(x)\, dx = 1 \quad \text{or} \quad \sum_{i=0}^{\infty} f(x_i) = 1 \tag{4-4}$$

It scales all probabilities so that an assured or certain event is assigned a probability value of unity, which is tantamount to requiring that each experiment have *some* outcome. This conclusion serves as a basis for defining an upper limit to the probability of an event. The second criterion, $f(x) \geq 0$, assigns zero probability to an impossible event, and the third is a criterion imposed for simplicity and clarity.

When one deals with discrete distributions, such as the binomial, it is sensible to refer, say, to $P(x = 2)$. However, for continuous distributions, or those characterized by a continuous infinity of arguments, it follows that $P(x = 2) = 0$. The cumulative functions $P(x \leq a) = F(a) = \int_{-\infty}^{a} f(x)\, dx$ and $P(x \leq b) = F(b) = \int_{-\infty}^{b} f(x)\, dx$ can be written without the equalities $P(x < a) = F(a)$ and $P(x < b) = F(b)$, because $P(x = a)$ and $P(x = b)$ are both precisely zero, thus adding nothing to the integration. If $b > a$,

$$P(a < x < b) = \int_{a}^{b} f(x)\, dx \tag{4-5}$$

whereupon it is manifest that probability can be thought of as the area bounded by the curve $f(x)$, by $x = a$, $x = b$, and by the axis of abscissae. The area under a point, or $P(x = a)$, is clearly zero.

For discrete distributions, a slightly different view prevails, because there is an implied interval surrounding every argument. Suppose the arguments x_i are weights, in pounds, taken from a household scale. Then the interval $x_0 = 0.5$ would include all weights 0 to 1 pound; $x_1 = 1.5$ all weights 1 to 2 pounds, etc., and $P(x = a)$ need not be zero.

There are many ways to specify a density function uniquely. One could plot or tabulate all the points for reference. It is simpler, although not always possible in a manageable fashion, to write the equation of the function. For example, consider the two functions

$$P(x = m) = p^m (1 - p)^{N-m} \binom{N}{m} \tag{4-6}$$

and

$$f(x) = \frac{1}{\sqrt{2\pi}\, \theta_2} \exp\left[-\frac{1}{2}\left(\frac{x - \theta_1}{\theta_2} \right)^2 \right] \tag{4-7}$$

Both can be shown to satisfy the three criteria for probability densities, whereupon complete specification of those densities requires the identification of merely a few parameters. Other functional representations are the substance of the structure of mathematical statistics. Suffice it here (1) to relate the general shape of a function's graph to its analytic formulation and (2) to gain an insight into the essential parameters characterizing the function. One such class of parameters, the moments of a distribution, is introduced to this purpose.

4-3   Moments of Distributions

Structural engineers deal with useful steel shapes, such as I-beams and wide-flange sections. They know that the particles of a wide-flange beam are distributed in a characteristic shape but that a unique specification requires additional data about size (or cross-sectional area) and proportion (or moments of inertia about some axes). These supplementary data are related to the moments of the cross-section; indeed, the centroid of the section is that point where the first moments (in two perpendicular directions) vanish, and about which the moments of inertia are minimized.

The analogy to statistical distributions is remarkably complete. It can be shown that if all the moments of a statistical distribution are known, the distribution is uniquely defined, and conversely. Therefore, it is essential to embark on a study of these important parameters. Suppose that some continuous distribution $f(x)$ is postulated; the first moment about an arbitrary axis $x = a$ is defined by

$$\mu_a = \int_{-\infty}^{\infty} (x - a) f(x) \, dx \qquad (4\text{-}8)$$

where the Greek letter μ is the standard notation for a moment and its subscript defines the axis $x = a$.

If $a = 0$, Eq. 4-8 refers to the first moment about the origin; this is so important in statistics that it has its own symbol, μ', and is called the *mean*. It is perhaps more familiar as the arithmetic *average*.[11] Thus

$$\mu' = \int_{-\infty}^{\infty} x f(x) \, dx \qquad (4\text{-}9)$$

In general, the rth moment about the origin is written

$$\mu_r' = \int_{-\infty}^{\infty} x^r f(x) \, dx \qquad (4\text{-}10)$$

and the set of moments for $r = 1, \ldots, \infty$ completely defines the function $f(x)$. When the origin of moments is at the mean, $\mu = 0$, and the rth moment about the mean is written without the prime. Thus

$$\mu_r = \int_{-\infty}^{\infty} (x - \mu')^r f(x) \, dx \qquad (4\text{-}11)$$

[11] Sometimes the prime is omitted where no confusion can result.

and again the set of moments for $r = 1, \ldots, \infty$ completely defines the function. The sets $\mu_r{'}$ and μ_r can be derived from each other. For example, if $r = 2$, $\mu_2{'} = \int x^2 f(x)\, dx$ and $\mu_2 = \int (x - \mu)^2 f(x)\, dx = \int x^2 f(x)\, dx - 2\mu \int x f(x)\, dx + \mu^2 \int f(x)\, dx = \mu_2{'} - 2\mu(\mu) + \mu^2(1)$, whence

$$\mu_2 = \mu_2{'} - \mu^2 \tag{4-12}$$

Similar derivations can be made for any moment about any axis.

The mean is a measure of central tendency in that it is a numerical representation of the center of gravity of the distribution $f(x)$. Generally, it does not appear among the observations but is a convenient distillation of the many data. However, it fails to give any indication of the nature of the dispersion of the values. For example, the sets $(49, 51)$, $(10, 90)$, $(40, 50, 60)$, and $(-50, 150)$ all have means of 50, but they vary widely in their dispersion. The second moment about the mean

$$\mu_2 = \int_{-\infty}^{\infty} (x - \mu{'})^2 f(x)\, dx = \mu_2{'} - \mu^2 \tag{4-13}$$

is called the *variance*, and it, too, is given a special symbol, σ^2, because of its great importance. Because $f(x)$ and $(x - \mu)^2$ are never negative, the variance is never negative; its positive square root, σ, is the *standard deviation*. Both the mean and standard deviation have the same dimensions as the original variate values. The first moment serves to measure the magnitude of the mean or the central tendency of the distribution; the second moment the magnitude of dispersion of the distribution. It is readily seen that a distribution with given mean and a large variance is more diffuse than one with the same mean but a small variance.

The computation of moments from sample data is a straightforward task. If the size of the sample is n, the sample mean is

$$\bar{x} = \sum_{i=1}^{n} x_i / n \tag{4-14}$$

where $\bar{x}$ replaces μ to indicate that a simple parameter rather than a population parameter is implied.[12] The sample variance is written

$$s^2 = \sum_{i=1}^{n} (x_i - \bar{x})^2 / (n - 1) \tag{4-15}$$

if the population mean is unknown or

$$s^2 = \sum_{i=1}^{n} (x_i - \mu{'})^2 / n \tag{4-16}$$

[12] The distinction between population values and their sample counterparts is generally noted by the use of Greek and Roman letters respectively.

if the population mean is known. The distinction between n and $(n - 1)$ in the denominators can be disregarded at first reading; indeed, Eq. 4-15 is often given as the definition of variance without further justification for the reduction in denominator (Secs. 4-5 and 4-8).

Use of Eq. 4-15 requires two passes through the data, the first to compute $\bar{x}$ and the second to compute $\Sigma(x_i - \bar{x})^2$ after $\bar{x}$ is known. But if the expansion

$$\frac{1}{n - 1}\Sigma(x_i - \bar{x})^2 = \frac{\Sigma(x_i^2 - 2\bar{x}x_i + \bar{x}^2)}{n - 1} = \frac{\Sigma x_i^2 - n\bar{x}^2}{n - 1} \qquad (4\text{-}17)$$

is made in keeping with Eq. 4-12, only one pass is necessary when a desk calculator or digital computer is used, because these devices can accumulate Σx_i and Σx_i^2 simultaneously. Thus, if $\Sigma x_i/n$ is written for $\bar{x}$, the variance is

$$s^2 = \frac{\Sigma x_i^2 - n(\Sigma x_i/n)^2}{n - 1} = \frac{\Sigma x_i^2}{n - 1} - \frac{(\Sigma x_i)^2}{n(n - 1)} \qquad (4\text{-}18)$$

Both Eqs. 4-12 and 4-18 state that the variance about the origin exceeds the variance about the mean by the mean squared. As before, recursive[13] computational schemes for higher moments can be generated.

4-4   Examples of the Use of Moments

Consider the data in Table 4-3.

Table 4-3   Sample Calculation of Moments

Magnitude of Observations	Frequency of Observations		
x_i	$f(x_i)$	$x_i f(x_i)$	$x_i^2 f(x_i)$
(1)	(2)	(3) = (2) × (1)	(4) = (3) × (1)
1	2	2	2
2	6	12	24
3	12	36	108
4	24	96	384
5	36	180	900
6	40	240	1440
7	36	252	1764
8	24	192	1536
9	12	108	972
10	6	60	600
11	2	22	242
Sums	200	1200	7972

[13] Recursive in that they can be expressed in terms of lower moments.

By Eq. 4-14, $\bar{x} = 1200/200 = 6$
By Eq. 4-18, $s^2 = 7972/199 - (1200)^2/(199 \times 200) = 3.88$
or $s = 1.97$

If these data are plotted as in Fig. 4-2, several interesting conclusions can be drawn.

1. The curve is symmetric about the mean, whereupon all odd moments about the mean vanish because every positive contribution to the sum $\Sigma(x_i - \mu')^m$

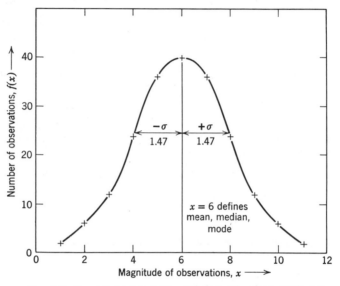

Fig. 4-2. Graphical presentation of information from Table 4-3.

for m odd, is balanced by a negative deviation. (The first moment about the mean is identically zero for every distribution.)

2. If a smooth curve is drawn through the data points, the points of inflection lie at a distance σ or 1.97 units from the mean.

3. The *mode*, or most frequent observation, is equal to the mean and also to the *median*, or central ranked observation, the median always equaling the mean for symmetric distributions, whereas the mode, in a U-shaped symmetric distribution as in Fig. 4-3, is not centrally located.

The mean—most frequently used of the three measures of central tendency—has statistical nobility in that it arises naturally from considerations of the moments of a distribution. It is easy to compute, and its reliability as a function of sample size is well understood. However, it is sensitive to the existence of a very few extreme values among the data. The median, less sensitive to outlying data, suffers because of theoretical considerations which generally make it less desirable than the mean. One such consideration is that the median is purely a positional measure of central tendency. The mode offers little analytical substance and hence does not often appear as a descriptive parameter.

If the first two moments, μ and σ^2, are known, much can be inferred about the parent population; indeed, the central problem of statistics involves (1) estimation of moments from sample parameters and (2) inferences about the population. The dimensionless ratio

$$c_v = \sigma/\mu \qquad (4\text{-}19)$$

defines the *coefficient of variation* of a distribution, and its magnitude conveys important information about the population. For example, it is

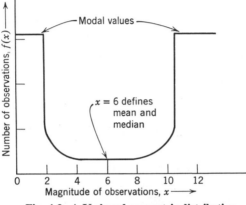

Fig. 4-3. A U-shaped symmetric distribution.

known that the coefficient of variation of annual flows for a large number of streams in the eastern United States lies in the range 0.2 to 0.4. Its value for the St. Lawrence River is much smaller because the Great Lakes regulate and stabilize the flow; a desert stream, subject to an enormous range of flows, is likely to show a high value of c_v. Thus certain general conclusions about the hydrologic regimen of a stream can be drawn simply by noting its c_v value. One can describe a stream as flashy, stable, etc., by examining only two moments. Further uses of moments are presented later.

4-5 Statistical Expectation

If x is a statistical variate, it is customary to write the symbol $E(x)$ to denote the operator *expectation* or *expected value* of x; expectation implying the average of x over all its possible values. Thus, if x is continuous,

$$E(x) = \int_{-\infty}^{\infty} x f(x)\, dx \qquad (4\text{-}20)$$

and if x is discrete

$$E(x) = \sum_{i=1}^{n} x_i f(x_i) \tag{4-21}$$

Other commonly used notation for the operator includes $<x>$ and Ex. From Eq. 4-12, we can write

$$E(x - \mu)^2 = E(x^2) - [E(x)]^2 \tag{4-22}$$

The whole spectrum of mathematical statistics is simplified by the use of the expectation operator. Like any other mathematical shorthand, it adds little to the substance of the theory but aids in the formalisms of analysis and manipulation.

Several commonly used expressions, given here without proof, are

$$E(x) = \mu, \quad \text{and} \quad E(x - \mu)^2 = \sigma^2 \tag{4-23}$$

$$E(\bar{x}) = \mu, \quad \text{and} \quad E(s^2) = (n - 1)\sigma^2/n \tag{4-24}$$

$$E(cx) = cE(x), \text{ if } c \text{ is constant} \tag{4-25}$$

and
$$E(xy) = E(x) \cdot E(y), \text{ if } x \text{ and } y \text{ are independent.} \tag{4-26}$$

These expressions will be justified later.

4-6   Approximations to the Binomial; the Normal Distribution

The binomial distribution is generally regarded as the fundamental distribution in statistics. This does not imply that it is the most useful on a day-to-day basis; rather that, because of its structural simplicity, it forms the basis for a set of approximating distributions that are the lifeblood of applied statistics.

The normal distribution, often referred to as the Gaussian[14] distribution, is by far the most widely used member of this set of approximations. It is a two-parameter symmetric distribution given by the equation

$$f(x) = \frac{1}{\sqrt{2\pi}\,\theta_2} \exp\left[-\frac{1}{2}\left(\frac{x - \theta_1}{\theta_2}\right)^2\right] \tag{4-27}$$

which is identical to the example of Eq. 4-7. Its first two moments

$$E(x) = \mu = \theta_1 \tag{4-28}$$

and
$$E(x - \theta_1)^2 = \sigma^2 = \theta_2{}^2 \tag{4-29}$$

define the distribution completely, and the function may be written

$$f(x) = \frac{1}{\sqrt{2\pi}\,\sigma} \exp\left[-\frac{1}{2}\left(\frac{x - \mu}{\sigma}\right)^2\right] \tag{4-30}$$

[14] After its formulator, the German astronomer and mathematician, Karl Friedrich Gauss (1777–1855).

The distribution is symmetric because no odd powers of the argument x appear in $f(x)$, and odd moments about the mean are zero. Indeed, a symmetric distribution function is defined as a function with vanishing third moment.

Figure 4-4 shows a symmetric binomial distribution, $p = 0.5$, for which $n = 20$. The number of successes, x, is the axis of abscissae, and $P(x)$ is the axis of ordinates. The arrowheads show $P(x)$ versus x, and the numeric values are, as usual, computed by $P(x) = \binom{20}{x} 0.5^x 0.5^{20-x} = 20!\,(0.5)^{20}/$ $[x!\,(20 - x)!]$. The smooth curve in Fig. 4-4 is derived from consideration of the moments of the binomial distribution. Theory gives

$$E(x) = np = \mu \tag{4-31}$$

and
$$E(x - \mu)^2 = npq = \sigma^2 \tag{4-32}$$

where $\sigma = \sqrt{npq}$ or $\sigma/n = \sqrt{pq/n}$ are referred to as sigma Bernoulli.[15] In

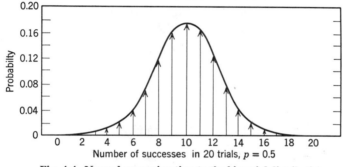

Fig. 4-4. Normal approximation to the binomial distribution.

our example, $\mu = np = 20 \times 0.5 = 10$, and $\sigma^2 = npq = 20 \times 0.5 \times 0.5 = 5$; whereupon we substitute 10 and 5 for μ and σ in Eq. 4-27. The agreement in Fig. 4-4 is excellent; it would be better if n were larger, or worse if p were a polar value (say, 0.1 or 0.9) rather than the central value 0.5. In fact, for very small, or very large, values of the binomial parameter p, the normal distribution is an unacceptable substitute and some other approximation, such as Poisson's distribution,[16] must be employed.

The Poisson distribution is based on the fact that when n of the binomial distribution is very large, the terms of the binomial, from the last backwards, approach values of $e^{-\mu}$, $e^{-\mu}\mu$, $e^{-\mu}\mu^2/2!$ $\cdots$ for the event happening

[15] After the Netherlands-Huguenot-Swiss mathematician Jacob Bernoulli (1654–1705), author of *Ars Conjectandi* (The art of conjecture), 1713.
[16] Named after the French mathematician Simeon Denis Poisson (1781–1840), author of *Recherches sur la probabilité des jugements* (Enquiry into the probability of conjecture), Paris, 1837; also known for the ratio of lateral to longitudinal strain named after him.

0, 1, 2, 3 $\cdots$ times, the general term being $e^{-\mu}\mu^a/a!$ for the event happening a times. Both mean and variance tend to equal μ in this distribution.

One might reasonably ask why the binomial should be replaced at all; the response runs along the following lines. The binomial is computationally awkward since it requires the evaluation of a combinatorial term which, in turn, depends upon sample size. Thus the distribution $P(x)$ must be reevaluated for each n, whereas n does not appear in the expression for the normal distribution. Furthermore, many natural phenomena seem to conform rather well to the normal distribution or to some distribution that can easily be rendered normal by making a data (logarithmic, square root, etc.) transform. The normal, being a continuous distribution, precludes the necessity of splitting the observed range into segments or intervals and, importantly, admits of negative arguments. But the most important feature of all is that the normal can be tabulated, once, by means of a simple data transform so that the entire distribution is written as a function of one parameter alone.

Let x be a normally distributed variate with mean μ and variance σ^2. This is customarily written

$$x \sim N(\mu, \sigma^2) \tag{4-33}$$

Define the variate

$$y = (x - \mu)/\sigma \tag{4-34}$$

and note the following properties:

$$E(y) = (1/\sigma)[E(x) - E(\mu)] = (1/\sigma)(\mu - \mu) = 0 \tag{4-35}$$

and $\quad E[y - E(y)]^2 = E(y - 0)^2 = E(y^2) = (1/\sigma^2)[E(x - \mu)^2]$

or, by definition of σ^2,

$$E(y^2) = \sigma^2/\sigma^2 = 1 \tag{4-36}$$

so that $\qquad\qquad\qquad y \sim N(0, 1^2) \tag{4-37}$

In words, y is normally distributed with zero mean and unit variance. Now, because the first two moments of the distribution of y are known,[17] and because y is known to be normally distributed, the function $f(y)$ can be tabulated and will serve as a basis for *all* other normal distributions. This transform, known as *standardization* or *normalization*, is one of the major tools of the statistician. For example, let x be the annual flow in a river and let $x \sim N(10, 3^2)$. Suppose that the probability that $13 < x < 16$ or, more generally, that $x_1 < x < x_2$ is desired. Let $t_1 = (x_1 - \mu)/\sigma = (13 - 10)/3 = 1$ and $t_2 = (x_2 - \mu)/\sigma = (16 - 10)3 = 2$, as illustrated in

---

[17] The reader is asked to accept the fact that if $x \sim N(\mu, \sigma^2)$, any linear transform of x is also normally distributed. A little reflection will convince him that this must be so.

Fig. 4-5, where the required probability is shaded. A table of the cumulative distribution $F(t)$ (Table I-6 in the Appendix) shows that the cumulative area from $-\infty$ up to $t = 2$ is 0.9772 and that the area up to $t = 1$ is 0.8413. The difference, 0.136, is the required answer. Of course the function $f(t)$ or, more fundamentally, the function $f(x)$ could be integrated[18] to give the same result, 0.136. Thus, use of the normal table precludes the necessity of integration.

It is possible to pose the obverse question: how large must x be to encompass 90% of all the values? The table indicates that $y = 1.28$ for

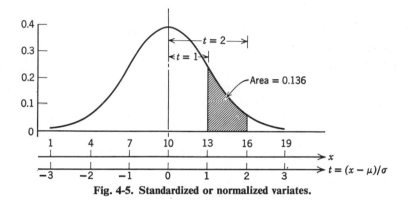

Fig. 4-5. Standardized or normalized variates.

90% of the area, whereupon $x = t\sigma + \mu = 3t + 10 = 3(1.28) + 10 = 13.84$, so that in the range $-\infty < x < 13.84$ one would expect to find 90% of all the possible observations.

The final, permanent tabulation of the normal curve is an obvious advantage over the cumbersome binomial, but again the skeptic might ask to what avail all this manipulation is offered. The reply represents a first contact with statistical inference. If the data are normal or near-normal, one can expect about 67% of the observations to lie within one standard deviation of the mean, about 95% to lie within two standard deviations of the mean, etc. These results may be used as in the following example.

Example 4-1. A certain production process is tested periodically by a sample of size 1000. Experience shows that the mean number of defective items is 10 with a standard deviation of 3. A particular sample produces 19 defectives. Should the entire batch

18

$$f(t) = \int_{1}^{2} \frac{1}{\sqrt{2\pi}(1)} \exp\left[-\frac{1}{2}\left(\frac{t-0}{1}\right)^2\right] dt; \quad \text{or}$$

$$f(x) = \int_{13}^{16} \frac{1}{\sqrt{2\pi}(3)} \exp\left[-\frac{1}{2}\left(\frac{x-10}{3}\right)^2\right] dx = 0.136$$

be rejected? The strategy involves computing the standardized value $t = (19 - 10)/3 = 3$ and asking a new question: How likely is it that a t-value as large as 3 will arise merely by chance? The table indicates 0.00135, whereupon *management*, not the statistician, makes the choice! The statistician, in effect, says that the process might be acceptable, because 0.135% of the time one is likely to get 19 defectives out of 1000. However, the processing unit could be out of adjustment; if so 19 out of 1000 is too high to tolerate. Generally, the acceptance level is in the area of 95%, or $\pm 1.96\sigma$. The management would thus reject the entire batch as lying outside the prescribed acceptable limit.

The normal distribution has many more uses and much more nobility than sketched here. Indeed, some truly remarkable results are obtained from and with the normal distribution. It must be left for the moment, but it will recur in further discussions of the applications of theory.

4-7 Curve Fitting, Least Squares, and Regression Analysis

Graphical and Simple Analytical Techniques. Turn now to further applications of theory. Oftentimes the engineer wishes to fit an analytic function to observed data or to evaluate the parameters of some prescribed functional representation. For example, theoretical considerations, such as a dimensional analysis, might indicate that experimental parameters, or certain combinations of parameters, are quadratically related. The three coefficients of the relationship can be deduced from a few measurements, whereupon the task of curve fitting is complete. To cite another example, consider the laboratory determination of the linear coefficient of thermal expansion of a certain solid. Suppose that experiments are performed under ideal conditions so that the effects of external influences are eliminated. The resulting pairs of points, length versus temperature, are likely to show very little scatter or deviation from a straight line, at least within a prescribed temperature range, and a sufficiently reliable linear representation or fit might, therefore, be attained by eye.

Examples of several commonly used functions and their graphic representations are tabulated in Table 4-4; the equations are given in their untransformed and transformed modes, and by using the straight-line form, curve fitting is accomplished by elementary algebraic manipulation or by eye. In all cases, y as the dependent variable is plotted along the ordinate, and x as the independent variable along the abscissa.

If in this table Eq. (i), $y = a + bx$, is taken as the basic example, reference to the sketches will show (1) that the intercept on the y-axis at $x = 0$ is $y = a$, and (2) that the slope of the line $dy/dx = (y_2 - y_1)/(x_2 - x_1) = b$. Using Eq. (ii), $y = ae^{bx}$ or $(\log y) = (\log a) + (b \log e)x$, as the functional example, it follows (1) that the intercept on the y-axis at $x = 0$ is $\log y = \log a$, or $y = a$, and (2) that the slope of the line $d(\log y)/dx = (\log y_2 - \log y_1)/(x_2 - x_1) = b \log e$. The remaining equations are dealt with in similar fashion.

A useful habit to acquire in curve fitting is to pass the straight line of best fit through the means of the observed values of x and y, or their respective transforms. A simple computation of the means fixes the position of the fitted line, and therefore the only remaining decision is to select the slope of the line.

Method of Least Squares. Postulate a linear relationship between population variates θ (dependent) and λ (independent). The equation is

$$\theta = \alpha + \beta(\lambda - \bar{\lambda}) \qquad (4\text{-}38)$$

where $\bar{\lambda}$ is the population mean of the independent variable and α and β are coefficients. In general, θ and λ are not available because observational and sampling errors introduce systematic bias or random perturbation into the measurements (say, y and x). Let these errors be disregarded for the moment, so that y may be written for θ and x for λ without error. The coefficients α and β are under estimate, and some criterion must be established for their evaluation. Let R_i be the residual corresponding to the ith observation, or the deviation between the computed value $\alpha + \beta(x_i - \mu_x)$ and the observed y_i. If the data display no deviation from a linear fit, all the residuals, R_i, are zero, and no curve-fitting problem exists. In general, the coefficients are chosen to satisfy some objective function in which the residuals, R_i, appear as arguments. Several feasible criteria are: (1) minimize the sum of absolute values of the residuals; (2) minimize the sum of squares of the residuals; and (3) visualize an inverse estimating function $x = a + b(y - \mu_y)$ and select the coefficients (α, β) and (a, b) such that β and b are reciprocals. Many other criteria could be offered, but these three are encountered most frequently.

For reasons that will become clear in subsequent paragraphs, the second alternative is the most useful in a large portion of cases. The formalism is outlined here.

Select α, β so as to minimize

$$\sum_{i=1}^{n} R_i^2 = \Sigma[\alpha + \beta(x_i - \mu_x) - y_i]^2 \qquad (4\text{-}39)$$

where n is the number of sample data. This is accomplished if the first derivatives of ΣR_i^2 with respect to α and β are zero; thus

$$\frac{\partial(\Sigma R_i^2)}{\partial \alpha} = 2\Sigma\left[R_i \frac{\partial R_i}{\partial \alpha}\right] = 2\Sigma[\alpha + \beta(x_i - \mu_x) - y_i] = 0$$

$$\frac{\partial(\Sigma R_i^2)}{\partial \beta} = 2\Sigma\left[R_i \frac{\partial R_i}{\partial \beta}\right] = 2\Sigma\{(\alpha + \beta(x_i - \mu_x) - y_i)x_i\} = 0$$

Table 4-4 Straight-Line Functions of Certain Equations

No.	Type of Equation	Shape of Curve on Arithmetic Paper for Positive Values of Constants	Equation in Straight-Line Form	Functional Plotting Ordinate Variable	Scale	Abscissa Variable	Scale
(i)	$y = a + bx$	(a)	$y = a + bx$	y	arith.	x	arith.
(ii)	$y = ae^{bx}$	(b)	$(\log y) = (\log a) + (b \log e)x$	y	log.	x	arith.
(iii)	$y = ax^b$	(c)	$(\log y) = (\log a) + b(\log x)$	y	log.	x	log.
(iv)	$y = a + \dfrac{b}{x}$	(d)	$y = a + b\left(\dfrac{1}{x}\right)$	y	arith.	$\left(\dfrac{1}{x}\right)$	arith.

	Equation	Transformation	Ordinate scale	Abscissa	Abscissa scale
(v)	$y = \dfrac{x}{a + bx}$	$\left(\dfrac{x}{y}\right) = a + bx$	$\left(\dfrac{x}{y}\right)$ arith.	x	arith.
(vi)	$y = \dfrac{a}{b + cx}$	$\left(\dfrac{1}{y}\right) = \left(\dfrac{b}{a}\right) + \left(\dfrac{c}{a}\right)x$	$\left(\dfrac{1}{y}\right)$ arith.	x	arith.
(vii)	$y = c + be^{ax}$	$\left(\log \dfrac{dy}{dx}\right) = (\log ab) + (a \log e)x$	$\left(\dfrac{\Delta y}{\Delta x}\right)$ log.	x	arith.
(viii)	$y = c + ax^b$	$\left(\log \dfrac{dy}{dx}\right) = (\log ab) + (b - 1)\log x$	$\left(\dfrac{\Delta y}{\Delta x}\right)$ log.	x	log.

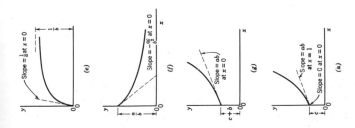

(e) Slope $= \frac{1}{a}$ at $x = 0$; $\frac{1}{b}$

(f) Slope $= -\frac{a}{b^2}$ at $x = 0$; $\frac{a}{b}$

(g) Slope $= ab$ at $x = 0$; $c + b$

(h) Slope $= ab$ at $x = 1$; Slope $= 0$ at $x = 0$; c

By summing over i and then dividing both equations by 2, the following simultaneous equations are found:

$$n\alpha + \beta\Sigma x_i - \beta n\mu_x - \Sigma y_i = 0$$

$$\alpha\Sigma x_i + \beta\Sigma x_i^2 - \beta\mu_x\Sigma x_i - \Sigma x_iy_i = 0 \tag{4-40}$$

But $\beta\Sigma x_i = \beta n\mu_x$, and α can be found explicitly as

$$\alpha = \frac{\Sigma y_i}{n} = \mu_y \tag{4-41}$$

whereupon

$$\beta(\Sigma x_i^2 - n\mu_x^2) = \Sigma x_iy_i - n\mu_x\mu_y$$

or

$$\beta = \frac{\Sigma x_iy_i - n\mu_x\mu_y}{\Sigma x_i^2 - n\mu_x^2} \tag{4-42}$$

Equations 4-40 are called the *normal* equations of the bivariate array (x_i, y_i), and, in general, there are as many simultaneous normal equations as there are parameters under estimate. Thus if some variable z is written as a linear function of u, v, w, x, and y, we would expect six simultaneous equations, one for each independent variable plus one constant. As the number of variables becomes large, manual solution of the resulting system of simultaneous equations becomes less attractive and the use of a digital computer appears desirable.

The line $y = \alpha + \beta(x - \mu_x)$ is called the *least-squares* fit to the data because α and β are chosen to minimize the sum of squares of residuals. The variation among the y-values is attributable to two sources, variation in x and random factors. For example, if y represents weight and x represents height, a portion of the variation in y, weight, among the n individuals in a sample can be attributed to their several heights. Of course there are other factors, such as body frame and nutrition, but having postulated a bivariate model as in Eq. 4-38, one is constrained to consider all other sources of weight variation as arising from random factors. The line-of-best-fit, or least-squares line, maximizes the explained or attributable portion of the variation in y because the unexplained portion, ΣR_i^2, is minimized.

Example 4-2. Find, by the method of least squares, the straight-line relationship between mean annual rainfall and altitude above sea level for the pairs of values[19] listed in Table 4-5.

$$\alpha = \bar{y} = 19.5; \quad \beta = \frac{\Sigma x_iy_i - n\mu_x\mu_y}{\Sigma x_1^2 - n\mu_x^2} = \frac{396.8 - 6(19.5)(2.20)}{51.14 - 6(2.20)^2} = 6.30;$$

and the completed estimator is $y = 19.5 + 6.30(x - 2.20)$ or $y = 5.64 + 6.30x$. The residuals R_i are: 5.0, −7.6, −0.5, 0.8, 3.4, and −1.0, the sum ΣR_i^2 is a minimum.

[19] These values are rounded figures for San Diego County, California. See D. W. Mead, *Hydrology*, McGraw-Hill Book Co., New York, 1919, p. 294.

Table 4-5   Least-Squares Calculations of Rainfall-Altitude Relationship

Mean Annual Rainfall, in.	Elevation above Sea Level, 1000 ft			Calculated
Observed y	Observed x	x^2	xy	y
44	5.3	28.1	233	39.0
20	3.5	12.3	70.0	27.6
24	3.0	9.0	72.0	24.5
14	1.2	1.44	16.8	13.2
12	0.48	0.23	5.8	8.6
3	−0.26	0.07	−0.8	4.0
Sums 117	13.22	51.14	396.8	116.9
Means 19.5	2.20	8.52	66.1	19.5

Elements of Regression Theory.[20]   Of all the possible criteria for estimating the coefficients α and β, ΣR_i^2 possesses the justification that the resulting fit minimizes the unexplained variation in y, the dependent variable. Consider now a general bivariate distribution $f(x, y)$. It is possible to generalize further to k variates, but the details become oppressive unless matrix notation beyond the scope of this book is introduced. For two variables the density can be represented by a warped surface, the volume under which is given by

$$\int_{-\infty}^{\infty} \int_{-\infty}^{\infty} f(x, y)\, dx\, dy = 1 \qquad (4\text{-}43)$$

Say that x and y are normally distributed: $x \sim N(\mu_x, \sigma_x^2)$ and $y \sim N(\mu_y, \sigma_y^2)$ The joint distribution of x and y is given by the equation

$$f(x, y) = \frac{1}{2\pi\sigma_x\sigma_y(1 - \rho^2)^{\frac{1}{2}}} \exp\left\{ -\frac{1}{2}\left[\frac{1}{(1 - \rho^2)}\right]\left[\left(\frac{x - \mu_x}{\sigma_x}\right)^2\right.\right.$$
$$\left.\left. + \left(\frac{y - \mu_y}{\sigma_y}\right)^2 - 2\rho\left(\frac{x - \mu_x}{\sigma_x}\right)\left(\frac{y - \mu_y}{\sigma_y}\right)\right]\right\} \qquad (4\text{-}44)$$

where ρ, the correlation coefficient, is a parameter of the joint distribution. For a given value of one of the variates, say x_0, y will be normally distributed. This is equivalent to passing a plane parallel to the y- and $f(x, y)$-axes and noting that the section is a normal curve. Because two parameters completely specify a normal distribution, the equation can be written for the particular normal distribution that corresponds to x_0 by

[20] Regression is that function which gives the expected value of one variate corresponding to a chosen particular value of a second variate.

finding $E(y \mid x_0)$ and $E(y^2 \mid x_0)$, where the symbol $\mid x_0$ denotes the condition that x_0 is known, i.e., the expectations of y and of y^2, given x_0, define the mean and variance of the conditional distribution of $(y \mid x_0)$. From the distribution $f(x, y)$, Eq. 4-44, the integral $E(y \mid x_0) = \int_{-\infty}^{\infty} y f(y \mid x_0) \, dy$ is formed. It yields the expected value

$$E(y \mid x_0) = \mu_y + \frac{\rho \sigma_y}{\sigma_x}(x_0 - \mu_x) \qquad (4\text{-}45)$$

The integral $E(y^2 \mid x_0) = \int_{-\infty}^{\infty} y^2 f(y \mid x_0) \, dy$ yields the associated variance $\sigma_y^2(1 - \rho^2)$.

Thus, for a given value x_0, $y \sim N[\mu_y + (\rho \sigma_y / \sigma_x)(x_0 - \mu_x), \sigma_y^2(1 - \rho^2)]$; in words, y is normally distributed with mean $\mu_y + (\rho \sigma_y / \sigma_x)(x_0 - \mu_x)$, a function of x_0, and with variance $\sigma_y^2(1 - \rho^2)$, independent of x_0. Because the parameter ρ is defined by

$$\rho = \frac{\Sigma x_i y_i - n \mu_x \mu_y}{(\Sigma x_i^2 - n \mu_x^2)^{\frac{1}{2}}(\Sigma y_i^2 - n \mu_y^2)^{\frac{1}{2}}} \qquad (4\text{-}46)$$

it follows that

$$\beta = \rho \sigma_y / \sigma_x \qquad (4\text{-}47)$$

whereupon the least-squares regression line, $y = \alpha + \beta(x - \mu_x)$, is seen to be identical to the line $E(y \mid x) = \mu_y + (\rho \sigma_y / \sigma_x)(x - \mu_x)$, which plots the expected value of y given x. This function, called a regression line, provides firm theoretical justification for the use of least-squares techniques to estimate one variable from another. If x and y values are transformed to standardized variables $u = (x - \mu_x)/\sigma_y$ and $v = (y - \mu_y)/\sigma_x$, the line of regression passes through the origin and has a slope equal to ρ.

The standard deviation $\sigma_y \sqrt{1 - \rho^2}$ is called the standard error of estimate of y and is a measure of the unexplained variance. When the x_i and y_i are colinear, $\rho = \pm 1$, and the standard error, or unexplained variance, is zero. When the x_i and y_i are unrelated, $\rho = 0$, and the standard error, or unexplained variation, is not reduced by virtue of the regression of y on x.

Figure 4-6 gives an example of a regression line. Note that Roman rather than Greek letters are used, because the observed points yield sample, not population, moments. The dashed lines in the figure show a band width of one standard error. For $x = 15$, the regression line estimate of y is $5.5 + 0.456(15 - 11.2) = 7.233$, but we can supplement the estimate by stating that 67% of the time y will lie in the range $6.827 < y < 7.639$, 95% of the time in the range $6.421 < y < 8.045$, and so forth, because the band width is 0.406.

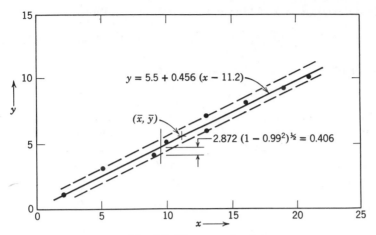

$$y = 5.5 + 0.456\ (x - 11.2)$$

$$2.872\ (1 - 0.99^2)^{\frac{1}{2}} = 0.406$$

Fig. 4-6. The regression line.

Data

y 1, 2, 3, 4, 5, 6, 7, 8, 9, 10
x 2, 4, 5, 9, 10, 13, 13, 16, 19, 21
$\bar{x} = 0.1 \times 112 = 12.2$
$\bar{y} = 0.1 \times 55 = 5.5$
$S_x^2 = 0.1(1622 - 1254.4) = 36.76;\ S_x = 6.060$
$S_y^2 = 0.1(385 - 302.5) = 8.25;\ S_y = 2.872$
$r = 0.99$
$b = 0.456$
$S_y(1 - r^2)^{\frac{1}{2}} = 0.406$

In Eq. 4-12, the formula $E(x^2) = \mu_2' = \mu^2 + \sigma^2$ was developed and the analogous relation for two variables $E(xy) = \mu_x\mu_y + \rho\sigma_x\sigma_y$ may be derived. If and only if x and y are independent, $\rho = 0$ and $E(xy) = \mu_x\mu_y$ as given in Eq. 4-26.

4-8 Reliability of Results; Sampling

Standard Errors. In interpreting results obtained by statistical analysis of quantitative information, it is important to have a measure of their reliability. One can intuit that reliability varies, in some way, with sample size.

To find the degree of reliability of a parameter such as the arithmetic mean, it is necessary to determine how a number of equally good means (i.e., similarly derived) are distributed. It is generally true (by the Central Limit Theorem) that the sample means form a normal distribution for which the central tendency and dispersion can be found. The reliability of the means is then indicated by a measure such as the standard deviation of the distribution of these means, $\sigma_{\bar{x}}$. This can be shown to be related to the standard deviation σ of the individual samples as follows:

$$\sigma_{\bar{x}}^2 = E(\bar{x} - \mu)^2 = E(\bar{x}^2) - 2\mu E(\bar{x}) + E(\mu^2) = E(\bar{x}^2) - \mu^2$$

But

$$\bar{x}^2 = (1/n^2)[x_1 + x_2 + \cdots + x_n]^2 = (1/n^2)[x_1^2 + x_2^2 + \cdots$$
$$x_n^2 + 2x_1 x_2 + \cdots]$$

Now there are $n(n - 1)/2$ cross-product terms like $2x_1 x_2$, the expectation of their sum being $[n(n - 1)/2]E(2x_i x_j) = n(n - 1)\mu^2$ if the x_i, x_j are independent.

The expectation of the n terms like x_i^2 is $nE(x_i^2) = n(\mu^2 + \sigma^2)$. Therefore $E(\bar{x}^2) = (1/n^2)[\mu^2 + \sigma^2 + n(n - 1)\mu^2]$ and

$$\sigma_{\bar{x}}^2 = (1/n)[\mu^2 + \sigma^2 + (n - 1)\mu^2] - \mu^2 = \sigma^2/n.$$

Accordingly the standard deviation of the mean computed from a sample of size n, or more succinctly, the standard error of the mean, is

$$\sigma_{\bar{x}} = \sigma/\sqrt{n} \tag{4-48}$$

This measure shows that, according to the tabulated probability integral, the chances are $2 \times 34.1 = 68.2\%$ that a mean determined from a similar collection of data will lie within $\pm\sigma_{\bar{x}}$ of the true mean. The reliability of other statistics is indicated by the standard deviation of their sampling distributions. A list of several measures and their standard errors follows for normal distributions.

Measure	Computation	Standard Error
mean	$\bar{x} = \Sigma x_i/n$	$\sigma/\sqrt{n}$
median	middle observation	$1.25\, \sigma/\sqrt{n}$
standard deviation	$s = \sqrt{\Sigma(x_i - \bar{x})^2/(n - 1)}$	$\sigma/\sqrt{2n} = 0.707\, \sigma/\sqrt{n}$
coefficient of variation	$c_v = s/\bar{x}$	$\sqrt{1 + 2c_v^2}/\sqrt{2n}$

This list provides the basis for an earlier statement that the median is less justifiable than the mean as a measure of central tendency; the reason, clearly, is that its standard error or sampling variance is larger, which is tantamount to saying that the mean is a more stable statistic.

Augmenting Hydrologic Records.   It often happens that two hydrologic records of related phenomena, say the runoff of two river systems in the same climatic region, exhibit significant correlation ρ. If one record (say runoff, x_i) is longer or more complete than the other (say runoff, y_i), the question arises as to whether the extra x_i values can reliably be used to augment or fill in the y-record. The answer depends upon whether the estimated values increase or decrease the standard error of the parameter under estimate. If computed values of y are to be used to help estimate the mean μ_y, the standard error of the mean is of interest; if the computed values are to be used to help estimate the variance σ_y^2, the standard error of the variance is of interest.

If n_1 is the length of concurrent record and n_2 the proposed extension, and if the x_i and y_i are normally distributed and serially uncorrelated, the critical cutoff value[21] of the correlation for improving the mean is

$$\rho = (n_1 - 1)^{-\frac{1}{2}}$$

For improving the variance, the critical value of ρ is of the order[22] of 0.8 for typical values of n_1 and n_2; conditions suitable for improving estimates of the variance are much more restrictive than those for improving the mean.

If ρ is less than the indicated value, more variance is added to the standard error by virtue of weak correlation than is removed by virtue of increased record length, and correlation should not be used to augment the records.[23]

An Algebraic Demonstration.   In Sec. 4-3 the distinction between two variance estimators was discussed and the preferred estimator for

$$\sigma^2 = [n/(n - 1)]s^2 \tag{4-49}$$

was given without proof. To fix firmly the use of the expectation operator and to show further applications of the evaluation of sampling errors, this important relation is derived which indicates that the same variance s^2 underestimates the population variance: $s^2 = E(x - \bar{x})^2 = E[(x - \mu) - (\bar{x} - \mu)]^2 = E[(x - \mu)^2 - 2(x - \mu)(\bar{x} - \mu) + (\bar{x} - \mu)^2] = \sigma^2 - E(\bar{x} - \mu)^2$. That $E(\bar{x} - \mu)^2$, the variance of the mean, is σ^2/n is known; thus $s^2 = \sigma^2 - \sigma^2/n = [(n - 1)/n]\sigma^2$, or σ^2 is estimated by $[n/(n - 1)]s^2$.

This concludes the discussion of sampling errors. The lesson to be learned is that every sample statistic has a corresponding sample error, and that the reliability of the statistic is a function of the standard error. The derivation of standard errors of a wide range of statistics is one of the major areas of the mathematical theory of statistics.

4-9   Further Topics in Correlation

Time Series.   When observations are arranged in order of occurrence to form *time series*, a study of the changing magnitudes of successive observations will discover trends, cycles or periodicities, and fluctuations.

[21] After H. A. Thomas, Jr.
[22] After J. R. Rosenblatt, personal communication, 1958.
[23] M. B. Fiering, On the Use of Correlation to Augment Data, *J. Am. Stat. Assoc.*, **57**, 20 (1962).

Trends are tendencies of the observations to increase or decrease with time; cycles or periodicities are tendencies to form successive maxima and minima like the crests and troughs of waves; and fluctuations are tendencies of the observations to change their magnitude explosively from time interval to time interval. Numerical examples of three time series, idealized to exhibit these three specific tendencies, are given in Table 4-6 and illustrated in Fig. 4-7.

Series A exhibits a perfect arithmetic trend; the magnitudes of successive observations, taken at equal time intervals, increase uniformly from 2 to 22. Series B records a simple cyclical variation or periodicity; the magnitudes of the observations move up and down systematically from a low

Table 4-6   Examples of Time Series

Time of observation	11	12	13	14	15	16	17	18	19	20	21
Magnitude of observation											
Series A (trend)	2	4	6	8	10	12	14	16	18	20	22
Series B (cycle)	6	4	6	12	18	20	18	12	6	4	6
Series C (fluctuation)	18	12	14	6	16	2	10	22	4	20	8

value of 4 to a high value of 20 to trace a sine-like wave. In series C, the magnitudes of the observations fluctuate from time interval to time interval between 2 and 22 with no apparent rhyme or reason.

A graphical representation of these three time series, as in Fig. 4-7, gives a good general impression of their nature, but it does not express their story in numbers. For that one must turn either to a determination of the equations of the curves traced by the series or to an identification of suitable parameters.

Trends, Cycles, and Periodicities.   The tendencies of observations to change in magnitude may be simple or complex. The function of the statistician is to discover the inherent regularity, if such exists, and to express it in numbers. The regularity of change in magnitude with time, inherent in Series A, is easily recognized. Because the observations increase in magnitude by a fixed number of units during each interval of time, the slope of the straight line fitting them best is an acceptable measure of the *generalized trend* of this arithmetic series. If the origin of the coordinate system is placed at the intersection of the arithmetic means of the times and magnitudes of the observations, the equation of the straight line of best fit becomes: $(y - \mu_y) = b(x - \mu_x)$, where $(y - \mu_y)$ and $(x - \mu_x)$ are the deviations of the magnitudes of the individual observations from their means. The constant b (a being zero) can be evaluated by least squares from the normal equation for a straight line as: $b\Sigma(x - \mu_x^2)/n - \Sigma(y - \mu_y)^2/n = 0$ or $b = \Sigma(x - \mu_x)(y - \mu_y)/\Sigma(x - \mu_x)^2$, which is in itself a simple

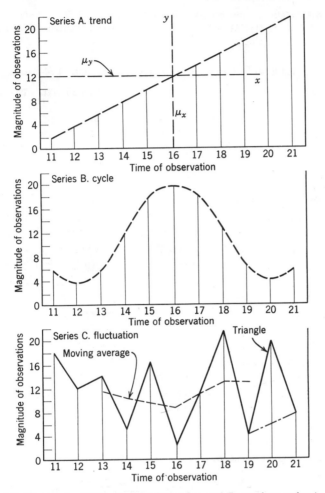

Fig. 4-7. Time series illustrating trends, cycles, and fluctuation; series A, B, and C.

expression for the trend. If the observations are made at regular time intervals, this expression can be further simplified by substituting the *order of the observations in time* (1, 2, 3, etc.) for the *time* itself. For n observations, the mean is then the $[(n + 1)/2]$th observation, and one can substitute for the deviation $(x_i - \mu_x)$ of the ith observation the value $[i - (n + 1)/2]$, with the following result:

$$(4\text{-}50)$$

$$b = \frac{\Sigma[i - (n + 1)/2](y - \mu_y)}{\Sigma[i - (n + 1)/2]^2} = \frac{12}{[n(n^2 - 1)]} \Sigma[i - (n + 1)/2](y - \mu_y)$$

Example 4-3.   Calculate the trend for Series A (see Table 4-7).

By Eq. 4-50, $b = \{12/[11(121 - 1)]\}220 = +2$. The trend, therefore, is $+2$ per unit interval of time, as noted before.

Table 4-7   Calculation of Trend (Example 4-3)

Observed time	11	12	13	14	15	16	17	18	19	20	21
Order, i	1	2	3	4	5	6	7	8	9	10	11
$[i - (n + 1)/2] = i - 6$	−5	−4	−3	−2	−1	0	+1	+2	+3	+4	+5
Observed magnitude	2	4	6	8	10	12	14	16	18	20	22
Deviation from mean $(y - \mu_y)$	−10	−8	−6	−4	−2	0	+2	+4	+6	+8	+10
$[i - (n + 1)/2](y - \mu_y) =$ $(i - 6)(y - \mu_y)$	50	32	18	8	2	0	2	8	18	32	50

Trends are not necessarily arithmetic. Geometric trends are quite common. The reductions in the death rates from typhoid fever, tuberculosis, and many other diseases in North America are examples. Since $(b \log e)$ is the trend of a geometric time series, the percentage change per unit time is $100[(y_{i+1} - \mu_y) - (y_i - \mu_y)]/(y_i - \mu_y) = 100(y_{i+1} - y_i)/(y_i - \mu_y) = 100(e^b - 1)$ for a positive trend (magnitudes increasing with time) and $(y_i - y_{i+1})/(y_i - \mu_y) = 100(1 - e^b)$ for a negative trend (magnitudes decreasing with time). The subscripts $(i + 1)$ and i denote observations a unit interval of time apart.

Moving Averages.   Most water-supply and wastewater data are not sufficiently extensive to identify long-swing cycles or periodicities. Possible periods do show up in plotted time series when random irregularities are suppressed. *Moving averages* (simple or weighted) of a convenient number of successive terms serve this purpose reasonably well in some instances. By averaging an odd number of successive observations, the average will coincide with the middle item which can be weighted for emphasis. Calling the observed magnitudes a, b, c, etc., examples of weighted moving averages are:

$$M_b = \frac{a + 2b + c}{4} ; \qquad M_c = \frac{b + 2c + d}{4}, \text{ etc.} \qquad (4\text{-}51)$$

or

$$M_c = \frac{a + 4b + 6c + 4d + e}{16} ; \qquad M_d = \frac{b + 4c + 6d + 4e + f}{16}, \text{ etc.}$$

$$(4\text{-}52)$$

The magnitudes of the weighting coefficients are arbitrary. An advantage of those shown here is that they lend themselves to systematic computations.

Example 4-4.   Calculate moving averages of types 4-51 and 4-52 for Series C. (See Table 4-8.) Column 3 = $a + b, b + c$, etc.; Col. 4 = $(a + b) + (b + c) = (a + 2b + c)$, etc.; Col. 5 = Col. 4/4 = $(a + 2b + c)/4$ etc.; Col. 6 = $(a + 2b + c)/4 + (b + 2c + d)/$

$4 = (a + 3b + 3c + d)/4$, etc.; Col. 7 $= (a + 3b + 3c + d)/4 + (b + 3c + 3d + e)/$
$4 = (a + 4b + 6c + 4d + e)/4$, etc.; Col. 8 $=$ Col. $7/4 = (a + 4b + 6c + 4d + e)/16$,
etc.

Table 4-8   Calculation of Moving Averages (Example 4-4)

Time	Magni-tude	First Reduction			Second Reduction		
(1)	(2)	(3)	(4)	(5)	(6)	(7)	(8)
11	$a = 18$						
12	$b = 12$	30					
13	$c = 14$	26	56	14.0			
14	$d = 6$	20	46	11.5	25.5		
15	$e = 16$	22	42	10.5	22.0	47.5	11.9
16	$f = 2$	18	40	10.0	20.5	42.5	10.6
17	$g = 10$	12	30	7.5	17.5	38.0	9.5
18	$h = 22$	32	44	11.0	18.5	36.0	9.0
19	$i = 4$	26	58	14.5	25.5	44.0	11.0
20	$j = 20$	24	50	12.5	27.0	52.5	13.1
21	$k = 8$	28	52	13.0	25.5	52.5	13.1

Fluctuation.   The magnitudes of the observations in Series A and C (Fig. 4-7) are the same. However, their order of occurrence is purposely different. In Series A, magnitudes progress smoothly from low to high; in Series C they fluctuate violently. Acceptable measures of fluctuation are the *standard fluctuation*[24] and *coefficient of fluctuation*, defined as follows:

$$\text{Standard fluctuation } F = \sqrt{\Sigma(\Delta'')^2/(n - 2)} \qquad (4\text{-}53)$$

$$\text{Coefficient of fluctuation } C_F = F/\mu \qquad (4\text{-}54)$$

Here Δ'' is the second difference in the magnitudes of successive observations, n is the number of observations, and μ is their mean. Graphically, the standard fluctuation is a measure of the area of the triangle formed by three successive observations (Fig. 4-7).[25]

Example 4-5.   Calculate the standard fluctuation and coefficient of fluctuation for Series A and C.
   1. In Series A, the first differences, Δ', all equal $+2$; the second differences, Δ'', therefore, all equal zero; and both F and C_F are zero.
   2. In Series C, the story is different. See Table 4-9.

[24] W. L. Crum, A Measure of Dispersion for Ordered Series, *Quarterly Publications of the American Statistical Association*, 17, 969 (1921).
[25] If y_1, y_2, and y_3 are the magnitudes of the last three observations in Series C, the area of the triangle formed by them at unit time intervals is: $\frac{1}{2}(y_1 + y_2) + \frac{1}{2}(y_2 + y_3) - \frac{3}{2}(y_1 + y_3) = \frac{1}{2}[(y_2 - y_1) - (y_3 - y_2)] = \frac{1}{2}$ (second-order difference).

Table 4-9   Calculation of Fluctuation

Magnitude	18	12	14	6	16	2	10	22	4	20	8
First difference Δ'		-6	$+2$	-8	$+10$	-14	$+8$	$+12$	-18	$+16$	-12
Second difference Δ''			$+8$	-10	$+18$	-24	$+22$	$+4$	-30	$+34$	-28
$(\Delta'')^2$			64	100	324	576	484	16	900	1156	784

1. By Eq. 4-53, the standard fluctuation is: $F = \sqrt{4404/9} = 22.1$.
2. The mean is: $\mu = 12$.
3. By Eq. 4-54, the coefficient of fluctuation is: $C_F = 22.1/12 = 1.84$, or 184%.

4-10   Operational Hydrology[26]

The preceding discussion of time series deals with manipulation of data to extract measures of trend, cycles, or fluctuation. Investigate now a mathematical model which describes the stochastic[27] nature of the underlying hydrologic structure in a river basin and attempt to extract efficient estimates of certain statistics. Suppose that the combined annual precipitation and snowmelt in a river basin is an independently distributed variable; i.e., the value in each year is independent of all previous values. In most basins the consequent stream flow is not independently distributed because the basin itself tends to perpetuate extreme flow values. For example, if a period of drought is followed by a period of normal precipitation, the basin tends to restore depleted groundwater levels before producing runoff; thus stream flows continue at a reduced level. Conversely, if a normal year follows a year of abundant precipitation, the basin soils are well filled and a high proportion of the incident precipitation runs off, resulting in yet another year of high flows. This persistence is characterized by the serial correlation coefficient, computed as in Eq. 4-46 with x_{i-1} replacing y_i. Thus

$$\rho = \frac{\sum_{i=2}^{n} x_i x_{i-1} - (n - 1)\mu^2}{(n - 2)\sigma^2} \tag{4-55}$$

Equation 4-55 is valid for n large, say greater than 15; for $n < 15$, the values μ^2 and σ^2 would have to be replaced by the products of means and standard deviations of the first $n - 1$ and last $n - 1$ values.

Let the following linear regression model be postulated:

$$x_{i+1} = \alpha + \beta(x_i - \mu) \tag{4-56}$$

[26] Also called synthetic records and hydrological synthesis. See A. A. Maass and others, *Design of Water-Resource Systems*, Harvard University Press, 1960, Chapter 12 by H. A. Thomas, Jr., and M. B. Fiering.
[27] From the Greek word *stochos*, mark or aim; hence, conjectural.

wherein x_i is the flow in year i, x_{i+1} is the estimated flow in year $i + 1$, α, β are coefficients, and μ is the mean annual flow. This recursion[28] model is deterministic in nature, i.e., there is no random or stochastic component to represent the statistical variation that inheres in certain hydrological phenomena. With respect to the first moment the expected value of x_{i+1}, $E(x_{i+1}) = \alpha = \mu$, which is appropriate. The model, however, is deficient with respect to the variance

$$\text{Var}(x_{i+1}) = E(x_{i+1})^2 - \mu^2 = \alpha^2 + \beta^2 E(x_i - \mu)^2$$
$$+ 2\alpha\beta E(x_i - \mu) - \mu^2 = \mu^2 + \rho^2\sigma^2 - \mu^2,$$

so that $\text{Var}(x_{i+1}) = \rho^2\sigma^2$, which is unacceptable unless $\rho = \pm 1$.

If, however, a random component $t\sigma\sqrt{(1 - \rho^2)}$ is added to Eq. 4-56, $\text{Var}(x_{i+1})$ is preserved because t, a random normal deviate with zero mean and unit variance, has $E(t) = 0$ and $E(t^2) = 1$. Thus, if

$$x_{i+1} = \alpha + \beta(x_i - \mu) + t\sigma(1 - \rho^2)^{\frac{1}{2}} \qquad (4\text{-}57)$$

it follows that $E(x_{i+1})^2 - \mu^2 = \mu^2 + \rho^2\sigma^2 - \mu^2 + \sigma^2(1 - \rho^2) = \sigma^2$. For non-normal x_i, higher moments can be preserved by suitable algebraic manipulation.

Of what use is the statistical or operational generation of hydrologic sequences by means of Eq. 4-57?

1. Statistics of derived distributions for which moments are difficult or impossible to evaluate can often be extracted from studies of a long sequence of operational or statistically generated values. Indeed, it may be necessary to use extremely long traces of flows for investigating unstable statistics, whereupon a digital computer becomes an invaluable aid.

2. Operational studies of engineering systems may be made using statistically generated inflow sequences. This technique is generally more realistic than subjecting the system to the historical record alone, whereupon the designer can more readily evaluate the effects of random perturbations on the proposed design. The use of a digital computer to simulate the operation of a system subject to long synthetic inflow traces is a promising avenue to further research.

The effects of serial correlation on the expected value and standard error of various parameters of derived distributions may readily be investigated. Thus, although the probabilities of various observed flow magnitudes will not change significantly in a long synthetic record, it is easy to investigate the severity of sustained low or high flows (as a function of ρ) using operational traces; an analytical solution might be hopeless.

[28] The term *recursion* signifies relationship between any value of a set and its preceding values.

Example 4-6. With reference to Fig. 4-6, let x be denoted by x_{i-1} and y by x_i, and let the two variables be normally distributed. Then, for some initial value x_0, say 2.0,

(a) $x_1 = 5.5 + 0.456(2.0 - 11.2) + 0.406t_1$, in accordance with Eq. 4-57. If t_1, taken from a table of random deviates, is -1.07, $x_1 = 0.97$.

(b) $x_2 = 5.5 + 0.456(0.97 - 11.2) + 0.406t_2$, and so forth.

4-11   Probability Paper

Although it is possible to express the normal summation curve or probability integral in straight-line form, it is simpler and sometimes more

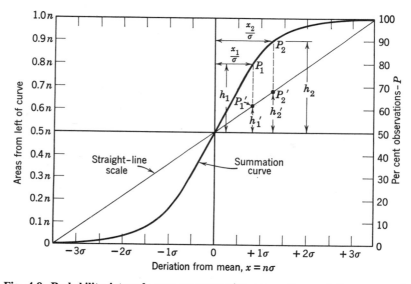

Fig. 4-8. Probability integral curve or summation curve of normal frequency and its translation into a straight line.

useful to develop a system of coordinates on which normal frequency distributions will plot as straight lines. How this is done is indicated in Fig. 4-8. There the origin of the coordinate system is placed at the halfway mark of the summation curve, and the horizontal scale of magnitudes is kept arithmetic. The vertical, originally arithmetic, scale is then compressed so that the distances h_1 and h_2 for the percentages P_1 and P_2 on the S-shaped summation curve are reduced to $h_1{}'$ and $h_2{}'$. These compressed distances identify the position of the percentages $P_1{}'$ and $P_2{}'$ on a new scale—called the probability scale—which converts the S-shaped curve into a straight line. As shown in Fig. 4-8, the relative magnitudes of $h_1{}'$ and $h_2{}'$ are given by the ratios: $h_1{}' : h_2{}' = (x_1/\sigma) : (x_2/\sigma) = x_1 : x_2$. A sample calculation will illustrate the development of the probability scale.

Example 4-7.   Determine the position of the 10% and 90% markings of a probability scale 10 in. long with end markings of 0.01% and 99.99%.

1. Place the 50% mark halfway from either end.
2. For 0.01% and 99.99% (each 49.99% from the center): $x/\sigma = \pm 3.72$ from Table I-6.
3. For 10% and 90% (each 40% from the center): $x/\sigma = \pm 1.28$ from Table I-6.
4. $h_1'/h_2' = (x_1/\sigma)/(x_2/\sigma)$, or $h_1' = h_2'(x_1/\sigma)$. For $h_2' = 5$ in., $x_2/\sigma = \pm 3.72$, and $x_1/\sigma = \pm 1.28$; or $h_1' = 5 \times 1.28/3.72 = 1.72$ in.

Therefore, place the 10% and 90% marks 1.72 in. to either side of the center of the scale.

The development and use of coordinate paper that incorporates a probability scale was first suggested by Hazen.[29] Any series of observations that is arithmetically normal will plot as a straight line on arithmetic probability coordinate paper. The straight line of best fit for a normal distribution passes through the intersection of the arithmetic mean μ with the 50% frequency, because half the observations lie to either side of the mean; and moreover, through the intersection of $\mu \pm \sigma$ with the 84.1% and 15.9% frequency respectively, because 34.1% of the observations lie within $x/\sigma = 1$ of the mean and $50 \pm 34.1 = 84.1\%$ and 15.9% respectively.

Conversely, an arithmetic probability plot indicates arithmetic normality of the frequency distribution when the observed points fall on a substantially straight line. If a straight line is fitted to the plotted points by eye, the approximate magnitudes of μ and the median can be read at the 50% frequency, and the approximate magnitude of $\mu \pm \sigma$ at the 84.1% and 15.9% frequencies respectively. Obviously, too, the expected frequency of any observation of given magnitude (and vice versa) can be read from the plot.

Example 4-8.   For the data given in columns 2 and 3 of Table 4-10, determine the moments of the arithmetically normal frequency curve of best fit, the plotting position of the observed points, and the calculated points through which the straight line of best fit on arithmetic probability paper must pass (Fig. 4-9). Necessary calculations are systematized in Table 4-10.

For any group, k, therefore, the number of observations equal to or less than the class mean is: $\sum_{1}^{k-1} f + \tfrac{1}{2} f_k$. For the sixth group, for example, $\sum_{1}^{5} f + \tfrac{1}{2} f_6 = 80 + 20 = 100$.

4-12   Geometrically Normal Frequency

Because the differences between logarithms of numbers decrease steadily as the numbers rise, a curve limited at it lower end by zero but otherwise unrestrained, sometimes becomes symmetrical, or *functionally normal*, when the logarithms of the observations are substituted for their arithmetic magnitudes.

[29] Allen Hazen, Storage to Be Provided in Impounding Reservoirs, *Trans. Am. Soc. Civil Engrs.*, 77, 1539 (1914).

A geometrically normal array of observations of a variable x is completely definable in terms of the geometric mean μ_g and the geometric standard deviation σ_g. By analogy to the arithmetically normal array:

$$\log x_g = \log x - \log \mu_g \quad \text{or} \quad x_g = x/\mu_g \tag{4-58}$$

$$\log \mu_g = (\Sigma \log x)/n \tag{4-59}$$

$$\log \sigma_g = \sqrt{\Sigma[\log^2 x_g/(n-1)]} = \sqrt{\Sigma[\log^2 x/(n-1)] - [n/(n-1)]\log^2 \mu_g} \tag{4-60}$$

$$y = [n/(\log \sigma_g \sqrt{2\pi})] \exp\{-1/2[(\log x_g)/(\log \sigma_g)]^2\} \tag{4-61}$$

Table 4-10   Calculation of Parameters and Plotting Position of Arithmetically Normal Frequencies (Example 4-8)

No. of Group	Magnitude of Grouped Observations as Class Mean, x	Number of Observations in Class Interval, f	$fx =$ (2) × (3)	Deviation from Mean, $x - \mu$	$f(x-\mu)^2$ (3) × (5)	Observations Equal to or Less Than Class Mean Number (see note)	Per Cent 100 × (7)/200
(1)	(2)	(3)	(4)	(5)	(6)	(7)	(8)
1	1	2	2	−5	50	1	0.5
2	2	6	12	−4	96	5	2.5
3	3	12	36	−3	108	14	7.0
4	4	24	96	−2	96	32	16.0
5	5	36	180	−1	36	62	31.0
6	6	40	240	0	0	100	50.0
7	7	36	252	+1	36	138	69.0
8	8	24	192	+2	96	168	84.0
9	9	12	108	+3	108	186	93.0
10	10	6	60	+4	96	195	97.5
11	11	2	22	+5	50	199	99.5
Sums		$n = 200$	1200	...	772	...	...

Arithmetic mean $\mu = \Sigma fx/n = 1200/200 = 6$.

Standard deviation $\sigma = \sqrt{\Sigma f(x-\mu)^2/(n-1)} = \sqrt{772/199} = 1.97$.

Middle ordinate $y_0 = n/(\sigma\sqrt{2\pi}) = 200/(1.97 \times 2.51) = 40.4$.

Equation of distribution $y = y_0/\exp[1/2(x-\mu)^2/\sigma^2] = 40.4/\exp[(x-6)^2/7.74]$

Note. Column 7, on the assumption that half the observations lie to either side of the class mean, is calculated as the sum of the observations below the class interval plus one-half the observations in the class interval.

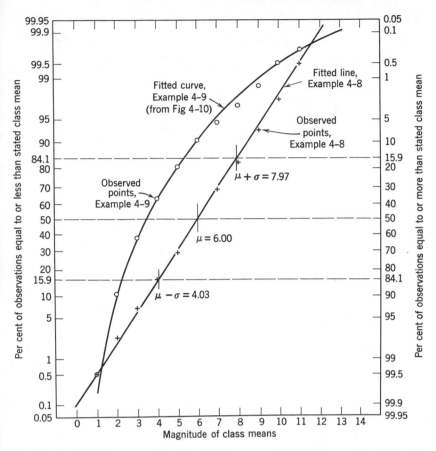

Fig. 4-9. Straight-line summation plot of a frequency distribution on arithmetic probability paper; Example 4-8. The geometric series from Example 4-9 (Fig. 4-10) is added for comparison.

Because x_g is expressed in terms of μ_g, σ_g is inherently a ratio to μ_g and so incorporates the concept of the coefficient of variation.

Analysis of geometrically normal distributions, too, is expedited by probability paper. A logarithmic scale replaces the arithmetic one, and the straight line of best fit passes through the intersections of μ_g with the 50% frequency, and $\mu_g\sigma_g$ with the 84.1% frequency or μ_g/σ_g with the 15.9% frequency respectively. In other words, the geometric mean and the median coincide, and $P_{84.1}/\mu_g = \mu_g/P_{15.9} = \sigma_g$.

The standard deviations of the geometric mean and the geometric standard deviation follow for geometrically normal series.

Measure	*Computation*	*Standard Error*
mean	$\log \mu_g = (\Sigma \log x)/n$	$(\log \sigma_g)/\sqrt{n}$
standard deviation	$\log \sigma_g = \sqrt{(\Sigma \log^2 x_g)/(n-1)}$	$(\log \sigma_g)/\sqrt{2n}$

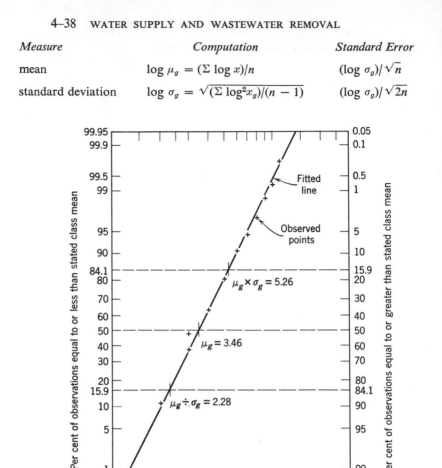

Fig. 4-10. Straight-line summation plot of a frequency distribution on logarithmic probability paper.

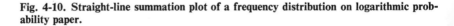

Example 4-9. For the data given in Columns (1) and (2) of Table 4-11, determine the constants of the geometrically normal frequency curve of best fit and the points necessary to plot the straight line of best fit on log-probability paper (Fig. 4-10). The necessary calculations are systematized in the table.

Accordingly, $\log \mu_g = 0.5390$ and $\mu_g = 3.46$; $\log \sigma_g = \sqrt{3.2541 \times 2/199} = 0.018$ and $\sigma_g = 1.52$; also $\mu_g \sigma_g = 3.46 \times 1.52 = 5.26$ can be plotted at 84.1% and $\mu_g/\sigma_g = 3.46/1.52 = 2.28$ can be plotted at 15.9%.

Table 4-11 Calculation of Geometrically Normal Frequencies

Magnitude of Observation, x	Number of Observations, f	Per Cent of Observations, $100f/n$	$\log x$ $\log (1)$	$(100f/n)$ $\log x$ $(3) \times (4)$	$\log x_g =$ $\log x -$ $\log \mu_g$ $(4) -$ $\log \mu_g$	$\log^2 x_g$ $(6)^2$	$(100f/n)$ $\log^2 x_g$ $(3) \times (7)$
(1)	(2)	(3)	(4)	(5)	(6)	(7)	(8)
1	2	1	0.0000	0.0000	−0.5390	0.2905	0.2905
2	40	20	0.3010	6.0200	−0.2380	0.0566	1.1320
3	66	33	0.4771	15.7443	−0.0619	0.0038	0.1254
4	38	19	0.6021	11.4399	+0.0631	0.0040	0.0760
5	30	15	0.6990	10.4850	+0.1600	0.0256	0.3840
6	10	5	0.7782	3.8910	+0.2392	0.0572	0.2860
7	6	3	0.8451	2.5353	+0.3061	0.0937	0.2811
8	4	2	0.9031	1.8062	+0.3641	0.1326	0.2652
9	2	1	0.9542	0.9542	+0.4152	0.1724	0.1720
10	1	0.5	1.0000	0.5000	+0.4610	0.2125	0.1063
11	1	0.5	1.0414	0.5207	+0.5024	0.2711	0.1356
Sums	$n = 200$	100.0	. . .	53.8966	. . .	. . .	3.2541
Means	. . .	. . .	. . .	0.5390	. . .	. . .	. . .

4-13 Concluding Remarks

This chapter has introduced a wide variety of new concepts in rapid-fire succession. The essential features, though, have been repeated often enough to stand out sharply. It has been seen repeatedly how the expectation operator can be applied to evaluate the standard error or sampling standard deviation of a statistic; this type of analysis is essential for application of theory to many practical problems. The use of normal tables and probability papers for elementary inferential analysis was demonstrated in several paragraphs; this, too, is an essential feature of applied statistics.

CHAPTER 5

Water and Wastewater Volumes

5-1 Volume and Rate Concepts

Good management and design of water-supply and wastewater-removal systems demand a good knowledge of the volumes and flows involved and their relation to population and time. Quantities often recorded in practice are:

(*a*) Total annual volumes in gallons (gal) or million gallons (mg).

(*b*) Average rates of draft or flow in gallons per day (gpd) or million gallons daily (mgd) = (*a*)/(365 or 366).

(*c*) Average rates of draft or flow in gallons per capita daily (gpcd) = (*b*)/(midyear population or tributary population).

(*d*) Average daily rates in gallons per person[1] connected to the system = (*b*)/(connected midyear population or tributary population).

(*e*) Average daily rates in gallons per service[2] = (*b*)/(number of services, active or total).

Because per capita and related figures generalize the experience, they are useful in comparing the records of different communities and estimating future needs of individual communities and areas. Fluctuations in flow are usefully expressed as percentage ratios of maximum or minimum monthly, weekly, daily, or hourly rates to average monthly, weekly, daily, and hourly rates respectively.

[1] Or *consumer* in water supply
[2] Or *tap* in water supply

Most water-supply and wastewater-disposal systems include relatively massive structures (dams, reservoirs, and treatment works) that are a long time in construction and are not readily expanded; they also include pipes and other conduits sunk into city streets and disrupting to traffic while they are being laid. Accordingly, the principal system components are purposely made large enough to satisfy community needs for a reasonable number of years. Selecting the initial or design capacity is not simple. It calls for skill in interpreting social and economic trends and sound judgment in analyzing past experience and predicting future requirements. Among needed estimates are the following:

1. The number of years, or *design period*, for which the proposed system and its component structures and equipment are to be adequate.
2. The number of people, or *design population*, to be served.
3. The rates of water use and wastewater release, or *design flows*, in terms of per capita water consumption and sewage discharge as well as industrial and commercial requirements.
4. The area to be served, or *design area*, and the allowances to be made for population density and areal water consumption and wastewater release from residential, commercial, and industrial districts.
5. The rates of rainfall and runoff, or *design hydrology*, for storm and combined sewerage.[3]

5-2 Design Periods

Design periods are chosen with the following factors in mind:

1. Useful life of component structures and equipment, taking into account obsolescence as well as wear and tear.
2. Ease, or difficulty, of extending or adding to existing and planned works, including a consideration of their location.
3. Anticipated rate of population growth, including possible shifts in community, industrial, and commercial development.
4. Going rate of interest on bonded indebtedness.
5. Performance of the works during their early years when they will not be loaded to capacity.

Change in purchasing power of money during the period of retirement of indebtedness is of no fundamental concern, but the longer the useful life, the greater the difficulty of extensions, the smaller the rate of growth, the lower the rate of interest, and the better the early performance, the farther into the future can designs be projected with economic justification. Design periods often employed in practice are shown in Table 5-1.

[3] This aspect of the problem is considered in Chap. 7.

Table 5-1 Design Periods for Water and Wastewater Structures

Type of Structure	Special Characteristics	Design Period, Year
Water supply		
Large dams and conduits	Hard and costly to enlarge	25–50
Wells, distribution systems, and filter plants	Easy to extend	
	When growth and interest rates are low*	20–25
	When growth and interest rates are high*	10–15
Pipes more than 12 in. in diameter	Replacement of smaller pipes is more costly in long run	20–25
Laterals and secondary mains less than 12 in. in diameter	Requirements may change fast in limited areas	Full development
Sewerage		
Laterals and submains less than 15 in. in diameter	Requirements may change fast in limited areas	Full development
Main sewers, outfalls, and intercepters	Hard and costly to enlarge	40–50
Treatment works	When growth and interest rates are low*	20–25
	When growth and interest rates are high*	10–15

* The dividing line is in the vicinity of 3% per annum.

5-3 Population Data

The most reliable information on the population of a given community or area at a designated time is obtained by a well-conducted official enumeration or census. The government of the United States has made a decennial census since 1790. Additional information may come from state enumerations, usually authorized for years ending in 5, and from special surveys made by public authorities or private agencies for governmental, social, or commercial purposes. U.S. Census dates and intervals[4] between

[4] U.S. Census Dates and Intervals.

Year	Date	Census Intervals, Years
1790–1820	First Monday in August	Approximately 10
1830–1900	1 June	Exactly 10, except 1820–1830
1910	15 April	9.875
1920	1 January	9.708
1930	1 April	10.250
1940–1960	1 April	Exactly 10

them were not standardized until the census of 1930 but were changed in attempts to find a time when most people are in their home communities and accessible to enumerators.

The information obtained is published by the Bureau of the Census, Department of Commerce. Political or geographic subdivisions for which population data are summarized include states, counties, metropolitan districts, cities, and towns, wards, and census tracts. An historical record beginning in 1790 lists cities with 100,000 inhabitants or more at the time of the last census; for smaller communities the historical record is shorter. Census-tract data offer the most complete geographic breakdown of information but are published for the larger cities only. However, they can be obtained from the Bureau by special arrangement.

5-4   Population Growth

Populations increase by births, decrease by deaths, increase or decrease by migration, and increase by annexation. Each of these elements is influenced by social and economic factors some of which inhere in the community; others are countrywide and even world wide in origin. Changes in birth and death rates in the United States since the First World War[5] must be interpreted in terms of (1) immigration restrictions which have decreased the proportion of young adults; (2) advances in maternal and child hygiene which have reduced maternal and infant mortality and the infectious diseases of childhood; (3) improvements in nutrition which have increased fertility and lowered the incidence of tuberculosis as well as other deficiency and infectious diseases; (4) discoveries in medicine which have decreased the prevalence and fatality of infectious diseases; and (5) fluctuations in the national economy which have lowered or raised the birth rate. Other factors, such as wars and disasters, have also come into play. Recognizing that birth and death rates move towards more or less stable values and that annexations or extensions of services can be anticipated, the most important and least predictable element of population change is commercial and industrial activity. This may produce sharp rises,

---

[5] Birth and death rates in the United States per 1000 population have been recorded as follows:

	1915	1920	1925	1930	1935	1940	1945	1950	1955	1960
Birth rate	30	28	25	21	19	19	20	24	25	24
Death rate	13	13	12	11	11	11	11	10	9	10
Rate of natural increase	16	15	13	10	8	8	10	15	16	14

slow growth, stationary conditions, or even marked declines in population.[6]

Were it not for these many and varying influences, populations would follow the growth curve characteristic of living things within limited space or with limited economic opportunity. The curve is S-shaped (Fig. 5-1), early growth taking place at an increasing, late growth at a decreasing rate as a saturation value or upper limit is approached. What the future holds for a given population depends upon where it is on the growth curve at a given time.

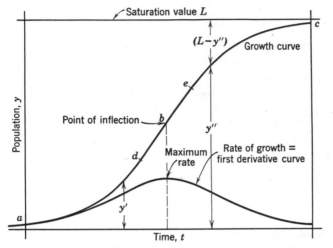

Fig. 5-1. Population growth idealized. Note geometric increase from *a* to *b*; straight-line increase from *d* to *e* (approximately); and first-order increase from *b* to *c*.

5-5   Short-Term Estimates and Long-Term Forecasts

Two types of population estimates are needed in the management and design of water and wastewater works: (*a*) estimates of midyear populations for current years and the recent past, and (*b*) forecast of populations for longer design periods.

Estimates for Current and Past Years. These are either intercensal estimates for the years between censuses or postcensal estimates for the years since the last census. Mathematically, midyear values are usually interpolated, or extrapolated, on the basis of arithmetic or geometric

[6] Examples are furnished by the growth of Detroit, Mich. (automobile industry), the decline of Providence, R.I. (textile industry), and the growth of Miami, Fla. (recreation).

City	1910	1920	1930	1940	1950	1960
Detroit	466,000	994,000	1,569,000	1,623,000	1,850,000	1,670,000
Providence	224,000	238,000	253,000	254,000	249,000	207,000
Miami	5,500	30,000	111,000	172,000	249,000	292,000

change. Growth is *arithmetic* if the population increase dy in the time interval dt is unvarying and independent of population size: i.e., $dy/dt = k_a$ where k_a is a constant. Growth is *geometric* if dy/dt is proportional to population size y; i.e., $dy/dt = k_g y$, where k_g is a proportionality factor. Integration between the limits y_e (population of earlier census) and y_l (population of later census) and the limits t_e (date of earlier census) and t_l (date of later census) yields:

$$k_a = (y_l - y_e)/(t_l - t_e) \quad \text{for arithmetic growth} \tag{5-1}$$

$$k_g = (\ln y_l - \ln y_e)/(t_l - t_e) \quad \text{for geometric growth} \tag{5-2}$$

Integration between the limits y_m (desired midyear population) and y_e or y_l, and between the limits t_m (desired date) and t_e or t_l, gives the midyear populations as follows:

Arithmetic estimate

Intercensal: $y_m = y_e + (y_l - y_e)(t_m - t_e)/(t_l - t_e)$ (5-3)

Postcensal: $y_m = y_l + (y_l - y_e)(t_m - t_l)/(t_l - t_e)$ (5-4)

Geometric estimate

Intercensal: $\log y_m = \log y_e + (\log y_l - \log y_e)(t_m - t_e)/(t_l - t_e)$

$$(5\text{-}5)$$

Postcensal: $\log y_m = \log y_l + (\log y_l - \log y_e)(t_m - t_l)/(t_l - t_e)$

$$(5\text{-}6)$$

Geometric estimates, therefore, use the logarithms of populations in the same way as the populations themselves are used in arithmetic estimates; also, arithmetic increase is seen to be analogous to growth by simple interest, geometric increase to growth by compound interest. The lower portion of the S-shaped growth curve in Fig. 5-1 is approximated by analogy to geometric increase (concave upward); the central portion by analogy to arithmetic increase (straight line); and the upper portion by analogy to first-order chemical kinetics[7] (concave downward). Choice of method is aided by an examination of the population curve traced by available census figures plotted on arithmetic-coordinate paper.

Example 5-1. A city[8] recorded a population of 111,000 in its earlier decennial census and 171,000 in its later one. Estimate the midyear (1 July) populations (1) for the fifth intercensal year and (2) for the ninth postcensal year by arithmetic increase and geometric increase. Assume a census date of 1 April.

[7] The first-order reaction is formulated in Vol. 2. Its application to population data is illustrated in Fig. 5-1 and involves an estimate of the limiting population or saturation value L.
[8] The figures used are rounded values for Miami, Fla., 1930 and 1940.

1. Intercensal estimate for fifth year. $t_m - t_e = 5.25$ yr; $t_l - t_e = 10.00$ yr; and $(t_m - t_e)/(t_l - t_e) = 5.25/10.00 = 0.525$.

Arithmetic	Geometric
$y_l = 171,000$	$\log y_l = 5.23300$
$y_e = 111,000$	$\log y_e = 5.04532$
$y_l - y_e = 60,000$	$\log y_l - \log y_e = 0.18768$
$0.525(y_l - y_e) = 31,500$	$0.525(\log y_l - \log y_e) = 0.09853$
$y_m = 142,500$	$y_m = 139,300$

2. Postcensal estimate for ninth year. $t_m - t_l = 9.25$ yr; $t_l - t_e = 10.00$ yr; and $(t_m - t_l)/(t_l - t_e) = 9.25/10.00 = 0.925$.

Arithmetic	Geometric
From (1) $y_l - y_e = 60,000$	$\log y_l - \log y_e = 0.18768$
$0.925(y_l - y_e) = 55,500$	$0.925(\log y_l - \log y_e) = 0.17360$
$y_l = 171,000$	$\log y_l = 5.23300$
$y_m = 226,500$	$\log y_m = 5.40660$
	$y_m = 255,000$

Note that geometric estimates are higher for postcensal years and lower for intercensal years.

One can arrive at supporting estimates of populations from sources that, in one way or another, reflect population growth. Examples are school enrollment, services of different utilities, commercial transactions, building permits, and health and welfare records. Suitable ratios derived from these sources will translate them into population values. Ratios of this kind vary locally and in time. They must be chosen with discretion. Although no general values obtain, the following orders of magnitude are not uncommon in North American communities:

Population: school enrollment = 5:1.
Population: number of water, gas, or electric services = 3:1.
Population: number of telephone services = 4:1.

Current estimates of the nation's population are made by the Bureau of the Census by adding to the last census population the differences between births and deaths[9] and between immigration and emigration. For states and other large population groups, current (postcensal) estimates are made in various ways. One of them, the *apportionment method*, is formulated as follows: If we let y equal the local population and Y the national population and apply the subscripts of Eq. 5-4,

$$y_m - y_l = (Y_m - Y_l)(y_l - y_e)/(Y_l - Y_e) \tag{5-7}$$

[9] The Bureau of the Census estimates that 92% of all births are recorded and 98% of all deaths. Adjustments are made for incomplete registration.

i.e., the apportionment method equates local increase to national increase times the ratio of local to national intercensal increase. Where a loss in population has been registered during the last intercensal decade, the Bureau of the Census recommends using the last census figure.

Forecasts for Design Periods. Long-range forecasts of population differ appreciably from postcensal estimates in method of attack. In order to identify the long-term swing rather than short-term fluctuations, the full record of population growth is quite generally employed. Forecasting methods include (1) mathematical curve fitting and (2) graphical studies.

S-shaped curves, like the growth curve, can be described by equations seeking a rational biological basis. One of the best known is the *logistic* curve which describes a theory of P. F. Verhulst[10] in mathematical terms and is not unlike some curves of chemical autocatalysis. Ordinarily, mathematical curve fitting is useful only in forecasts for large population groups, namely, large cities and states or nations.

Pearl's formulation of Verhulst's population theory describes a logistic curve (Fig. 5-2) in the form

$$y = \frac{L}{1 + m \exp nt} = \frac{L}{1 + \exp(\ln m + nt)} \tag{5-8}$$

where y is the population at time t from an assumed origin, L is the upper limit or saturation population, and m and n are coefficients that can be calculated from observed or graphically generalized values of y. If only three pairs of characteristic values, y_0, y_1, y_2 at times $t_0 = 0$, t_1, and $t_2 = 2t_1$ extending over the useful range of the census populations, are chosen, as suggested by McLean,[10] the saturation value and coefficients of the curve are calculated from the three simultaneous equations as: $L = [2y_0y_1y_2 - y_1^2(y_0 + y_2)]/(y_0y_2 - y_1^2)$, $m = (L - y_0)/y_0$, and $n = (1/t_1) \ln [y_0(L - y_1)]/[y_1(L - y_0)]$. Instead, it may be convenient to develop a logistic scale for fitting straight lines to observed pairs of values. To do this, populations are expressed in terms of an estimated and graphically verified saturation magnitude L. The per cent saturation $P = 100y/L = 100/(1 + m \exp nt)$ or $\ln [(100 - P)/P] = \ln m + nt$. This becomes the equation of a straight line with ordinate intercept $\ln m$ and slope n for $\ln [(100 - P)/P]$ plotted against t or values of $\ln [(100 - P)/P]$ scaled in either direction from a 50-percentile or middle ordinate.

Example 5-2. In two periods, each of 20 years, a city[11] grew from 30,000 to 172,000 to 292,000. Find (1) the saturation population, (2) the coefficients, and (3) the equation of a logistic curve satisfying the experienced growth.

[10] See Raymond Pearl, *Medical Biometry and Statistics*, W. B. Saunders Co., Philadelphia, Chapter 18, 1940; and J. C. McLean, *Civil Eng.*, **22**, 133 and, importantly, 886 (1952).

[11] Rounded values for Miami, Fla., 1920–1960.

1. Because $y_0 = 30,000$; $y_1 = 172,000$; and $y_2 = 292,000$,

$$L = [2 \times 30 \times 172 \times 292,000 - (172)^2 \times 322,000]/[30 \times 292 - (172)^2]$$
$$= 313,000; \text{ moreover,}$$

2. $m = (313 - 30)/30 = 9.43$, and

$$n = 0.05 \ln (30 \times 141)/(172 \times 283) = 0.05 \times (-2.442) = -0.122, \text{ and}$$

3. $y = 313/[1 + 9.43 \exp (-0.122)t]$.

This curve is plotted in Fig. 5-2 both arithmetically and logistically.

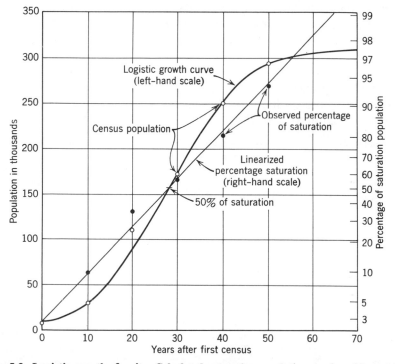

Fig. 5-2. Logistic growth of a city. Calculated saturation population, confirmed by graphical good straight-line fit, is 313,000. Right-hand scale is plotted as log $[(100 - P)/P]$ about 50 % at the center.

Plots of population against time generally exhibit trends that can be carried forward to the end of design periods. The eye of a skilled interpreter of population growth will guide his hand to extend population curves into what appear to be reasonable forecasts without committing the forecaster to a particular mathematical system. For this reason, graphical forecasts are much used by engineers. Sketching in the past growth of similar, but larger, communities may be helpful or harmful. The historical periods entering into comparisons of this kind are fairly certain to be quite unlike, and the future of a given community will presumably be other than the past of a different community once of about the same size, even though the two places were or are now similar in their constitution and composition.

Somewhat different in principle is the forecasting of populations by projecting into the future, not a growth curve, but its first derivative, a rate-of-growth curve. For convenience, the rate of growth can be expressed as the intercensal percentage increase in population, adjusted, if necessary, for variations in census dates. Comparisons with rates of growth of other, larger populations are also possible but should be justified. Plotting rate of growth against population density provides additional information.

Arithmetic scales are most generally useful in plotting population data. However, a logarithmic (geometric) population or rate-of-growth scale sometimes brings observed points into line and simplifies their projection. Straight-line projections are given mathematical justification by *least-squares* procedures including determination of a coefficient of correlation and its standard error (Sec. 4-7).

Example 5-3.   The design period for the water works of a community of 164,000 at the time of the last census is 30 years. Estimate the design population from a study of its past rate of growth, assuming (*a*) an arithmetic trend and (*b*) a geometric trend in rate of growth.   The recorded decadal populations of the community[12] and rates of growth prior to the last census are given in Table 5-2 together with the calculations necessary to fit trends to the rates by the method of least squares.

Table 5-2   Least-Squares Calculations for Example 5-3

	Population, x, in Thousands	Decadal Rate of Growth, y, %	$\log y$	x^2	xy	$x \log y$
	42.0	26.7	1.4265	1,764	1,121	59.91
	53.2	50.2	1.7007	2,830	2,671	90.48
	79.9	23.8	1.3766	6,384	1,901	109.99
	98.9	39.6	1.5977	9,781	3,916	158.01
	138.0	18.8	1.2742	19,044	2,595	175.84
Sums	412.0	159.1	7.3757	39,803	12,204	594.23
Means	82.4	31.8	1.4751	7,961	2,441	118.85

1. Calculate the trends in rate by Eqs. 4-41 and 4-42.
   (*a*) Arithmetic trend in rate: $y = 44.2 - 0.150x$.
   (*b*) Geometric trend in rate:

$$\log y = 1.6638 - 0.00211x \quad \text{or} \quad y = 46.1 \exp{(-5.27 \times 10^{-3}x)}$$

2. Plot the observations and fitted trends in Fig. 5-3.

[12] Rounded values for Hartford, Conn., from 1880 to 1940, merely for illustration of method.

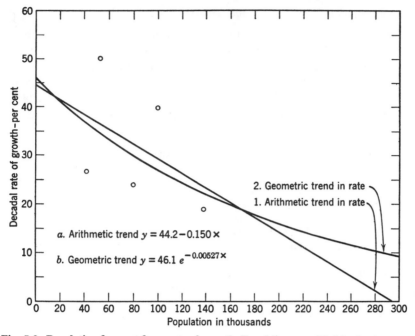

a. Arithmetic trend $y = 44.2 - 0.150 \times$

b. Geometric trend $y = 46.1\ e^{-0.00527 \times}$

Population in thousands

Fig. 5-3. Population forecast from rate of growth. Trend lines are fitted by least squares.

3. Estimate the population from the decadal rates of growth read from Fig. 5-3 or calculated from the fitted equations. The results are shown in Table 5-3. Here decadal increase = per cent growth × population/100; and population = preceding population + increase.

Table 5-3   Calculation of Estimated Populations (Example 5-3)

Years after Last Census	Population in Thousands a	b	Decadal Growth Rate, % a	b	Increase a	b
0	164	164	19.6	19.4	32	32
10	196	196	14.8	16.4	29	32
20	225	228	10.5	13.9	21	32
30	246	260	...	...	...	...

Forecasts must consider areal or geographic restriction of population growth as well as changing social, economic, and political effects. Some of these may, in a sense, be catastrophic to growth (footnote 5).

5-6   Population Distribution and Density

Estimates of the total population of a community or district are needed in the design and management of water and wastewater systems as a whole. Distribution of water and collection of wastewater within the area call, in addition, for estimates of population density and nature of occupancy and use of component areas or districts. Population density is generally expressed as the number of persons per acre. A classification of areas and expected population densities is shown in Table 5-4.

Table 5-4   Common Population Densities

	Persons per Acre
1. Residential areas	
(a) Single-family dwellings, large lots	5–15
(b) Single-family dwellings, small lots	15–35
(c) Multiple-family dwellings, small lots	35–100
(d) Apartment or tenement houses	100–1000 or more
2. Mercantile and commercial areas	15–30
3. Industrial areas	5–15
4. Total, exclusive of parks, playgrounds, and cemeteries	10–50

Suitable values derive from studies of present and possible future subdivision of typical blocks. For example, small lots, 50 ft × 150 ft, facing a 60-ft street in a block 600 ft long and 300 ft wide, run 24 to the block and $43,560/(660 \times 360/24) = 4.4$ to the acre. For single-family dwellings, the population density then becomes $4.4 \times 5 = 22$ persons per acre, assuming 5 persons per dwelling unit. Much can be learned from fire-insurance maps, aerial maps, and field surveys.

Population distribution within communities can be identified by examining census tract reports for the larger cities of the United States and ward reports for the smaller ones. Changes in occupancy and use must be forecast, as well as changes in population density or saturation. Some zoning ordinances define the nature of occupancy as well as the bulk of the buildings allowed to be erected. They are useful instruments for estimating reasonable design values. Unfortunately, ordinances are subject to repeal, modification, and re-interpretation.

Possible changes should be allowed for, wherever this can be reasonably done. The smaller the district and the lower its population density, the greater is the possible departure from average values. This is exemplified in Eq. 5-9, which approximates graphical values proposed by Greeley and Stanley.[13]

$$\frac{D_{max}}{D} = [2.90 - \log p \exp(-2.57 \times 10^{-2} D)] \exp(-2.57 \times 10^{-2} D) \quad (5\text{-}9)$$

[13] Calvin Davis, *Handbook of Applied Hydraulics*, 2nd Ed., McGraw-Hill Book Co., New York, p. 1017, 1952.

Here D_{max} is the probable maximum number of persons per acre in a district containing p per cent of the population, and D is the average number of persons per acre. For $D = 20$ and $p = 10$, for example, $D_{max}/D = 1.38$ and $D_{max} = 28$ persons per acre.

5-7 Water Consumption

Service pipes supply water to dwellings, mercantile or commercial properties, industrial establishments, and public buildings. The water used is classified accordingly. The quantities delivered in North American communities tend towards values shown in Table 5-5, but with wide variations, because of differences in (1) climate, (2) standards of living, (3) extent of sewerage, (4) type of mercantile, commercial, and industrial activity, (5) cost of water, (6) availability of private water supplies, (7)

Table 5-5 Normal Water Consumption

Class of Consumption	Quantity, gpcd	
	Normal Range	Average
Domestic	15–70	50
Commercial and industrial	10–100	65
Public	5–20	10
Water unaccounted for	10–40	25
Total	40–230	150

quality or properties of water for domestic, industrial, and other usages, (8) distribution-system pressures, (9) completeness of meterage, and (10) system management.

Water rates are generally classified, according to annual consumption per service, as:

Domestic rate	less than 300,000 gal
Intermediate rate	300,000 to 3,000,000 gal
Manufacturing rate	more than 3,000,000 gal

The domestic rate permits about 16 persons to draw water at a rate of 50 gpcd through a single service.

A breakdown of domestic water consumption apportions the various uses as follows:[14] 41% to flushing toilets; 37% to washing and bathing;

[14] C. N. Durfor and Edith Becker, Public Water Supplies of the 100 Largest Cities in the United States, 1962, *U.S. Geology Survey, Water Supply Paper* 1812, 5 (1964).

6% to kitchen use; 5% to drinking water; 4% to washing clothes; 3% to general household cleansing; 3% to watering the garden; 1% to washing the family car.

5-8 Factors Affecting Consumption

Domestic Consumption. Extremes of heat and cold increase water consumption: hot and arid climates by more bathing, air conditioning, and irrigation; cold climates by water bled through faucets to keep service pipes and building distribution systems from freezing. High standards of living mean heavy draft of water for kitchen, bathrooms, and laundry, lawn and garden sprinkling, car washing, and unit or central air conditioning.

Where sewerage systems are not extended in pace with water distribution systems, private sewage disposal facilities may become overloaded and break down.

Commercial and Industrial Consumption. Some enterprises, hotels and hospitals, for example, use much water; so do industrial establishments[15] like breweries, canneries, laundries, paper mills, and steel mills.

The less water costs, the higher, ordinarily, is its consumption, particularly for industrial purposes. Rough rules from North American experience are (1) that consumption varies inversely as the *manufacturing rate* and (2) that rate increases may, for a time, reduce consumption by about one-half their percentage rise. When groundwater sources are abundant within communities or other suitable water sources are easily accessible, large users are encouraged to develop supplies of their own for special purposes such as air conditioning, condensing, and manufacturing processes.

Consumption in General. Public supplies are the systems of choice when they deliver water that is clean, palatable, and of unquestioned safety for drinking and culinary uses; when the water is soft for washing and cool for condensing; and when it meets the quality needs of industry. Wide use of bottled waters is, in a sense, a measure of public disapprobation. Yet private sources are sometimes dangerous, even when they are palatable.

Water is discharged, more or less in orifice flow, through faucets and similar outlets, as well as through leaks in mains and faulty plumbing; therefore, flow varies about as the square root of the pressure head. Accordingly, high pressures result (1) in rapid discharge and increased waste of water through fixtures and (2) in increased leakage as a whole. Operating pressures in excess of about 60 psig are no longer so important for fire fighting as they were before the advent of motor pumpers.

[15] Industrial water requirements are discussed in Vol. 2.

Meterage encourages thrift and normalizes water demand. Meter consciousness depresses domestic use abnormally when meters are first put in, but draft does return eventually to a defendable norm. A distinction must be made between *per cent of services* metered and *per cent of consumption* metered. Understandably, large consumers are given meters first, and this effects a greater per capita reduction in consumption than occurs later. Ordinarily, meters should adjust consumption in keeping with size and type of community. The cost of metering water, including meter reading and repair, is substantial. Consequently, it is good management to balance cost of meterage against value of water conserved by reduction of waste. There have been instances in which reduction has been large enough to permit postponing otherwise needed extensions of supplies.

No distribution system is absolutely tight. Where the main supply and the water delivered to consumers or used in other ways (for example, in washing filters and flushing streets, mains, and sewers) are fully metered, about 85% of the supply should reasonably be accounted for; if estimates of water used in fighting fires are added, the uses of 90% or more of the supply should be identified. Because leakage is independent of draft, it is evaluated more logically in gpcd than as a percentage of the total. New cast-iron water mains generally lost 100 to 500 gpd per mile of pipe per inch diameter before the introduction of preformed joints. Because 500 people are normaly served by a mile of 8-in. pipe in North American cities, between (100 to 500) × 8/500 = 2 to 8 gpcd were then lost from distribution systems. By comparison, a leaky water-closet tank wastes 60 and a dripping faucet 12 gpd.

Leakage detection is an important function in the management of older systems. Superficial signs of leaks are: high night flows in water mains and service pipes, excessive flows in sewers, abnormal drops in pressure, water running in gutters, moist pavements, persistent seepage, and unusually green vegetation (in droughts and dry climates). Purposeful detection includes placing sounding rods on accessible piping or driving rods into the ground near mains to test for moist earth; employing electronic amplifiers to pick up the sound of running water; inspecting premises for leaky plumbing; placing weak and short-lived radioactive tracers in mains and probing for radioactivity of the flowing water and the ground; and conducting water-waste surveys. A common technique of survey crews is sequential isolation and testing of comparatively small sections of the system. All or but one or two valves on mains feeding into individual sections are closed, and the amount of entering water is determined in some convenient way (Sec. 16-9).

Future Consumption. As North American cities have grown, their per capita use of water has commonly risen by about one-tenth the percentage increase in population. A city gaining in population by 50%, therefore, increases its per capita water consumption by about 5%. Water uses are bound to become larger as summer air conditioning becomes common. However, the different structures cooled need not draw more than 5 to 35 gpcd at maximum rate during the summer or more than 0.5 to 4.5 gpcd on an annual basis if cooling water is conserved in evaporative condensers or cooling towers. Automatic household appliances (dishwashers, home laundries, and garbage grinders) further increase per capita rates of consumption.

5-9   Variations in Demand

Water consumption changes with the seasons, the days of the week, and the hours of the day. There are major seasonal peaks during summer heat and drought when large volumes of water are drawn to refresh man and his domestic animals, water lawns and gardens, fill swimming and wading pools, and feed the washers or cool the condensers of air-conditioning equipment. Minor seasonal peaks occur during extreme winter cold (1) when water is run to waste in order to keep household services and pipes from freezing and (2) when there is much leakage from pipe joints because metals contract with cold. Among seasonal uses of water in industry are the processing of agricultural products at times of harvest, and shifts of draft between private groundwater supplies in the summer and public surface-water supplies in the winter to draw profit from lower water temperatures. Day to day variations reflect household and industrial activity: Sundays for rest and Mondays for washing. Hour to hour fluctuations produce a peak close to noon and a trough in the small hours of the morning. Normal variations in draft must be known if supply pipes, service reservoirs, and distributing pipes are to be properly dimensioned. Moreover, there must be suitable allowances for sudden, heavy, and unpredictable drafts to fight fires. The volume of water actually used in quenching fires is relatively small, but the rate at which it must be supplied is high and becomes of determining influence in sizing the distribution systems of small and middle-group North American communities.

Normal Variations.   The smaller the community, the more variable is the demand; the shorter the period of flow, the wider is the departure from the mean. Variations are conveniently expressed as ratios to the mean. There are large differences between communities. Common values are:

Ratio	Normal Range	Average
Maximum day: average day	(From 1.2 to 2.0):1	1.5:1
Maximum hour: average hour	(From 2.0 to 3.0):1	2.5:1

Fire Demand. To extinguish fires and keep them from flaring into conflagrations, fire supply must be fitted to the bulk, congestion, fire resistance, and content of buildings. Because the character of the so-called high-value or congested districts of North American communities is a function of their size, their fire demand is likewise a function of their size. For other parts of communities, fire-flow estimates are based upon the nature and congestion of component buildings. Industrial and commercial properties have requirements of their own. The existence of private fire supplies, storage, and pumps is a modifying factor.

In North America fire protection is normally based upon recommendations of the National Board of Fire Underwriters. This fact-finding organization is supported by fire-insurance companies. A principal activity is the grading of public water supplies for adequacy of their fire protection services.[16] Careful and continuing analyses of water demands experienced during fires in different kinds of communities underlie formulations of general standards by the Board. From these, the designer should depart only for good and sufficient reasons. Among the many factors taken into account by the Board in fixing upon standard fire flows is the probable loss of water from connections broken during large fires. The general requirements of the National Board are summarized below.[17]

1. Within the central, congested, high-value district, the rate Q in gpm,[18] at which water must be available to check a serious conflagration, varies with the population P in thousands in accordance with the following relationship for communities of 200,000 people or less:

$$Q = 1020\sqrt{P}(1 - 0.01\sqrt{P}) \tag{5-10}$$

2. The central portion of communities with populations in excess of 200,000 requires capacities of 12,000 gpm and 2000 to 8000 gpm in addition for a second fire.

3. For residential districts the required fire flow varies from 500 gpm to 6000 gpm.

As previously stated, the actual volume of water withdrawn from the system to fight fires in the course of a year is almost negligibly small.

Coincident Draft. It is hardly conceivable that water will continue to be drawn at maximum rate for general community purposes while a serious fire is raging. Accordingly, the total draft probably does not equal

[16] *Standard Schedule for Grading Cities and Towns of the United States*, National Board of Fire Underwriters (now the American Insurance Association), New York, 1942.

[17] A more detailed statement is deferred until Chap. 13.

[18] This is the customary unit for rating pumps, fire streams, and ground-water yields; 1000 gpm = 1.44 mgd.

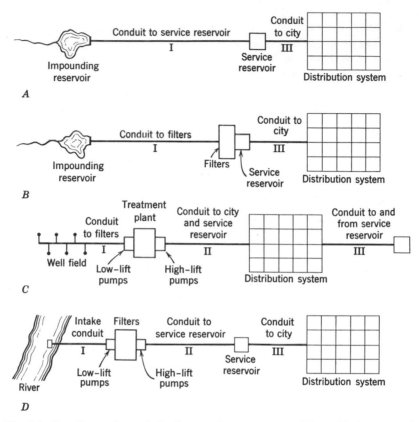

Fig. 5-4. Capacity requirements for the constituent structures of four typical water-works systems. The service reservoir is assumed to take care of hourly fluctuations, fire drafts, and emergency reserve.

		Capacity of System, mgd			
Structure	Required Capacity	A	B	C	D
1. River or well field	Maximum day			22.5	22.5
2. Conduit I	Maximum day	22.5	22.5	22.5	22.5
3. Conduit II	Maximum day	....	....	....⎫	22.5
4. Conduit III	Coincident draft and fire	35.7	35.7	35.7⎬	35.7
5. Low-lift pumps	Maximum day plus reserve	....	....	30.0	30.0
6. High-lift pumps	Maximum hour plus reserve	....	....	45.0	50.0
7. Filters or treatment plant	Maximum day plus reserve	....	24.0	24.0	24.0
8. Distribution system to high-value district	Coincident draft and fire	35.7	35.7	35.7	35.7

the sum of the fire demand and maximum *hourly* draft. Instead, the sum of the fire demand and *maximum daily* rate (150% of the average daily rate) appears to be reasonable in all but unusual situations.

Example 5-4. Each of the four water works systems shown in Fig. 5-4 serves a community with an estimated future population of 100,000. Estimate the required capacities of their constituent structures for an average water consumption of 150 gpcd and a distributing reservoir so sized that it can provide enough water to care for differences between hourly and daily flows and for fire demands and emergency water requirements. Fundamental calculations are:

1. Average daily draft = 150 × 100,000/1,000,000 = 15 mgd.
2. Maximum daily draft = coincident draft = 1.5 × 15 = 22.5 mgd.
3. Maximum hourly draft = 2.5 × 15 = 37.5 mgd.
4. Fire flow to high-value district = $1020\sqrt{100}(1 - 0.01\sqrt{100}) = 9180$ gpm, or 9.180 × 1.44 = 13.2 mgd.
5. Coincident draft plus fire flow = 22.5 + 13.2 = 35.7 mgd.
6. Provisions for breakdowns and repairs of pumps and water purification units by installing at least one reserve unit give the following capacities:

   Low-lift pumps: 2 × average daily draft = 2.0 × 15 = 30 mgd = $\frac{4}{3}$ × 22.5 (max. daily draft).

   High-lift pumps: 3 × average daily draft = 3.0 × 15 = 45 mgd, or $\frac{4}{3}$ × 37.5 = 50 mgd (max. hourly draft).

   Filters and the like: 1.6 × average daily draft = 1.6 × 15 = 24 mgd, or 22.5 mgd (max. daily draft).

The resulting capacities of the four systems shown in Fig. 5-4 are summarized below that figure.

5-10   Demand and Drainage Loads of Buildings

The demand load of a building depends upon the number and kinds of fixtures and the probability of their simultaneous operation. Different fixtures are furnished with water at different rates as a matter of convenience and purpose. Expressed in cubic feet per minute (cfm), or fixture units, these rates become whole numbers of small size. Common demand rates are shown in Table 5-6.

It is quite unlikely that all fixtures in a building system will draw water or discharge it at the same time. A probability study of draft demands by Hunter[19] suggested the relationships plotted in Fig. 5-5. In practice, the values shown are modified as follows:

1. Demands for service sinks are ignored in calculating the total fixture demand.

2. Demands of supply outlets, such as sill cocks, hose connections, and air conditioners, through which water flows more or less continuously for a

[19] Roy B. Hunter, Methods of Estimating Loads in Plumbing Systems, *National Bureau of Standards, Report* BMS 65 (1940). See also Housing and Home Finance Agency, *Housing Research Paper* 15 (1951).

Table 5-6 Fixture Rates

Type of Fixture and Supply (1) and Discharge (2)	Rates of Supply and Discharge, cfm	
	Private Buildings	Public and Office Buildings
Wash basin, faucet—(1) and (2)	1	2
Water closet, (2) only	6	8
flush tank, (1) only	3	5
flush valve, (1) only	6	10
Urinal		
(stall or wall), flush tank (1) only	. . .	3
(stall or wall), flush valve	. . .	5
(pedestal), flush valve	. . .	10
Bathtub or shower, faucet or mixing valve	2	4
Bathroom group (2) only	8	. . .
flush tank for closet, (1) only	6	. . .
flush valve for closet, (1) only	8	. . .
separate shower head, (1) only	2	. . .
separate shower stall, (2) only	10	. . .
Kitchen sink, faucet 2	2	4
Laundry trays (1 to 3), faucet	3	. . .
Combination fixture, faucet	3	. . .
Service sink, faucet (hotel or restaurant)	. . .	3
Sill cock	$\frac{2}{3}$	$\frac{2}{3}$

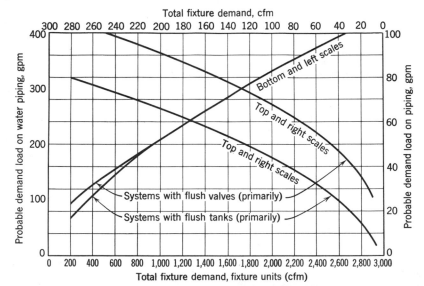

Fig. 5-5. Demand load on water piping. (*After Hunter.*)

considerable length of time, are added to the probable flow rather than the fixture demand.

3. Fixtures supplied with both hot and cold water exert reduced demands upon main hot-water and cold-water branches (not fixture branches). An allowance of three-fourths of the demand shown in Table 5-6 for individual fixtures is suggested.

Example 5-5. A two-story dwelling contains the following fixtures: a pair of bathroom groups, an additional water closet, an additional washbasin, a kitchen sink, a laundry tray, and a sill cock. All water closets are served by flush tanks. Find the demand load.

From Table 5-6: 2 bathroom groups @ 6 = 12; 1 water closet = 3; 1 washbasin = 1; 1 kitchen sink = 2; 1 laundry tray = 3; total = 21 cfm.

From Fig. 5-5, the probable flow in the building main will be 15 gpm plus 5 gpm for the sill cock, or a total of 20 gpm.

Like demand load, the drainage load placed on different parts of the system does not equal the sum of the discharge rates of individual fixtures. Not all of them are likely to be operated at the same instant or in such manner as to concentrate the full flow at a given point in the system. The larger the system, the steadier is the flow and the smaller the intensity of flow. In this respect, building-drainage systems behave, on a small scale, like sewerage systems (Sec. 5-11). Moreover, the time factor varies with differences in fixture distribution and complicates the estimation of a reasonable load. Probable discharges are greater for an individual horizontal branch than for the stack into which it empties; greater, too, for an individual stack than for the building drain in which it terminates. As a consequence, allowable ratios of fixture load to design discharge are relatively small for horizontal drains, larger for stacks, and greatest for building drains. These complicating factors make it impossible to show the relation between fixture discharge and drainage load by simple curves as was done in Fig. 5-5 for water piping.

5-11 Wastewater Flows

Flows in public sewers include one or more of the following: spent waters, groundwater seepage,[20] and stormwater runoff.

Spent Water. Spent waters are, primarily, portions of the public supply discharged into sewers from the drainage systems of buildings. Secondarily, they are made up of water drawn from private sources for air conditioning, industrial processes, and similar purposes. Sixty to 70% of the total water supplied generally becomes wastewater. The remainder is used up in watering lawns and gardens, flushing streets, fighting fires, generating steam, and satisfying miscellaneous household, commercial,

[20] Also called infiltration, but generally identified as seepage in this book.

and industrial purposes. Commercial areas discharge about 20,000 gpd per acre. That industrial wastewaters vary widely in volume follows from what has been said about industrial water consumption.

Groundwater. Groundwater, both *vadose* and *phreatic* (Fig. 6-5), seeps into street and building sewers through the leaky joints and manholes of older systems and through cracked pipes. Seepage potential varies with (1) height of the groundwater table above sewer inverts, (2) rainfall, snow-melt, and soil permeability, and (3) workmanship in constructing manholes and laying sewers and their connections to buildings. To suit the conven-ience of the designer, seepage rates are stated in various ways. Common allowances before the advent of preformed joints were:

A: 500 to 5000 gpd per acre; average, 2000.

B: 5000 to 100,000 gpd per mile of sewer, including house connections; average 30,000.

C: 500 to 5000 gpd per mile of sewer per inch diameter (average 2500) plus 100 gpd per manhole.

Ranges in values are broad because of variations in rainfall, percolation into the ground, height of groundwater table, and size and nature of area drained. The low values in A, B, and C are for sewers laid above the ground-water table. The high values are for sewers laid below the groundwater table, unless cast-iron or cement-asbestos pipe is substituted for vitrified tile or concrete pipes or preformed joints are used. Conversion from A to B and C is a function of (1) sewer length per acre (in North American communities, 115 ft for average development and 300 ft for full develop-ment); (2) sewer diameter (12 in. or less for almost 95% of the total length of sewers, if building connections are included); and (3) distances between manholes (generally less than 400 ft).

Example 5-6. Find A, B, and C for an annual rainfall of 48 in., one-half of which filters into the ground, a quarter of it eventually reaching the sewerage system.

$A = 48 \times \frac{1}{2} \times \frac{1}{4} \times 43{,}560 \times 7.5/365 = 450$ gpd/acre.

$B = 450 \times 5280/300 = 8000$ gpd/mile for full development.

For a 12-in. sewer and $5280/350 = 15$ manholes/mile, $C = (8000 - 15 \times 100)/12 = 550$ gpd/mile and inch diameter.

The degree of seepage is found by gaging sewers in the early morning hours and subtracting a small amount for spent-water flows. There is no seepage when sewers are laid with permanent underdrains that empty into nearby drainage channels. Initial system tightness is tested by gaging sewer flows before fixtures are connected. Sewers lose water to the ground as well as taking in groundwater flows.

Stormwater. The amounts of runoff from precipitation are large and overshadow the flow of sanitary sewage in combined systems. Separate sanitary systems should be free of stormwater, but they seldom are.

Illicit connections from roofs and from yard and foundation drains add to flows as do manhole covers that are not tight. Amounts vary with the effectiveness of regulations and countermeasures. Rates are as high as 70 gpcd and average 30 gpcd. A rainfall of 1 in. per hr on 1200 sq ft of roof creates a flow of 12.5 gpm or 17,800 gpd; spread over an acre, 1 in. per hr equals 1.008 cfs of runoff. Leakage through manhole covers may add 20 to 70 gpm when there is as much as 1 in. of water on the streets.

Example 5-7. What is the degree of separation of stormwater from roof leaders of houses 20 ft by 30 ft occupied by 5 persons when the rainfall intensity is 1 in. per hr and the stormwater flow in the sewers is 50 gpcd?

1. Storm runoff = 20 × 30 × 1 × 17,800/(1200 × 5) = 1780 gpcd.
2. Per cent non-enforcement = 100 × 50/1780 = 3%.

Gagings of sanitary sewers and flow meters at treatment works will record the amounts of illicit stormwater as differences between normal dry-weather flows and flows immediately following intense rains.

5-12 Variations in Flow

Flow in storm and combined sewers follows the pattern of runoff from precipitation. Fluctuations are sharp and high. Flows in sanitary sewers vary with water consumption, but fluctuations are damped, because only part of the sewage comes from the water supply; seepage of groundwater is relatively steady; and open-channel flow allows water to rise and fall in the system. Rising levels store flows, falling levels release them. Moreover, the instantaneous flow at a given point is a composite of upstream waters collected at different times. The greater the distance to a given point, the greater is the time of flow or concentration. Indeed, a long *time of concentration* irons out peak discharges not only in rivers and storm sewers, but also in sanitary sewers. Hence, formulations of expected variations in flow are quite like flood-flow and flood-routing procedures.

Minimum flows edge upward for much the same reasons that peak discharges are brought down. Estimates of damping effects by H. M. Gifft[21] reduce closely to the following equations:

$$Q_{max}/Q_{ave} = 5.0/P^{1/6} \qquad (5\text{-}11)$$

and

$$Q_{min}/Q_{ave} = 0.2P^{1/6} \qquad (5\text{-}12)$$

or

$$Q_{max}/Q_{min} = 25.0/P^{1/3} \qquad (5\text{-}13)$$

Here Q_{max}, Q_{ave}, and Q_{min} are respectively the maximum, average, and minimum rates of flow of domestic sewage and P is the population in thousands. The complementarity of the damping effects of maximum and

[21] H. M. Gifft, Estimating Variations in Domestic Sewage Flows, *Waterworks & Sewerage*, **92**, 175 (1945); a somewhat different approach has been recommended by J. C. Geyer and J. J. Lentz in a report to the Federal Housing Administration (1964).

minimum flows is understandable. Shape as well as size of area served (represented here by population) determines the degree of damping.

Widely used relationships for flows of domestic sewage from areas of moderate size are:

Maximum daily flow $= 2 \times$ average daily flow
Maximum hourly flow $= 1.5 \times$ maximum daily flow, or
$\qquad 3 \times$ average daily flow
Minimum daily flow $= \frac{2}{3} \times$ average daily flow
Minimum hourly flow $= \frac{1}{2} \times$ minimum daily flow, or
$\qquad \frac{1}{3} \times$ average daily flow

Example 5-8. Estimate the average, peak, and low rates of flow in a district sanitary sewer serving 9000 people, an area of 600 acres, and a community of 45,000 people with an average water consumption of 150 gpcd.

1. Spent water: $0.7 \times 150 = 105$ gpcd.
2. Maximum hour: $3 \times 105 = 315$ gpcd.
3. Minimum hour: $\frac{1}{3} \times 105 = 35$ gpcd.
By Eq. 5-11, $Q_{max} = 105 \times 5.0/(9)^{1/6} = 360$ gpcd.
By Eq. 5-12, $Q_{min} = 105 \times 0.2(9)^{1/6} = 30$ gpcd.
4. Proportion of total population served: $100 \times 9000/45,000 = 20\%$.
5. Average population density: $9000/600 = 15$ persons/acer.
By Eq. 5-9, maximum population density:
$\qquad D_{max} = 15[2.90 - \log 20 \exp(-2.57 \times 10^{-2} \times 15)] \exp(-2.57 \times 10^{-2} \times 15)$.
$\qquad = 21$ persons/acre.
6. Rainwater: 30 gpcd (assumed).
7. Infiltration: 2000 gpd/acre (assumed).
8. Average rate of flow: $21(105 + 30) + 2000 = 4840$ gpd/acre, if storm water is included.
9. Peak rate of flow: $21(315 + 30) + 2000 = 9250$ gpd/acre.
10. Low rate of flow: $21(35 + 30) + 2000 = 3370$ gpd/acre.

5-13 Rural Systems

The volumes of water used under rural conditions and the resulting wastewaters vary downward in magnitude from values common for urban areas. Minimum use of piped water in dwellings is about 20 gpcd; about 50 gpcd is average. Rural schools, overnight camps, and factories (excluding manufacturing uses) draw about 25 gpcd, restaurants 10 gpcd on a patronage basis, and work or construction camps 45 gpcd. By contrast, resort hotels have to supply about 100 gpcd and rural sanatoria or hospitals about twice as much.

Livestock and irrigation needs are additional. Dairy cows drink about 15 gpcd, horses, mules, and steers about 12 gpcd, hogs 4 gpcd, sheep 2 gpcd, chickens 0.04 gpcd, and turkeys 0.07 gpcd. The overall water requirements for dairy cows, including water for cleansing and cooling, are about 35 gpcd. Greenhouses may need as much as 70 gpd per 1000 sq ft, and garden crops about half this amount.

Water requirements of troops rise from an absolute minimum of 0.5 gpcd in combat through 2 to 5 gpcd on the march or in bivouac and 15 gpcd in temporary camps up to 50 or more gpcd in permanent military installations.

Wastewaters are of the same order of magnitude, but with some loss.

As discussed before, rates of water use and wastewater release are set by the water requirements and discharge capacities of different fixtures. In comparison with municipal sewage, the wastewaters of rural habitations and similar buildings are likely to be smaller and more fluctuating in volume; fresher and more concentrated; and quite warm, greasy, and soapy as fixtures are operated to waste. There is substantially no flow at night; the active period is only about 16 hours.

CHAPTER 6

Elements of Hydrology

6-1 Definitions and Scope

Hydrology[1] is the science of water in nature: its properties, distribution, and behavior. As such, it provides basic information for the management of water resources within the framework of our hydraulic and hydrological economy: water supply and wastewater disposal, drainage and irrigation, navigation and river regulation, water power and flood control.

Water Resources of the Earth. The volumes of water on the earth are large. The oceans and seas alone are calculated to hold 324×10^6 cu miles[2] of water, and it is estimated that 6 to 7×10^6 cu miles are locked up in the polar ice caps. Together these water masses account for about 97% of the total water resource.[3] Unfortunately, neither one of them is immediately available for water supply; seawater because each liter contains 35 grams of salt, and polar ice because it is so far away from the habitable portions of the globe.

This leaves as the useful waters of the earth the 1.67×10^5 cu miles of fresh water in lakes and streams, permeable soils, and the atmosphere; somewhat less than 3% in the atmosphere, derived, to be sure, by evaporation of salt as well as fresh water; the remainder split almost equally between surface and ground. However, these portions of the hydrosphere are not static; water circulates. Ten to 12×10^4 cu miles fall annually from the skies as rain or snow, about a fourth onto the continents and islands,

---

[1] From the Greek *hydor*, water, and *logos*, science.
[2] 1 cu mile = 1.47×10^{11} cu ft or 1.10×10^{12} gal.
[3] R. Colas, Producing Fresh Water from Sea Water, *L'Eau*, **49**, 205 (1962).

the remainder onto the oceans; 0.9 to 1.2 × 10^4 cu miles run off the surface of the land; and the ground yields, more or less safely, as much as 0.4 × 10^4 cu miles of water. In overall estimates, about a third of the land masses are well watered, the remaining two thirds semiarid and arid. As a final statistic, the total number of water molecules upon the earth is close to 45 × 10^{45}.

Branches of Hydrology. In relation to the atmosphere, hydrology deals (1) with rainfall and other forms of precipitation: their causes, origin, occurrence, magnitude, distribution, and variation and (2) with the return of moisture to the atmosphere by evaporation, sublimation, and transpiration.[4] As part of the broad science of meteorology, which encompasses all atmospheric phenomena, the study of atmospheric waters is called hydrometeorology.

Surface-water hydrology deals with runoff or stream flow and its variations; storage in ponds, lakes, and reservoirs; physical features of river and lake systems; and the origin and behavior of surface waters in general. Known as hydrography, this branch of hydrology is devoted to (1) waters flowing in brooks and rivers (potamology[5]); (2) fresh waters standing in ponds, lakes, and reservoirs (limnology[5]); and (3) salt waters filling the seas and oceans of the world (oceanography).

Groundwater hydrology considers the origin, nature, and occurrence of subsurface water, its infiltration into the ground, passage or percolation through open formations, and its seepage from them.

Some aspects of hydrology have no immediate application in water and wastewater engineering. To conserve space, most of them are omitted from this chapter or touched upon but briefly.

6-2 The Water Cycle

Precipitation, percolation, runoff, and evaporation are stages in the cycle of water, which is without beginning or end (Fig. 6-1). Of the water driven to earth, some falls directly upon water surfaces; some flows overland and makes its way into brooks and rivers, ponds, lakes, and reservoirs, or seas and oceans; some is returned at once to the atmosphere by evaporation from water and land surfaces, and by evaporation and transpiration from vegetation; and some sinks into the soil.

Of the water entering the earth's skin, part is held near the surface whence some of it evaporates directly and some is taken up by vegetation to be returned to the atmosphere by transpiration. The remainder of the infiltering

---

[4] *Sublimation* is passage of a solid to the vapor state without intermediate melting. *Transpiration* is evaporation or exhalation of water or water vapor from plant cells—leaf cells, for example—and corresponds to perspiration in animals.

[5] From the Greek, *potamos*, a river; and *limne*, a lake.

water settles downward by gravity until it reaches the groundwater table to join the subterranean reservoir within the earth's crust. Most of the groundwater eventually discharges at the surface of the earth through springs and seepage outcrops, or it passes, at or below the water line, into streams and standing bodies of water, including the oceans (Fig. 6-5).

The water flowing in brooks and rivers is derived, only in small part, from direct precipitation, in largest volume from rain running off the

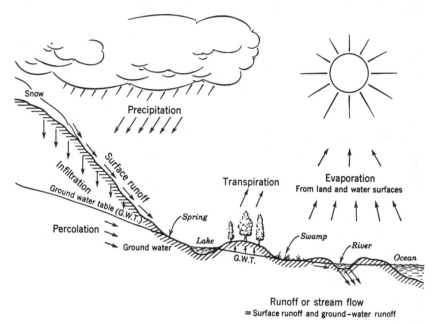

Fig. 6-1. The water cycle.

surface of the earth, and in steadiest amounts as *dry-weather flow* from the lowering of lakes, ponds, and reservoirs and from groundwater seepage.

Evaporation and precipitation are the principal driving forces in the water cycle. Solar radiation is the source of needed energy. Runoff and percolation shift the scene of its evaporation laterally along the earth's surface; atmospheric circulation does so for its condensation and precipitation.

6-3   Data Collection[6]

The adequacy of water resources can be assessed only in hydrological terms. Collection and analysis of needed information are a prime

---

[6] W. B. Langbein and W. G. Hoyt, *Water Facts for the Nation's Future*, Ronald Press, New York, 1958.

responsibility of government in general, and of water authorities, in particular. Without adequate information, water resource development becomes an economic uncertainty and an engineering gamble. Chances may have to be taken at the start of resource development; undoubtedly, they were in the early history of the United States, but they cannot be justified for the long pull.

Rain Gaging. In the United States, a Weather Service was organized in the Army Signal Corps in 1870, and the Weather Bureau was established in 1891. Currently the Bureau maintains more than 10^5 standard rain gages (Sec. 6-6) or one for about 250 sq miles.[7] Some two-thirds of the rain gages are nonrecording, and under cooperative observation. The more informative recording rain gages have multiplied more rapidly since 1940, radar storm-tracking stations being added after the Second World War. The average length of record of nonrecording stations is close to 50 years; only a few go back a century or more.

Snow Surveys. Snowfall is identified routinely at rain gaging stations. Snow surveys are special undertakings that keep an inventory of the important frozen or winter storage of water in high mountains which is or may be released to lowlands during the summer. Snow surveys began in 1910. They are a present responsibility of the Soil Conservation Service, which was organized in 1939. More than a thousand snow courses are now traversed annually in cooperation with states and hydraulic or agricultural interests.

Stream Gaging. The yield of upland catchments of moderate size was first measured in the 1860's by cities in need of water. Before that time the Corps of Engineers had gaged only the great rivers of the country. The Geological Survey, created in 1879, established a nationwide stream gaging network in 1894. Its program is supported by state as well a federal funds. Over the years, more than ten thousand stations have been operated. Their present density per 1000 sq miles varies from 0.5 (Nevada) to 11 (New Jersey). All too few have been assigned to small, and consequently flashy, streams draining areas of less than 1000 sq miles. Because the total length of United States surface streams is about three million miles, there is one gaging station in about four hundred miles.

Groundwater Studies. Responsibility for reporting on groundwater was given the Geological Survey in 1895, but no significant scale of operation was achieved until the 1920's. States share the expense of this program, too. Fluctuations of water levels are measured now in about ten thousand observation wells. It is comforting to know that subsurface water stored at useful depths of less than 2500 ft equals the total recharge of the ground during 16 average years.

[7] These and subsequent data are for the coterminous United States only.

Other Measurements.   Desmond Fitzgerald[8] made careful measurements of evaporation before 1885, and many thousands of observations have been accumulated since the turn of the century. Today the Weather Bureau collects information from several hundred land pans, but monthly measurements of Lake Mead evaporation comprise one of the few regular reservoir studies currently in progress. New and important measurements are connected with field tests of evaporation reduction by monolayers of fatty alcohols (Sec. 11-5).

6-4 Precipitation

Atmospheric moisture precipitates in large amounts as rain, snow, hail, or sleet; it condenses in small amounts as dew, frost, and rime. The most important causes of precipitation are external and dynamic, or internal, cooling; dynamic cooling implying the reduction in the temperature of the atmosphere accompanying its expansion as air masses rise or are driven to high altitudes. The observed drop in temperature is called the *lapse rate.* Within the troposphere, up to 7 miles above ground level in the middle latitudes, the lapse rate is about 3 F in 1000 ft; but it is quite variable within the first 2 or 3 miles and may, at times, be negative. An increase in temperature with altitude, or negative lapse rate, is called an *inversion.* Adiabatic expansion cools ascending air by about 5.5 F in 1000 ft if no moisture is precipitated; but, if the dew point is reached, the latent heat of evaporation is released, and the rate of the resultant *retarded* or *wet adiabatic* rate of cooling drops to about 3.2 F in 1000 ft.

Air is stable and will not ascend by convection when the lapse rate is lower than both the wet and dry adiabatic rates of cooling. Otherwise, its temperature would become less and its density more than the temperature of its surroundings as it is moved into the higher altitude. If the lapse rate is greater than the dry adiabatic rate, rising air becomes warmer and lighter than the air along its upward path. Hence, it continues to ascend and remain *unstable.* If the lapse rate lies between the wet and dry adiabatic rates, the air remains stable when moisture is not condensing but becomes unstable as soon as precipitation sets in. This *conditional stability* is one of the requirements for successful rainfall stimulation. Dry ice or silver iodide may then provide the nuclei that trigger precipitation and convert stable into unstable air. Nevertheless, rainfall can be heavy only in the presence of a continuing supply of moisture. In other words, cloud seeding becomes favorable only when atmospheric conditions are already conducive to natural precipitation. Accordingly, seeding appears to hold out some, but not much, hope for rainmaking.

[8] Superintendent engineer of the Western Division of the Boston, Massachusetts, Water Works for which Chestnut Hill Reservoir was the distribution center.

Moist air is moved upward principally by: (1) convective currents to cause *convective* rainfalls; (2) hills and mountains to produce *orographic* rainfalls; and (3) cyclonic circulation to generate *cyclonic* rainfalls.

Convective Precipitation. Convective precipitation is exemplified by tropical rainstorms. Air masses near the earth's surface absorb heat during the day, expand, and take up increasing amounts of water vapor with a specific gravity near 0.6 relative to dry air. The air mass becomes lighter; almost exclusively vertical currents are induced and carry the mass to higher altitudes where it is exposed to colder surroundings and expands under reduced pressure. Under both external and dynamic cooling, water vapor is condensed, and precipitation follows.

Orographic Precipitation. Precipitation is orographic when horizontal currents of moist air strike hills or mountain ranges that deflect the currents upwards. In North America the rainfalls of the Pacific Northwest and the Southern Appalachians furnish examples of this type of precipitation.

Example 6-1. Coastal air with a temperature of 60 F and a dew point of 54 F is forced over a mountain range that rises 4000 ft above sea level. The air then descends to a plain 3000 ft below. If the dew point is lowered at a rate of 1.1 F in 1000 ft, find (1) the height at which condensation will begin; (2) the temperature at the mountain top; (3) the temperature on the plain beyond the mountain assuming that condensed moisture precipitates before the air starts downward.

1. If H_c is the elevation at which condensation begins and T_c and D_c are respectively the air and dew-point temperatures at this elevation, $T_c = D_c$ when condensation starts, and $T_c = 60 - 5.5 \times 10^{-3}H_c = D_c = 54 - 1.1 \times 10^{-3}H_c$. Hence $H_c = 1360$ ft. Air cools at the dry adiabatic rate below this elevation and at the retarded adiabatic rate above it.

2. The temperature at the top of the mountain is: $60 - 1.36 \times 10^3 \times 5.5 \times 10^{-3} - (4 - 1.36) \times 10^3 \times 3.2 \times 10^{-3} = 44$ F.

3. If the descending air warms at the dry adiabatic rate, the temperature on the plain becomes: $44 + 3 \times 10^3 \times 5.5 \times 10^{-3} = 60.5$ F.

Cyclonic Precipitation. Cyclonic precipitation is associated with unequal heating of the earth's surface and build-up of pressure differences that drive air from points of higher to points of lower pressure. Major temperature effects are: (1) temperature differences between equator and poles, producing so-called planetary circulation; and (2) unequal heating of land and water masses, forming secondary areas of high and low pressure on sea and land and consequent atmospheric circulation.

Differences in the earth's relative rotary speed between equator and poles deflect tropical air currents moving towards the poles. This explains the general easterly direction of cyclonic disturbances over the North American continent as well as the rotary or cyclonic motion of horizontal air currents converging at points of low pressure.

In the continuous planetary circulation of the atmosphere between equator and poles, warm, moisture-laden, tropical air masses travel poleward, are cooled and precipitate their moisture along the way. Ultimately, they are transformed into cold, dry, polar air. A return movement drives polar air masses towards the equator, and there is heavy precipitation when tropical and polar air masses collide. The light, warm, tropical air cools,

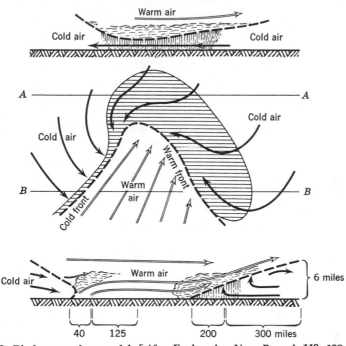

Fig. 6-2. Bjerkness cyclone model. [*After Engineering News-Record, 119,* 198 (1937).]

The central part of the figure shows the wind distribution in the horizontal found in any well-organized disturbance. The double arrows represent warm air currents; the single arrows cold currents. The upper portion of the figure shows a vertical section through *AA* of the central figure; the lower portion a vertical section through *BB*. The vertically striated areas indicate precipitation.

and precipitates its moisture as it is forced up and over the heavy polar air. Collisions between tropical and polar air masses normally account for the protracted general rainfalls and accompanying floods of the central and eastern United States. When, for unknown reasons, polar air does not return towards the equator in the usual manner, there may be serious droughts.

The Bjerkness cyclone model, Fig. 6-2, identifies the movements of warm and cold air masses in the usual type of cyclonic storm. Precipitation is indicated on the plan by shading. The cross-sections suggest the manner in which warm air is forced upward by cold air. At the *cold front*, the colder air wedges itself below the mass of warm air and usually advances southward and eastward in the northern hemisphere. At the *warm front*, the warm air is forced to climb over the retreating wedge of cold air and usually advances northward and eastward in the northern hemisphere. When there is little or no movement at the boundary of the air masses, the front is called *stationary*. When the cold front overtakes the warm front and lifts all the warmer air above the surface, the front is said to be *occluded*.

Cyclonic storms are eddies in the vast planetary circulation between equator and poles. They are generally several hundred miles in diameter, and their rotational and lateral motions are both relatively slow. Cyclones are distinctly different from the violent whirlwinds of tornadoes or hurricanes. In the central or low-pressure portion of cyclonic disturbances, moisture is precipitated from the rising air, while fair weather usually prevails in surrounding high-pressure areas.

The storms of most importance on the North American continent as a whole originate over the Pacific Ocean, strike the coast of the northern United States or Canada, swing south and east over the central or northern United States, and generally escape through the St. Lawrence Valley to the Atlantic Ocean. Storms born in the Gulf of. Mexico drift northward· over the continent and out to sea.

The three types of precipitation—convective, orographic, and cyclonic— seldom occur by themselves. Most precipitation in the temperate regions of the earth results from a combination of two or more causes. Examples are (1) the rainfall of the Pacific slopes which accompanies cyclonic storms forced upward by the Rocky Mountains; and (2) local thunderstorms which are both cyclonic and convective in origin.

About a third of the water falling on continental land masses reaches the oceans as runoff. The remainder is returned to the atmosphere by evaporation and transpiration. Of the vaporized water, a small part is reprecipitated; but the major part is transported over the oceans. Accordingly, the stream flow from continents represents the net water loss from circulating air masses as they precipitate and re-evaporate moisture in their course across the land.

6-5 Droughts

Droughts are defined as periods when crops fail to mature for lack of rainfall or when precipitation is insufficient to support established human activities. Drought conditions prevail when annual rainfall is deficient or poorly distributed in time; or when annual precipitation is concentrated in a few heavy rainfalls that drain away rapidly. Droughts impose a critical demand (1) upon works designed to furnish a continuous and ample amount of water and (2) upon streams expected to carry away domestic and industrial effluents without nuisance. Statistical studies of past droughts suggest a strong tendency for self-perpetuation. Some dry spells are broken ultimately only by a change in the seasons.

6-6 Measuring Precipitation

The *cooperative observer* stations of the United States measure rainfall in standard cylindrical can gages, 2 ft high and 8 in. in diameter (Fig. 6-3).

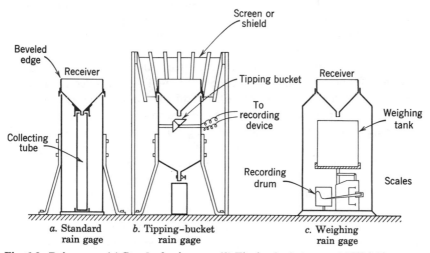

Fig. 6-3. Rain gages: (*a*) Standard rain gage; (*b*) Tipping-bucket gage; (*c*) Weighing gage.

A funnel-shaped inset receives and discharges the catch to a central measuring tube of such diameter that 1 in. on a standard measuring stick inserted in the tube equals 0.1 in. of rainfall.

The *official* Weather Bureau stations register rainfall accumulations during short intervals of time. Engineers base their designs of storm drainage systems and forecasts of flood stages for streams on records of this kind. The continuous-recording gages, shown in Fig. 6-3, are in common use. In the *tipping bucket* a twin-compartment bucket is balanced in such a way that the compartments fill, tip, and empty reciprocally. In the *weighing gage*, the rain concentrating from a receiving funnel is weighed on recording scales. In both gages, measurements are traced by movements of a pen on charts operated by clockworks. The screen or shield shown in Fig. 6-3*b* keeps precipitation from being swept past the gage by high winds.

Standard gages will measure snowfalls more satisfactorily if their receiving funnels and collecting tubes are removed and the naked can is inverted and used as a *cookie cutter* to collect samples of snow from undrifted places. The snow is melted without loss by adding known amounts of warm water. Volumes in excess of added amounts are recorded as inches of precipitation. Some snows are feathery and dry, others compact and wet. Their water equivalent varies accordingly. An average value to remember is 10 in. of snow to 1 in. of water.

The amount of precipitation falling as snow increases rapidly with elevation. Because most rain-gaging stations are situated at relatively low altitudes, more accurate methods are needed for determining snowfall on high-lying watersheds in regions where winter snows provide much of the annual runoff or spring thaws provoke serious floods. In one method sampling stations are located along a *snow course* traversing the drainage system. An observer walks the course and, at suitable intervals, samples the snow blanket with a hollow-tube collector. The water content of the sample is found by weighing the tube or by melting the collected snow. In another method a battery of four or five shielded snow gages is placed 200 or 300 ft apart in a location typifying average conditions on the watershed. The water equivalent of the snow falling during given periods of time is computed from the weight increment of the containers.

Regional or countrywide rainfall experience is generalized by isohyetal (equal rainfall) lines on suitable maps. In the coterminous United States, the 20-in. isohyetal line divides the country into two distinct climatological regions lying roughly to either side of the 100th meridian. In the well-watered east, enough rain falls for normal agriculture and water supply. In the arid west, water development is restricted by the amount that can be collected and stored for use during the dry season.

Errors in precipitation measurements are caused by the following:

1. Wind eddy currents sweeping rain and snow over gages set on top of the ground. Less than the true ground-level rainfall is caught. However, it is possible to shield standard rain gages, in ways developed by Hall and Nipher for example, and to approximate the catch obtained when the rim of the gage is set flush with the ground.

2. Obstructions—trees, bushes, fences, and buildings—cast a rain shadow. To avoid it, gages are placed in the clear by a distance greater than the height of the tallest obstruction. If gages must be put on a roof, they should be centered in the largest available flat area.

Engineers should be fully aware of the limitations of precipitation records. Aside from errors of measurement, areal variations in precipitation may be large, even over small stretches of country. In the circumstances, a single gage cannot yield representative information.

6-7   Evaporation and Transpiration[9]

Evaporation raises the storage requirements of reservoirs and lowers the yield of lakes and ponds. Swamps and other wet surfaces, too, return much water to the atmosphere.

Evaporation from Water Surfaces.   Rates of evaporation from open water surfaces vary with the temperature or vapor pressure of the water and the air in contact with it, and, furthermore, with wind speed, barometric pressure, and water quality. Because these factors are by no means independent, individual effects are not clear cut. In general, evaporation and gas transfer have much in common.

1. For high differences between the maximum vapor pressure at water-surface temperature and the actual pressure of aqueous vapor in the overlying air, evaporation is rapid; for small differences, evaporation is slow; for negative differences, there is condensation.

2. At the temperatures of natural waters, the vapor pressure is almost doubled for every rise of 10 C (18 F). Hence temperature affects evaporation profoundly; yet the slow warming and cooling of deep bodies of water make for relatively even evaporation.

3. Films of still air above a water surface soon become saturated with moisture, and evaporation practically ceases. Within limits, wind stimulates evaporation by displacing moisture-laden films with relatively dry air.

4. As pressures drop, evaporation rises, but altitude has little effect because of counterbalancing changes in temperature. Fast rates of evaporation at high altitudes are caused, in large measure, by greater wind velocities.

5. Rates of evaporation are decreased slightly when salt concentrations are high.

Rohwer's formula[10] illustrates the dependence of evaporation on the factors just cited:

$$E = 0.497(1 - 1.32 \times 10^{-2}p_a)(1 + 0.268w)(V - v) \qquad (6\text{-}1)$$

where E is the evaporation in inches a day; p_a is the barometric pressure in inches of mercury; w is the wind velocity in miles per hour; and V and v are the vapor pressures in inches of mercury at the water temperature and dew-point temperature of the atmosphere respectively.

[9] The vapor pressure or vapor tension of water is the maximum gaseous pressure exerted at a given temperature by water vapor in contact with a water surface. The pressure of water vapor in air not saturated with aqueous vapor equals the vapor pressure of water at the *dew-point* temperature of the air, namely, the temperature at which the air would be saturated by the moisture actually in it. In other words, vapor pressure is the partial pressure exerted by the water vapor in the atmosphere and, in accordance with Dalton's law, evaporation is proportional to it (Vol. 2).

[10] C. Rohwer, Evaporation from Free Water Surfaces, *U.S. Dept. Agr., Tech. Bull.* 271 (1931).

Example 6-2. Estimate the evaporation for a day during which the following averages obtain: water temperature = 60 F; maximum vapor pressure $V = 0.52$ in.; air temperature = 80 F; relative humidity = 40%; vapor pressure $v = 1.03 \times 0.40 = 0.41$ in.; wind velocity $w = 8$ mph; and barometric pressure $p_a = 29.0$ in. Hg. By Eq. 6-1,

$$E = 0.497(1 - 1.32 \times 10^{-2} \times 29.0)(1 + 0.268 \times 8)(0.52 - 0.41) = 9.41 \times 10^{-2} \text{ in.}$$

Thermodynamic formulations relate evaporation to the difference between solar radiation and heat accounted for as (1) back radiation, (2) heat stored in the water, and (3) heat lost in other ways.

Evaporation from Land Surfaces. Wet soil loses water rapidly to the atmosphere; moist soil does so more slowly. Immediately after a rainstorm, water, intercepted by vegetation or present in films, pools, or puddles on roofs and pavings, starts to evaporate at about the rate of loss from shallow water. As the free moisture disappears, evaporation slows down. Interstitial moisture is evaporated internally or drawn to the surface by capillarity before it evaporates. Soil characteristics and depth to groundwater are governing factors. Where the water table lies 3 ft or more down, there is little evaporation after the surface layers have dried out. Because cultivated soils lose less water than uncultivated soils the practice of loosening soils to conserve moisture prevails.

Transpiration. The amounts of water transpired vary with the kind and maturity of vegetation, conditions of soil moisture, and meteorological factors. On the whole, the continents return more water to the atmosphere by transpiration than by evaporation. The total areal expanse of the leaves in a forest is very great in comparison with land and water exposures. Moreover, some plants can draw water from considerable depths and transpire it. Estimates for the United States place the proportion of precipitation lost to the atmosphere by evaporation and transpiration from forests and land uses and from surface reservoirs and phreatophytes[11] as high as 70%.

6-8 Measuring Evaporation and Transpiration

Evaporation from water surfaces is commonly measured by exposing pans of water to the atmosphere and recording evaporation losses by systematic measurements or self-registering devices. Both floating and land pans have been used (Fig. 6-4). Neither one is fully satisfactory. The standard (Class A) measuring device of the Weather Bureau is a 4-ft galvanized iron pan, 10 in. deep, supported on a grid of 2-in. by 4-in. timbers that raise the pan slightly above the ground to promote air circulation. A hook gage in a stilling well identifies changes in water level.

[11] Phreatophytes, from the Greek *phreas*, a well, and *phyton*, a plant, are deep-rooted, water-seeking plants.

Temperature, rainfall, and wind speed are also recorded. The anemometer is placed next to and just above the pan. Observed losses are not the same as for floating pans of different materials, color, or depth; nor are they the same as for natural or impounded bodies of water.

Pan evaporation is translated empirically to lake evaporation by the equation

$$E = \frac{CE'(V - v)}{V' - v'} \tag{6-2}$$

where primed letters pertain to pan conditions, the others to lake conditions.[12] The coefficient C is said to average 0.7. In most of the United

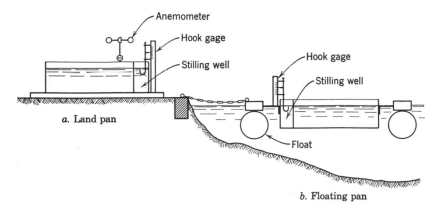

a. Land pan

b. Floating pan

Fig. 6-4. Evaporating pans.

States, mean annual evaporation from water surfaces equals or exceeds mean annual rainfall.

Together, transpiration and evaporation are referred to as *evapotranspiration* or *consumptive use*. They are measured experimentally by agriculturalists in a number of ways. In one of them evaporation is equated to the difference between rainfall on a plot of ground and water collected by underdrains; in another, soil-water level is held constant in a tank filled with representative materials growing representative plants. If the tank bottom is pervious, the resulting lysimeter[13] measures consumptive use as the difference between (1) water falling on or applied to the surface and (2) water draining from the bottom, corrections being made for changes in soil moisture. Data of this kind are generally of limited use to water supply engineers, but it is good to have some concept of the order of magnitudes

[12] M. A. Kohler, Lake and Pan Evaporation, *U.S. Geol. Survey Circ.* **229**, 127 (1952).
[13] From the Greek *lysis*, dissolving, because water percolating through early lysimeters was examined for substances taken into solution.

involved. For example, the transpiration ratio, or weight of water transpired by a plant per unit weight of dry matter produced exclusive of roots, increases stepwise from about 350 for Indian corn through wheat and rice to almost 800 for flax; and from about 150 for firs through oaks to almost 400 for birches.

Empirical formulations of consumptive use are generally based on temperature records. A relationship proposed by Lowry and Johnson,[14] for example, reads as follows:

$$U = 0.9 + 1.5 \times 10^{-4} \, \Sigma(T_m - 32) \qquad (6\text{-}3)$$

where U is the consumptive use in feet (acre-feet/acre), and T_m is the daily maximum temperature in degrees Fahrenheit for the growing season (last to earliest frost). Hence $\Sigma(T_m - 32)$ is the sum of the degree days. When $\Sigma(T_m - 32) = 4 \times 10^4$, for example, U becomes 2.4 ft. Adding the proportion of daylight hours during specific months in the frost-free period, Blaney and Criddle[15] arrived at the equation:

$$U' = K\Sigma p T' \qquad (6\text{-}4)$$

where the new factors are K, an empirical coefficient for specific crops varying from 0.6 for small vegetables to 1.2 for rice, and p, the monthly percentage of daylight hours in the year, the consumptive use U' being measured in inches for a given period of time, and T' being the mean monthly temperature.

6-9   Percolation

The term percolation is employed in this book to describe the passage of water into, through, and out of the ground. Together, Figs. 2-4 and 6-5 show the conditions in which water occurs below the surface of the ground. Only water in the saturated zone can be withdrawn from subsurface sources, the development of groundwater supplies depending upon the yields actually obtainable and their cost. Unwanted entrance of groundwater into manholes and pipes is an important matter in sewerage design.

Groundwater is derived directly or indirectly from precipitation: (1) directly as rainwater and snowmelt that filter into the ground, seep through cracks or solution passages in rock formations, and penetrate deep enough to reach the groundwater table; (2) indirectly as surface water from streams, swamps, ponds, lakes, and reservoirs that filters into the ground

[14] R. L. Lowry and A. F. Johnson, Consumptive Use of Water for Agriculture, *Trans. Am. Soc. Civil Engrs.*, **107**, 1243 (1942). Shannon's determination of frost depth takes a similar form; see Eq. 12-11.
[15] H. F. Blaney and W. D. Criddle quoted by R. D. Goodrich, *Trans. Am. Soc. Civil Engrs.*, **122**, 810 (1957).

through permeable soils when the groundwater table is lower than free water surfaces. Streams that recharge the ground are known as *influent* streams; streams that draw water from the ground as *effluent* streams.

The water table tops out the zone of saturation; the capillary fringe overrides it. The fringe varies in thickness from a foot or so in sand to as

Under-saturated Zone or Zone of Aeration	Soil water is near enough to the surface to be reached by the roots of common plants. Some soil water remains after plants begin to wilt.	
	Stored or pellicular* water adheres to soil particles and is not moved by gravity.	
	Gravity or vadose** water moves down by gravity throughout zone.	
Suspended Water	Capillary water occurs only in the capillary fringe at bottom of the zone of aeration.	
Saturated Zone Ground Water or Phreatic† Water	Free water occurs below the water table. Movement controlled by the slope of the water table.	
	Confined or artesian water occurs beneath a confining stratum. Moves laterally as water in a pressure conduit.	
	Fixed ground water occurs in subcapillary openings of clays, silts, etc. Not moved by gravity.	
	Connate‡ water entrapped in rocks at the time of their deposition.	

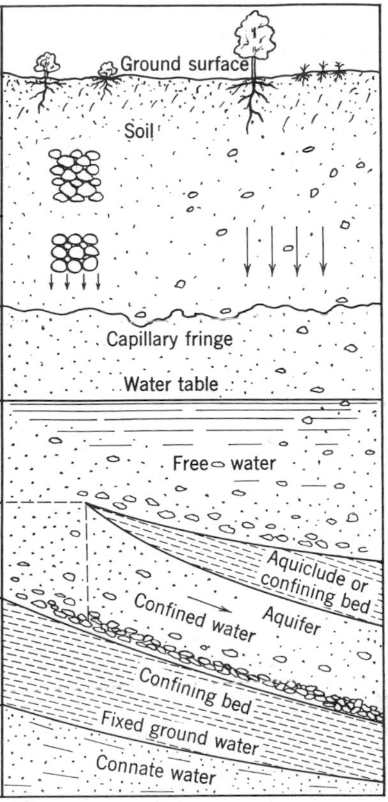

* Latin *pellis* skin   ** Latin *vadere* going.
† Greek *phreas* a well.   ‡ Latin *connatus* born together.

Fig. 6-5. Occurrence and distribution of subsurface water. (After C. F. Tolman, Ground Water, McGraw-Hill Book Co., New York, 1937.)

much as 10 ft in clay. It rises and falls with the water table, lagging behind to become thicker above a falling table and thinner above a rising table. Evaporation is increased when capillarity lifts water to, or close to, the ground surface. Pollution spreads out along the water table and is lifted into the fringe. There it is trapped and destroyed in the course of time. Hydraulically, an aquifer dipping beneath an impervious geological stratum has a piezometric surface, not a groundwater table.

How much rain filters far enough into the ground to become ground-water is quite uncertain. Among governing factors can be listed:

1. Hydraulic permeability. Permeability, not merely pore space, determines the rate of infiltration of rainfall and its passage to the groundwater table. Only rarely does freezing not reduce permeability.

2. Turbidity. Suspended matter picked up by erosion of tight soils clogs the pores of open soils.

3. Rainfall patterns and soil wetness. Light rainfalls have time to filter into the ground, heavy rainfalls do not. Wet soils are soon saturated; dry soils store water in surface depressions and their own pores. Some stored water may reach the groundwater table eventually. Heavy rains compact soil, and prolonged rains cause it to swell. Both reduce surface openings. Air displacement from soils opposes filtration; sun cracks and biological channels speed it up.

4. Ground cover. Vegetation retards runoff and increases surface evaporation as well as retention and transpiration of soil water. Effects such as these are most marked during the growing season.

5. Geology. Geological structure has much to do with infiltration. Examples are (a) lenses of impervious materials which intercept incoming water and keep it from reaching the groundwater table; and (b) confining layers of tight materials which direct water into closed-channel flow. Independent zones of saturation above lenses of impervious materials store *perched* water; continuous zones of saturation (aquifers) lying between impervious materials hold *artesian* water.

6. Surface slope. Steep slopes hasten surface runoff and reduce infiltration.

The earth's crust is porous to depths of 2 to 8 miles. Beyond that, pressures are so great that plastic flow closes all interstices.

6-10 Groundwater Discharge

In nature, subsurface waters are discharged from the ground: (1) to the surface through springs and seepage outcrops (hydraulic discharge); and (2) to the atmosphere from the soil or through vegetation (evaporative discharge).

Hydraulic discharge takes place wherever the groundwater table intersects the land surface. Geologic and hydraulic conditions that combine to force the return of groundwater to the earth's surface as springs include: (1) outcroppings of impervious strata covered by pervious soils or other water-bearing formations; (2) overflows of subterranean basins in limestone or lava; (3) leakage from artesian systems through faults that obstruct flow; and (4) steep surface slopes that cut into the water table. In humid regions, groundwater may seep into streams throughout their length.

Evaporative discharge from soil is commonly confined to the belt of soil water, but it also affects aquifers passing within capillary distance from the land surface. Plants seek moisture at whatever levels their roots can thrive, usually from the belt of soil water or the capillary fringe. Trees and *phreatophytes* may draw water from as far down as the zone of saturation, *xerophytes*[16] only from the zone of aeration. Ways of natural discharge of subsurface waters are illustrated in Figs. 6-1 and 2-4. Evaporative discharge is normally confined to a few feet in humid climates, and about 20 ft in dry climates. The roots of phreatophytes may reach downward as far as 50 ft.

Differences between rates of *recharge* and *discharge* are correlated with changes in water stored in the saturation zone. During wet weather, the water table rises; during dry weather, it falls. Because the dry-weather flow of most surface streams is supported by groundwater discharge, correlation between low stream flows and groundwater levels is good, too, and observed coefficients can be used to predict ground storage.

Pumping intrudes into the natural regimen of subsurface waters. Recharge, discharge, and storage are forced to seek new equilibria. Lowering the water table may decrease and even stop natural discharge, but increase natural recharge, especially in soils bordering on surface streams. How much water can be salvaged economically by lowering the water table through pumping depends on the cost of lifting water from increasing depths. If the water table is to remain at a designated level, average rates of withdrawal and recharge must be alike under the conditions generated.

Among other factors affecting groundwater levels are: (1) seasonal variations in evaporation and transpiration; (2) diurnal fluctuations in transpiration; (3) changes in barometric pressure; (4) passage of moving loads, trains for example, over artesian formations; (5) land and ocean tides; and (6) earthquakes. Fluctuations in levels registered by a continuous recording gage on an observation well seldom have one cause only. Records must, indeed, be analyzed with much care if underground hydrological cycles are to be fully understood.

6-11 Measuring Percolation

As explained in Sec. 6-8, infiltration into various soil types supporting different kinds of vegetation is measured in lysimeters. The variables are many, and groundwater flow and yield can be related to rainfall information only in very simple geological situations such as isolated sand dunes. Nevertheless, it is reasonable, for comparative or bookkeeping purposes, to express annual results in the same units as rainfall. Infiltration of about half the rainfall is not unusual. No more will be said here, because the quantitative assessment of infiltration and groundwater yield is so large a topic that it is assigned to a full chapter in this book (Chap. 9).

[16] From the Greek *xeros*, dry, and *phyton*, plant.

6-12   Runoff

Water derived directly from precipitation flows over the ground into water courses as surface, storm, or flood runoff. However, the amounts of water actually reaching streams are reduced by infiltration, evaporation, and other losses along the way.

Dry-Weather Flows.   Water flowing in streams during dry spells, or when precipitation falls as snow without melting, is known as *dry-weather flow* or *dry-weather runoff*. It is composed of water stored in the ground and impounded in lakes, ponds, swamps, and other backwaters. Accordingly, the dry-weather yield of streams comes both from *natural surface storage* and *natural ground storage*. In some river basins with headwaters at high altitudes, much of the summer runoff is derived from melting snowfields. In the absence of snowmelt or surface storage, streams lying above the groundwater table at all stages of flow are *ephemeral* (short-lived); streams lying above the summer groundwater level *intermittent*.

Runoff from Rainfall.   Runoff from rainfall is influenced chiefly by (1) the intensity, duration, and distribution of precipitation; (2) the size, shape, cover, and topography of the catchment area; and (3) the nature and condition of the ground. Some of these factors are constant, others vary seasonally. Generally speaking, conditions that tend to promote high surface runoff—high rates of rainfall, steep slopes, frozen or bare and heavy soils, for example—are also conditions that tend to reduce dry-weather flows.

Runoff from Snowmelt.   Streams fed by snowfields and glaciers possess certain unique runoff characteristics because of the following subsidiary factors: (1) heat melt, (2) condensation melt, and (3) rainfall melt. Fresh, clean snow reflects about 90% of the incident sunlight. Warm, still air, too, causes little melting, because the thermal conductivity of air is small [about 1.1 Btu/(hr·sq ft·in.) at 32 F when the temperature difference is 1 F]; but there is condensation of moisture and rapid melt when the vapor pressure of the air is higher than that of the snow. Because the heat of condensation of water vapor is 1073 Btu/lb at 32 F and the heat of fusion of ice is only 144 Btu/lb, condensation of 1 in. of moisture results in $1073/144 = 7.5$ in. of melt. Rain falling on snow produces relatively less melting by comparison, namely, $(T - 32)/144$ for each inch of rain, T being its temperature in degrees Fahrenheit and equaling the wet-bulb temperature of the air. Even when $T = 60.8$ F, for example, an inch of rain induces only $(60.8 - 32)/144 = 0.2$ in. of melt. In more general terms, each degree day above 32 F can result in 0.05 to 0.15 in. of melt. This is the degree-day factor.

For snow packs on mountainsides, an areally weighted average temperature can be computed for the melting zone. The lower boundary of this zone is drawn by the snow line; the upper boundary by the contour lying above the observation station by about 1000/3 times the difference between the observed temperature and 32 F. The assumption is made that the temperature of the atmosphere drops by approximately 3 F for each 1000-ft lift in elevation.

Example 6-3. The snow line of a 14,000-ft mountain range lies 8000 ft above sea level. (1) For a mean daily temperature of 47 F at an observation station 7000 ft above sea level, find the upper boundary of the melting zone and the temperature at the snow line. (2) Assuming a melting zone of 100 sq miles, and a degree-day factor of 0.10 in., find the anticipated daily runoff in mgd and cfs.
  1. Elevation of freezing level = 8000 + 1000(47 − 32)/3 = 13,000 ft, and temperature at snow line = 47 − 3 × 1 = 44 F.
  2. For an average temperature of (44 + 32)/2 = 39 F or 7 degree days, the total anticipated melt becomes 7 × 0.1 × 100 = 70 sq mile in.; 17.37 × 70 = 1220 mgd; or 1220 × 1.547 = 1880 cfs.

6-13 Measuring Runoff

No studies of surface-water supplies, storm and combined sewerage systems, and wastewater disposal can advance to the design stage without thorough evaluation of pertinent runoffs, their magnitude and variability. Accordingly, two subsequent chapters are devoted to discussions of this topic. Stream gaging itself is based on an understanding of open-channel flow. Measuring devices are many: current meters, floats, weirs, and surveying instruments; measuring techniques involve chemicals, radioactive tracers, and persistent dyes. Each of the devices and techniques has its own advantages and disadvantages, and each has its peculiar range of usefulness. Once established at a stable cross-section, and rated by suitable means, gage height need be the sole measure of record, automatic records being traced by vertical movements of a float in a stilling well. Occasional checks of actual runoff will reinforce the validity of the rating curve which relates measured discharge to measured gage height.

6-14 Good Records and Their Uses

Collection of representative hydrological information should be encouraged at every opportunity if the water potential of a river system is to be fully understood and put to use. As has been said of the Upper Nile[17], "It must not be imagined for a single instant that these long lists of figures are dead things. In the hands of competent and original-minded engineers,

[17] Sir William Willcocks and J. I. Craig, *Egyptian Irrigation*, E. & F. N. Spon, Ltd., London, 3rd ed., 1913.

they have within them as great a potency of life as the fabled dragon's teeth, and, when sown up and down, may chance to spring up armed men."

Rainfall Records. Although precipitation is the ultimate source of all water supplies, it should be understood at the outset that water supply studies should be based, whenever possible, on direct measurements: runoff records for surface-water supplies and groundwater flows for groundwater supplies. Nonetheless, hydrologists will and should continue to look for useful relations between rainfall and runoff and between rainfall and infiltration; and engineers will and should put these relations to work in the absence of direct measurements. However, the links in the chain of hydrological sequences still remain too weak to be placed under much stress. If this is kept in mind, rainfall records need not be eschewed by engineers. Instead they can be put to use to good purpose in the business of water supply and drainage by giving a wider conception of variations to be expected. For example, they illuminate the possibility of the drought that comes but once in a century or the storm that visits a region but once in a score of years; they suggest cycles and trends and identify variations in areal distribution of normal and unusual rainfalls; and they lend form to predictions of runoff in hydraulic systems, such as storm drains and canals still to be built.

Runoff Records. As soon as serious thought is given to the development of a catchment area, actual measurements of runoff should be started. Even the first year's results will tell much because they can be amplified by feedback; for example, by cross-correlation between short-term runoff observations of the river basin under study and long-term records of neighboring or otherwise similar systems. If rainfall records for the watersheds in question are long, correlation of rainfall ratios with runoff ratios for the period of recorded stream flow in each basin provides a reasonable foundation for extending the shorter record.[18] Generally speaking, comparative studies of hydrographs or duration curves are more reliable than correlations of precipitation and other hydrological information; but there are exceptions.

Records of the intermittent runoff from small areas yet to be drained by storm sewers are neither numerous nor of much use. Rates of flow change markedly when drainage systems are constructed and go into operation, and they are bound to change further as communities grow and age. Accordingly, continuous records supported by imaginative estimates of

[18] In the United States precipitation is recorded for the calendar year, runoff for the water year, October 1 to September 30. This difference must not be forgotten in comparing annual runoff and rainfall values. For the water year, the autumnal equinox marks, in a rough and general way, the average yearly low point in natural storage of groundwater and surface flows.

runoff to be drained away in stormwater systems in a growing urban complex have much to commend them.

Flow measurements in existing sewers are hard to translate into design values for other sewers, unless the new drains are to be situated in similar, normally nearby, catchments. Even then, there remains the uncertainty of future change.

Flood-flow estimates must look to unusual as well as normal experience. The range and number of useful observations is best extended by resorting to as much hydrological information as can be assembled. Fortunately, the labor of correlating pertinent data has been greatly reduced by access to high-speed computers. By combining modern computational methods with modern statistical procedures, it has become possible to harvest information in far greater measure than before and, in a sense, to generate operational sequences of hydrological information of great significance.

CHAPTER 7

Rainfall and Runoff

7-1 Reasons for Engineering Analysis

Sanitary engineers are concerned mainly with two kinds of rainfall and runoff information for given drainage areas: (1) records of water collected in fixed calendar periods (days, weeks, month, and years) and (2) records of intensities and durations of individual rainstorms and flood flows. Studies of water yield underlie the safe and economic development of surface-water supplies by continuous draft and by storage. They cast some light, too, upon groundwater production and are needed in gaging the pollutional load that can safely be imposed upon water courses into which sewage and industrial wastes are emptied. Studies of rainfall intensities and flood runoff are starting points in the design of storm and combined sewers and their appurtenances. Moreover, they provide information on (1) the proper dimensioning of spillways and diversion conduits for dams and similar structures, (2) the location and protection of water and waste-water works within the flood plain of streams, and (3) the proper proportioning of rainwater collection works.

In favorable circumstances, available hydrological data apply directly to the site of the structure to be built or protected. More often, information is incomplete or obtainable only for places some distance away. All manner of data must then be collated to arrive at reasonable estimates of expected rainfall or runoff.

7-2 Annual Rainfall and Runoff

Analysis of annual rainfall and runoff records for trends and cycles, although of general interest, is seldom immediately profitable. Only rarely are records long enough to distinguish periodic from random variations. Analysis of arrayed observations, on the other hand, often yields useful information in comparative hydrology.

Both rainfall and runoff form frequency distributions skewed to the right because of the constraint imposed by the lower limit of annual rainfall or runoff. The limit is generally greater than zero but smaller than the recorded minimum. It stands to reason that there must be an upper limit as well, but its value is more flexible and, from the standpoint of water supply, also less important. In spite of these acknowledged difficulties, most records of rainfall and runoff can be generalized with fair success as arithmetically normal series and somewhat better as geometrically normal series. Reasonably accurate comparisons can be had, therefore, in terms of the observed or sample arithmetic mean μ and standard deviation σ or the geometric mean μ_g and standard deviation σ_g. Fits between observed and calculated values become still closer when a parameter of skewness is introduced, as indicated, for example, in Sec. 7-8 for flood flows. For ordinary purposes, mean annual values and coefficients of variation, $c_v = \sigma/\mu$, will suggest the comparative safe yields of water supplies developed with and without storage. Draft is then generalized as a proportion of the mean annual rainfall or runoff, whatever the basis of measurement happens to be.

Rainfall. Where populations have grown significantly on the North American continent, mean annual rainfalls generally range upward from 10 in. to almost 80 in. For the well-watered regions, the coefficient of variation is as low as 0.1; for the arid regions as high as 0.5. Statistically, this implies that a deficiency as great as half the mean annual rainfall is expected to occur in arid regions as often as a deficiency of only one-tenth the mean annual rainfall, or less, in the well-watered ones.[1] High values of c_v, therefore, signify low maintainable drafts or high storage requirements.

Within a given region, the coefficient of variation for different rainfall stations is substantially uniform. Excessive differences can generally be traced to improper location or false readings of gages. Accordingly, they offer a check on the records.

Runoff. Losses by evaporation and transpiration, together with unrecovered infiltration, reduce annual runoff below annual rainfall. However, so much depends upon the seasonal distribution of rainfall that it is not possible to establish a direct and reliable relationship between the two.

[1] Reference to the probability integral, Table I-6, will show that deficiencies, or negative deviations from the mean, equal to or greater than $c_v\mu = \sigma$ are to be expected $100 - 84.1 = 15.9\%$ of the time or $1/0.159 =$ once in 6.3 years because $t = (x - \mu)/\sigma$. These calculations, however, are only approximately true because normality is assumed where skewness exists.

There is likewise no direct relationship between their variability. On the North American continent, the mean annual runoff from catchment areas contributing flow to water supplies ranges from about 5 to 40 in., and the coefficients of variation lie between 0.15 and 0.75. As shown in Example 7-1, the fact that the mean annual runoff is usually less than the mean annual rainfall, whereas the variation in stream flow is about half again as great as the variation in precipitation, makes for unsteady runoff-rainfall ratios.

Example 7-1. Analyze the 26-year record of a stream[2] in the north-eastern United States and of a rain gage[2] situated in a neighboring valley and covering the identical period of observation (Table 7-1).

Table 7-1   Record of Annual Rainfall and Runoff (Example 7-1)

Order of Occur-rence	Rainfall, in.	Runoff, in.	Order of Occur-rence	Rainfall, in.	Runoff, in.
1	43.6	26.5	14	48.9	25.4
2	53.8	35.5	15	66.3 (max.)	39.9
3	40.6	28.3	16	42.5	23.3
4	45.3	25.5	17	47.0	26.4
5	38.9 (min.)	21.4	18	48.0	29.4
6	46.6	25.3	19	41.3	25.5
7	46.6	30.1	20	48.0	23.7
8	46.1	22.7	21	45.5	23.7
9	41.8	20.4	22	59.8	41.9 (max.)
10	51.0	27.6	23	48.7	32.9
11	47.1	27.5	24	43.3	27.7
12	49.4	21.9	25	41.8	16.5 (min.)
13	40.2	20.1	26	45.7	23.7

1. The arrayed data produce the results shown in Table 7-2. To test the reliability of the different parameters, their standard deviations are appended. The chances are 68.2% (namely, 2 × 34.1) that the magnitudes of the individual parameters will not vary by more than the stated deviation.

2. Each year of record covers 100/26 = 3.85% of the experience. The values in each array, because they are not grouped, are plotted on probability paper at $100k/(n + 1) = 100k/27\%$ in Fig. 7-1. This method of locating the plotting position (Sec. 7-5) reconciles the left-hand and right-hand probability scales and permits inclusion of all observed values. Only an arithmetic plot is shown. On it, the arithmetically normal curve of best fit is a straight line, the geometrically normal curve a curved line. The straight line passes through the intersection of the mean with the 50% frequency and through that of $\mu \pm \sigma$ with the 84.1% or 15.9% value (Sec. 4-11). The curve of geometric

[2] The Westfield Little River, which supplies water to the city of Springfield, Mass., the rain gage being situated at the West Parish filtration plant. The years of record are 1906 to 1931 (Table 7-1).

Table 7-2 Statistical Parameters of Rainfall and Runoff (Example 7-1)

	Rainfall	Runoff	Runoff-Rainfall Ratio, %
1. Length of record, n, yr	26	26	...
2. Arithmetic mean, μ, in.	46.8 ± 1.2	26.6 ± 1.1	57
3. Median, μ_d, in.	46.3 ± 1.5	25.5 ± 1.4	55
4. Geometric mean, μ_g, in.	$46.5 \overset{\times}{\div} 1.02$	$26.1 \overset{\times}{\div} 1.04$	56
5. Arithmetic standard deviation, σ, in.	6.0 ± 0.8	5.8 ± 0.8	97
6. Coefficient of variation, c_v, %	12.9 ± 1.8	21.8 ± 3.2	169
7. Geometric standard deviation, σ_g	$1.13 \overset{\times}{\div} 1.02$	$1.24 \overset{\times}{\div} 1.03$	110

normality is traced by values read from a similar straight line of best fit passing through μ_g at 50%, $\mu_g \times \sigma_g$ at 84.1%, and μ_g/σ_g at 15.9% on logarithmic-probability paper (Sec. 4-12).

3. Examination of the results and the plot (Fig. 7-1) shows the following:

(a) Both records are fitted approximately by an arithmetically normal distribution but somewhat better by a geometrically normal distribution.

(b) A little over half the annual rainfall appears as stream flow. The range of recovery is from 39 to 70%.

(c) Runoff is more variable than rainfall; about 1.7 times as much, as measured by c_v.

(d) The probable lower limits of rainfall and runoff are fairly well defined by the plot, namely 30 in. for rainfall and 10 in. for runoff.

(e) The magnitudes of maximum and minimum yields expected once in 2, 5, 10, 20, 50, and 100 years, i.e., 50, 20, 10, 5, 2, and 1% of the time, as read from the curves of best fit, are summarized in Table 7-3.

Table 7-3 Expected Rainfall and Runoff Frequencies (Example 7-1)

Maximum values may be exceeded, minimum values may not be reached.

Frequency, Once in Stated Number of Years	By Arithmetic Normality				By Geometric Normality			
	Rainfall, in.		Runoff, in.		Rainfall, in.		Runoff, in.	
	Max.	Min.	Max.	Min.	Max.	Min.	Max.	Min.
2	47	47	27	27	47	47	26	26
5	52	42	31	22	52	42	32	22
10	54	39	34	19	54	40	35	20
20	56	37	35	17	56	38	37	18
50	59	35	39	15	59	36	41	17
100	60	33	40	13	61	35	43	16

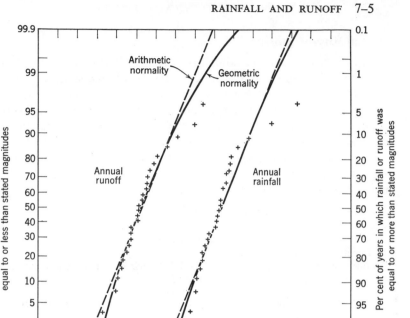

Fig. 7-1. Frequency distribution of annual rainfall and runoff plotted on arithmetic-probability paper.

7-3 Storm Rainfall

Storms sweeping over the country deposit their moisture in fluctuating amounts during different intervals of time and over varying areas. A single recording rain gage measures the point rainfall only and reflects but imperfectly the conditions of precipitation prevailing over the area as a whole. In these circumstances, statistical averaging is relied upon to offset individual departures from the norm. Given the records of one or more recording rain gages within or reasonably near a given area, rainfall is found to vary in intensity (1) during the course or duration of individual storms, (2) throughout the area covered by individual storms, and (3) from storm to storm. These variations establish respectively: (1) the time-intensity or intensity-duration relationship of individual storms, (2) the areal distribution of individual storms, and (3) the frequency of storms of given intensity and duration.

7-4 Intensity of Storms

The intensity, or rate, of rainfall is conveniently expressed in inches per hour, and it happens that an inch of water distributed over an acre in an hour closely equals a cubic foot per second; more precisely, 1.008 cfs. Rainfall is often most intense near the beginning of storms, but this is not necessarily so. By convention, storm intensities are expressed as arithmetic mean rates of precipitation during specified periods. This makes them progressive means for increasing periods of time. They are highest for short time intervals and decline steadily with the length of the rainfall. Time-intensity calculations are illustrated in Example 7-2.

Example 7-2. Given an automatic rain-gage record, find the progressive arithmetic mean rate, or intensity, of precipitation for various durations. The record[3] is shown in Cols. 1 and 2 of Table 7-4. Necessary calculations are added in Cols. 3 to 7, Cols. 5 to 7 being independent of preceding columns.

In this example, the maximum rate of rainfall during a 5-min period (0.54 in.) was experienced between the thirtieth and thirty-fifth minute.

Table 7-4 Time and Intensity of a Storm Rainfall (Example 7-2)

Rain-Gage Record				Time-Intensity Relationship		
Time from Beginning of Storm, min	Cumu-lative Rainfall, in.	Time Interval, min	Rainfall during Interval, in.	Duration of Rain-fall, min	Maximum Total Rainfall, in.	Arithmetic Mean Intensity, in. per hr
(1)	(2)	(3)	(4)	(5)	(6)*	(7)
5	0.31	5	0.31	5	0.54	6.48
10	0.62	5	0.31	10	1.07	6.42
15	0.88	5	0.26	15	1.54	6.16
20	1.35	5	0.47	20	1.82	5.46
25	1.63	5	0.28	30	2.55	5.10
30	2.10	5	0.47	45	3.40	4.53
35	2.64	5	*0.54*	60	3.83	3.83
40	3.17	5	0.53	80	4.15	3.11
45	3.40	5	0.23	100	4.41	2.65
50	3.66	5	0.26	120	4.59	2.30
60	3.83	10	0.17			
80	4.15	20	0.32			
100	4.41	20	0.26			
120	4.59	20	0.18			

* Column 6 records maximum rainfall in consecutive periods. It proceeds out of Col. 4 by finding the value, or combination of consecutive values, that produces the largest rainfall for the indicated period. Col. 7 = 60 × Col. 6/Col. 5.

[3] Storm of October 27–28, 1908, at Jupiter, Fla.

7-5   Frequency of Intense Storms

The greater the intensity of storms, the rarer is their occurrence or the smaller their frequency. Roughly, the highest intensity of specified duration reported in a station record of n years, called the n-year storm, has a frequency of once in n years. The next highest value has a frequency of twice in n years, or a recurrence interval of $n/2$ years and is called the $n/2$-year storm.

However, this does not allow for chance variations in observed magnitudes; nor does it make for rational plotting or good identification of the recurrence interval of intense storms.

Plotting Position.   If m equally reliable records of n years were available, the average largest magnitude would be the median of the m largest observed magnitudes in each record of n years. In a statistical sense, therefore, the highest intensity associated with a given duration in a single record of n years will probably be exceeded as an average only once in $n/(1 - 0.5) = 2n$ years, and the next highest intensity once in $n/(2 - 0.5) = 0.67n$ years. In general terms, therefore, the observation of kth largest magnitude in an array is likely to be reached or exceeded but once in $n/(k - 0.5)$ years. Here k is the number of observations reaching or exceeding that magnitude in the arrayed record. This method of calculating frequencies is less conservative but more rational than when n is divided by k. A third method has been suggested in Example 7-1, where the frequency of occurrence of the kth magnitude is calculated to be once in $(n + 1)/k$ intervals of time. A fourth and statistically well defined but somewhat laborious convention for locating the plotting position[4] is $3(n^2 - 1)/[k(3n - 1) - (n + 1)]$. Finally, the probability that a storm equaling or exceeding the kth-year storm will occur in any series of n years is $1 - (1 - p)^n$, where $(1 - p)^n$ is the probability of its nonoccurrence. For example, the chance of the 10-year storm occurring in a 5-year period is $1 - (1 - \frac{1}{10})^5 = 0.41$ or 41%.

Recurrence Intervals.   The recurrence interval I is the calendar period, normally in years, in which the kth highest or lowest value in an array covering n calender periods is expected to be equaled or exceeded statistically. The associated per cent of time is $100/I$. The fifth value in a 30-year series, for example, can be calculated to have a recurrence interval of $n/k = \frac{30}{5} = 6$ years or 16.7% of the time; $(n + 1)/k = \frac{31}{5} = 6.2$ years or 16.1%; $n/(k - 0.5) = 30/4.5 = 6.7$ years or 15.0%; or $3(n^2 - 1)/[k(3n - 1) - (n + 1)] = 6.5$ years or 15.4% of the time, depending upon the chosen formulation.

[4] Suggested by H. A. Thomas, Jr.

By pooling all observations irrespective of their association with individual storm records, a generalized intensity-duration-frequency relationship is obtained. Some effort can be spared in the preparation of rainfall records for analysis if, at the outset, storms of low intensity are eliminated from consideration. The following empirical relationships suggest the lower limits of the intensities that should ordinarily be included in the analysis of North American station records:

$$i = 0.6 + 12/t \quad \text{for the northern United States} \qquad (7\text{-}1)$$

$$i = 1.2 + 18/t \quad \text{for the southern United States} \qquad (7\text{-}2)$$

Here i is the intensity of rainfall in inches per hour and t is its duration in minutes. For a duration of 10 min, for example, intensities below 3 in. per hr in the southern states need not receive attention. The storm recorded in Example 7-2 exhibits double this intensity. Storm rainfall can be analyzed in many different ways. However, all procedures start from a summary of experience such as that shown in Example 7-3. The data obtained may be used directly, or after smoothing (generally graphical) operations that generalize the experience. The developed intensity-duration-frequency relationships may be expressed in tabular or graphical form or as equations.

Example 7-3. The number of storms of varying intensity and duration recorded by a rain gage[5] in 45 years are listed in Table 7-5. Determine the time-intensity values for the 5-year storm.

Table 7-5 Record of Intense Rainfalls (Example 7-3)

Duration, min	Number of Storms of Stated Intensity (inches per hour) or More												
	1.0	1.25	1.5	1.75	2.0	2.5	3.0	4.0	5.0	6.0	7.0	8.0	9.0
5							123	47	22	14	4	2	1
10					122	78	48	15	7	4	2	1	
15				100	83	46	21	10	3	2	1	1	
20			98	64	44	18	13	5	2	2			
30	99	72	51	30	21	8	6	3	2				
40	69	50	27	14	11	5	3	1					
50	52	28	17	10	8	4	3						
60	41	19	14	6	4	4	2						
80	18	13	4	2	2	1							
100	13	4	1	1									
120	8	2											

[5] Record for New York City from 1869 to 1913.

If it is assumed that the 5-year storm is equaled or exceeded in intensity $\frac{45}{5} = 9$ times in 45 years, the generalized time-intensity values may be interpolated from the summary by finding (a) for each specified intensity the duration that is equaled or exceeded by nine storms and (b) for each specified duration the intensity that is equaled

Table 7-6   Calculation of Storm Frequencies (Example 7-3)

a. Duration, min	5	10	15	20	30	40	50	60	80	100
a. Intensity, in. per hr	6.50	4.75	4.14	3.50	2.46	2.17	1.88	1.66	1.36	1.11
b. Intensity, in. per hr	1.0	1.25	1.5	1.75	2.0	2.5	3.0	4.0	5.0	6.0
b. Duration, min	116.0	89.9	70.0	52.5	46.7	29.0	25.7	16.0	9.3	7.5

or exceeded by nine storms. Interpolation proceeds along a broken diagonal line both vertically and horizontally. The results obtained are brought together in Table 7-6 and Fig. 7-2. A smooth curve drawn through them traces the course of the 5-year storm-rainfall. Similar calculations for the 1-, 2-, and 10-year rainfalls yield the remaining members of the family of curves included in Fig. 7-2.

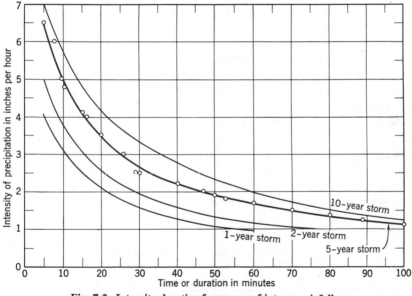

Fig. 7-2. Intensity-duration-frequency of intense rainfalls.

7-6   Formulation of Intensity-Duration-Frequency Relationships

Time-intensity curves like those in Fig. 7-2 are immediately useful in the design of storm-drainage or collection systems and in flood-flow analysis. Instead of being preserved and communicated as graphical records, the curves can be formulated (1) in individual equations that express the time-intensity relationships for specific frequencies only or (2) in a single equation that generalizes the intensity-duration-frequency relationships as a whole.

Good fits are usually obtained by an equation of the form

$$i = cT^m/(t + d)^n \qquad (7\text{-}3)$$

where i is the intensity in inches per hour, t the duration in minutes, T the frequency of occurrence in years, and c, d, m, and n are regional coefficients and exponents. Their order of magnitude is about as follows in North American experience: $c = 5$ to 50; $d = 0$ to 30; $m = 0.1$ to 0.5; and $n = 0.4$ to 1.0.

The problem of fitting Eq. 7-3 to a station record can be tackled either graphically or by least squares. For storms of specified frequency, Eq. 7-3 reduces to $i = A(t + d)^{-n}$, where $A = cT^m$.

Graphical Fitting.   Because the equation $i = A(t + d)^{-n}$ can be transformed to read: $[\log i] = \log A - n[\log (t + d)]$, direct plotting of i against t on log-log paper for individual frequencies produces curves that become straight lines when trial values of d are added to the observed values of t. A single value of d must be found that will place the resultant values of $(t + d)$ along a family of straight lines having the same slope for all frequencies. This slope establishes the value of n. Values of A can then be calculated, or they can be read as ordinates at $(t + d) = 1$ if this point appears on the plot. To determine c and m, the derived values of A are plotted on log-log paper against T for the frequencies studied. Because $[\log A] = \log c + m[\log T]$, the slope of the resulting straight line of best fit gives the values of m, and the value of c is read on the ordinate at $T = 1$.

Least-Squares, or Graphical, Fitting.   For least-squares fitting, the equation $A = cT^m$ presents no difficulty when it is written in straight-line form. A fitting, either least-squares or graphical, of the equation $i = A(t + d)^{-n}$ is somewhat more taxing.

The straight-line form of this equation is

$$\log\left(-\frac{di}{dt}\right) = \log n - \frac{1}{n}\log A + \left(1 + \frac{1}{n}\right)\log i \qquad (7\text{-}4)$$

If the storm intensities are recorded at uniform intervals of time, the slopes $(-di/dt)$ of the intensity-duration curves at i_{k+1} are closely approximated by the relation

$$-\frac{di}{dt} = \frac{i_k - i_{k+2}}{t_{k+2} - t_k} \qquad (7\text{-}5)$$

where the subscripts k, $k + 1$, and $k + 2$ denote the sequence of the pairs of observations in the series. A better fit is commonly obtained if the data below 60 min are separated for analysis from the data for longer durations.

Example 7-4 is restricted to a duration of 60 min and graphical fitting without benefit of least squares.

Example 7-4. Fit Eq. 7-3, $i = cT^m(t + d)^n$, to the 60-min record of intense rainfalls presented in Example 7-3.

Plot the values for the 5-year storm shown in Table 7-6 on double logarithmic paper (Fig. 7-3). The high-intensity short-duration points are seen to bend away from a straight line drawn through them by eye. However, they are brought into line by adding 2 min to their duration periods, i.e., $(t + d) = (t + 2)$. How the equation of this line $i = A/(t + d)^n = 26/(t + 2)^{0.66}$ is derived is shown in Fig. 7-3. Similar plots for the

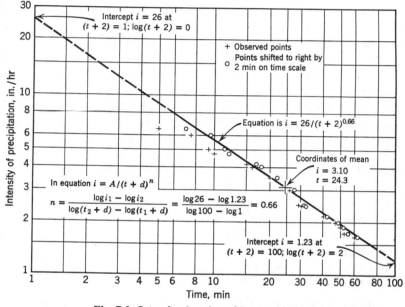

Fig. 7-3. Intensity-duration of 5-year rainstorm.

other storms included in Fig. 7-2 would yield parallel lines of good fit. The intercepts A of these lines on the i-axis at $(t + d) = 1$ themselves plot as a straight line on double logarithmic paper against the recurrence interval T. Hence $A = cT^m$, where numerical values for $c = 16$ and $m = 0.21$ are found in the same fashion as A and n, to complete the numerical evaluation of the coefficients and with them the relationship

$$i = \frac{cT^m}{(t + d)^n} = \frac{16T^{0.31}}{(t + 2)^{0.66}}$$

7-7   Storm Runoff and Flood Flows

The flood flows descending the water courses of river basins or collected in the storm drains or combined sewers of municipal drainage districts are derived from rains that fall upon the tributary watershed. The degree of their conversion into runoff is affected by many factors, especially in the varied environment of urban communities. Component effects and their relative importance must, therefore, be clearly recognized in the interpretation of storm runoff or flood experience in relation to intense rainfalls.

As has been said before, flows normally reach their crest at a given point on a stream or within a drainage scheme when runoff from rainfall begins to pour in from all parts of the tributary area. There are exceptions to this rule, but they are few. An important exception is a storm traveling upstream or sweeping across a catchment area so rapidly that runoff from distant points cannot reach the point of concentration until long after the central storm has moved on. Diminution of effective area or retardance of this kind is rarely taken into consideration in American practice; but it should be in some circumstances. Because rainfall eventually decreases in intensity with increasing duration, the shorter the elapsed time or *time of concentration* in which the entire area is tributary to the *point of concentration*, the larger are the flows.

The time of concentration is shortest for small, broad, steep areas with rapidly shedding surfaces. It is lengthened by dry soil, surface inequalities and indentations, vegetal cover, and storage in water courses, on flood plains, and in reservoirs. The volume of runoff is swelled by snow and ice melt, infiltration from bank storage, and release of water from impoundages either on purpose or by accident. Maximum rates obtain when storms move downstream at speeds that bring them to the point of discharge in about the time of concentration, making it possible for the runoff from the most intense rainfall to arrive at the point of discharge at nearly the same instant.

Among the ways devised for estimating storm runoff or flood flows for engineering designs are the following:

1. Statistical analyses based upon observed records of adequate length. Obviously these can provide likely answers. Unfortunately, however, recorded information is seldom sufficiently extensive to identify critical magnitudes directly from experience. Information must be generalized to arrive at rational extrapolations for the frequency or recurrence interval of design flows or the magnitude of flows of design frequency.

2. Statistical augmentation of available information (a) through cross-correlation with recorded experience in one or more adjacent and similar basins for which more years of information are available; (b) through correlation between rainfall and runoff when the rainfall record is longer than the runoff record (but see Sec. 4-8); and (c) through statistical generation of additional values (Sec. 4-10).

3. *Rational* estimates of runoff from rainfall. This is a common procedure in the design of storm and combined sewers that are to drain (a) an existing built-up area and satisfy anticipated change in the course of time, or (b) an area about to be added to a municipal drainage scheme.

4. Calculations based on empirical formulations not devised specifically from observations in the design area but reasonably applicable to existing watershed conditions. Formulations are varied in structure and must be selected with full understanding of the limitations of their derivation. At best, they should be applied only as checks of statistical or rational methods.

Where failure of important engineering structures is sure to entail loss of life or great damage, every bit of hydrological information should be adduced to arrive at economical but safe design values. Hydraulic models may also be helpful.

7-8 Statistical Analysis of Runoff

Records of maximum daily, weekly, monthly, or annual runoff form frequency distributions that are skewed to the right, implying that their means lie to the right of their modes. Records of this kind can be generalized roughly as geometrically normal series, more closely as Pearsonian Type III and Gumbel distributions, or graphically as partial duration curves.

The Type III Pearsonian Distribution. In the family of frequency distributions postulated by Karl Pearson,[6] Type III lends itself well to generalization of hydrological phenomena that appear to possess a lower limit greater than zero but no upper limit. The equation for this distribution contains more coefficients than the geometrically normal distribution and identifies departure from this kind of normality. Its equation, referred to the mean as its origin, is

$$y = y_0\{1 + [(x - \mu) + d]/a\}^{\gamma a} \exp\{-\gamma[(x - \mu) + d]\} \qquad (7\text{-}6)$$

Notation is as follows:

y = ordinate or frequency of runoff of specified magnitude
y_0 = modal ordinate or frequency of modal runoff
x = abscissa or magnitude of runoff
a = departure of lower limit from mode
d = difference between mode and mean magnitude
μ = mean magnitude
σ = standard deviation
γ = a measure of both variability and skewness.

The lower limit of Eq. 7-6 lies at $(x - \mu) + d = -a$, y being zero, but there is no upper limit (see sketch above Table 7-7). Determination of the coefficients a, $d = \mu - \mu_0$, and γ can be accomplished by direct mathematical methods. However, calculations are greatly simplified by a table of areas similar in concept to the table for the normal distribution (Table I-6). Table 7-7 is a short version of such a table based upon Foster's

[6] British statistician (1857–1936), noted also for the product-moment formula for the coefficient of correlation as the slope of the straight line best fitting pairs of observations in two related series. The normal distribution is Type VII in Pearson's series.

Table 7-7   Short Table of Areas under Pearson's Type III Skew Frequency Distribution Curve

Values of $t = (x - \mu)/\sigma$ for stated values of the area from the lower limit, $\mu - (a + d)$, to stated value of t for skewness $d/\sigma = $ (mean − mode)$/\sigma$

Area A from lower limit

Area B = Total area − area A

Area A

Lower limit

Mode Mean
μ_0 μ

y_0 a d y x

Values of Area A as Per Cent of Total Area	Deviation $t = (x - \mu)/\sigma$ for stated skewness $d/\sigma = $ (mean − mode)$/\sigma$														
	0.0	0.1	0.2	0.3	0.4	0.5	0.6	0.7	0.8	0.9	1.0	1.2	1.4
0.01	−3.73	−3.32	−2.92	−2.53	−2.18	−1.88	−1.63	−1.42	−1.25	−1.11	−1.00	...	...
0.1	−3.09	−2.81	−2.54	−2.28	−2.03	−1.80	−1.59	−1.40	−1.24	−1.11	−1.00	...	...
1.0	−2.33	−2.18	−2.03	−1.88	−1.74	−1.59	−1.45	−1.32	−1.19	−1.08	−0.99	−0.83	−0.71
5	−1.65	−1.58	−1.51	−1.45	−1.38	−1.31	−1.25	−1.18	−1.11	−1.04	−0.97	−0.82	−0.71
10	−1.28	−1.25	−1.22	−1.19	−1.16	−1.12	−1.08	−1.05	−1.00	−0.95	−0.90	−0.79	−0.70
20	−0.84	−0.85	−0.85	−0.86	−0.86	−0.86	−0.85	−0.84	−0.82	−0.80	−0.78	−0.71	−0.65
50	−0.00	−0.03	−0.06	−0.09	−0.13	−0.16	−0.19	−0.22	−0.25	−0.28	−0.30	−0.35	−0.38
80	+0.84	+0.83	+0.82	+0.80	+0.78	+0.76	+0.74	+0.71	+0.68	+0.64	+0.61	+0.54	+0.47
90	+1.28	+1.30	+1.32	+1.33	+1.34	+1.34	+1.35	+1.34	+1.33	+1.32	+1.30	+1.25	+1.20
95	+1.65	+1.69	+1.74	+1.79	+1.83	+1.87	+1.90	+1.93	+1.96	+1.98	+2.00	+2.01	+2.02
99	+2.33	+2.48	+2.62	+2.77	+2.90	+3.03	+3.15	+3.28	+3.40	+3.50	+3.60	+3.78	+3.95
99.9	+3.09	+3.38	+3.67	+3.96	+4.25	+4.54	+4.82	+5.11	+5.39	+5.66	+5.91	+6.47	+6.99
99.99	+3.73	+4.16	+4.60	+5.04	+5.48	+5.92	+6.37	+6.82	+7.28	+7.75	+8.21	...	...
99.999	+4.27	+4.84	+5.42	+6.01	+6.61	+7.22	+7.85	+8.50	+9.17	+9.84	+10.51	...	...
99.9999	+4.76	+5.48	+6.24	+7.02	+7.82	+8.63	+9.45	+10.28	+11.12	+11.96	+12.81	...	...

calculations.[7] By Pearson's definition[8] skewness equals (mean − mode)/σ. For Type III curve,

$$\text{Skewness } \frac{d}{\sigma} = \frac{\Sigma(x - \mu)^3}{2\sigma\Sigma(x - \mu)^2} \tag{7-7}$$

Finding the skewness for Pearson's Type III curve involves, therefore, calculation of $\Sigma(x - \mu)^3$ as well as $\Sigma(x - \mu)^2$. The reliability of the parameter of skewness, like that of other statistics, is a function of the number of observations. Because the numerical value of skewness increases with the number of observations, n, Hazen[9] suggested that the calculated skewness be multiplied by a factor $(1 + 8.5/n)$ in the analysis of runoff records. The calculations necessary to fit a Type III curve to observed flood flows are illustrated in Example 7-5.

Example 7-5.   Given the 20-year record of flood runoff of a stream draining 48.5 sq miles of hilly country in the northeastern United States,[10] plot Pearson's Type III curve of best fit and determine the magnitude of the flood expected to be equaled or exceeded once in 50, 100, 200, and 1000 years.

1. The observed flood flows are recorded in Table 7-8 together with the calculations necessary to determine the arithmetic mean μ, the standard deviation σ, and the skewness d/σ.

Number of observations $n = 20$; arithmetic mean $\mu = 910/20 = 45.5$; standard error $\sigma = \sqrt{\Sigma x^2/(n - 1)} = \sqrt{12,676/19} = 25.9$; coefficient of variation $c_v = 25.9/45.5 = 0.57$; skewness $d/\sigma = \Sigma(x - \mu)^3/[2\sigma\Sigma(x - \mu)^2] = 551,400/(2 \times 25.9 \times 12,700) = 0.838$; adjusted skewness $(d'/\sigma) = 0.838(1 + 8.5/20) = 1.20$.

The coefficient of variation of the flood flows is observed to be more than twice as large as the coefficient of variation in annual flows (Sec. 7-2).

2. The coordinates necessary to plot the summation curve of best fit are obtained from Table 7-7 as shown in Table 7-9.

3. Observed points and the curve of best fit are plotted in Fig. 7-4 on arithmetic-probability paper. The fit is good. It would be still better, especially in the lower, though less important, reaches, if maximum monthly, weekly, or daily values had been analyzed instead of yearly ones. Arithmetic-probability paper is selected in this instance only for convenience in plotting. Logarithmic scales might have taken the place of the probability scale or the runoff scale, or both scales.

4. The magnitudes of the floods expected to be equaled or exceeded once in 50, 100, 200, and 1000 years are

50-year flood = 125 csm read at 98%	or 2%
100-year flood = 143 csm read at 99%	or 1%
200-year flood = 163 csm read at 99.5%	or 0.5%
1000-year flood = 213 csm read at 99.9%	or 0.1%

[7] H. A. Foster, Theoretical Frequency Curves, *Trans. Am. Soc. Civil Engrs.*, **87**, 142 (1924).
[8] The Pearsonian definition of skewness is used here rather than that of Hazen, who defines the coefficient of skewness as twice the Pearsonian skewness for Type III curve.
[9] Allen Hazen, *Flood Flows*, John Wiley & Sons, New York, 1930.
[10] The Westfield Little River in Massachusetts for the years from 1910 to 1929.

Table 7-8 Observed Flood Flows and Calculation of Statistical Parameters (Example 7-5)

Maximum Annual Flood Flow, csm	Deviation from Mean $(x - \mu)$	$(x - \mu)^2$	$(x - \mu)^3$	Per Cent of Years Flood Is Not Exceeded
(1)	(2)	(3)	(4)	(5)
17	−28.5	812	− 23,100	4.8
18	−27.5	756	− 20,800	9.5
24	−21.5	462	− 9,900	14.3
24	−21.5	462	− 9,900	19.0
31	−14.5	210	− 3,000	23.8
31	−14.5	210	− 3,000	28.6
34	−11.5	132	− 1,500	33.3
35	−10.5	110	− 1,200	38.1
36	− 9.5	90	− 900	42.8
36	− 9.5	90	− 900	47.6
38	− 7.5	56	− 400	52.4
43	− 2.5	6	0	57.2
46	+ 0.5	0	0	61.9
47	+ 1.5	2	0	66.7
51	+ 5.5	30	+ 200	71.5
59	+13.5	182	+ 2,500	76.3
60	+14.5	210	+ 3,000	81.0
63	+17.5	306	+ 5,400	85.8
91	+45.5	2,070	+ 94,200	90.5
126	+80.5	6,480	+521,700	95.2
Sums 910	...	12,676	+551,400	...

Table 7-9 Calculated Frequency of Flood Flows (Example 7-5)

Area A Table 7-7 (1)	$(x - \mu)/\sigma$ from Table 7-7 (2)	$(x - \mu)$ $25.9 \times$ (2) (3)	Flood Flow x (3) + 45.5 csm (4)
1	−0.83	− 21.5	24.0
5	−0.82	− 21.2	24.3
10	−0.79	− 20.5	25.0
20	−0.71	− 18.4	27.1
50	−0.35	− 9.1	36.4
80	+0.54	+ 14.0	59.5
90	+1.25	+ 31.3	76.8
95	+2.01	+ 52.1	97.6
99	+3.78	+ 97.9	143.4
99.9	+6.47	+167.5	213.0

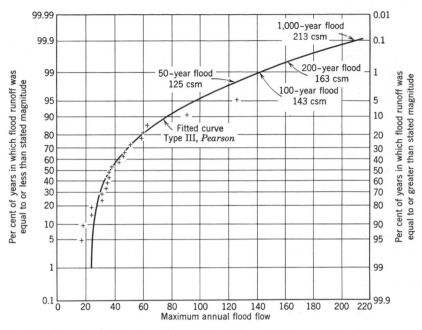

Fig. 7-4. Frequency distribution of annual flood flows plotted on arithmetic-probability paper and fitted by Pearson's Type III curve.

Physically, the maximum flood that can occur on a given stream is limited by the size of the drainage area and the maximum rate at which atmospheric water can be transported to it. Long records of floods suggest a limit of once in 50 to 200 years. Uncertainty of estimate by extrapolation suggests using the 1000-year or 100,000-year value in the design of major structures.

Gumbel's Distribution. E. J. Gumbel[11] has assumed that extreme values of stream flow conform to the theoretical distribution of extreme values as follows:

$$F(x) = 1 - \exp\left[\exp\left(-b\right)\right] \qquad (7\text{-}8)$$

where b is the dimensionless variable $(x - \mu + 0.450\sigma)/0.780\sigma$ because the deviation of the modal flood from the mean annual flood is approximately $-0.577\sigma\sqrt{6}/\pi = -0.450\sigma$. For example, if the mean annual 24-hr flood of a stream is 288×10^3 cfs with a standard deviation of 113×10^3 cfs, $b = (700 - 288 + 0.450 \times 113)/(0.780 \times 113) = 5.25$ for a flood of

[11] E. J. Gumbel, Floods Estimated by the Probability Method, *Eng. News-Record,* **134,** 833 (1945); also see *Maximum Possible Precipitation,* Hydrometeorological Report No. 23, Dept of Commerce, Washington, D.C. 1947.

700×10^3 cfs, and

$$F(x) = 1 - \exp[\exp - 5.25) = 0.005$$

or the recurrence interval $I = 1/(5 \times 10^{-3}) = 200$ years approximately.

The Partial Duration Curve. Some engineers prefer graphical or purely empirical methods of attack, such as analyses of peak-flood distributions irrespective of the time interval in which floods have occurred in a given record. Ordinal floods, second, third, etc., to the maximum in any one year but larger than the maximum of some other year are, therefore, included. If the peak floods—up to three or four times the number of years, months, or weeks of record—are arranged and numbered in order of decreasing magnitudes, the resulting array can be plotted as a flood expectancy or partial duration curve with the average recurrence interval I as the abscissa and the size of flood as the ordinate. The recurrence-interval principle can be applied also in the analysis of storm rainfalls (Sec. 7-5). Information of this kind plots as a more or less straight line when floods or storm rainfalls causing them are related to the logarithms of their recurrence intervals.

7-9   Rational Estimates of Runoff from Rainfall

Among ways of estimating runoff from specific rainfalls, two are of general interest: the rational method and the unit hydrograph method.

The Rational Method. This method postulates that

$$Q = cia \tag{7-9}$$

where Q is the rate of runoff at a specified place, a is the tributary drainage area, i is the average intensity of rainfall, and c is the runoff-rainfall ratio, called the runoff coefficient. Because $i = A/(t + d)^n$ (Sec. 7-6), where $d > 0$ and $n \leq 1$, whereas $a = kt^2$ if the velocity of travel towards the point is considered uniform, and a increases faster with time than i decreases (Sec. 7-4), it follows that Q is generally maximized when the entire area is tributary to the point of concentration. This has been said before, but is worth further elucidation by the present equations.

Of the three factors included in Eq. 7-9, a is found from a regional map or survey, i is determined for a storm of duration equal to the time of concentration (Secs. 3 to 6 of this chapter), and c is estimated from the characteristics of the catchment area. The time of concentration is found (1) for flood discharge by estimating average velocities of flow in the principal drainage channels of the tributary area; and (2) for runoff from sewered areas by estimating the time required for runoff to enter the sewerage system from adjacent surfaces (called the *inlet time*) and adding to it the time of flow in the sewers or storm drains proper. Because rapid inflow from tributaries generates flood waves in the main stem of a river system, flood velocities are often assumed to be 30 to 50% higher than normal rates of flow (Sec. 14-9).

The selection of suitable values for c in estimating runoff from sewered areas is discussed more fully in connection with the design of storm drains and combined sewers (Chap. 15). In the translation of rainfall into flood flows, c varies seasonally, regionally, and locally. For the eastern United States, Bernard[12] has suggested (1) a limiting value, c_{max}, varying from about 0.3 to 1.5, with the highest values for the northern portion of the country where melting snow and ice add to immediate runoff from spring rains; and (2) reducing the limiting coefficient to that of the selected flood frequency in accordance with the relation

$$c = c_{max}(T/100)^m \qquad (7\text{-}10)$$

on the assumption that the limiting coefficient has a frequency of once in 100 years, T being the frequency of occurrence in years and m a coefficient, both in accordance with Eq. 7-3.

Example 7-6. For the region studied in Example 7-3, estimate the 1-year and 10-year flood runoff from 1 sq mile on the assumption that c_{max} is 1.0 and the time of concentration t is 60 min.

From Eq. 7-3

$$\text{1-year intensity } i = 16/(62)^{0.66} = 1.1 \text{ in./hr}$$
$$\text{10-year intensity } i = (16 \times 10^{0.31})/(62)^{0.66} = 2.1 \text{ in./hr}$$

2. From Eq. 7-10

$$\text{1-year magnitude } c = 1.0(0.01)^{0.31} = 0.24$$
$$\text{10-year magnitude } c = 1.0(0.1)^{0.31} = 0.49$$

3. From Eq. 7-9

$$\text{1-year runoff } Q = 0.24 \times 1.1 \times 1.0 \times 640 = 170 \text{ cfs}$$
$$\text{10-year runoff } Q = 0.49 \times 2.1 \times 1.0 \times 640 = 660 \text{ cfs}$$

The Unit Hydrograph. In dry weather, or when precipitation is frozen, the residual hydrograph or base flow of a river is traced by water released from storage in the ground or in ponds, lakes, reservoirs, and backwaters of the stream. Immediately after a rainstorm, the rate of discharge rises above base flow by the amount of surface runoff entering the drainage system. That portion of the hydrograph rising above the base flow can be isolated from it and is a measure of the true surface runoff (Fig. 7-5). The *unit hydrograph* method stems from studies of simple geometric properties of the surface-runoff portion of the hydrograph in their relation to an *effective rain* that has fallen during a *unit* of time, such as a day or an hour, and that, by definition, has produced surface runoff.

[12] M. Bernard, Modified Rational Method of Estimating Flood Flows, Appendix A of *Low Dams*, National Resources Committee, Washington, 1938.

The important geometric properties of the unit hydrograph of surface runoff illustrated in Fig. 7-5 are:

1. The abscissal length measuring time duration above base flow is substantially constant for all unit-time rains.

2. Sequent ordinates, measuring rates of discharge above base flow at the end of each time unit, are proportional to the total runoff from unit-time rains irrespective of their individual magnitudes.

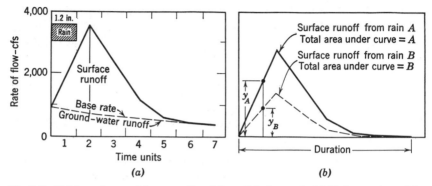

Fig. 7-5. Origin and geometric properties of the unit hydrograph. (a) Hydrograph resulting from unit-time rain. See Example 7-7. (b) Distribution graph showing geometric properties of unit hydrograph; $y_A : A = y_B : B$; base duration is constant.

3. Ratios of individual areas to the total area under the hydrograph, measuring the amount of water discharged in a given interval of time, are constant for all unit hydrographs of the same drainage area. These distribution ratios are generally referred to as the *distribution graph*, even when they are not presented in graphical form.

4. Rainstorms extending, with or without interruption, over several time units, generate a hydrograph composed of a series of unit hydrographs superimposed in such manner as to distribute the runoff from each unit-time rain in accordance with the successive distribution ratios derived from unit-time rainfalls.

These geometric properties do not apply when runoff originates in melting snow or ice, or when the speed of flood waves in streams is changed appreciably as river stages are varied by fluctuating flows. Time is an important element of the procedure, and rainfall data must be available for unit times shorter than the time of concentration of the drainage area. Unit times as long as a day can be employed successfully only for large watersheds (1000 sq miles or more). For sheds of 100 to 1000 sq miles, Sherman[13] has suggested values of 6 to 12 hr; for sheds of

[13] O. E. Meinzer, *Hydrology*, McGraw-Hill Book Co., New York, p. 524, 1942.

20 sq miles, 2 hr; and for very small areas one-fourth to one-third the time of concentration. The unit hydrograph method is illustrated in Example 7-7.

Example 7-7. 1. Given the rainfall and runoff records of a drainage area of 620 sq miles, determine the generalized distribution of runoff (the distribution graph) from isolated unit-time rainfalls. This involves first of all a search for records of isolated rainfalls and for records of the resulting surface runoff. The basic data for a typical storm are shown in Table 7-10 together with necessary calculations. Development of

Table 7-10 Observations and Calculations for Unit Hydrograph (Example 7-7)

| Sequence of Time Units | Observed Rainfall, in. | Runoff, cfs | | Estimated Distribution of Surface Runoff | | Average Distribution Ratio for 10 Storms, % |
		Observed Total	Estimated Base Flow	cfs	%	
(1)	(2)	(3)	(4)	$(5) =$ $(3) - (4)$	$(6) =$ $100(5)/6200$	(7)
1	1.20	1,830	870	960	15.5	16
2	0.03	3,590	800	2,790	45.0	46
3	0.00	2,370	690	1,680	27.1	26
4	0.00	1,220	600	620	10.0	10
5	0.00	640	510	130	2.1	1
6	0.00	430	410	20	0.3	1
7	0.00	350	350	0	0.0	0
Totals	...	...	...	6,200	100.0	100

this table is straightforward, except for Col. 4, which records the estimated base flow. This can be derived only from a study of the general hydrograph of the stream in combination with all related hydrological observations of the region.

2. Apply the average estimate of runoff distribution to the observed rainfall sequence presented in Table 7-11.

The calculations in Table 7-11 need little explanation except for Col. 3, the estimated loss of rainfall due principally to infiltration. This estimate rests on all available information for the region. It is discussed in principle in Sec. 7-9 and in Chap. 9. Column 5 is identical with Col. 7 of Table 7-10. Column 6 is the net rain of 0.5 in., during the first time unit multiplied by the distribution ratio of Col. 5. Columns 7, 8, and 9 are similarly derived for the net rains during the subsequent time units. Column 10 gives the sums of Cols. 6 to 9, and Col. 11 converts these sums from inches to cubic feet per second. If the base flow is estimated and added to the surface runoff shown in Col. 11, the hydrograph becomes complete.

The unit hydrograph method is useful in estimating magnitudes of unusual flood flows, in forecasting flood crests during storms, and in the manipulation of storage on large river systems. It has the important property of (1) tracing the full hydrograph resulting from a storm rather than being confined to a determination of the peak flow alone; and (2) producing useful results from short records. For small drainage areas, the

Table 7-11   Application of Unit Hydrograph Method (Example 7-7)

Sequence of Time Units	Rainfall, in.			Average Runoff Distribution Ratio, %	Distributed Runoff for Stated Time Units, in.				Compounded Runoff	
	Observed	Estimated Loss	Net		1st	2nd	3rd	5th	in.	cfs*
(1)	(2)	(3)	(4) = (2) − (3)	(5)	(6)	(7)	(8)	(9)	(10)	(11)
1	1.8	1.3	0.5	16	0.08	...	...	...	0.08	1,300
2	2.7	1.6	1.1	46	0.23	0.18	...	...	0.41	6,900
3	1.6	1.1	0.5	26	0.13	0.50	0.08	...	0.71	11,900
4	0.0	0.0	0.0	10	0.05	0.29	0.23	...	0.57	9,500
5	1.1	0.2	0.9	1	0.01	0.11	0.13	0.14	0.39	6,500
6	0.0	0.0	0.0	1	0.00	0.01	0.05	0.42	0.48	8,000
7	0.0	0.0	0.0	0	0.00	0.01	0.01	0.23	0.25	4,200
8	0.0	0.0	0.0	0	0.00	0.00	0.00	0.09	0.09	1,500

* Rate of runoff in cubic feet per second = inches × 26.88 × 620 sq miles = 16,700 cfs if the time unit is a day. For other time units multiply by reciprocal ratio of length of time to length of day.

method depends upon the readings of a recording rain gage. Many refinements in procedure and aids to the rationalization of the various steps continue to be developed by hydrologists and engineers.

7-10   Flood-Flow Formulas

Flood-flow formulas are empirical evaluations of drainage-basin characteristics and hydrological factors falling rationally within the framework of the relation $Q = cia$. Frequency relations are implied even when they are not expressed in frequency terms. Time-intensity variations, likewise, are included, but (indirectly) as functions of the size of area drained. Equation 7-9 is thereby reduced to the expression $Q = Ca^m$, where m is less than 1. This follows from what has been said before about relative changes in i and a with t; namely, $i = A/(t + d)^n$ and $a = kt^2$. For d close to zero, therefore, $i = \text{constant}/(a^{n/2})$ and, substituting i in Eq. 7-9, $Q = \text{constant } a^{1-n/2} = Ca^m$, where $m = 1 - n/2$. Because n varies from 0.5 to 1.0 (Sec. 7-6), m must and does vary in different formulations from 0.8 to 0.5. The value of C embraces the maximum rate of rainfall, the runoff-rainfall ratio of the watershed, and the frequency factor. An example is the Fanning formula listed in Table 7-12 together with other flood-flow formulas in which certain component variables or their influence upon runoff are individualized.

Table 7-12 Examples of Flood-Flow Formulas

Individualized Variable	Author and Region	Formula
None	Fanning, New England	$Q = Ca^{5/6}$, where $C = 200$ for a in sq miles
Rainfall intensity and slope of watershed	McMath, St. Louis, Mo.	$Q = cia^{4/5}s^{1/5}$, where s = slope in ‰ and $c = 0.75$ for a in acres or 480 for a in sq miles
Shape and slope of watershed	Potter, Cumberland Plateau	$Q = ca^{7/6}/(l/s^{1/2})$, where l = length of principal waterway in miles, s = slope of waterway in ft/mile, and $c = 1920d$ for a in sq miles, the 10-year peak flood and a factor d relating the basin to the base station at Columbus, Ohio
Shape, slope, and surface storage of watershed	Kinnison and Colby, New England	$Q = (0.000036h^{2.4} + 124)a^{0.95}/(rl^{0.7})$, where h = median altitude of drainage basin in ft above the outlet; $r = \%$ of lake, pond, and reservoir area; l = average distance in miles to outlet; and a = sq miles
Frequency of flood	Fuller, U.S.A.	$Q = Ca^{0.8}(1 + 0.8 \log T)(1 + 2a^{-0.3})$, where T = number of years in the period considered, and C varies from 25 to 200 for different drainage basins and a in sq miles

These examples are chosen only as illustrations of forms of flood-flow formulas. They are not necessarily the best forms, nor should they be applied outside the area for which they were derived.

The flood-flow characteristics of United States drainage basins have been compared by developing their envelope curve on a Q versus a plot as a function of $\sqrt{a}$ and identifying their Meyers rating from the equation

$$Q = 100p\sqrt{a} \qquad (7\text{-}11)$$

where Q is the extreme peak flow in cfs; p is the percentage ratio of Q to a postulated ultimate maximum flood flow of $Q_u = 10,000\sqrt{a}$; and a is the drainage area, which must be 4 sq miles or more. In the Colorado River basin, the Meyers rating is only 25%; in the northeastern United States seldom more than 50%; in the lower Mississippi basin as much as 64% as an average.

Fuller's formula is of particular interest because it incorporates a frequency factor and is countrywide in scope. It was developed in sequence as follows:

1. The average annual 24-hr flood:

$$Q_{av} = Ca^{0.8} \qquad (7\text{-}12)$$

2. The most probable maximum 24-hr flood in T years:

$$Q_{max} = Q_{av}(1 + 0.8 \log T) \qquad (7\text{-}13)$$

3. The most probable peak discharge in T years:

$$Q = Q_{max}(1 + 2a^{-0.3}) \qquad (7.14)$$

Inspection of these equations suggests the nature of their graphical derivation from observed flood flows. For the United States, C varies from 25 to 200. It should be noted that Fuller's maximum flood in T years is the

Table 7-13   Fuller's Flood Frequency Values

Type of Structure	Damage in Case of Failure	Values of $(1 + 0.8 \log T)$
Temporary works during construction	Slight	1.5–2
Minor permanent structures	Slight	2–3
Temporary works	Considerable	2–3
Major permanent structures	Material	3–5
Major permanent structures	Material and disastrous	5–6

most probable value to occur in that period rather than the value that is equaled or exceeded once in that period. Because Fuller assumes that the most probable value is the arithmetic mean of the group of *exceeding* values, flood flows calculated by his formula are generally higher than those determined by common statistical procedures for equal periods. Thomas[14] has shown that Fuller's frequency factor $(1 + 0.8 \log T)$ has a rational basis and is more completely expressed as

$$(1 - 0.45c_v + 1.80c_v \log T).$$

[14] Unpublished study by H. A. Thomas, Jr.

The variability in runoff of different streams is thereby related to c_v, the coefficient of variation. Fuller[15] has recommended using the values of the frequency factor $(1 + 0.8 \log T)$ shown in Table 7-13.

Example 7-8. For the New England drainage area of 48.5 sq miles in Example 7-5, calculate (1) the Meyers rating and (2) the magnitude of the maximum peak flood to be expected in 100 years by Fuller's formula.

1. Example 7-5 gives the 200-year flood as 163 csm or $163 \times 48.5 = 7900$ cfs. Assuming that the 200-year value is the maximum, $p = 7900/(100\sqrt{48.5}) = 11.3\%$. This is a reasonable value for the region.

2. Example 7-5 gives the arithmetic mean peak flood as 45.5 csm; hence

$$C = \frac{Q}{a^{0.8}(1 + 2a^{-0.3})} = \frac{45.5 \times 48.5}{48.5^{0.8}(1 + 2 \times 48.5^{-0.3})} = 61$$

This, too, is a reasonable value for the region. For a normal value of $C = 60$,

$$Q = 60 \times 48.5^{0.8}(1 + 0.8 \log 100)(1 + 2 \times 48.5^{-0.3}) = 5{,}700 \text{ cfs or } 118 \text{ csm}$$

The flood flow to be equaled or exceeded once in 100 years is given in Example 7-5 as 143 csm. Fuller's empirical 100-year frequency factor is $(1 + 0.8 \log T) = 2.6$. Thomas's rational 100-year frequency factor for $c_v = 0.57$ (Example 7-5) is $(1 - 0.45c_v + 1.8c_v \log T] = (1 - 0.45 \times 0.57 + 1.8 \times 0.57 \times 2) = 2.8$.

In a statistical sense, droughts are unusual occurrences in much the same significance as floods and can be analyzed in much the same manner. Both rainfalls of small magnitude and the resulting runoff can be identified statistically.

[15] W. E. Fuller, Flood Flows, *Trans. Am. Soc. Civil Engrs.*, **77**, 564 (1914). Mr Fuller (1879–1935) was a partner of Allen Hazen and later Professor of Civil Engineering at Swarthmore College.

CHAPTER 8

Storage and Runoff Control

8-1 Importance in Water Supply and Wastewater Disposal

In nature the runoff from drainage areas is held back in varying degree by lakes and ponds and in the channels, backwaters, and banks of streams and other water courses. In times of drought these natural accumulations are released and reduce the severity of low water; in times of flood they are replenished, lower the flood peaks, and reduce the severity of high water. Both low and high water control are important in regional water management.

In the absence of adequate natural storage, engineers construct impounding reservoirs. More rarely they excavate storage basins in lowlands adjacent to streams. Natural storage, too, can be regulated. Control works (gates and weirs or sills) on outlets of lakes and ponds are examples.

Some storage works are designed to serve a single purpose only; others to include a number of different functions and preserve the broader economy of natural resources. Common purposes include:

1. Water supply for household, farm, and industry.
2. Dilution and natural purification of sewage and other municipal and industrial wastewaters.
3. Irrigation of arable lands.
4. Harnessing of water power.
5. Low-water regulation for navigation.
6. Preservation and cultivation of useful aquatic life.
7. Recreation—fishing, boating, and bathing.
8. Control of destructive floods.

The greatest net benefit may accrue from a judicious combination of reservoir functions in multipurpose developments. The choice of single-purpose storage systems should indeed be justified fully.

Storage is provided when stream flow is inadequate or rendered unsatisfactory by heavy pollution. Release of stored waters then swells flows and dilutes pollution. Storage itself also affects the quality of the waters impounded. Both desirable and undesirable changes may take place. Their identification is the responsibility of *limnology*, the science of lakes or, more broadly, of inland waters (Vol. 2).

If they must receive wastewaters—principally municipal sewage and industrial process waters—stream flows should be adjusted to the pollutional load imposed upon them. Low-water regulation, as such, is made possible by head-water or upstream storage, but lowland reservoirs, too, may aid dilution and play an active part in the natural purification of river systems. Whether over-all results are helpful or not depends upon the volume and nature of wastewater flows and the chosen regimen of the stream.

8-2 Safe Yield of Streams

In the absence of storage, the safe yield of a river system is its lowest dry-weather flow; with full development of storage, the safe yield approaches the mean annual flow. The economical yield generally lies somewhere in between. The attainable yield is modified: (1) by evaporation; (2) by bank storage; (3) by seepage out of the catchment area; and (4) by silting.

Storage-yield relations are illustrated in this chapter by calculations of storage to be provided in impounding reservoirs for water supply. However, the principles demonstrated are also applicable to other purposes and uses of storage.

8-3 Storage as a Function of Draft and Runoff

A dam thrown across a river valley impounds the waters of the valley. Once the reservoir has filled, the water drawn from storage is eventually replenished by the stream, provided runoff, storage, and draft are kept in proper balance. The balance is struck graphically or analytically on the basis of historical records or replicates generated by suitable statistical procedures of operational hydrology (Sec. 4-10).

Assuming, as in Fig. 8-1, that the reservoir is full at the beginning of a dry period, the maximum amount of water S that must be withdrawn from storage to maintain a given average draft D equals the maximum cumulative difference between the draft D and runoff Q in a given dry period, or

$$S = \text{maximum value of } \Sigma(D - Q) \tag{8-1}$$

To find S, $\Sigma(D - Q)$ is summed arithmetically or graphically. The mass diagram or Rippl[1] method illustrated in Fig. 8-1 is a most convincing and useful demonstration of finding $\Sigma(D - Q) = \Sigma D - \Sigma Q$. The shorter the interval of time for which runoff is recorded, the more exact is the result. As the maximum value is approached, therefore, it may be worth while to shift to short intervals of time: from monthly to daily values, for example.

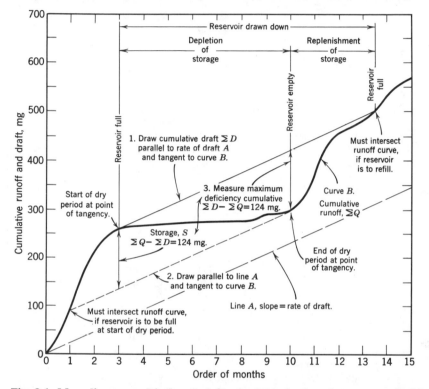

Fig. 8-1. Mass diagram or Rippl method for the determination of storage required in impounding reservoirs. Basic runoff values are for the Westfield Little River, near Springfield, Mass., for March 1914 to March 1915. A constant draft of 750,000 gpd/sq mile = 23 mg/sq mile for a month of 30.4 days is assumed.

The additional storage identified by such a shift may be as much as 10 days of draft.

Assuming that inflow and drafts are repeated cyclically, in successive sets of T years, Thomas and Fiering[2] have developed a *sequent peak* procedure for determining minimum storage for no shortage in draft based upon two needed cycles. Example 8-1 illustrates their procedure. Also

[1] W. Rippl, The Capacity of Storage Reservoirs for Water Supply, *Proc. Inst. Civil Engrs.*, **71**, 270 (1883).
[2] H. A. Thomas, Jr., and M. B. Fiering, personal communication.

Table 8-1 Calculation of Required Storage (Example 8-1)

(Runoff, draft, and storage are expressed in mg/sq mile)

Order of Months (1)	Recorded Runoff, Q (2)	Estimated Draft, D (3)	$Q - D$ (4)	$\Sigma(Q - D)^*$ (5)	Storage $S = P - T$ (6)	Waste, W (7)	Reservoir State† (8)
1	94	27	+67	67	67	0	R
2	122	27	+95	162	162	0	R
3	45	30	+15	$177P_1$	176	1	S
4	5	30	−25	152	151	0	F
5	5	33	−28	124	123	0	F
6	2	30	−28	96	95	0	F
7	0	27	−27	69	68	0	F
8	2	27	−25	44	43	0	F
9	16	30	−14	30	29	0	F
10	7	36	−29	$1T_1$	0	0	E
11	72	33	+39	40	39	0	R
12	92	30	+62	102	101	0	R
1	94	27	+67	169	168	0	R
2	122	27	+95	264	176	87	S
3	45	30	+15	$279P_2$	176	15	S
4	5	30	−25	254	151	0	F
5	5	33	−28	226	123	0	F
6	2	30	−28	198	95	0	F
7	0	27	−27	171	68	0	F
8	2	27	−25	146	43	0	F
9	16	30	−14	132	29	0	F
10	7	36	−29	$103T_2$	0	0	E
11	72	33	+39	142	39	0	R
12	92	30	+62	$204(P_3)$	101	0	R

* P = peak; T = trough.
† R = rising; F = falling; S = spilling; E = empty.

Col. 2: These are observed flows for the Westfield Little River, near Springfield, Mass., for March 1914 to February 1915. Operational replicates might have been used instead (Sec. 4-10).

Col. 3: The values 27, 30, 33, and 36 mg/sq mile = 0.89, 0.11, 1.09, and 1.18 mgd/sq mile respectively for 30.4 days/month. For a total flow of 462 mg/sq mile in 12 months the average flow is $462/365 = 1.27$ mg/sq mile, and for a total draft of 360 mg the development is $100 \times 360/462 = 78\%$.

Col. 4: Positive values are surpluses, negative values deficiencies.

Col. 5: P_1 is the first peak, and T_1 is the first trough in the range P_1P_2, where P_2 is the second higher peak; similarly T_2 is the second trough in the range $P_2(P_3)$ presumably.

Col. 6: The required maximum storage $S_m = \max(P_j - T_j) = P_m - T_m = P_1 - T_1 = 177 - 1 = 176$ in this case. The fact that $P_2 - T_2 = 279 - 103 = 176$

recommended is the development of runoff traces by the operational methods described in Sec. 4-10. Equation 4-56 is translated into a stochastic model of monthly runoff values by the following equation:

$$Q_{i+1} = \bar{Q}_{j+1} + \beta_j(Q_i - \bar{Q}_j) + t_i\sigma_{j+1}(1 - \rho_j^2)^{\frac{1}{2}} \tag{8-2}$$

where Q_i is the runoff during month i and Q_{i+1} is the estimated runoff during month $i + 1$, both reckoned from the start of the operational sequence; $\bar{Q}_j$ is the expected, i.e., the mean value of record during month j and $\bar{Q}_{j+1}$, similarly, the expected or mean value of record during month $j + 1$ within a repetitive cycle of 12 months; β_j is the regression or, in this case, recursion coefficient for estimating flow in month $j + 1$ from flow in month j; t_i is a random normal deviate with zero mean and unit variance taken from a table of random deviates; σ_{j+1} is the standard deviation of flows in month $j + 1$; and ρ_j is the correlation coefficient between the runoff in month j and month $j + 1$. Equation 8-2, as suggested by Thomas and Fiering, therefore characterizes a circular random walk, a model in which the first two terms on the right-hand side of the equation establish a linear relationship between the flows in month $i + 1$ and i and the third term is a random additive component or stochastic operator.

The index j can run *cyclically* from 1 to 12 (one year of 12 monthly flows); the index i *sequentially* from zero to any wanted number of months such as $50 \times 12 = 600$ months for an hydraulic structure or system with an expected life of 50 years, for example, or $600 \times 10 = 6000$ months for 10 sets of 50-year sequences. Therefore the index j refers to observed or sample data; the index i to operational traces. Given a table of random deviates and the $4 \times 12 = 48$ parameters ($\bar{Q}_j$, σ_j, and β_j for each of 12 monthly flows and ρ_j for each pair of consecutive months), the computer calculation of Q_{i+1} becomes straightforward.

Example 8-1.   From the recorded monthly mean runoff values shown in Col. 2, Table 8-1, find the required storage for the estimated rates of draft listed in Col. 3, Table 8-1.

For variable drafts and inclusion of varying allowances for evaporation from the water surface created by the impoundage, the analytical method possesses distinct advantages over the graphical method. The principal

---

also implies that there is seasonal rather than over-year storage. Storage at the end of month i is $S_i = \min \{S_M, [S_{i-1} + (Q_i - D_i)]\}$; for example, in line 2, $S_M = 176$ and $[S_{i-1} + (Q_i - D_i)] = 67 + 95 = 162$, or $S_i = 162$; in line 3, however, $S_M = 176$ and $[S_{i-1} + (Q_i - D_i)] = 126 + 95 = 221$ or $S_i = S_M = 176$.

Col. 7: The flow wasted $W_i = \max \{0, [(Q_i - D_i) - (S_M - S_{i-1})]\}$; for example, line 3, $(Q_i - D_i) - (S_m - S_{i-1}) = 15 - (176 - 162) = 1$ or $W_i = 1$; in line 3 of the second series, however, $(Q_i - D_i) - (S_m - S_{i-1}) = 15 - (176 - 176) = 15$. There is no negative waste.

value of the Rippl method, indeed, is not for the estimation of storage requirements but for determining the yield of catchment areas upon which storage reservoirs are already established.

8-4 Design Storage

Except for occasional series of dry years and very high developments, seasonal storage generally suffices in the well-watered regions of North America. Water is plentiful, stream flows do not vary greatly from year to year, reservoirs generally refill within the annual hydrologic cycle, and it does not pay to go in for high or complete development of catchment areas. In semiarid regions, on the other hand, water is scarce, stream flows fluctuate widely from year to year, runoff of wet years must be conserved for use during dry years, and it pays to go in for high developments. In these circumstances, operational records of adequate length become important along with machine computation.

Given a series of storage values for the flows observed or generated statistically, the engineer must decide which value he will use. Shall it be the highest on record, or the second, third, or fourth highest? Obviously, the choice depends upon the degree of protection to be afforded against water shortage. This must be fitted into drought experience, which is a function of the length of record examined. To arrive at a reasonable answer, he may resort to a statistical analysis of the arrayed storage values and an economically justifiable design storage. Storage values equaled or exceeded but once in 20, 50, or 100 years, i.e., 5, 2, and 1% of the time, are often considered. For water supply, Hazen[3] suggested employing the 5% value in ordinary circumstances. In other words, design storage should be adequate to compensate for a drought of a severity not expected to occur oftener than once in 20 years. In still drier years, it may be necessary to curtail the use of water, by limiting, or prohibiting, lawn sprinkling and car washing, for example.

Restricting water use is irksome to the public and a poor way to run a public utility. As a practical matter, moreover, use must be cut down well in advance of anticipated exhaustion of the supply. It would seem logical to consider not only the frequency of curtailment but also the depletion at which conservation should begin. In practice, the *iron ration* generally lies between 20 and 50% of the total water stored. Requiring a 25% reserve for the drought that occurs about once in 20 years is reasonable. An alternative is a storage allowance for the drought to be expected once in 100 years. This is slightly less in magnitude than the combination of a 25% reserve with a once-in-20-years risk.

[3] Allen Hazen, Storage to Be Provided in Impounding Reservoirs, *Trans. Am. Soc. Civil Engrs.*, **77**, 1539 (1914).

In undeveloped areas, few records are even as long as 20 years. Estimation of the 5, 2, and 1% frequencies, or of recurrence intervals of 20, 50, and 100 years, then requires extrapolation from available data. Probability plots lend themselves well to this purpose. However, they must be used with discretion. Where severe droughts in the record extend over several years and require annual rather than seasonal storages, the resulting series of storage values becomes nonhomogeneous and is no longer strictly subject to ordinary statistical interpretations. They can be made reasonably homogeneous by including, besides all truly seasonal storages, not only all true annual storages, but also those seasonal storages that would have been identified within the periods of annual storage if the drought of the preceding year or years had not been measured. Plots of recurrence intervals should include minor storages as well as major ones. The results of these statistical analyses are then conveniently reduced to a set of draft-storage-frequency curves.

Example 8-2.   Examination of the 25-year record of runoff from an eastern stream[4] shows that the storages listed in Table 8-2 are needed in successive years to maintain a draft of 750,000 gpd per sq mile.

Table 8-2   Storage Requirements (Example 8-2)

Order of year	1	2	3	4	5	6	7	8	9	10	11	12	13
Calculated storage, mg	47	39	104	110	115	35	74	81	124	29	37	82	78
Order of year	14	15	16	17	18	19	20	21	22	23	24	25	
Calculated storage, mg	72	10	117	51	61	8	102	65	73	20	53	88	

Estimate the design storage requirement probably reached or exceeded but once in 20, 50, and 100 years.

1. The 25 calculated storage values arrayed in order of magnitude are plotted on arithmetic-probability paper in Fig. 8-2 at $100k/26 = 3.8$, 7.7, 11.5%, etc. A straight line of best fit is identified in this instance, the arithmetic mean storage being $\mu = 67$ mg and the standard deviation $\sigma = 33$ mg.

The storage requirements reached or exceeded once in 20, 50, and 100 years, or 5, 2, and 1% of the time, are read as 123, 137, and 146 mg respectively. Probability paper is used because it offers a rational basis for projecting the information beyond the period of experience. The once-in-20-years requirement with 25% reserve suggests a design storage of $123/0.75 = 164$ mg per sq mile of drainage area.

3. It should be noted that the coefficient of variation of the calculated storage $c_v = 100 \times 33/67 = 50\%$ is more than twice the variability of runoff ($c_v = 22\%$) for closely the same period of observation (Example 7-1).

4. For comparison with other river records, draft and storage may be expressed in terms of the mean annual flow (MAF); storage may also be expressed in terms of daily draft. For a mean annual flow of 26.6 in., or $26.6 \times 0.0477 = 1.27$ mgd per sq mile (Example 7-1).

[4] The Westfield Little River near Springfield, Mass., for the years 1906 to 1930.

(a) Draft = 750,000 gpd/sq mile = 100 × 0.750/1.27 = 59% of MAF.

(b) Storage requirement equalled or exceeded once in 20 years = 123 mg/sq mile, or (100 × 123)/(1,27 × 365) = 27% of MAF.

(c) Storage requirement = 123/0.750 = 164 days of draft, or nearly half a year when 10 days are added to compensate for the use of monthly averages rather than daily stream flows.

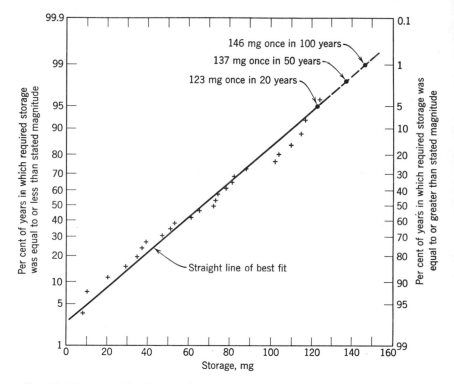

Fig. 8-2. Frequency distribution of required storage plotted on arithmetic-probability paper.

When more than one reservoir is built on a stream, the overflow from each impoundage passes to the reservoir next below in the valley, together with the runoff from the intervening watershed. The amount of overflow is determined from the storage analysis for each year or for the critical year. If the reservoirs are operated jointly and those downstream are drawn on first, all reservoirs may be considered to be combined at the most-downstream location, provided the area tributary to each reservoir is large enough to fill its reservoir during the season of heavy runoff. The last-mentioned point requires special study.

8-5   Generalized Storage Values

Hazen[5] has shown by an analysis of countrywide information that it is possible to base regional storage requirements on the mean annual flows of streams and their coefficients of variation. A partial summary of Hazen's generalized storage values is given in Table 8-3; and its use is illustrated in Example 8-3.

Table 8-3   Generalized Storage Values for Streams East of the Mississippi River, and in Oregon and Washington

(Both draft and storage are expressed in terms of the mean annual flow of the stream. The coefficient of variation in annual flows is designated c_v.)

Draft	

Draft	Storage for Stated Values of c_v						Deduction for 30 Days' Ground Storage
	0.20	0.25	0.30	0.35	0.40	0.45	
0.9	0.85	1.05	1.31	1.60	1.88	2.20	0.074
0.8	0.54	0.64	0.78	0.97	1.19	1.39	0.066
0.7	0.39	0.43	0.50	0.62	0.76	0.92	0.058
0.6	0.31	0.32	0.34	0.40	0.49	0.60	0.049
0.5	0.23	0.23	0.24	0.26	0.32	0.39	0.041

Example 8-3.   For the eastern stream dealt with in Fig. 8-1 and Example 8-2, find the generalized storage for a draft of 750,000 gpd per sq mile on the assumption that the coefficient of variation in annual flow is 0.22 and the mean annual flow 1.27 mgd (Example 7-1).

1. The draft is 59% of MAF as shown in Example 8-2.
2. For 59% and $c_v = 0.22$, Table 8-3 lists a storage of 0.30MAF or $0.30 \times 1.27 \times 365 = 139$ mg/sq mile.
3. For 30 days' ground storage, deduct, according to Table 8-3, 0.048 from 0.30, making it 0.25MAF or $0.25 \times 1.27 \times 365 = 116$ mg/sq mile.

The agreement between the results obtained by normal analytical procedures and by Hazen's generalized storage values is good.

8-6   Loss by Evaporation, Seepage, and Silting

When an impounding reservoir is filled, the hydrology of the inundated area and its immediate surroundings is changed in a number of respects; (1) the reservoir loses water by evaporation to the atmosphere and gains water by direct reception of rainfall; (2) rising and falling water levels alter the pattern of groundwater storage and movement into and out of the surrounding reservoir banks; (3) at high stages, water may seep from the reservoir through permeable soils into neighboring catchment areas

[5] Allen Hazen, *American Civil Engineering Practice*, R. W. Abbett, ed., John Wiley & Sons, New York, p. 1446, 1930, p. 18–09, 1956, as revised by Richard Hazen.

and so be lost to the area of origin; and (4) quiescence encourages sub-sidence of settleable suspended solids and silting of the reservoir.

Water-Surface Response.   The response of the new water surface is to establish new hydrological equilibria (1) through loss of the runoff once coming from the land area flooded by the reservoir Qa (closely), where Q is the areal rate of runoff of the original watershed, and a is the water surface area of the reservoir; and through evaporation from the water surface Ea, where E is the areal rate of evaporation; (2) through gain of rainfall on the water surface Ra, where R is the areal rate of rainfall. The net rate of loss or gain is $[R - (Q + E)]a$; a negative value records a net loss and a positive value a net gain.

Individual factors vary within the annual hydrologic cycle and from year to year. They can be measured. Exact calculations, however, are commonly handicapped by inadequate data on evaporation. Required hydrological information should come from local or nearby observation stations, areas of water surface being determined from contour maps of the reservoir site. The mean annual water surface, normally about 90% of the reservoir area at spillway level, is sometimes substituted to simplify calculations.

For convenience, the water-surface response is expressed in one of the following ways:

1. Revised runoff: $Q_r = Q - (Q + E - R)(a/A)$ (8-3)
2. Equivalent draft: $D_e = (Q + E - R)(a/A)$ (8-4)
3. Effective catchment area: $A_e = A - a[1 - (R - E)/Q]$ (8-5)

Here A is the total catchment area and a the reservoir surface area, and the values obtained are used as follows in recalculating storage require-ments: Q_r replaces Q; $D + D_e$ replaces D; and A_e replaces A. A fourth allowance calls for raising the flow line of the reservoir by $Q + E - R$ expressed in units of length yearly. In rough approximation the spillway level is raised by a foot or two in the eastern United States.

Example 8-4.   A mean draft of 30.0 mgd is to be developed from a catchment area of 40.0 sq miles. First calculations ask for a reservoir area of 1500 acres at flowline. The mean annual rainfall is 47.0 in., the mean annual runoff 27.0 in., and the mean annual evaporation 40.0 in. Find (1) the revised mean annual runoff, (2) the equivalent mean draft, (3) the equivalent land area, and (4) the adjusted flowline.

1. By Eq. 8-3, the revised annual runoff is: $Q_r = 27.0 - (27.0 + 40.0 - 47.0)0.9 \times 1500/(640 \times 40.0) = 27.0 - 1.1 = 25.9$ in.

2. By Eq. 8-4, the equivalent mean draft is: $D_e = 1.1$ in., or 52,000 gpd/sq mile, and the effective draft is $30.0 + 40.0 \times 0.052 = 32.1$ mgd.

3. By Eq. 8-5, the equivalent land area is: $A_e = 40.0 - (0.9 \times 1500/640) \times [1 - (47.0 - 40.0)/27.0] = 40.0 - 1.6 = 38.4$ sq miles.

4. The adjusted flowline is: $Q + E - R = 27.0 + 40.0 - 47.0 = 20$ in., equaling $20 \times 0.9 = 18$ in. at spillway level.

Seepage. If the valley enclosing a reservoir is underlain by porous strata, water may be lost by seepage. Subsurface exploration alone can foretell how much. Seepage is not necessarily confined to the dam site. It may occur wherever the sides and bottom of the reservoir are sufficiently permeable to permit water to escape through the surrounding hills.

Silting. Soil erosion on the watershed causes reservoir silting. Both are undesirable. Erosion destroys arable lands. Silting destroys useful storage. How bad conditions are in a given catchment area depends principally upon soil and rock types, ground surface slopes, vegetal cover, methods of cultivation, and storm-rainfall intensities.

Silt accumulations cannot be removed economically from reservoirs by any means so far devised. Dredging is expensive, and attempts to flush out deposited silt by opening scour valves in dams are fruitless. Scour only produces gullies in the silt. In favorable circumstances, however, much of the heaviest load of suspended silt can be guided through the reservoir by opening large sluices installed for this purpose. Flood flows are thereby selected for storage in accordance with their quality as well as their volume.

Reduction of soil erosion is generally a long-range undertaking. Involved are: proper farming methods, such as contour plowing; terracing of hillsides; reforestation or afforestation; cultivation of permanent pastures; prevention of gully formation through construction of check dams or debris barriers, and revetment of stream banks.

In the design of impounding reservoirs for silt-bearing streams, suitable allowance must be made for loss of capacity by silting. Understandably, deposition is most severe in reservoirs that are large in volume relative to inflow; more especially impoundments serving flashy and therefore strongly erosive streams. The proportion of sediment retained is called its *trap efficiency*. A simple calculation will show that 2000 mg per l of suspended solids equals 8.3 tons per mg and that an acre-foot of silt weighs almost 1500 tons if its unit weight is 70 lb per cu ft. In some parts of the United States,[6] the volume of silt V_s in acre-feet deposited annually can be approximated by the equation

$$V_s = cA^n \qquad (8\text{-}6)$$

where A is the size of the drainage area in square miles, and c and n are coefficients with a value of $n = 0.77$ for southwestern streams and values of c varying from 0.43 through 1.7 to 4.8 for low, average, and high deposition respectively, the corresponding values for southeastern streams

[6] For basic information, see H. M. Eakin, Silting of Reservoirs, *U.S. Dept. Agr. Tech. Bull.*, 524, 1939, and J. E. Jenkins, C. E. Moak, and D. A. Okun, Sedimentation in Reservoirs in the Southeast, *Trans. Am. Soc. Civil Engrs.*, **III, 68,** 3133 (1961).

being $c = 0.44$ only and $n = 1.0$. The similarity of this empirical relationship to a flood-flow formula is not surprising. Understandably, the magnitudes of c and n, here reported, apply only to the regions for which they were developed.

A plot of trap efficiency against the proportion of the mean annual flow stored in a reservoir traces curves quite similar to curves for the expected performance of settling basins of varying effectiveness (Vol. 2). Close to 100% of the sediment transported by influent streams may be retained in reservoirs storing a full year's tributary flow. Trap efficiency drops to a point between 65 and 85% when the storage ratio is reduced to 0.5 (half a year's inflow) and to 30 to 60% when the storage ratio is lowered to 0.1 (5 weeks' inflow). Silting is often fast when reservoirs are first placed in service and may be expected to proceed towards a steady state as time goes on. An annual silting rate of 1.0 acre-ft per sq mile of watershed corresponds roughly to a yearly reduction in storage of 0.3 mg per sq mile. because an acre 3 ft deep is closely 1 mg.

8-7 Area and Volume of Reservoirs

The surface areas and volumes of water at given horizons are found from a contour map of the reservoir site. Areas enclosed by each contour line are planimetered, and volumes between contour lines are calculated. The *average-end-area method* is generally good enough for the attainable precision of measurements.

For uniform contour intervals h and successive contour areas $a_0, a_1, \ldots a_n$, the volume V of water stored up to the nth contour is

$$V = \tfrac{1}{2}h[(a_0 + a_1) + (a_1 + a_2) + \cdots + (a_{n-1} + a_n)]$$
$$= \tfrac{1}{2}h\left(a_0 + a_n + 2\sum_1^{n-1} a\right) \tag{8-7}$$

For general use, surface areas and volumes are commonly plotted against contour elevations as in Fig. 8-3. It should be noted that volumes must be determined from the surface-area curve by planimetering the area enclosed between the curve and its ordinate.[7] For impounding reservoirs, the volume curve is approximated mathematically by the equation

$$V = cH^m \tag{8-8}$$

where H is the height of water at the dam and c and m are coefficients for a given reservoir site. Consequently, the area curve is approximated by the

---

[7] The vertical scale implied by elevations generally leads engineers to plot elevations as ordinates. Figure 8-3, therefore, is not in consonance with the injunction to plot as the ordinate the variable to be found.

first derivative, or

$$A = cmH^{m-1} \tag{8-9}$$

Plotted on logarithmic scales, both curves approximate straight lines from which c and m can be determined. The indicated magnitude of m is about 3.

In reservoir operation, a small amount of water lies below the invert of the reservoir outlet. Constituting the dregs of the impoundage, this water is of poor quality. The associated reduction in *useful storage* is offset, in

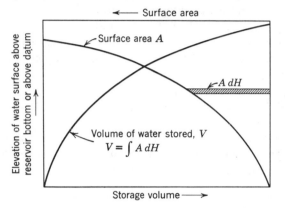

Fig. 8-3. Surface area of a reservoir and volume of water stored.

general, by bank storage released from the soil as the reservoir is drawn down. Moreover, the water below the outlet sill does form a conservation pool for fish and wildlife.

Surface areas and volumes enter not only into the solution of hydrological problems but also into the management of water quality such as the control of algae by copper sulfate.

8-8   Spillway Capacity and Flood Routing

Impounding reservoirs must have spillways that can safely discharge the maximum peak flood the storage works are expected to pass. To be on the safe side, entrant floods are assumed to occur when the reservoir is full. Before the maximum head on the spillway can be developed, however, flood waters will back up in the reservoir and fill the space between spillway level and flood crest. As a result, the flood peak is reduced, often by enough to lower the required discharge capacity of the spillway appreciably. However, if construction of the reservoir deprives the stream of significant amounts of valley storage within the reservoir site, studies of flood routing must make proper allowances for lost storage.

In other respects, retardation of floods by storage above spillway level is a function of reservoir inflow rates I, water storage S above spillway level, and reservoir outflow rates Q. These variables are so irregular that they cannot be generalized mathematically. In the circumstances, engineers proceed to stepwise analyses of pertinent hydraulic sequences: varying inflow, changing water level, and varying outflow. For a specified time element, Δt,

$$Q\,\Delta t = I\,\Delta t - \Delta S \qquad (8\text{-}10)$$

Assuming average rates of inflow and outflow closely equal to the arithmetic means of the rates obtaining at the beginning and end of time intervals Δt, mechanical integration proceeds to evaluate $Q\,\Delta t$ as $\Delta t(Q_k + Q_{k+1})/2$; $I\,\Delta t$ as $\Delta t(I_k + I_{k+1})/2$; and ΔS as $(S_{k+1} - S_k)$. Here the subscripts k and $(k+1)$ denote successive instants of time differing by Δt. Substituting in Eq. 8-10 and bringing associated outflow and storage terms together:[8]

$$\left(\frac{S_{k+1}}{\Delta t} + \frac{1}{2}Q_{k+1}\right) = \left(\frac{S_k}{\Delta t} - \frac{1}{2}Q_k\right) + \tfrac{1}{2}(I_k + I_{k+1}) \qquad (8\text{-}11)$$

Equation 8-11 provides a useful means for determining the outflow pattern produced by a given inflow pattern. The resulting *flood routing* procedure is best explained by an example (Example 8-5).

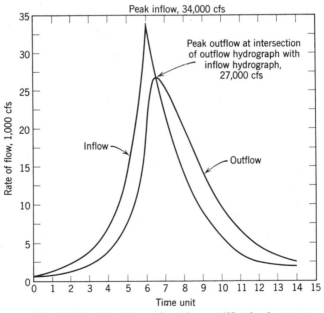

Fig. 8-4. Flood routing or flood-flow modification by storage.

[8] Spillway discharge $Q = CL(H - H_0)^{3/2}$ by the common weir formula, while storage $S = V - V_0 = c(H^m - H_0^m)$ as indicated in Eq. 8-8. Here H_0 is the water depth at spillway level, $H - H_0$ the spillway head, and L the weir length.

Example 8-5. From the predicted hydrograph of a stream in flood (Fig. 8-4), construct the outflow hydrograph to be expected from a reservoir of known storage characteristics impounding the stream under the runoff conditions assumed to prevail during the flood.

The following assumptions are made: length of spillway tentatively selected $L = 250$ ft; appropriate weir coefficient $C = 3.8$; and time interval $\Delta t = 3$ hr $= 10,800$ sec.

1. Determine, for increasing heads H, the outflow Q and storage S above spillway level. To do this, the surface area A of the reservoir must be found from a curve like that in Fig. 8-3.

2. Calculate the corresponding functional rates of storage $(S/\Delta t)$, $[(S/\Delta t) - \frac{1}{2}Q]$, and $[(S/\Delta t) + \frac{1}{2}Q]$ as in Table 8-4.

Table 8-4   Calculation of Functional Rates of Storage (Example 8-5)

Head on Spillway H, ft	Reservoir Area, A acres	Calculated Outflow, Q cfs	Calculated Storage S above Spillway level, acre-ft	Functional Rates of Storage		
				$S/\Delta t$, cfs	$S/\Delta t - \frac{1}{2}Q$, cfs	$S/\Delta t + \frac{1}{2}Q$, cfs
(1)	(2)	(3)	(4)	(5)	(6)	(7)
0	670	0	0	0	0	0
1	700	950	685	2,760	2,285	3,235
2	730	2,680	1,400	5,650	4,310	6,990
3	760	4,940	2,145	8,650	6,180	11,120
4	790	7,600	2,920	11,770	7,970	15,570
5	820	10,620	3,725	15,020	9,710	20,330
6	850	13,950	4,560	18,390	11,415	25,365
7	885	17,600	5,425	21,900	13,100	30,700
8	920	21,500	6,330	25,500	14,750	36,250
9	960	25,700	7,270	29,300	16,450	42,150
10	1,000	30,100	8,250	33,300	18,300	48,400

Col. 1: Assumed values; heads differing by 1 ft.
Col. 2: From area curve similar to Fig. 8-3.
Col. 3: From $Q = CLH^{3/2} = 3.8 \times 250 \times H^{3/2}$ or straight-line plot on log-log paper (Fig. 8-5).
Col. 4: By Eq. 8-7: $\frac{1}{2}h[A_0 + A_n) + 2\sum_{1}^{n-1} A]$.
Col. 5: Col. 4 $\times$ 43,560/10,800 = 4.03 $\times$ Col. 4.
Col. 6: Col. 5 $-$ $\frac{1}{2}$ Col. 3.
Col. 7: Col. 5 $+$ $\frac{1}{2}$ Col. 3 = Col. 6 + Col. 3.

3. Plot the rates of discharge and storage against the heads on the spillway. This is done in Fig. 8-5. The resulting curves, known as *routing curves* and *discharge curves*, allow the stepwise graphical determination of spillway heads and outflows at the chosen time intervals, 3 hr in this instance.

4. In Fig. 8-5 add the average rate of inflow $\frac{1}{2}(I_k + I_{k+1})$ for each specified time interval to the corresponding value of $[(S_k/\Delta t) - \frac{1}{2}Q_k]$ in accordance with Eq. 8-11, and find at the resulting magnitude of $[(S_{k+1}/\Delta t) - \frac{1}{2}Q_{k+1}]$ the spillway head and dis- charge that must obtain in order to satisfy these relationships. To establish a starting point, it is assumed that the reservoir is in equilibrium at the initial rate of inflow of 700 cfs shown in Fig. 8-4, the head on the spillway being

$$H = [Q/(CL)]^{2/3} = [700/(3.8 \times 250)]^{2/3} = 0.82 \text{ ft.}$$

Necessary calculations are shown in Table 8-5.

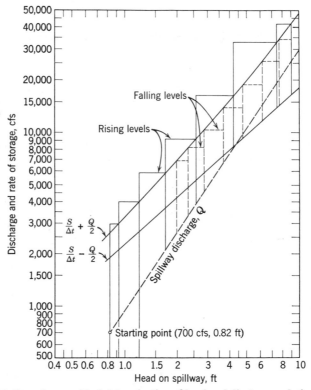

Fig. 8-5. Stepwise graphical determination of head and discharge relationships in routing a flood through an impounding reservoir. See Eq. 8-11: $[(S_{k+1}/\Delta t) + \frac{1}{2}Q_{k+1}] = [(S_k/\Delta t) - \frac{1}{2}Q_k] + \frac{1}{2}(I_k + I_{k+1})$.
Example: $(S_{k+1}/\Delta t + \frac{1}{2}Q_{k+1}) = 1,900 + 1,050 = 2,950$; $H = 0.92$ and $(S_{k+1}/\Delta t + \frac{1}{2}Q_{k+1}) = 2,100 + 1,900 = 4,000$; $H = 1.2$.

5. Plot the calculated outflow hydrograph against the observed inflow hydrograph. This is done in Fig. 8-5. It is seen that storage above spillway level lowers the peak flow from 34,000 cfs to 27,000 cfs, i.e., to 80% of its uncontrolled magnitude. Ac- cordingly, the head on the spillway is 9.2 ft (Fig. 8-5).

Table 8-5   Calculation of Reservoir Outflows (Example 8-5)

Time Number	Observed Inflow I, cfs	$\frac{1}{2}(I_k + I_{k+1})$ Average Inflow, cfs	$S/\Delta t - Q/2$ At Beginning of Time Interval	$S/\Delta t + Q/2$ At End of Time Interval	Head on Spillway, ft	Out-flow Q, cfs
(1)	(2)	(3)	(4)	(5)	(6)	(7)
0	700	......	......	......	0.817	700
1	1,400	1,050	1,900	2,950	0.920	840
2	2,400	1,900	2,100	4,000	1.20	1,250
3	4,000	3,200	2,700	5,900	1.70	2,100
4	7,000	5,500	3,700	9,200	2.55	3,870
5	15,000	11,000	5,400	16,400	4.20	8,170
6	34,000	24,500	8,300	32,800	7.40	19,100
7	22,000	28,000	13,700	41,700	8.95	25,400
8	14,000	18,000	16,200	34,200	7.65	20,010
9	9,000	11,500	14,200	25,700	6.10	14,300
10	6,000	7,500	11,500	· 19,000	4.70	9,680
11	3,400	4,700	9,300	14,000	3.70	6,760
12	2,500	2,950	7,400	10,350	2.85	4,570
13	2,200	2,350	5,900	8,250	2.30	3,310
14	2,000	2,100	4,850	6,950	1.95	2,590

Col. 1: Each time interval is 3 hours.

Col. 2: The observed inflow is taken from the chosen flood hydrograph of the stream before impoundage. See Fig. 8-4.

Col. 3: Average of successive values in Col. 2.

Col. 4: Value of $[(S/\Delta t) - \frac{1}{2}Q]$ at beginning of time interval read during construction of Fig. 8-5.

Col. 5: Value of $[(S/\Delta t) + \frac{1}{2}Q]$ at end of time interval = Col. 4 + Col. 3 in accordance with Eq. 8-11.

Cols. 6 and 7. Read from Fig. 8-5 with exception of the initial values: 0.82 ft and 700 cfs. These identify the starting point of the step integration.

The principles involved in this as well as numerous other methods of flood routing can be put to use also in studies of the effect of channel storage, detention or retardation basins, and other types of storage upon flood flows and flows in general.

A rough determination of whether it will pay to perform calculations such as these can be made from generalized estimates suggested by Fuller[9] (Table 8-6). If the outflow is reduced to 90% or less of the inflow, more accurate calculations are normally justified.

[9] W. E. Fuller, Flood Flows, *Trans. Am. Soc. Civil Engrs.*, **70**, 564 (1914).

Table 8-6   Generalized Estimates of Reservoir Outflows

Ratio of storage above spillway level to flood flow in 24 hours, %	5	10	20	30	40	50	60	70
Ratio of peak outflow to peak inflow, %	99	97	93	86	77	65	53	40

Example 8-6.   The maximum 24-hour flood flow in Example 8-5 is 27,000 acre-ft. For a maximum allowable head on the spillway of 10 ft and a storage above spillway level of 8250 acre-ft, find the ratio of peak outflow to peak inflow from Fuller's values (Table 8-6):

1. Ratio of storage above spillway level to 24-hour flood $100 \times 8,250/27,600 = 30\%$.
2. From Fuller's values, ratio of peak outflow to peak inflow $= 86\%$.
3. The value ascertained in Example 8-5 was 80%, the maximum head on the spillway being 9.2 ft.

Because Fuller's outflow ratio is less than 90%, a more accurate determination is warranted.

The principles set forth in the preceding sections of this chapter are applicable also to the storage and regulation of storm-water runoff collected by combined municipal drainage schemes. Storm-water stand-by or holding tanks used for this purpose may be incorporated in the collecting system itself or become auxiliary units in sewage-treatment works (Sec. 3-6).

CHAPTER 9

Groundwater Flow

9-1   Groundwater Sources

The hydrology and hydraulics of groundwater flows have received some attention in Secs. 2-6 and 6-9 to 6-11. The present chapter evaluates the hydrologic, geologic, and hydraulic properties of groundwater sources more closely and gives its attention to their influence on groundwater capture for water supply. It will be apparent, too, that some of the properties have a bearing (1) on the storage of surface waters and runoff and (2) on the escape of water from conduits or drains, on the one hand, and its entrance into them, on the other hand.

The factors governing the availability of groundwater, although they are difficult to evaluate, are no less real and measurable than the factors determining the yield of surface supplies. By contrast, however, available quantitative information is generally meager and fragmentary. Indirect evidence, principally of a geologic nature, must be adduced to arrive at useful conclusions. For major developments, the services of a competent geologist are, indeed, essential. In the absence of long records of the behavior of developed groundwater sources or extensive scientific investigations, the engineer must base his decisions on past experience with similar supplies and upon the behavior of test wells.

9-2   Groundwater Geology

The wide variation in texture and stratigraphy of the earth's crust is reflected in the manner of occurrence of both free and confined groundwaters. The water table may lie at or near the earth's surface as in streams and swamps, or it may be several thousand feet down. Groundwater may flow through caverns, crevices, and solution passages at velocities comparable to the velocities of turbulent surface streams (1 or more fps), or it may move in laminar flow through the capillary interstices of soils and rocks at velocities of only a few feet a year. Aquifers may be thick and isotropic[1] as well as homogeneous, or they may consist of a variety of layers, lenses, and tortuous bands of different materials. Detailed acquaintance with the geology of groundwater areas is essential to a knowledge of the capacity of water-bearing formations. Surface geology and exposures by mining, quarrying, and related operations must be supplemented by *well logs*. These are records of the nature and depth of the strata encountered in sinking wells.[2] Combined with measurements of capacity, logs furnish the most important information to be had without the aid of test-well or geophysical reconnaissance.

Geologically, the earth's crust is made up of rocks and soils. The rocks are igneous, sedimentary, and metamorphic in origin; the soils are derived from the rocks by weathering of rock exposures.

9-3 Water-Bearing Rocks

The *intrusive igneous* rocks are dense in texture and would be barren of water were it not for rock fissures and cracks. The width of resulting openings is generally small (seldom more than 1 mm), and the openings die out with depth. The numbers of inclined joints intersected by wells decreases rapidly, from about 4 per 100 ft down to the 100-ft level to less than 1 per 100 ft below the 400-ft level. Understandably, therefore, the groundwater from intrusive rocks is derived from depths that generally do not exceed 300 ft. Of the intrusive rocks, basalt is a good aquifer, rhyolite a poor one. Weathering of the granites produces the silica sands and gravels that, after transportation, abrasion, and sorting by wind and water, form the most productive water-bearing soils.

The *extrusive igneous* rocks may be very porous and contain cracks, holes, and extensive caverns. Some lava formations[3] yield water in abundance.

Of the four common varieties of *sedimentary* rocks (limestones and related calcareous rocks, shales, sandstones, and conglomerates), the *limestones* are usually dense and impervious. However, they are the most soluble of all rocks and, where they have been subjected to the leaching action of water containing dissolving carbon dioxide or organic acids, they

---

[1] Possessing the same properties in all directions; from the Greek *isos*, equal, and *tropic*, changing.

[2] Many states require the keeping of well logs and their filing with a state authority or the U.S. Geological Survey.

[3] For example, in the northwestern United States and the Hawaiian Islands.

are honeycombed by solution passages and caverns. Underground streams and lakes are formed in the course of time, and these may overflow at the surface to create large springs.[4] *Shales*, produced by the consolidation of clays, are generally impervious and act as aquicludes. *Sandstones*, by contrast, may be very pervious. Their water-bearing capacity depends upon the extent to which the pores of constituent sand grains are filled with cementing materials. Quartzites, composed of silica sands completely filled with cementing siliceous materials, are like granites in density and imperviousness; loosely cemented sandstones are among the most productive aquifers. The water-bearing capacity of the consolidated or cemented heterogeneous mixtures of materials that constitute *conglomerates* varies considerably. As a rule, they are quite tight. Good aquifers are sometimes encountered in limestones and sandstones at depths in excess of a mile. However, most groundwater developments are less than 2000 ft deep.

None of the *metamorphic* rocks is an important water producer. *Marble*, like the limestone from which it is created, is soluble and may yield water from solution channels. *Slates* and *schists*, which originate in shales, are relatively impervious, but they transmit some water along joints, cleavage cracks, and fractures. *Gneiss* resembles, in its structural and water-bearing properties, the intrusive granites from which it is generally derived.

In North America, the important water-bearing rock formations lie at considerable depths below the earth's surface and generally carry water under artesian pressure.[5] The supplies obtained from cavernous limestones near the surface are an exception.

9-4 Water-Bearing Soils

Although the water-bearing rocks of the United States are important sources of water, the areas served by them are small within the country as a whole. Greater yields of water are derived from the soils of the overburden in which free and artesian conditions of flow exist.

---

[4] Examples are numerous, particularly in Florida and in the Ozarks of Missouri and Arkansas.

[5] The great artesian systems of the United States are: (1) the extensive paleozoic system of the east-central region, where shales confine water in sandstones and limestones, e.g., the well-known Potsdam sandstone in Wisconsin and northern Illinois; (2) the Roswell system in New Mexico, where a cavernous permian limestone furnishes large quantities of water for irrigation; (3) the Atlantic and Gulf coastal plain systems, in which dipping formations of pervious cretaceous and tertiary sands and gravels or sandstones and limestones are interbedded with clays or shales; and (4) the cretaceous artesian systems of the Great Plains, in which water is confined under great pressure in extensive sandstones lying below thick, dense shales, e.g., the productive Dakota sandstone that underlies parts of Wyoming, Colorado, North and South Dakota, Nebraska, and Minnesota.

The size classification of soil particles developed by the Bureau of Chemistry and Soils of the U.S. Department of Agriculture and by the International Society of Soil Science is shown in Table 9-1.

Sands and gravels are by far the most important water-bearing soils. They have high specific yields and permeabilities (Sec. 9-6) and are ordinarily so situated that replenishment is rapid. Uniform or well-sorted sands and gravels are the most productive; mixed materials containing clay are least so—for example, boulder clay deposited beneath ice sheets. Transported

Table 9-1   Size Classification of Soil Grains

Diameter of Grain, cm

Soil	U.S. Dept. of Agriculture	International Society of Soil Science
Fine gravel (grit)	2×10^{-1} to 10^{-1}	
Coarse sand	10^{-1} to 5×10^{-2}	2×10^{-1} to 2×10^{-2}
Medium sand	5×10^{-2} to 2.5×10^{-2}	
Fine sand	2.5×10^{-2} to 10^{-2}	2×10^{-2} to 2×10^{-3}
Very fine sand	10^{-2} to 5×10^{-3}	
Silt	5×10^{-3} to 5×10^{-4}	2×10^{-3} to 2×10^{-4}
Clay	5×10^{-4} or less	2×10^{-4} or less

material is generally more permeable than material in immediate contact with the mother rock. Most sand and gravel beds have been deposited in shallow, active water: (1) in seas, lakes, or river beds as *alluvia*; (2) at the mouth of canyons as *outwash cones*; or (3) along the edge of retreating ice sheets as *outwash plains*. Because the origin of these soils and the depth and motion of the transporting water have varied in time, the deposits generally include alternating layers of varying size and grading. Beds deposited in lakes and seas are often extensive; outwash cones or river channels usually contain relatively small lenses of sand and gravel confined between layers of less pervious materials.[6]

Clays and *silts*, although porous, are generally quite impervious. They are poor aquifers and significant only (1) when they confine or interfere with the movement of water through the more pervious soils and (2) when they supply water to permeable formations by consolidation.

[6] The largest supplies of groundwater in the United States come from the following sand and gravel deposits: (1) glacial outwash plains north of the Ohio and Missouri rivers and in New England; (2) valley fill in the western mountain region; (3) tertiary and quaternary deposits in the quaternary terrace and lowland deposits in the Atlantic and Gulf coastal plains.

Where rock outcrops at the surface, the rate of water intake is likely to be small. If, on the other hand, the rock is covered by porous and permeable soils, the rate of infiltration is often good, and the overburden becomes, in a sense, a reservoir from which water feeds steadily into the underlying rock. The thicker the water-bearing mantle, the greater, in general, is the safe yield from rocks as well as from the soil itself. Topography, or surface relief, is also important. The steeper the slope, the more effectively does it shed rainfall and runoff from melting snow. Valleys and outwash plains and cones not only accumulate the heaviest overburden but they are, ordinarily, areas of least slope and so in a position to intercept and retain abundant quantities of groundwater.

9-5 Geophysical Exploration

Geological formations differ in their gravitational, magnetic, seismic, electric, acoustic, and radioactive properties. These can be translated into geological terms from the known behavior of similar formations. Geophysical exploration or prospecting provides needed information. Variations in gravity and of the earth's magnetic field are measured with the aid of the gravity meter and the magnetometer. Although these instruments do not determine the presence of water itself, they suggest the presence and location of favorable geological structures. Acoustic and seismic methods measure the speed of travel of sound and shock waves through underground formations. Dependence of wave velocity upon the density of the materials through which it passes makes possible a geophysical analysis of the test area. The presence of water makes itself felt, too. Wave reflection is measured when interest is centered on deep strata, wave refraction when the water-bearing formation is near the surface of the earth (Fig. 9-1a).[7]

The apparent resistivity, ρ_a, of the ground is defined by the equation

$$\rho_a = RA/L \qquad (9\text{-}1)$$

where R is the measured resistance in ohms of a formation of length L and cross-section A normal to the direction of current flow. In saturated porous formations, the resistivity is governed primarily by water content in accordance with the equation

$$\rho_a/\rho_w = (3 - f)/2f \qquad (9\text{-}2)$$

where ρ_w is the resistivity of the water and f is the porosity ratio.

Resistivity of the formations and their contained water is determined by impressing a current on electrodes inserted in the ground and measuring

[7] Daniel Linehan and Scott Keith, Seismic reconnaissance for groundwater development, *J. New England Water Works Assoc.*, **63**, 76 (1949).

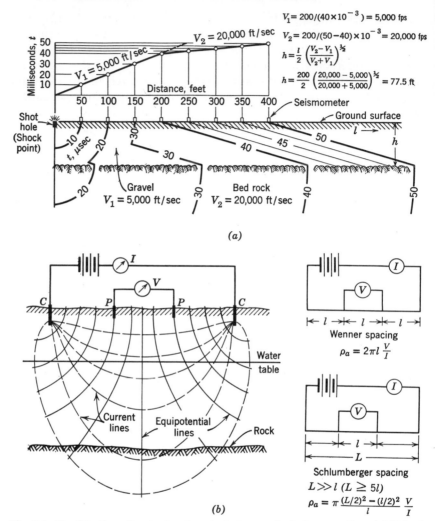

Fig. 9-1. Identification of water-bearing strata by geophysical prospecting. (a) Seismic refraction. (*After Linehan and Keith.*) (b) Electric resistivity. (*After Mooney and Wetzel.*)

the potential between two intermediate points. Mooney and Wetzel[8] have developed curve-matching techniques for interpreting the data obtained by the Wenner or third-point arrangement shown in Fig. 9-1b. Electrical resistivity surveys are most useful in identifying the boundaries between fresh water and salt water and in areas where the stratigraphy and properties of the formation are fairly well known.

[8] H. M. Mooney and W. W. Wetzel, *The Potentials about a Point Electrode and Apparent Resistivity Curves for a Two-, Three-, and Four-layered Earth*, University of Minnesota, Minneapolis, 1956.

9-6   Groundwater Hydrology

In the study of a particular groundwater source, surface collection areas and underground conduits and reservoirs must be identified, and hydrologic behavior of the system must be discovered. Estimates of safe yield require evaluation of the following factors: (1) the quantities of water added to the formation by infiltration of rain, melting snow and ice, and surface waters; (2) the volume of water stored within the isolated system as measured by the porosity, thickness, and areal extent of the water-bearing soil or rock formation; (3) the rate at which the water moves through the ground and can be withdrawn from it, which is a function of its permeability and available hydraulic gradients; and (4) the amount of water lost from the ground by evaporation and transpiration, by effluent seepage into streams and other surface bodies of water, by flow from springs, and by underground routes of escape. At the same time, the effect of pumping, or other induced withdrawal of water from the ground, must be taken into account. Withdrawal upsets the natural hydrologic and hydraulic balance, water levels fall, directions of movement change, return of water to the surface or to the atmosphere by natural processes may be reduced, and infiltration may be increased.

The General Hydrologic Equation.   Hydrological equilibrium is expressed by the following equation:

$$\Sigma R = \Sigma D + \Delta S \tag{9-3}$$

where ΣR denotes the various hydrological factors of recharge and ΣD those of discharge, ΔS being the associated change in storage volume. More specifically, the recharge is composed of:

1. Natural infiltration derived from rainfall and snowmelt.
2. Infiltration from surface bodies of water.
3. Underflow.
4. Leakage through confining layers or water displaced from them by compression.
5. Water derived from diffusion, charging, and water-spreading operations.

Conversely, the discharge includes:

1. Evaporation and transpiration.
2. Seepage into surface bodies of water.
3. Underflow.
4. Leakage through confining layers or absorbed by them through the reduction of compression.
5. Water withdrawn through wells and infiltration galleries or basins.

As shown in Eq. 9-3, determination of the safe yield of an aquifer is quite analogous to finding the permissible draft from a surface supply

(Sec. 8-2). The hydrological inventory of a water-producing area includes, in addition to evaluation of the three terms in Eq. 9-3, a consideration of rainfall and surface runoff. The larger the area, the greater are the difficulties of obtaining accurate measurements or close estimates of inventory components.[9]

Recharge and Discharge. When the bulk of the water received by an aquifer is derived from surface streams by infiltration, the progressive reduction in surface flow along the water course is the principal measure of recharge.[10] The intake of rain and melting snow is more difficult to determine. It requires a knowledge of losses by evaporation and transpiration and of the water needed to satisfy the field-moisture capacity or *specific retention* of the soil.

The amount of water entering the ground from diffusion, charging, spreading, and recycling operations is generally a matter of record or can be made so. Discharge of groundwater by evapotranspiration is confined to formations in which the capillary fringe rises to the root zone or the surface. Discharge of groundwater by seepage sustains the dry-weather flow of streams and may be determined from changes in dry-weather flow along a stream's course. The amount of water withdrawn through groundwater works is read from records of draft. Underflow and leakage may either recharge or discharge a basin, or do both. The difficulty of evaluating the degree of leakage and underflow does not lessen its importance.

In some basins in the arid west of the United States, natural discharge becomes negligible when groundwater levels are lowered by heavy pumping. Average recharge must then equal average withdrawal, if storage, as reflected by water levels, is not to continue downward towards exhaustion. Such situations can be examined by plotting a moving average (Sec. 4-9) of annual withdrawal against a moving average of annual change in water level for a statistically significant number of years. Average discharge and recharge should come into balance at the withdrawal rate for which there is no water-level change.

Storage. The volume of water within a saturated formation of rock or soil equals its pore space. This is generalized in terms of the *porosity*, or ratio f of pore, void, or interstitial volume to total volume of rock or soil. The *voids ratio* or ratio of pore volume to solid volume, $e = f/(1 - f)$, is also a useful concept in groundwater hydraulics and soil mechanics. As shown in Fig. 9-2, there are two limiting arrangements, or packings, of spherical particles of uniform diameter in contact with each other: the

---

[9] In the United States, experimental stations for the intensive study of groundwater hydrology are maintained by the Soil Conservation Service and the Forest Service. The publications of these services hold much of interest.

[10] This is true, for example, in some parts of the western U.S.

orthogonal, or cubic, and the rhombic, or rhombohedral. Freshly deposited silt may possess a very high porosity (up to 80%). A common porosity of natural sands and gravels is 40%. The value for sandstones is more nearly 20%. However, porosity is a static quality of rocks and soils. It is not of itself a measure of perviousness or permeability. These are dynamic qualities that have no meaning in the absence of flow (Sec. 9-7).

Not all the water stored in a geological formation can be withdrawn by normal engineering operations. Accordingly, there is a difference between total storage and useful storage. The quantity that will drain off by gravity is called the *specific yield*; its counterpart is the *specific retention*. Specific yields vary from zero for plastic clays to 30% or more for uniform sands and gravels. Most aquifers have specific yields of 10 to 20%.

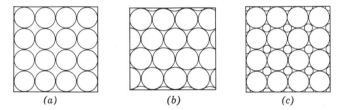

(a)   (b)   (c)

Fig. 9-2. Effect of arrangement and size variation of grains upon porosity. (*a*) Orthogonal packing; porosity = 47.64%. (*b*) Rhombic packing; porosity = 25.95%. (*c*) Two sizes, orthogonal; porosity 43.92%.

If the hydrological inventory is begun and ended at the same values of groundwater storage, specific yields need not be identified. In North America, water accumulates in the ground, as well as in surface reservoirs, from fall to spring and is depleted during the growing season. As previously stated, the U.S. Geological Survey selects September 30 as the end of the *water year*. At this time, annual depletion of groundwater generally stops and recharge begins. To the extent that storage is the same from year to year, the accuracy of annual inventories is improved. Changes in storage are based on recorded water levels in observation wells. Volumes are calculated from water-table contours or the piezometric surface.

The variation in the storage of an artesian basin is generally small. It is sometimes expressed as a *storage coefficient* or ratio of the volume of water released from the full depth of the aquifer through a unit area of its base when the piezometric surface of the basin drops by a unit of height. The range of values lies between 5×10^{-5} and 5×10^{-3}. Along with leakage through aquicludes, the relative volumes are small, but the associated absolute magnitudes may be appreciable when areas and pressure differences are large. Storage coefficients and specific yields become substantially identical when groundwater conditions are free.

Ground storage is relatively large, and deficits may be incurred over many years. Ultimately, however, they must be offset by recharge, if the source is not to fail.

9-7 Hydraulics of Groundwater

Water filtering into the ground passes downward to the zone of saturation before it moves laterally in the direction of greatest slope of the groundwater table or piezometric surface. This slope is the hydraulic gradient of underground flow. Like the hydraulic gradient of open channels and pipes, it is a measure of the frictional resistance to flow, the energy lost being dissipated as heat. Because recharge, discharge, and storage fluctuate, flow is both unsteady and nonuniform, and the hydraulic gradient is not stationary. During replenishment, the water table rises, the gradient steepens, and flow increases. During dry spells, the opposite takes place. Ordinarily, the hydraulic grade line slopes in the direction of the ground surface, but the degree of slope is not necessarily the same. Flow may be free as in an open channel or confined as in a pipe. Flow may be *laminar* when pores or crevices and associated velocities or Reynolds numbers are low. Flow may be *turbulent* when cracks or solution passages and associated velocities or Reynolds numbers are high.

An aquifer that offers little resistance to flow is called *pervious* or *permeable*; conversely, an aquifer that offers much resistance is called *impervious* or *impermeable*. The nature of the system of pores, rather than their relative volume, determines resistance to flow at given velocities. Permeability and porosity are not synonymous terms. For example, clays with porosities of 50% are quite impervious; sandstones with porosities of 15% or less are quite pervious.

In nature, the rate of groundwater movement and slope of the groundwater table, or piezometric surface, are not large. In aquifers of high yield, velocities of 5 to 60 ft a day are associated with hydraulic gradients of 10 to 20 ft per mile. Underflow through gravel deposits may travel several hundred feet per day, but flows as low as a few feet per year may also be economically useful.

9-8 Capillary Rise

Water is held above the true water table by capillary action and forms a capillary fringe. If the interstices are small, the quantity of water in this partially saturated layer of soil may be significantly large.

Surface tension, or intermolecular cohesion, determines the height to which water will rise in the capillary channels of fine-grained soils and porous rocks. As shown in Fig. 9-3, the capillary rise h of water of specific weight γ in contact with air of specific weight γ_a in a tube of diameter d

establishes a weight of water $\frac{1}{4}\pi d^2(\gamma - \gamma_a)h$ that must be supported by a force produced by the surface tension σ of the water being exerted along the line of contact of the water surface with the tube and forming a contact angle α with its vertical walls. The magnitude of this supporting force is $\pi d\sigma \cos \alpha$. Equating the weight of water to the supporting force and solving for the capillary rise,

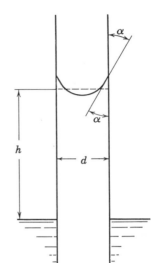

Fig. 9-3. Capillary rise of a liquid in a tube.

$$h = \frac{4\sigma \cos \alpha}{d(\gamma - \gamma_a)} \qquad (9\text{-}4)$$

For an air-water interface, a contact angle of zero degrees, which obtains in a glass tube that has been cleaned and moistened, and σ in dynes per centimeter, γ and γ_a equaling ρg and $\rho_a g$ respectively,

$$h = \frac{4\sigma}{gd(\rho - \rho_a)} = \frac{\sigma}{245d} \text{ cm} \qquad (9\text{-}5)$$

because the specific weight of air (1.25×10^{-3} gm/cm³ at 10 C) is so small and the specific weight of water is so close to unity.

Example 9-1. How high will water at a temperature of 10 C rise in a capillary tube 0.1 mm in diameter?

From Eq. 9-5 and for a surface tension of 74.2 dynes/cm (Table I-4):

$$h = \frac{74.2}{245 \times 0.01} = 30.3 \text{ cm} = 1 \text{ ft}$$

9-9   Darcy's Law

Although Hagen[11] and Poiseuille[12] were the first to propose that the velocity of flow of water and other liquids through capillary tubes is proportional to the first power of the hydraulic gradient, credit for verification of this observation and for its application to the flow of water through the ground or, more specifically, its filtration through sand, must go to

---

[11] Gotthilf Heinrich Ludwig Hagen (1797–1874), Ueber die Bewegung des Wassers in engen cylindrischen Röhren (On the flow of water in narrow cylindrical tubes), *Ann. Physik und Chemie*, **46**, 423 (1889).

[12] Jean Louis Poiseuille (1799–1869), French physician interested in the flow of fluid through arteries and veins, Recherches expérimentales sur le mouvement des liquides dans les tubes de très petits diamètres (Experimental investigations of the flow of liquids in tubes of very small diameter). *Roy. Acad. Sci. Inst. France Math. Phys. Sci., Mem.* **9**, 433 (1846). Translated by W. H. Herschel, Easton, Pa., 1940.

Darcy.[13] The relationship, known as Darcy's law, may be written

$$v = Ks \tag{9-6}$$

where v is not the actual pore velocity but the face or approach velocity, or the quantity of water flowing through a unit gross cross-sectional area; s is the gradient, or the loss of head per unit length in the direction of flow; and K is the coefficient of permeability (hydraulic conductivity) or the proportionality constant for water of a given temperature flowing through a given material. Because s is a dimensionless ratio, K has the dimensions of velocity and is in fact the velocity of flow associated with a hydraulic gradient of unity. Because the value of K varies inversely as the kinematic viscosity v of the flowing liquid (Table I-3), measurements of K are generally referred to a standard water temperature such as 60 F or 10 C. The ratio of the viscosity at the standard temperature to the observed temperature is the necessary correction factor, or

$$K_1/K_2 = v_2/v_1 \tag{9-7}$$

The upper limit of Darcy's law[14] lies at Reynolds numbers of 1 to 10. There inertial forces become significant. However, there is no turbulence below Reynolds numbers of 60 to 700. These are generally reached as water approaches well screens in coarse-grained sandy soils. No lower limit has been observed, even at vanishingly small hydraulic gradients—a few inches in a mile, for instance.

The magnitude of K is expressed in various units, depending upon the interests of the investigator and the system of measurements employed. The U.S. Geological Survey has chosen as its *standard coefficient of permeability* the flow of water in gpd at 60 F through a cross-sectional area of 1 sq ft under a unit gradient. Values of 2×10^{-4} to 10^5 have been observed, but the coefficients of most good aquifers lie between 10 and 5×10^3. The *field coefficient of permeability* relates flow to the ambient water temperature, a cross-sectional area 1 mile wide and 1 ft thick, and a hydraulic gradient of 1 ft per mile. The two coefficients are the same at a groundwater temperature of 60 F. The *coefficient of transmissibility* is obtained by multiplying the standard coefficient of permeability by the saturated height, or thickness, of the aquifer, in feet.

[13] Henri Philibert Gaspard Darcy (1803–1858), French engineer, member of the Corps des Ponts et Chaussées stationed at his native Dijon, *Les fontaines publiques de la Ville de Dijon* (The public wells of the city of Dijon), V. Dalmont, Paris, 1856; English translation by J. J. Fried, *Water Resources Bull.*, *Am. Water Resources Assoc.*, **1**, 4 (1965).
[14] As determined by evaluation of the constituent terms proposed in Volume 2 for the filtration of water through granular materials.

Magnitudes of the coefficient of permeability in various classes of soils are systematized in Fig. 9-4. Only for granular deposits can calculations be based upon measurable characteristics of soil grains and water (Vol. 2).

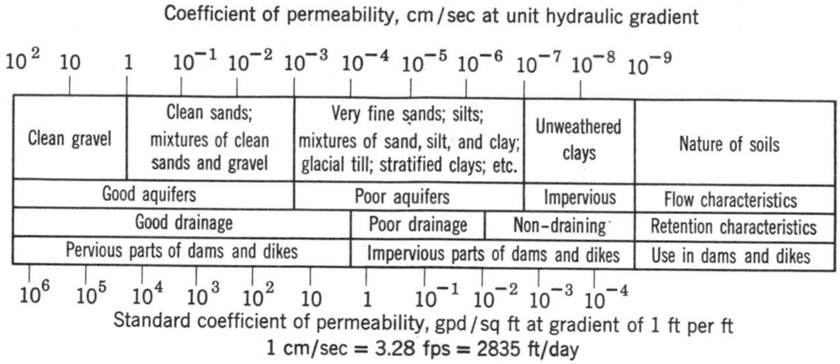

Coefficient of permeability, cm/sec at unit hydraulic gradient

10^2 10   1 10^{-1} 10^{-2} 10^{-3} 10^{-4} 10^{-5} 10^{-6} 10^{-7} 10^{-8} 10^{-9}

Clean gravel	Clean sands; mixtures of clean sands and gravel	Very fine sands; silts; mixtures of sand, silt, and clay; glacial till; stratified clays; etc.	Unweathered clays	Nature of soils
Good aquifers		Poor aquifers	Impervious	Flow characteristics
Good drainage		Poor drainage	Non–draining	Retention characteristics
Pervious parts of dams and dikes		Impervious parts of dams and dikes		Use in dams and dikes

10^6 10^5 10^4 10^3 10^2 10   1 10^{-1} 10^{-2} 10^{-3} 10^{-4}
Standard coefficient of permeability, gpd/sq ft at gradient of 1 ft per ft
1 cm/sec = 3.28 fps = 2835 ft/day

Fig. 9-4. Magnitude of the coefficient of permeability for different classes of soils. (*After Arthur Casagrande.*)

Example 9-2. (1) Estimate the velocity of flow (ft/day) and the discharge (gpd) through an aquifer of very coarse sand 1000 ft wide and 50 ft thick when the slope of the groundwater table is 20 ft/mile. (2) Find the standard coefficient of permeability and the coefficient of transmissibility on the assumption that the water temperature is 60 F.

1. From Fig. 9-4 choose a coefficient of permeability of $K = 1.0$ cm/sec $= 2835$ ft/day. Because $s = 20/5280$, Eq. 9-6 states that $v = 2835 \times 20/5280 = 11$ ft/day and $Q = 11 \times 1000 \times 50 \times 7.5 \times 10^{-6} = 4.1$ mgd.

2. The standard coefficient of permeability is $2835 \times 7.5 = 2.13 \times 10^4$, and the coefficient of transmissibility becomes $2.13 \times 10^4 \times 50 = 1.06 \times 10^6$.

9-10   Measurement of Permeability

Soil permeability is measured either in the laboratory or in the field. Laboratory determinations are precise but not necessarily representative of actual conditions. The samples that can be tested are relatively small, and their natural packing is easily disturbed. It follows that the observed results are useful only when the true texture of the aquifer is closely approximated by collecting undisturbed samples and the aquifer is substantially homogeneous throughout the gathering ground. If the aquifer contains alternating layers of pervious and impervious materials or lenses of different perviousness, laboratory findings become meaningless.

Available laboratory instruments include the *falling-head permeameter* shown in Fig. 9-5. The rate Q and head h decline with time as water flows through a sample of cross-section A and depth l.

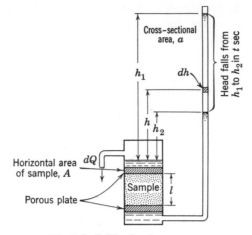

Fig. 9-5. Falling-head permeameter.

For heads h_1 and h_2 at the beginning and end of a time interval t, and for a cross-sectional area a of the standpipe, the differential equation for the rate of flow dQ under a head h in time dt is

$$dQ = -\frac{a\,dh}{dt} = K\frac{h}{l}A\frac{v_0}{v} \qquad (9\text{-}8)$$

where v and v_0 are the kinematic viscosities at the observed and reference temperature respectively. By transformation and integration,

whence

$$\int_0^t dt = \frac{al}{KA}\frac{v}{v_0}\int_{h_1}^{h_2} -\frac{dh}{h} \quad \text{or} \quad t = \frac{al}{KA}\frac{v}{v_0}\ln\frac{h_1}{h_2}$$

$$K = \frac{al}{tA}\frac{v}{v_0}\ln\frac{h_1}{h_2} \qquad (9\text{-}9)$$

Field determinations of permeability are generally made in one of two ways: (1) by measuring the hydraulic gradient and velocity of water movement in the ground or (2) by observing the discharge and drawdown of pumped wells. Pumping tests are described in Sec. 9-14.

The observed velocity is the true average rate of motion through the interstices of the aquifer. Because not all the interstices carry water, the average interstitial velocity v_f becomes $v/(k_f f)$, where k_f is the proportion of effective pore space. Hence the effective porosity lies somewhere between the gross porosity and the specific yield. Its determination has not received attention commensurate with its importance.

On the basis of effective porosity, effective velocity, and hydraulic gradient,

$$K = (k_f f v_f / s)(v / v_0) \qquad (9\text{-}10)$$

The effective or true average velocity of groundwater is measured in the field by noting the time required for a salt, dye, or radioactive tracer to traverse the distance between an injection well and an observation well lying in the direction of water movement. Time of arrival is determined electrically or by titration when salt solutions are injected, by visual observation or colorimetry when dyes are added, and by a Geiger counter or scintillator when radioactive tracers are introduced into the flow. The distance between the wells divided by the time required for half the added substance to be recovered is the effective, or median, velocity. Groundwater pollution can be traced in similar fashion. Uranin, a sodium salt of fluorescein, is an especially useful dye because it remains visible in dilutions of $1:(14 \times 10^7)$ without a fluoroscope and $1:(10^{10})$ with one. Radioactive tracers must be short-lived but otherwise unaffected by the soil through which they pass. Tritium (hydrogen 3) is a good example. Salt solutions must not be strong enough to change the physical properties of the groundwater.

9-11 Steady Flow into Wells

Groundwater movement towards a well can be formulated in accordance with the principles of Dupuit and Forchheimer,[15] when the well penetrates to the sole of the aquifer, the flow is steady, and the water table or the piezometric surface, as the case may be, is horizontal. Actually the water table or the piezometric surface is rarely horizontal, and flow is seldom steady. Changes in pumping and recharge rates and in amounts of water stored in the aquifer interfere. However, the usefulness of Dupuit's formulation can be expanded by introducing potential flow theory to cover confined aquifers in which the piezometric surface is inclined. The theory of steady flow has also been extended to leaky confining beds and other situations.

9-12 Unconfined Steady Flow

For radial flow from a concentric outer boundary (Fig. 9-6), the discharge through any cylindrical surface of radius x and height y is

$$Q = 2\pi K x y (dy/dx) \qquad (9\text{-}11)$$

[15] Arsène Jules Emile Juvenal Dupuit (1804–1866), French engineer, member of the Corps des Ponts et Chaussées, and author of *Études théoriques et·pratiques sur le mouvement des eaux courantes* (Theoretical and practical studies of the movement of running waters), 2nd ed., Dunod, Paris, 1863; also Information No. 10, Central Organization for Applied Scientific Research in the Netherlands (T.N.O.), the Hague, 1964. For Forchheimer's contributions, see footnote 26.

where Q is the rate of flow into the well, and x and y are the coordinates of any point on the Dupuit cone of depression or drawdown curve. The component variables are $2\pi xy$, the area through which flow takes place, and $K(dy/dx)$ the velocity. By integration

$$Q \ln x = \pi K y^2 + c \qquad (9\text{-}12)$$

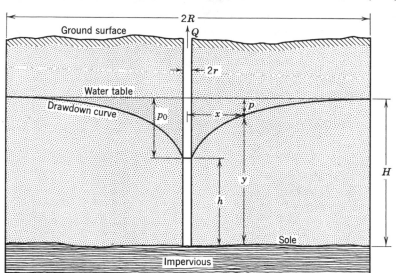

Fig. 9-6. Water-table well in a groundwater reservoir.

and for $y = h$ at $x = r$ (r being the radius of the well) and $y = H$ at $x = R$ (R being the radius of the circle of influence or distance of the outer boundary from the center of the well),

$$Q = \frac{\pi K(H^2 - h^2)}{\ln (R/r)} = \frac{1.36K(H^2 - h^2)}{\log (R/r)} \qquad (9\text{-}13)$$

Because H is constant, the quantity $(H^2 - h^2)$ increases at a declining rate as h is reduced. Thus successive increases in drawdown reduce the specific capacity of water-table wells. For a constant value of R the logarithmic ratio of the radius of the circle of influence to the radius of the well and its inverse relation to the yield indicate that increasing the size of a well does not greatly increase its yield. For example, a 2-ft well will yield only 15 to 30% more water than a 3-in. well.

9-13 Confined Steady Flow

For the conditions depicted in Fig. 9-7, where m is the thickness of the aquifer,

$$Q = 2\pi K x m(dy/dx) \qquad (9\text{-}14)$$

Integrating between the limits $x = r$ for $y = h$ and $x = R$ for $y = H$,

$$Q = \frac{2\pi Km(H - h)}{\ln (R/r)} = \frac{2\pi Km \, p_0}{\ln (R/r)} \tag{9-15}$$

The discharge is seen to be proportional to the drawdown $H - h = p_0$. The yield per unit drawdown, or *specific capacity*, of artesian wells has been observed to remain fairly constant at all reasonable values of drawdown.

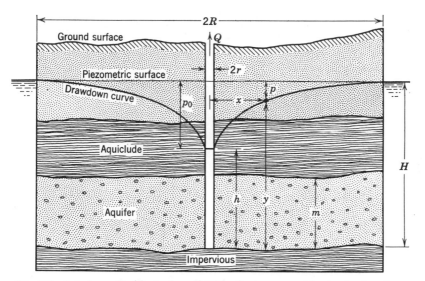

Fig. 9-7. Artesian well with steady radial flow from a concentric circular boundary.

Equation 9-15 may be rewritten

$$p_0 = \frac{Q \ln (R/r)}{2\pi Km} \tag{9-16}$$

If $T = Km$ is the transmissibility in gpd per ft width of aquifer, Q is gpm and $2 \ln (R/r) = F(u)$, Eq. 9-16 becomes

$$p_0 = (1440/4\pi)(Q/T)F(u) \tag{9-17}$$

In this form, the equation for steady flow can be compared with the formulations for unsteady flow of Sec. 9-14.

Partial Penetration of Well Screens. If the bottom of a well penetrates or is screened a distance $h_s < m$ in a confined aquifer of thickness m, the flow Q_p for a given drawdown will be less than, or the drawdown for a given flow greater than, when the well is screened over the full thickness of the aquifer. For partial penetration, the drawdown in the well, p_w, is given by the relationship:[16]

$$p_w = \frac{Q_p}{4\pi K} \left[\frac{2}{h_s} \ln \frac{\pi h_s}{2r} + \frac{0.2}{m} \right] \qquad (9\text{-}18)$$

which is valid for $1.3h_s \leq m$ and $h_s/2r \geq 5$. Because the drawdown at distances greater than $2m$ from the well is not significantly different from the drawdown of a fully penetrating well, the total drawdown for a partially penetrating well is

$$p_w = \frac{Q_p}{2\pi K} \left[\frac{1}{h_s} \ln \frac{\pi h_s}{2r} + \frac{0.1}{m} - \frac{1}{m} \ln \frac{R}{2m} \right] \qquad (9\text{-}19)$$

and the ratio of discharge Q_p from a partially penetrating well to the discharge Q of a fully penetrating well for a given drawdown p_w becomes

$$\frac{Q_p}{Q} = \frac{\ln (R/r)}{(m/h_s) \ln (\pi h_s/2r) + 0.10 + \ln (R/2m)} \qquad (9\text{-}20)$$

Artesian Well with Sloping Piezometric Surface. The paths of flow, or flowlines, around an unpumped well can be represented by a series of equally spaced parallel lines, $A, B, \ldots$ as in Fig. 9-8. The flowlines for a

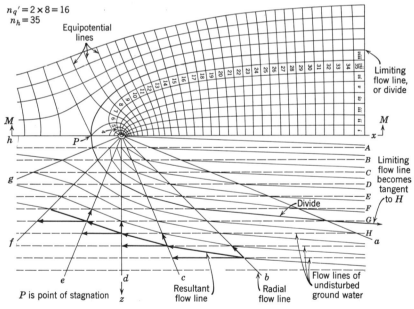

Fig. 9-8. Flow net of a single artesian well.

[16] G. J. de Glee, *Over grondwasserstroomingen bij wateronttrekking door middel van putten* (On groundwater flow through water withdrawal by means of wells), J. Waltman, Jr., Delft, 1930.

pumped well with horizontal piezometric surface, as formulated in Eq. 9-12, may be represented by radial lines a, b, ... as in Fig. 9-8. Superposition of these two systems of lines produces, by vector addition, the true paths of flow for a pumped well when the piezometric surface is inclined as shown in Fig. 9-8. Vectors can be added only when the figure is so constructed that the quantities of water flowing between adjacent parallel lines and between adjacent radial lines are equal. For this to be so, the number of parallel flow paths in the width of aquifer carrying the quantity of water pumped must equal the number of radial flow paths around the pumped well (16 each in Fig. 9-8). The equipotential lines cross the flowlines at right angles. If they are given the same spacing as the flowlines, they create an orthogonal flow net. The apex of the limiting flowline in Fig. 9-8 establishes the point of stagnation P. The line itself demarcates the divide between water drawn into and passing by the well. The flow pattern of this outer region, incidentally, is that past a solid object of the form traced by the limiting flowline.

For flow through a unit depth of aquifer, Eq. 9-15 becomes

$$q = \frac{2\pi K(H - h)}{\ln (R/r)} \qquad (9\text{-}21)$$

whence

$$K(H - h) = (q/2\pi) \ln (R/r) \qquad (9\text{-}22)$$

This is the velocity potential ϕ_r for radial flow towards a well. For the radial system of Fig. 9-8, $R^2 = x^2 + z^2$. Hence

$$\phi_r = (q/2\pi) \ln (R/r) = (q/4\pi) \ln [(x^2 + z^2)/r^2] \qquad (9\text{-}23)$$

The velocity potential of the undisturbed groundwater flow in the x direction is $\phi_0 = v_0 x$ and that of the combined flow is the sum of the two, i.e., $\phi = \phi_0 + \phi_r$. The point of stagnation downstream from the well is found by equating the x component of the velocity to zero and solving for x_0, or

$$v_x = \partial\phi/\partial x = v_0 + (q/2\pi)[x/(x^2 + z^2)] = 0 \qquad (9\text{-}24)$$

Because $z = 0$, furthermore,

$$x_0 = -q/(2\pi v_0) = -Q/(2\pi m K s) \qquad (9\text{-}25)$$

If z_0 is the distance between the well and the lines for undisturbed flow to which the limiting flowline or divide becomes asymptotic, the flow Q is intercepted from a width of aquifer $2z_0$. Thus $Q = 2z_0 m K s$ and $z_0 = -\pi x_0$.

Example 9-3. If the well in Fig. 9-8 penetrates an aquifer 40 ft thick and draws water laterally from a distance of 56 ft, the piezometric surface being lowered significantly for a distance of 140 ft upstream from the well by a drop in head of 30 ft at the well: (1) what is the yield of the well if the coefficient of permeability of the aquifer is 3.28×10^{-4} fps and the piezometric slope of the undisturbed groundwater is 40 ft in 140 ft; and (2) what is the distance of the point of stagnation from the well?

1. Because the yield of the well must equal the rate of flow of the tributary groundwater, $Q = Ksa = 3.28 \times 10^{-4} \times (40/140) \times 2 \times 56 \times 40 = 0.42$ cfs or 272,000 gpd.

2. The point of stagnation is identified by Eq. 9-25, in which $q = 0.42/40 = 1.05 \times 10^{-2}$ cfs and $v_0 = Ks = 3.28 \times 10^{-4} \times (40/140) = 9.37 \times 10^{-5}$ fps, as $x_0 = 1.05 \times 10^{-2}/(2\pi \times 9.37 \times 10^{-5}) = 17.8$ ft.

The width of the aquifer from which flow is intercepted is: $2z_0 = 2\pi x_0 = 2\pi \times 17.8 = 112$ ft, and $z_0 = 56$ ft.

9-14   Unsteady Flow into Wells

Theis[17] originated and Jacob,[18,21] Wenzel,[19] and Cooper and Jacob[20] have developed equational relationships for the flow of water into wells in which the pumping period is an added variable. This important advance in the hydraulics of wells has done away with the need for reaching the steady-flow or equilibrium conditions required for the application of earlier formulations.

Because the gradual approach of the cone of depression towards a steady state is produced primarily by the removal of water from storage as the cone deepens, a storage coefficient comes into play. Storage coefficient and transmissibility are then referred to as the *formation constants* of the aquifer.

The original development of the Theis equation derives from an analogy to the flow of heat toward a *sink* or point at which heat is removed at a uniform rate. The analogous quantities are:

Thermodynamic	*Notation*	*Hydraulic*
Rate of heat flow	Q	Rate of fluid flow
Temperature	p	Pressure
Temperature gradient	p/x	Pressure gradient
Conductivity	T	Transmissibility
Specific heat	S	Specific yield or storage coefficient

[17] C. V. Theis, The Relation between the Lowering of the Piezometric Surface and the Rate and Duration of Discharge of a Well Using Ground Storage, *Trans. Am. Geophys. Union*, **16**, 519 (1935).

[18] C. E. Jacob, On the Flow of Water in an Elastic Artesian Aquifer, *Trans. Am. Geophys. Union*, **21**, 574 (1940).

[19] L. K. Wenzel, Methods for Determining Permeability of Water-Bearing Materials, *U.S. Geol. Survey Water Supply Paper* 887, facing page 89 (1942).

[20] H. H. Cooper, Jr., and C. E. Jacob, A Generalized Graphical Method for Evaluating Formation Constants and Summarizing Well-Field History, *Trans. Am. Geophys. Union*, **27**, 526 (1946).

[21] C. E. Jacob, Drawdown Test to Determine Effective Radius of Artesian Well, *Trans. Am. Soc. Civil Engrs.*, **112**, 1047 (1947).

The mathematical solution of the heat-flow problem was transferred directly to the hydraulic problem, the equation being

$$p = \frac{Q}{4\pi Km} \int_u^\infty \frac{e^{-u}\, du}{u} = \frac{Q}{4\pi Km} W(u) \qquad (9\text{-}26)$$

Here $W(u)$ is the integral function of u, the lower limit u being defined as

$$u = x^2 S/(4Kmt) \qquad (9\text{-}27)$$

where S is the *storage coefficient* and t the time during which the well has been pumped. For $Km = T$, the coefficient of transmissibility in gpd per foot of width, Q the uniform rate of pumping in gpm, x the distance from the well in ft, t the time of pumping in days, and p the drawdown in ft,

$$p = \frac{1440Q}{4\pi T} \int_u^\infty \frac{e^{-u}\, du}{u} = \frac{114.6Q}{T} W(u) \qquad (9\text{-}28)$$

and

$$u = 1.87(S/T)(x^2/t) \qquad (9\text{-}29)$$

When flow is unconfined, the storage coefficient S equals the specific yield expressed as a decimal fraction. For an artesian aquifer, S equals the volume of water released, by virtue of compression, from storage within the column of the aquifer underlying a unit surface area during a unit drawdown of the piezometric surface.

The exponential integral of Eqs. 9-26 and 9-28 is called the *well function of u*, $W(u)$. It can be solved by expansion into the convergent series

$$W(u) = -0.5772 - \ln u + u - \frac{u^2}{2 \times 2!} + \frac{u^3}{3 \times 3!} - \cdots \qquad (9\text{-}30)$$

A series of values of $W(u)$ for values of u expressed as $N \times 10^n$ is given in Table I-7 of the Appendix.

9-15   Determination of Formation Constants (Overlay Method)

The magnitudes of the formation constants can be found by measuring the drawdowns in observation wells while the well under study is being pumped at a constant rate. For drawdown values, or rates of flow, other than those observed, the formation constants are assumed to remain unchanged within the area of influence. This is not necessarily true.

If Q, S, and T are considered constant, the quantities $114.6Q/T = C_1$ and $x^2/(ut) = T/(1.87S) = C_2$ in Eqs. 9-28 and 9-29, respectively, are also constant, and it follows that

$$\log C_1 = \log p - \log W(u) \qquad (9\text{-}31)$$

and

$$\log C_2 = \log (x^2/t) - \log u \qquad (9\text{-}32)$$

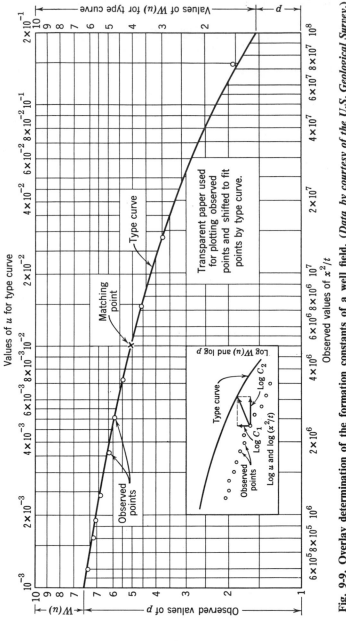

Fig. 9-9. Overlay determination of the formation constants of a well field. (*Data by courtesy of the U.S. Geological Survey.*)

Based on field tests the values of C_1, C_2, $W(u)$, and u are determined as follows:

1. The measured values of p are plotted logarithmically as ordinates against values of x^2/t as abscissas.

2. Values of $W(u)$ taken from Table I-7 are plotted as ordinates on the same diagram against values of u as abscissas.

3. Curves are drawn through the two sets of points, the curve through the second set of points being called the *type curve*.

4. It follows from the method of plotting and from Eqs. 9-31 and 9-32 that for every point on the p against x^2/t curve there is a corresponding point on the $W(u)$ against u curve which is displaced vertically by a fixed distance representing log C_1 and horizontally by a fixed distance representing log C_2. Therefore, a fixed amount of vertical and horizontal shift will bring the two curves into coincidence as in Fig. 9-9.

5. If transparent paper for a plot of the observed data is placed over the type curve and shifted horizontally and vertically until a best fit of the plotted points to the type curve is obtained, then any matching point will identify the values of $W(u)$ and u corresponding to the values of p and x^2/t by which Eqs. 9-28 and 9-29 can be solved for T and S.

Example 9-4.   For purposes of illustration, Fig. 9-9 shows observed data fitted to the type curve as if a transparency of the observed data had been moved into place over the type curve.

1. Selecting the point $p = x^2/t = 5 \times 10^6$ as the matching point, the formation constants T and S are computed for the observed values of $Q = 350$ gpm and $x = 225$ ft from the derived values of $u = 10^{-2}$ and $W(u) = 4.0$, as

$$T = 114.6QW(u)/p = 114.6 \times 350 \times 4/5 = 3.2 \times 10^4 \text{ gpd/ft}$$

and

$$S = uT/(1.87x^2/t) = 10^{-2}(3.2 \times 10^4)/[1.87(5 \times 10^6)] = 3.4 \times 10^{-5}$$

2. For 10 days of pumping at 700 gpm, Eq. 9-29 states that

$$u = 1.87[(3.4 \times 10^{-5})/(3.2 \times 10^4)](225^2/10) = 1.0 \times 10^{-5}$$

Reading the value of $W(u) = 10.9$ from Table I-7, Eq. 9-28 gives

$$p = 114.6(7 \times 10^2)10.9/(3.2 \times 10^4) = 27 \text{ ft}$$

3. If the well is gravel-packed with an outside diameter of the gravel wall of 24 in., the drawdown at the well itself after 10 days of pumping at 700 gpm is given in similar fashion by calculation of

$$u = 1.87[(3.4 \times 10^{-5})/(3.2 \times 10^4)](1/10) = 2.0 \times 10^{-10}$$

whence $W(u) = 21.75$, from Table I-7, and

$$p = 114.6(7 \times 10^2)21.75/(3.2 \times 10^4) = 54 \text{ ft}$$

9-16   Approximate Determination of Formation Constants

Jacob[21] has developed the following quick method for evaluating T and S. For values of $u < 0.02$ the terms beyond ln u in Eq. 9-30 may be neglected to give:

$$p = 114.6(Q/T)\{-0.5722 - 2.303 \log [1.87(S/T)(x^2/t)]\} \quad (9\text{-}33)$$

If observed values of p and t are plotted on arithmetic and logarithmic scales respectively, the points for the higher values of t, corresponding to $u < 0.02$, will fall along a straight line (Fig. 9-10). Pairs of values for two points along this line can be introduced into Eq. 9-33 to determine the coefficient of transmissibility T. Substitution of the point values in Eq. 9-33 gives

$$p_2 - p_1 = 264(Q/T) \log (t_2/t_1) \qquad (9\text{-}34)$$

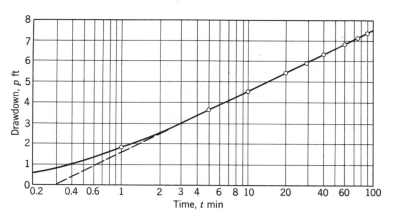

Fig. 9-10. Approximation of formation constants. (*Data by courtesy of the U.S. Geological Survey.*)

The storage coefficient S can then be calculated by reading the straight line value of t_0 at $p = 0$ and substituting it in the following empirical approximation, where t_0 is in days,

$$S = 0.3Tt_0/x^2 \qquad (9\text{-}35)$$

With the formation constants T and S known, Eq. 9-33 gives the draw-down for any desired values of x and t, provided only that u as calculated from Eq. 9-29 is less than 0.02. Even in cases where this is not so, the quick method becomes a useful guide for selecting a suitable matching point in the overlay method.

Example 9-5. For purposes of illustration, Fig. 9-10 shows the data for Example 9-4 ($Q = 350$ gpm and $x = 225$ ft) plotted on semilogarithmic paper, a straight line being drawn through the points for the higher values of t.

1. Selecting the points $t_1 = 1$ min, $p_1 = 1.6$ ft, and $t_2 = 10$ min, $p_2 = 4.5$ ft,

$$T = 264Q[\log (t_2/t_1)]/(p_2 - p_1) = 264 \times 350[\log (10/1)]/(4.5 - 1.6) = 3.2 \times 10^4 \text{ gpd/ft}$$

Because the straight line intersects the $p = 0$ axis at $t_0 = 0.3$ min,

$$S = 0.3Tt_0/x^2 = 0.3(3.2 \times 10^4)0.3/[(225)^2 \times 1440] = 3.0 \times 10^{-5}$$

2. For 10 days of pumping at 700 gpm, Eq. 9-29 shows that

$$u = 1.87(3.9 \times 10^{-5})(5.06 \times 10^4)/[(3.2 \times 10^4)10] = 1.15 \times 10^{-5}$$

Because this is less than 0.02, p can be calculated from Eq. 9-33 as

$$p = [114.6 \times 700/(3.2 \times 10^4)](-0.5772 - 2.3 \log 1.15 \times 10^{-5}) = 29 \text{ ft.}$$

9-17   Determination of Transmissibility by Observing Recovery

In the absence of an observation well, the coefficient of transmissibility can be determined more accurately by measuring the recovery of water levels in the well under test after pumping has stopped than by measuring

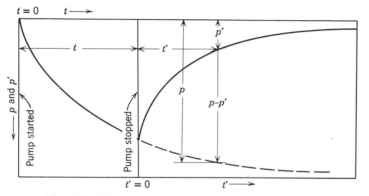

Fig. 9-11. Water-level recovery after pumping has stopped.

drawdown in the well during pumping. To this purpose, the well is pumped long enough to be drawn down appreciably. The pump is then stopped, and the rise of water level within the well is determined (Fig. 9-11). If t and p are respectively the time from starting the pump and the drawdown during pumping, and t' and p' are corresponding values after shutting the pump down and during recovery, Eq. 9-33 becomes

$$p - p' = 114.6(Q/T)\{-0.5772 - 2.303[\log 1.87(S/T)(x^2/t')]\} \quad (9\text{-}36)$$

where x is the well radius to the face of the aquifer (or the distance to an observation well) and p and p' are corrected for gravel, screen, and well losses so that they will apply also to the face of the aquifer.

Subtracting Eq. 9-33 for p from Eq. 9-36 for $p - p'$ and simplifying,

$$p' = 114.6(Q/T)[2.303 \log (t/t')] \quad (9\text{-}37)$$

Plotting p' on an arithmetic scale against t' or t/t' on a logarithmic scale, a straight line is obtained from which the coefficient of transmissibility T can be read.

9-18   Validity of Field-Test Results

The equations developed in Secs. 9-9 to 9-17 apply rigidly only when: (1) the aquifer is homogeneous and infinite in areal extent; (2) the well penetrates the entire thickness of the aquifer; (3) the coefficients of transmissibility and storage are constant at all times and places; and (4) water is released from storage as soon as the cone of depression develops.

When the coefficient of transmissibility is determined from field tests, it establishes an average value for much of the aquifer. This is not necessarily true when the magnitude of the coefficient is based on laboratory tests of permeability. The coefficient of transmissibility of an unconfined aquifer changes with time, because the thickness of the saturated soil becomes less as the water table is lowered by pumping. The selection of large values for x and t reduces this effect. The error introduced by delayed release of water from storage is minimized by prolonged pumping. The fact that aquifers are never infinite in extent may be accounted for by applying the method of images (Sec. 10-10).

9-19   Behavior of Groundwater in Contact with Salt Water[22]

Fresh water is found in contact with salt water most frequently (1) on islands, peninsulas, spits, or bars surrounded by or near the sea and (2) in artesian aquifers that outcrop in the sea. Under these conditions, the yield of fresh water and encroachment of salt water upon freshwater sources are exemplified by the dynamics of fresh water in sand, volcanic, and coral islands in the sea.

Depending upon the nature of the subsoil, rainwater percolates downward to join the body of fresh water supported, as an underground lens, upon the denser salt water. As shown in Fig. 9-12, the movement of fresh water is downward and outward within this lens. During rainy seasons, the water table rises and the bottom of the lens sinks. In the fluctuating boundary of contact between fresh and salt water, there is a concentration gradation from fresh through brackish to salt. Under static conditions, the thickness of the lens at any time and place is controlled by the height of the water table above sea level, because the freshwater column must balance the saltwater pressure at the bottom of the lens in accordance with the Ghyben-Herzberg principle.[23,24] If, as shown in Fig. 9-12, h_f is the thickness

[22] H. H. Cooper, Jr., F. A. Kohout, H. R. Henry, and R. E. Gover, Sea water in coastal aquifers, *U.S. Geological Survey, Water Supply Paper* 1613-C (1964).

[23] W. B. Ghyben, Nota in Verband met Voorgenomen Putboring nabij Amsterdam, (Notes in connection with bored wells near Amsterdam), *Tijdschrift van het Koninklijk Instituut van Ingenieurs*, **21** (1888–1889).

[24] B. Herzberg, Die Wasserversorgung einiger Nordseebäder (The water supply of some North Sea resorts), *Gasbeleuchtung und Wasserversorgung*, **44**, 815, 842 (1901).

of the lens in any vertical plane, conditions of equilibrium require that $h_f s_f = h_s s_s$ or $(h_f - h_s)s_f + h_s s_f = h_s s_s$, and

$$h_s = [s_f/(s_s - s_f)](h_f - h_s) \qquad (9\text{-}38)$$

For the normal specific gravities of seawater (1.025) and fresh water (1.000), therefore,

$$h_s = 40(h_f - h_s) \qquad (9\text{-}39)$$

If, for example, the water table rises 4 ft above sea level, the theoretical depth of the freshwater lens below sea level is $40 \times 4 = 160$ ft. However,

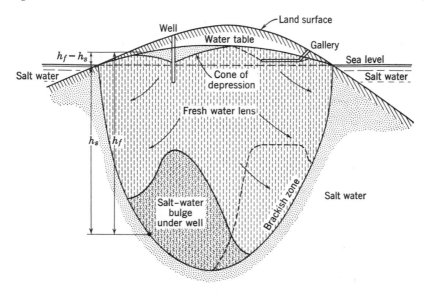

Fig. 9-12. Dynamics of a freshwater lens in contact with salt water.

when fresh water flows from the soil into the sea, the static balance is upset, and the maximum depth[25] of fresh water exceeds $40(h_f - h_s)$.

As shown in Fig. 9-12, pumping reduces the thickness of the freshwater lens and forms an upward bulge at the freshwater and saltwater interface. The volume of fresh water that can be withdrawn before this bulge is fully established equals the sum of (1) the volume of water stored between the original freshwater table and the stable cone of depression, (2) the volume of fresh water displaced by salt water in forming the bulge in the bottom of the freshwater lens, and (3) the volume of water percolating downward into the zone of influence around the well. Because the volume of fresh water displaced is often large, the water table may fall slowly through a number of years of pumping.

[25] M. K. Hubbert, The Theory of Groundwater Motion, *J. Geol.,* **48,** 785 (1940).

The water in flat freshwater lenses lying on top of the salt water penetrating permeable formations, such as coral and lava, may be withdrawn through galleries constructed above sea level (Fig. 9-12).

9-20   Flow Patterns or Nets

Continuity of flow requires that for a given element of time the volume of water entering an elemental mass of soil from one or more directions must equal the volume of water leaving in one or more directions, provided

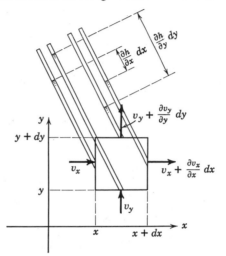

Fig. 9-13. Two-dimensional flow in isotropic materials.

there is no change in the mass or its void space. For two-dimensional flow (Fig. 9-13), the equation formulating this statement is

$$v_x \, dy + v_y \, dx = \left(v_x + \frac{\partial v_x}{\partial x} \, dx \right) dy + \left(v_y + \frac{\partial v_y}{\partial y} \, dy \right) dx \qquad (9\text{-}40)$$

whence

$$\frac{\partial v_x}{\partial x} + \frac{\partial v_y}{\partial y} = 0 \qquad (9\text{-}41)$$

For the three-dimensional case, therefore,

$$\frac{\partial v_x}{\partial x} + \frac{\partial v_y}{\partial y} + \frac{\partial v_z}{\partial z} = 0 \qquad (9\text{-}42)$$

In accordance with Darcy's law, moreover, $v_x = K \, \partial h / \partial x$, $v_y = K \, \partial h / \partial y$, $v_z = K \, \partial h / \partial z$, and it follows that

$$\frac{\partial^2 h}{\partial x^2} + \frac{\partial^2 h}{\partial y^2} + \frac{\partial^2 h}{\partial z^2} = 0 \qquad (9\text{-}43)$$

This is the Laplace differential equation for steady flow of water through a homogeneous, isotropic medium.

For unidirectional flow, all terms in the series but one drop out, and $d^2h/dx^2 = 0$. If x measures the length of path in the direction of flow, d^2h/dx^2 becomes the derivative of the Darcy equation, $dh/dx = v/K$, where v is constant and independent of x. The unidirectional flow pattern through a confined aquifer, shown in Fig. 9-14, is an example. For a unit width of aquifer of thickness m, $dh/dx = Q/(Km)$ and the head decreases uniformly at the rate v/K or $Q/(Km)$.

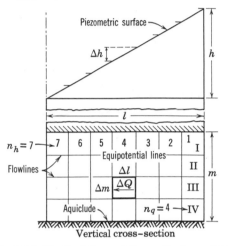

Fig. 9-14. Idealized flow net for confined parallel flow.

If the flowlines in any vertical section of the aquifer (in the direction of flow) are so spaced that the quantity ΔQ encompassed by adjacent paths distant Δm from each other respectively is the same, and the head lost in the distance Δl along the line of flow is Δh,

$$\frac{\Delta h}{\Delta l} = \frac{\Delta Q}{K \, \Delta m} \quad \text{or} \quad \frac{\Delta Q}{\Delta h} = K \frac{\Delta m}{\Delta l} \qquad (9\text{-}44)$$

If ΔQ and Δh are to be the same, the ratio $\Delta m/\Delta l$ must be constant, provided the value of K does not change. All rectangles must then be identical in size and shape. In the special case of uniform flow, Δm and Δl may be made equal for convenience. The component lines of the resulting flow net bound squares of equal size. The unidirectional case elucidates the fundamental principle of the flow net, first explored by Forchheimer.[26]

[26] Philip Forchheimer, *Hydraulik*, Teubner, Leipzig, 1930. Forchheimer (1852–1933) was professor of hydraulics at Aachen, Germany, and Graz, Austria. His two books on hydraulics, unabridged and abridged, were referred to by his students, facetiously but warmly, as the big and little Forchheimers.

The flow net, for which ΔQ and Δh are constant, throughout the field of motion may be further analyzed as follows.

If there are n_q paths of flow, the total flow is $Q = n_q \Delta Q$. If there are n_h equipotential drops, the total potential drop is $h = n_h \Delta h$ and $\Delta h = h/n_h$. Hence, in accordance with Darcy's law, $v = K \Delta h/\Delta l$ and $Q = \Delta m K \Delta h/\Delta l$, or

$$Q = Kh(n_q/n_h)(\Delta m/\Delta l) \tag{9-45}$$

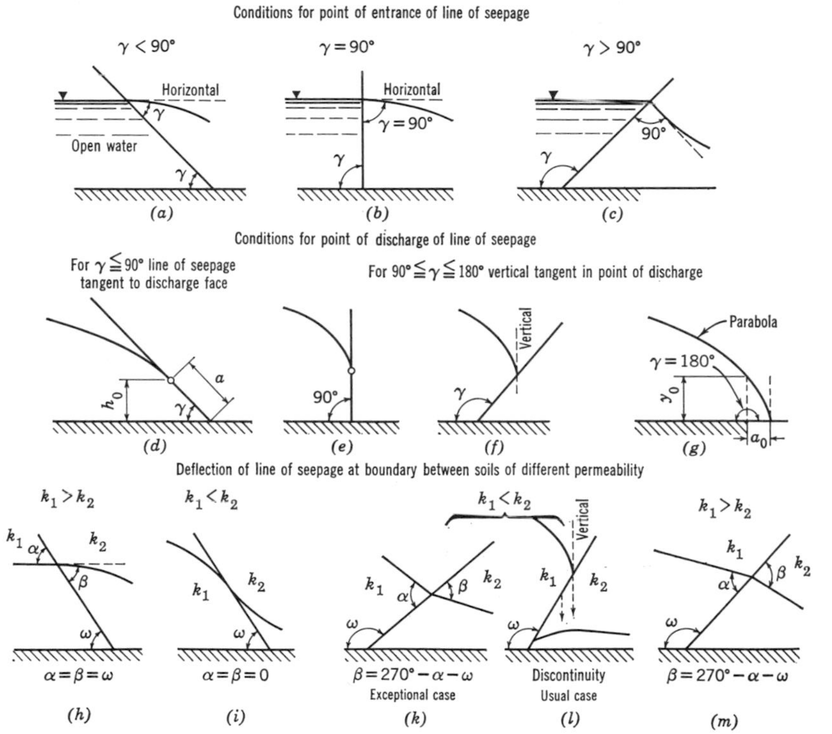

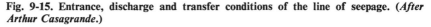

Fig. 9-15. Entrance, discharge and transfer conditions of the line of seepage. (*After Arthur Casagrande.*)

In the particular case of $\Delta l = \Delta m$, the equation reduces to

$$Q = khn_q/n_h \tag{9-46}$$

In the general case of two-dimensional flow, the third term in Eq. 9-43 drops out, and the equation describes two families of curves that intersect at right angles. The geometrical properties of these curves afford a graphical solution for almost every two-dimensional seepage problem. Equation 9-46 applies, but the velocity $v = \Delta Q/\Delta m$ is not constant, and Δl changes in proportion to Δm for a constant value of $\Delta h = h/n_h$. The blocks of the flow net are no longer equal, but they are orthogonal solids, similar in two dimensions and equal in the third. Conformance of the network to Eq. 9-46 requires that there be but one ratio of n_q/n_h. Had twice as many potential drops been assumed in Fig. 9-14, for instance, the number of radial flow paths would have had to be doubled.

The entrance, discharge, and transfer conditions that govern the line of seepage, or uppermost flowline, have been identified by Casagrande[27] and are illustrated in Fig. 9-15. The boundary conditions must be superimposed upon the general requirements laid down by Forchheimer if the flow net is to conform to the conditions that actually obtain.

Example 9-6. Figure 9-16 illustrates the construction of a flow net for a horizontal drain or collecting pipe in an unconfined aquifer for conditions when the water table passes through points A and A'. If the drain is fairly long and the area serving it is correspondingly large, two-dimensional, nonuniform flow can be assumed. Total flow then equals the discharge through a cross-section of unit thickness multiplied by the length of the collector. The flow net is developed as follows:

1. Draw a cross-section of the collector and aquifer to a convenient scale. Because the field is symmetrical about BC, only one-half need be drawn. Show the known (or assumed) water table elevation at A.
2. Choose a starting place. Whereas DCB is known to be a flow path boundary, it would be difficult to make a start by estimating the potential distribution along it. Along flowline AB the potential drops Δh are known to be constant, but the location of this flowline cannot readily be estimated. However, appreciation of the nature of the flow suggests that if A is somewhat farther from the drain than is the sole of the aquifer, the flow beneath A will be essentially horizontal and fairly uniform throughout the depth. Therefore, we can start by assuming that equipotential line AD is approximately vertical and that we can divide it into equal increments, Δm.
3. Working from line AD, sketch by successive trials the system of orthogonal lines that fulfills the requirements (a) that all elemental areas approximate squares; (b) that the vertical distances, Δh, between intersections of equipotential lines with the water table AB are the same (this is because the water pressure is constant, i.e., atmospheric, along the water table, and change in potential is associated with change in elevation only); and (c) that the discharge at the drain satisfies the applicable boundary conditions of Fig. 9-15.

On completion of a satisfactory orthogonal system, the flow into the collector can be calculated by Eq. 9-46.

If $h = 4.8$ ft, $m = 13.4$ ft, and $K = 10^{-1}$ cm/sec $= 3.28 \times 10^{-3}$ fps for clean sand and gravel (Fig. 9-4), the seepage from each direction per foot of collector is $q = 3.28 \times 10^{-3} \times 4.8 \times 7/11$, because $n_q = 7$ and $n_h = 11$. Hence $q = 1.0 \times 10^{-2}$ cfs/ft, and $Q = 2 \times 1.0 \times 10^{-2} \times 10^2 = 2.0$ cfs/100 ft from both sides.

9-21   Numerical Analyses and Analog Models

Numerical analyses, physical models, and analog computers are used extensively in studies of flow patterns in groundwater basins and around

[27] Arthur Casagrande, Seepage through Dams, *J. New Eng. Water Works Assoc.*, **51**, 139 (1937).

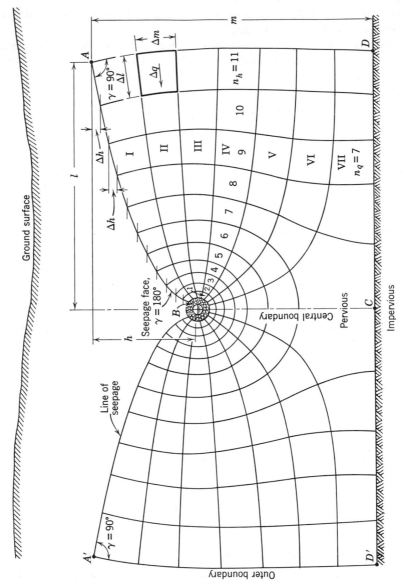

Fig. 9-16. Equipotential net for the flow of water into a drain.

well fields. Methods of numerical analysis are based on the iteration or relaxation methods developed by Southwell.[28,29]

A variety of models have been used. In the sand model, dyes trace the paths of streamlines along transparent plates, and piezometers measure the pressure potential. Both three-dimensional and unsteady flow can be studied. Viscous fluid models consist of parallel transparent plates spaced close enough to maintain laminar flow. Unsteady flows with irregular boundaries and nonuniform permeabilities can be investigated, but only for two-dimensional flows. Models of this kind were developed by Hele-Shaw.[30] The simpler forms of electrical models are convenient only for studying steady-state two-dimensional situations. More elaborate electrical models, commonly called electronic[31] or analog[32] computers, may be of service in investigating either two- or three-dimensional unsteady flow. If the variations in coefficients of permeability and storage (Sec. 9-4) are known, these can be simulated.

Analogs for groundwater systems are constructed of resistors and capacitors arranged in two- or three-dimensional networks. If the mesh size of the network is small in comparison with the areal extent of the aquifer, network response to excitation will simulate the response of the aquifer. Connections at the junctions are shown in Fig. 9-17, where arrangement (a) is for a two-dimensional net, (b) for a three-dimensional net, and (c) for two-dimensional flow in an aquifer with a leaky confining bed represented by a resistor to ground. Figure 9-17(d) shows the excitation and read-out equipment.

The finite difference form of a two-dimensional laminar flow may be written

$$T = \left(\sum_{2}^{5} h_i - 4h_1 \right) = L^2 S \frac{\partial h}{\partial t} \qquad (9\text{-}47)$$

where T and S are respectively the coefficient of transmissibility and the storage coefficient, as defined in Sec. 9-14, h_i is the head or potential at the points, represented by junctions 2, 3, 4 and 5 in Fig. 9-17a, and L is the distance between points so represented and the junction (1) in question. The electric potentials in the vicinity of a junction are represented by

[28] R. V. Southwell, *Relaxation Methods in Engineering Science*, Oxford University, London, 1940.
[29] D. K. Todd, *Ground Water Hydrology*, John Wiley & Sons, New York, 1959, p. 314.
[30] H. S. Hele-Shaw, Stream Line Motion of a Viscous Film, *Rep. 68th Meeting, British Assoc. Adv. Sci.*, **136** (1899).
[31] H. E. Skibitzke, Electronic Computers as an Aid to the Analysis of Hydrologic Problems, *Int. Assoc. Scientific Hydrology*, Commission on Subterranean Waters, Publication No. 52, 347 (1960).
[32] W. C. Walton, Electric Analog Computers and Hydrogeologic Systems Analysis in Illinois, *Jour. Tech. Div. Nat. Water Well Assoc., Ground Water*, **2**, 28 (1964).

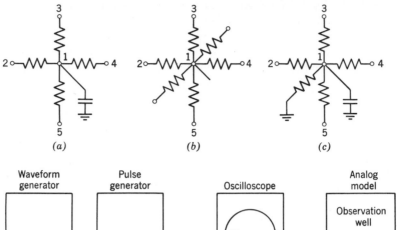

(a)   (b)   (c)

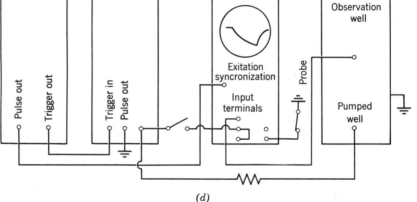

(d)

Fig. 9-17. Elements of an analog model of groundwater flow.

the analogous equation

$$\frac{1}{R} = \left(\sum_{2}^{5} E_i - 4E_1 \right) = C \frac{\partial E}{\partial t} \tag{9-48}$$

where R is the resistance, C the capacitance, and E the electrical potential. Four scale ratios connect the units of the hydraulic and electric systems: $V = K_1 H$, gallons and coulombs; $h = K_2 E$, feet and volts; $Q = K_3 I$, gpd and amperes; and $t_d = K_4 t_s$, days and seconds.

The excitation-response apparatus consisting of waveform and pulse generators and an oscilloscope is shown in Fig. 9-17d. The wave form generator triggers and synchronizes the pulse generator and oscilloscope. The pulse length is proportional to time and its height is proportional to the pumping rate. The cathode tube portrays a time-voltage curve analogous to the time-drawdown graph for an observation well. A resistance between the pulse generator and the model permits calculating the pumping rate in gpm from the equation

$$Q = E_R K_3/(1.44 \times 10^3 R_i) \qquad (9\text{-}49)$$

The time-voltage graphs are converted to drawdown curves by the appropriate scale ratios. Electric analogs of this type have been used successfully to study many complex situations. Inherent in these models is a degree of flexibility not found in others.

CHAPTER 10

Groundwater Collection

10-1 Facts and Foibles

Discovery and development of groundwater supplies is a straightforward engineering undertaking and should be pursued in this sense. That it requires an understanding of pertinent geological, hydrological, and hydraulic factors has been pointed out in Chapters 1, 2, 6, and 9. Contrary to popular belief, groundwater sources cannot be located by divining rods; nor is groundwater necessarily safe in quality and inexhaustible in volume.

Faith in water dowsing is without scientific foundation. A divining rod, generally a forked twig bent outward at its free ends by the dowser, is held by him in delicate equilibrium. The slightest motion of his wrists tilts the fork sharply downward. Subterranean waters have nothing to do with this maneuver of the divining rod or with the misguided or misguiding dowser.

Unquestioned faith in the hygienic safety of groundwater is likewise ephemeral. Water derived from solution passages in limestone and related geological formations or from a polluted catchment area close to the groundwater works must be looked upon with suspicion. To be sure, sands and other fine-grained soils or rocks may intercede to remove contaminants and pollutants from percolating waters, provided they are forced to travel through reasonable thicknesses of geological structures of this kind. However, there are contaminants—nitrates and fluorides in high concentration, for example—that are not removed even by the best of soils or rocks. Not surprisingly, therefore, outbreaks of water-borne disease have been traced to groundwaters as well as surface waters. Because there are many more groundwater supplies in much of the world, the number of outbreaks has, indeed, been larger than for surface water supplies. That the number of cases of disease has normally been smaller is due to the generally lower capacity of many, if not most, groundwater supplies. Generally speaking, the area nearest the intake works is the area to be safeguarded. Of some interest, too, are false beliefs in the provenance of groundwaters and the persistence of their yield. It is true that some groundwaters are transported in suitable aquifers over great distances. The Dakota sandstone, mentioned in Chap. 9, is an example. However, the volumes of flow are limited strictly to the area of their intake, i.e., the extent of their catchment, and the amount of rainfall or streamflow reaching the permeable formations.[1] Nor does depth alone ensure the adequacy of what is often miscalled an artesian supply, when wells are drilled into dense Archean rock. No groundwater source is inexhaustible. An overpumped development will fail, no matter where it is situated; and overdraft near the sea will let salt water intrude into an overpumped aquifer.

Good management of the groundwater resource, finally, requires definition of a system of laws, rights and equities that is easily understood and readily enforced.

In spite of difficulties of this kind, the ground may afford a naturally purer, cheaper, and more satisfactory supply of water than can the surface of the earth. If available waters are conserved, and, if necessary, supplemented by suitable recharge from surface sources, they can serve well and for long periods of time. If they are not husbanded with care and caution, they will fail in quantity and deteriorate in quality. Here and there they may even have to be abandoned.

The purpose of the present chapter is to discuss the essential constructional features of groundwater developments, the hydraulics associated with the draft of groundwater, and the available means for the maintenance and care of collecting works and for the conservation of the source.

10-2   Common Features of Collection Works

Pumping is the central feature of most groundwater works. For satisfactory performance, the suction lift, including entrance and pipe losses, must be held below 25 ft. When the water table is farther down than that, the collecting piping or conduit leading to the pump and the pumping unit itself must be lowered below ground level, or individual wells must be equipped with deep-well pumps. Infiltration galleries convey their flows by gravity to pump wells, from which the water is lifted to purification works or directly to the community. Gravity flow, like that from upland

[1] Sandy islands, such as Nantucket and Martha's Vineyard off the southern shore of Massachusetts, and necks of sand, such as Cape Cod, do not have intakes in the granites of the White Mountains of New Hampshire some 200 miles away. Instead, the fresh waters drawn from their sands are derived solely from local rainfall.

surface sources, is rarely possible. Exceptions are springs at the base of mountains, collecting tunnels driven into hillsides, and flowing artesian wells that lie high enough above the community. Suction and gravity conduits—suction conduits in particular—are vulnerable to pollution from sources in their immediate surroundings.

As it is drawn from the ground, water releases the gases it may contain. If it does, it must be passed through an air-separating tank from which the desorbed gases are evacuated by pumping. At the same time or sequently, sand or other soil granules pulled into the water from the aquifer have to be removed. A sand separator does this by impingement or sedimentation. Pumps and piping are then protected against abrasion.

Well-sinking is a specialized art that has evolved along a number of more or less regional lines. In the United States, well drillers are generally given much latitude in the choice of a suitable method. What they undertake to do is to sink a well of specified size at a fixed price per foot. Ordinarily, therefore, the engineer gives his attention, not so much to drilling operations, as to the adequacy, suitability, and economy of proposed developments and the location of the works. In addition, he is called on (1) to select the size, number, and arrangement of wells, (2) to specify the pumping and appurtenant equipment, (3) to make sure that a reliable contractor is employed, (4) to supervise the testing and development of completed wells, (5) to see that the wells and piping are properly disinfected before being placed in service, and (6) to assure the prevention of contamination of the operating supply from both surface and underground sources of pollution.

The size, number, and arrangement of wells are determined by the amount and depth of water to be tapped, the hydrology and hydraulics of available aquifers, and proposed methods of pumping.

Large *dug wells*, 6 ft or more in diameter, are generally constructed only where groundwater is shallow and storage within the well will compensate for fluctuations in the rate of pumping. Where the permeability of the ground is too low to keep a single well supplied with enough water, several wells may take its place.

Groups of shallow wells can be pumped by connecting them to suction lines leading to a common pumping station. For a scheme of this kind to work, the well strainers, or bottom of the drop pipes, must remain submerged, and suction lines must be airtight. The principal disadvantage of this design is that the wells must usually be spaced so closely (50 to 200 ft on centers) that the cones of depression or circles of influence overlap too much for good efficiency. Only the water filtering into the surface of the field or flowing laterally into it is collected. Pumping an entire field of closely spaced wells may be no more productive of water than pumping a selected group of properly spaced wells (Sec. 10-9).

Well diameters should be dimensioned in concordance with drawdown and yield. However, well-sinking methods and space requirements for pumping machinery actually govern well size more often than do hydraulic considerations. Strainers or screens and riser pipes should be large enough to keep entrance losses and other flow resistances within reasonable limits at maximum pumping rates. Riser-pipe velocities are commonly held down to 2 or 3 fps.

Construction methods depend primarily on the nature of the soil or rock to be penetrated. Costs of construction vary with size, depth, and design, and with the equipment and experience of local drillers. Designs improve and costs are lowered as regional geological and hydrological information becomes available. Good *well logs* are helpful if they give (1) accurate descriptions of formations encountered, (2) rates of drill penetration, and (3) amounts of water tapped, as well as other pertinent information. On completion of the well, the driller's log may be complemented (1) by calipering for size and caving zones; (2) measuring subsurface conditions by electric potentials and resistivities, and (3) determining porosities and moisture contents by gamma and neutron rays.

Entering into the design and operation of an optimal system are questions of depth, spacing, diameter, pumping rate, and other pertinent matters, as well as the hydrology and hydraulics of the source.

10-3 Well Construction

Wells are generally sunk in one of the four ways by which kinds of wells are distinguished.

Dug Wells. Small dug wells are generally excavated by hand. In loose overburden, they are cribbed with timber, lined with brick, rubble, or concrete, or cased with large-diameter vitrified tile or concrete pipe. In rock, they are commonly left unlined. Excavation is continued until water flows in more rapidly than it can be bailed out. Dug wells should be completed structurally when the water table is at or near its lowest level. Otherwise, they may have to be deepened later on (Fig. 10-1a).

Large and deep dug wells are often constructed by sinking their liners as excavation proceeds. The lead ring has a steel cutting edge; new rings are added as excavation progresses (Fig. 10-1b). Caissons allow the well to penetrate 15 to 20 ft below the water table.

Driven and Jetted Wells. Wells can be driven into relatively shallow sand formations. As shown in Fig. 10-2, the driving point is attached to a strainer or perforated section of pipe. To reduce friction, the point is somewhat larger than the casing. The driving weight is commonly suspended from a block attached to a tripod. In hard ground a cylindrical shoe equipped with water jets loosens the soil and washes it to the surface.

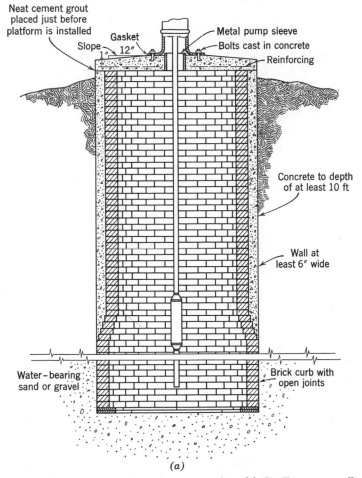

Neat cement grout
placed just before
platform is installed

Gasket

Metal pump sleeve

Bolts cast in concrete

Slope   1″   12″

Reinforcing

Concrete to depth
of at least 10 ft

Wall at
least 6″ wide

Water-bearing
sand or gravel

Brick curb with
open joints

(a)

Fig. 10-1. Dug wells and their sanitary protection. (*a*) Small masonry well.

Batteries of driven wells may be connected to a suction header to supply enough water.

Bored Wells. Wells can be bored with hand or power augers into sufficiently cohesive (noncaving) soils. Above the water table, the soil is usually held in the auger, which must then be raised from time to time to be cleaned. Below the water table, sand may wash out of the auger and have to be removed from the bore hole by a bailer or sand pump. As the well becomes deeper and deeper, sections of rod are added to the auger stem. Bits up to 36 in. in diameter have been used successfully, and wells have been enlarged in diameter up to 48 in. by reaming. A concrete, tile, or

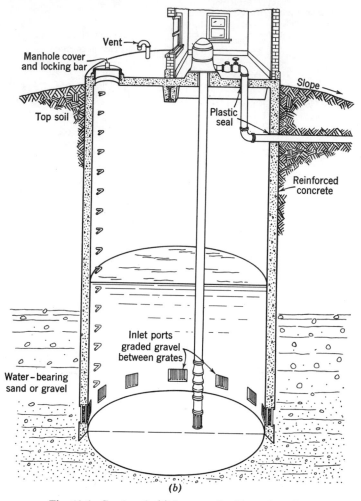

Fig. 10-1. *Continued.* (*b*) **Large well with cutting edge.**

metal casing is inserted in the hole and cemented in place before the strainer is installed.

Drilled Wells. Drilled wells are sunk either by percussion or rotary drilling. The following three methods are generally preferred:

Percussion Drilling. Drilling with cable tools is common in the United States. The string of tools includes a blunt or chisel-edged bit, a drill stem, jars, and a rope socket, all connected by tapered screw joints. A crank arm, reciprocating pulley, or walking beam lifts and drops the tools within a wet hole. The drill rope must be slightly elongated when the bit strikes bottom.

The return spring in the rope then keeps the bit from sticking or the tools from jamming. As their name implies, the *jars* (two heavy, loose, chainlike links) help to jar the bit loose on the upstroke. The driller turns the bit and judges the performance of the tools by the feel of the drill rope.

Blunt bits are used in soft material; chisel edges in hard rock. The drilling edge is somewhat larger than the shank to give working clearance. The

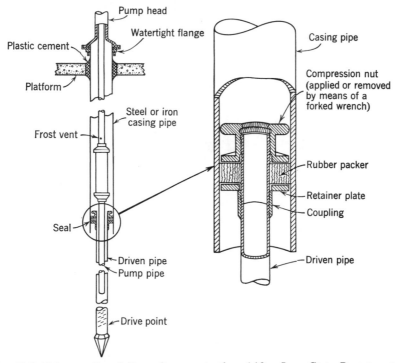

Fig. 10-2. Driven well and its sanitary protection. (*After Iowa State Department of Health.*)

loosened material is removed by a bailer attached to a sand line. Water is added when there is not enough natural flow into the well for drilling and bailing. Should the hole cave, a casing would be inserted and the drilling continued with a smaller bit.

Rotary Drilling. In rotary drilling, a cutting bit is attached to a hollow drill rod rotated rapidly by an engine-driven rotary table. Either water or a suspension of colloidal clay is pumped down the drill pipe, flows through openings in the bit, and transports the loosened material to the surface. The clay suspensions are designed to reduce loss of drilling fluid into permeable formations, lubricate the rotating drill pipe, bind the

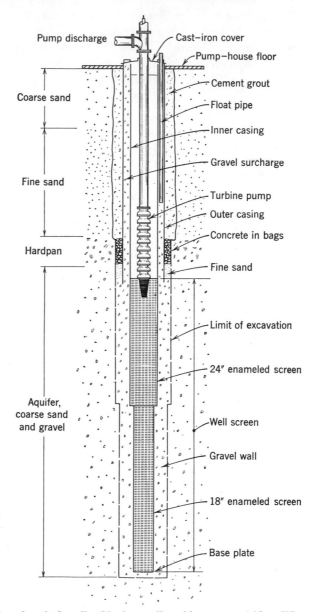

Fig. 10-3. Gravel-packed well with deep-well turbine pump. (*After Wisconsin State Board of Health.***)**

wall against caving, and suspend the cuttings. In drilling for water, the thick drilling clay may be forced into the aquifer and reduce the flow into the well. New methods of reaming and flushing have largely overcome difficulties of this kind. Where the supply of water is ample, *reverse circulation* does away with difficulties of caving without sealing the aquifer. To this purpose, clear water is poured into the annulus outside the drill pipe while a pump creates suction within the pipe. High upward velocities in the drill pipe clear coarse materials from the hole.

Percussion Reverse-Circulation Drilling.[2] In this form of drilling, a percussion bit sliding on the outside of the drill pipe breaks up boulders encountered by the drill. Drill pipes may be as much as 8 in. in diameter. Large fragments of rock can be removed through them. Holes up to 6 ft in diameter and 700 ft in depth are rapidly excavated in valley fills and other heterogenous unconsolidated materials. Sand added to the circulating water will reduce the water required to offset losses into the formations being drilled.

10-4 Gravel-Wall and Collector Wells

The area of influence of wells can be increased by enlarging their effective diameter. Gravel-wall and collector wells do this.

As shown in Fig. 10-3, an envelope of gravel placed outside the well screen creates a gravel wall and with it a larger intake envelope. This reduces the velocity of water leaving the aquifer and forms a filter that keeps sand out of the well. A well hole is first drilled and reamed to the desired diameter (24 in. or more). An outer casing is then cemented in place, and the aquifer is cleaned before a smaller inner casing carrying the well screen is inserted. After this, gravel is fed into the annulus between the two casings. A plunger operated rapidly up and down inside the casing helps to compact the gravel. Gravel-wall wells may suck in sand when they are first placed in operation, and some gravel may slip into the surroundings and have to be replaced from time to time.

Collector wells will extract relatively large supplies of groundwater from valley fills and other alluvial deposits of high permeability and ample rate of recharge. The central shaft of collector wells is a concrete caisson some 15 ft in internal diameter and finished off below the water table with a thick concrete plug. From this shaft, radial collectors, 6 or 8 in. in diameter, are jacked horizontally into the water-bearing formation through ports near the bottom of the caisson. A number of collector pipes may be installed and developed in the same fashion as ordinary vertical wells.

[2] Mario Massareuti, Percussion—Reverse Circulation Water-Well Drilling System Designed and Developed in Italy, *Ground Water*, *J. Nat. Water Well Assoc.*, **2**, 2, 25 (1964).

10-5 Cementing and Sealing

The exterior pipe or casing of a drilled well should be sealed in place by filling the annular space between the casing and the well hole with cement grout or other impermeable material down to the aquifer or water table. This cuts off downward flow of nearby water, avoids erosion of the hole, protects the casing against exterior corrosion, and delays failure of the well when the casing rusts out.

Sealing-grout is prepared by adding 4 to 6 gal of water to each 94-lb bag of cement. The grout is pumped more easily if lime, clay, mica, or cellulose flakes (or other lubricants) are added. Moreover, less grout is then lost into formations above the aquifer. Grouting is continuous. Injection is into the bottom of the annulus and displaces water and drilling mud from the space as the grout rises to the surface. The hole diameter should be at least 4 in. larger than the diameter of the casing. Well calipers will establish below-ground dimensions. Casings are usually cemented in place before drilling into the aquifer. Otherwise, grout must be kept out of the aquifer while the annulus is being filled with cement.

Cementing not only assures withdrawal of safe water from water wells; it also prevents contamination of valuable water resources from deep wells intended to dispose of brines and other industrial wastes. Moreover, cementing simplifies filling and sealing wells at the end of their useful life. A properly cemented well is shown in Fig. 10-4.

10-6 Well Strainers

After the cement grout has set, the hole is continued downward until a strainer or screen comes into line with the aquifer. Good well strainers offer little resistance to flow yet keep out unwanted sand. In aquifers of fine, uniform material, screen openings must be small enough to exclude the fines. In aquifers of widely varying particle size, well capacity is improved if strainer openings allow fines to enter the well while coarse particles stay behind within increased void space. A graded filter is thereby generated around the well. In sand, fines up to 50 to 80% of the total may be withdrawn. Backflushing or high rates of pumping may help to do this (Sec. 10-8).

Well strainers are commonly either perforated casings or fabricated screens. Perforated casings are generally used in uncemented wells when relatively large openings are permissible. They may be machine-perforated at the factory or slotted in place after installation.

The beveled openings of fabricated well screens commonly enlarge inward to clear the slots of sand that might otherwise lodge in them. Corrosion-resistant screens are more durable, but also more expensive, than

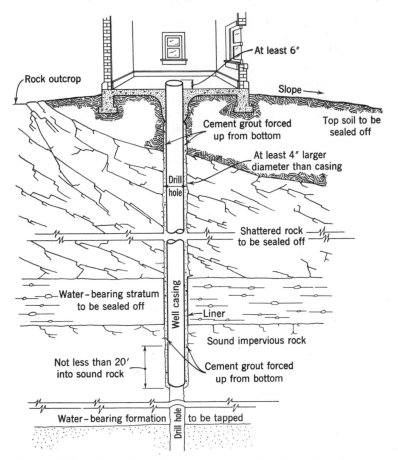

Fig. 10-4. Drilled well and its sanitary protection. (*After Iowa State Department of Health.*)

slotted casings. Metals suitable for well screens have been given the following order of preference:[3] Monel metal, supernickel, Everdur metal, silicon bronze, silicon brass, red brass, and stainless steel.

10-7 Pumping Equipment

Many types of well pumps are on the market to suit the wide variety of capacity requirements, depths to water, and sources of power. In the United States almost all well pumps are driven by electric motors (Chap. 16).

Domestic systems commonly employ one of the following pumps: (1) for lifts under 25 ft, a small reciprocating or piston pump; for lifts up to 125 ft,

[3] *Tentative Standard Specifications for Deep Wells*, prepared by the American Water Works Association.

a centrifugal pump to which water is lifted by recirculating part of the discharge to a jet or ejector; and (3) for lifts that cannot be managed by jet pumps, a cylinder pump installed in the well and driven by pump rods through a *jack* mounted at the well head. Systems of choice normally incorporate pressure tanks for smooth pressure-switch operation. The well itself may provide enough storage to care for differences between demand rates in the house and flow rates from the aquifer. This is why domestic wells are seldom made less than 100 ft deep, even though the water table may lie only a few feet below the ground surface. Deep wells and pump settings maintain the supply when groundwater levels sink during severe droughts or when nearby wells are drawn down steeply.

Large-capacity systems are normally equipped with centrifugal or turbine pumps driven by electric motors. A sufficient number of pump bowls are mounted one above the other to provide the pressure necessary to overcome static and dynamic heads at lowest water levels. Figure 10-3 shows a turbine pump installed in a well. Figure 10-5 illustrates a motor installation for driving a pump from the surface. For moderate quantities and lifts *submersible* motors and pumps, assembled into a single unit, are lowered into the well. The water being pumped cools the compact motors normally employed. Large-capacity wells should be equipped with suitable measuring devices. Continuous records of water levels and rates of withdrawal offer the means for checking the condition of the equipment and the behavior of the source of supply. This is essential information in the study and management of the groundwater resource.

10-8 Well Development and Testing

Flushing, surging, testing, and equipping wells before they are put into service are called *well development*. To clear clay from the aquifer near the well, Calgon $(NaPO_3)_6$, or muriatic acid (commercial HCl) may be added to the water during surging. Temporary equipment can provide the required high pumping rate and backflushing. When sand no longer enters the well, the *specific capacity*, or yield per foot of drawdown of the installation, is determined by pumping at different rates for a sufficient length of time to approach fairly stable water levels. The information obtained is put to use in selecting permanent equipment and determining the hydraulic characteristics of the aquifer and the well. To find safe, long-time yields, however, the hydrology of the aquifer must be fully explored (Chap. 9).

10-9 Interference of Wells

When the areas of influence of two or more pumped wells overlap, the draft of each well affects the drawdown of the other or others. Interference may become so severe in closely spaced wells that well groups could behave

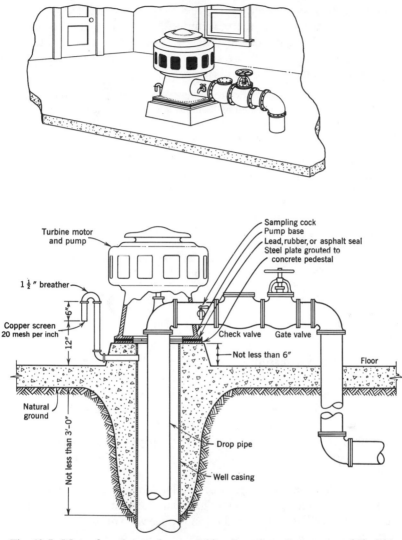

Fig. 10-5. Motor for submerged pump. (*After Iowa State Department of Health.*)

like a single well producing a single large cone of depression. When this is so, the discharge-drawdown relationships can be studied in this sense. A heavily pumped well field may have a circle of influence many miles in diameter. Wells within a circle of their own, a mile or so in diameter, could then behave like a single group. By contrast, lightly pumped, shallow wells in unconfined aquifers may register no interference when they are 100 ft apart or even less so.

The equations for unsteady flow, Sec. 9-14, allow calculating the drawdown of individual wells in the presence of interfering wells. To the drawdown of the well as an isolated unit are then added, one at a time, the drawdowns caused by each of the interfering wells. An example will illustrate the calculations to be performed.

Example 10-1.   Assuming that two wells, respectively 1000 ft and 2000 ft distant on a straight line, are added to the well of Example 9-4, find: (1) the expected drawdown in each well when the first well is pumped at a rate of 700 gpm for 10 days, and (2) the drawdown in each well when all three are pumped at a rate of 700 gpm for 10 days.

1. As shown in Example 9-4, the drawdown of the first well is 54 ft. The drawdown of the well 1000 ft away is calculated from $u = 1.87[(3.4 \times 10^{-5})/(3.2 \times 10^4)](10^6/10) = 2 \times 10^{-4}$, whence $W(u) = 7.94$ (Table I-7). It follows that $p = 114.6(7 \times 10^2) 7.94/(3.2 \times 10^4) = 20$ ft. Similarly, the drawdown of the second well is given by $u = 1.87[(3.4 \times 10^{-5})/(3.2 \times 10^4)](4 \times 10^6/10) = 8 \times 10^{-4}$, whence $W(u) = 6.55$. Accordingly, $p = 114.6(7 \times 10^2)6.55/(3.2 \times 10^4) = 16$ ft.

2. If all three wells are pumped at a rate of 700 gpm, the drawdown in the first and third wells will be the sum of their own drawdown and the drawdowns in one well 1000 ft away and the other well 2000 ft away, or $(54 + 20 + 16) = 90$ ft. At the same time, the drawdown of the second or central well will be its own drawdown together with twice the drawdown in a well 1000 ft away, or $(54 + 2 \times 20) = 94$ ft.

10-10   The Method of Images

In formulating both steady and unsteady flow into wells (Secs. 9-6 and 9-7), the aquifer was assumed to be unlimited in areal extent. If, under equilibrium conditions, the circle of influence of a well or well field fails to extend to the bounds of the aquifer or to the source of replenishment, the assumption of an infinite aquifer introduces no difficulty. However, this assumption is invalidated when (1) streams, outcrops, and topographic divides lie within the radius of influence; (2) formation boundaries, folds, and faults confine the aquifer to a few miles; and (3) waterbearing valley fills are of small breadth ($\leq$ 100 ft).

To deal with these influences, Lord Kelvin's method of images[4] for the analysis of electrostatic phenomena has been put to use for the solution of groundwater problems.[5] The method introduces one or more image wells— i.e., the traces of identical wells at equal distances beyond the boundary— in such manner that the superimposed effect of the image well produces the necessary limiting conditions at the boundary. Solutions for a variety of boundary conditions are then possible.

[4] William Thomson Kelvin (1824–1907), Baron of Largs, British physicist, known also for establishing the absolute temperature scale (named in his honor) and for contributions to thermodynamics in general.

[5] C. V. Theis, The Effect of a Well on the Flow in a Nearby Stream, *Trans. Am. Geophys. Union*, **21**, 734 (1940). J. G. Ferris, Ground-Water Hydraulics as a Geophysical Aid, *Michigan Dept. Conservation, Lansing, Mich., Tech. Rept.* 1 (1948).

Figure 10-6 illustrates the effect of a stream lying within the area of influence of a well. If there is enough percolation from the stream to keep the aquifer lying beneath its bed saturated with water, the stream surface

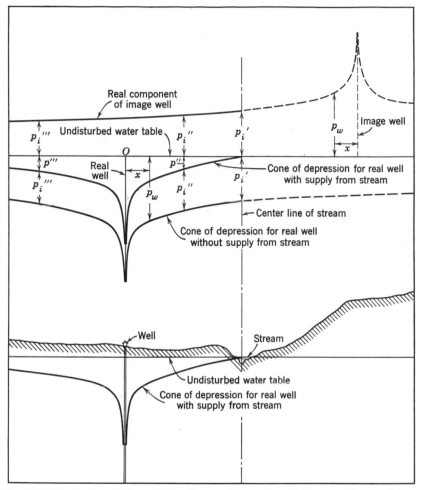

Fig. 10-6. Application of the method of images to a well receiving water from a stream. *Idealized.*

becomes an established equipotential line and so, too, a fixed boundary or limiting condition. To construct the modified cone of depression, the well cone is first drawn as if there were no boundary. A doubly mirrored image of the well is then constructed on the opposite side of the boundary and becomes the equivalent of a recharge well of the same capacity as the real well. Within the nature of this construction, the rise in water table of the real well by discharge of the image well brings the cone of depression to the water surface of the stream. The reduction in drawdown of the real well is then given by the recharge line of the image well lying above the real well. Addition of this line to the cone of depression of the real well satisfies the limit of the problem and so is a solution.

The solid lines in Fig. 10-6 identify the drawdown and recharge of the real well and image wells in the real region; the dotted lines do so in the image region.

Example 10-2.   If the well of Example 9-4 lies 1000 ft from a stream that can supply water to the ground fast enough to hold the water table at the surface along the stream course, (1) find the drawdown in the well after 10 days' pumping at 700 gpm, and (2) sketch the profile of the intersection of the cone of depression with a vertical plane through the well normal to the stream.

Table 10-1   Calculation of Cone of Depression (Example 10-2)

Distance from Real Well	Depression without Supply from Stream	Build-up from Image Well	Depression with Supply from Stream
x, ft	p_u, ft	p_i, ft	p, ft
1000 right	19.8	−19.8	0
500 right	23.4	−17.8	5.6
100 right	31.4	−16.7	14.7
10 right	43.0	−16.4	26.6
1 right and left	54.4	−16.4	38.0
10 left	43.0	−16.4	26.6
100 left	31.4	−16.2	15.2
500 left	23.4	−15.3	8.7
1000 left	19.8	−14.4	5.4

1. As shown in Example 9-4, the drawdown without supply from the stream is 54 ft. The image recharge well is 2000 ft distant and will, therefore, have a build-up of 16 ft as calculated for the drawdown at this distance in Example 10-1. Thus the resultant drawdown is $(54 - 16) = 38$ ft.

2. For $T = 3.2 \times 10^4$ gpd per ft, $S = 3.4 \times 10^{-5}$, and $Q = 700$ gpm, needed values of u are calculated from Eq. 9-29 for various assumed values of x. Corresponding values of $W(u)$ are found in Table I-7, and values of p are calculated from Eq. 9-28. The results are tabulated in Table 10-1 and plotted in Fig. 10-2.

A well penetrating valley fill, between impermeable walls constituting aquicludes within the area of influence, is another example of problems that can be solved by the method of images. Because there can be no flow across the boundary of the aquicludes, the cone of depression of the well must intersect at right angles the vertical planes representing the average boundary positions. Mirrored images of the real well establish the limiting conditions. Exclusion of flow that would have occurred in the absence of the aquicludes makes it necessary to subtract from the cone of depression of the real well the depression of the water table featured by the cone of depression of the image wells. The solution of a problem of this kind is shown in Fig. 10-7. Two image wells are not enough, because the intersection, at either boundary of the depression produced by the image beyond the opposite valley wall, leaves an unbalanced head potential. A second set of images at twice the distance from the real well eliminates this error. However, it leaves, in turn, a reduced discrepancy at the opposite boundaries. Hence, a series of images must be introduced on each side of the well. Other situations will suggest themselves to the reader.

10-11   Galleries and Drains

Infiltration galleries are suitably constructed (1) as marginal drains along hillsides, (2) at right angles to the underflow of valleys, (3) parallel to streams towards which upland flow is traveling, and (4) above sea level on islands and along coasts where saltwater intrusion is to be avoided.

For maximum yield, galleries should lie at the full depth of the aquifer. Large galleries are constructed of masonry or concrete with numerous openings. They are built in open trenches or tunneled through the ground. Surrounding them with gravel will increase their intake. Tile drains laid with open joints in gravel-filled trenches are used to collect shallow waters. Sometimes they radiate from springs and dug wells to boost their yields.

The capacity of galleries built across a valley may be increased by sinking a cutoff wall of concrete into the ground to dam up the underflow and force its entrance into an upstream collecting system.

In the most favorable circumstances, an infiltration gallery situated on the impervious sole of an unconfined aquifer intercepts all the natural underground flow. As shown in Fig. 10-8, the flow pattern is nonuniform in but two dimensions when a steady state has been reached. Consequently, the approximate amount of water drawn into such a gallery can be determined by flow-net principles (Sec. 9-9). The situation can also be dealt with in more direct mathematical terms. As proposed by Dupuit,[6] the following simplifying assumptions must be made: (1) the soil is isotropic and incompressible; (2) the tangent of the angle of inclination of the water table, i.e., its slope, is substantially equal to its sine; and (3) the flow is uniform and horizontal throughout the depth of the aquifer.

In accordance with Darcy's law and the notation of Fig. 10-8, the discharge per unit length of gallery then becomes

$$q = Ky\, dy/dx \tag{10-1}$$

[6] Jules Dupuit, *Études théoretiques et practiques sur le mouvement des eaux* (Theoretical and practical studies of the movement of waters), Paris, 1863, 2nd ed.

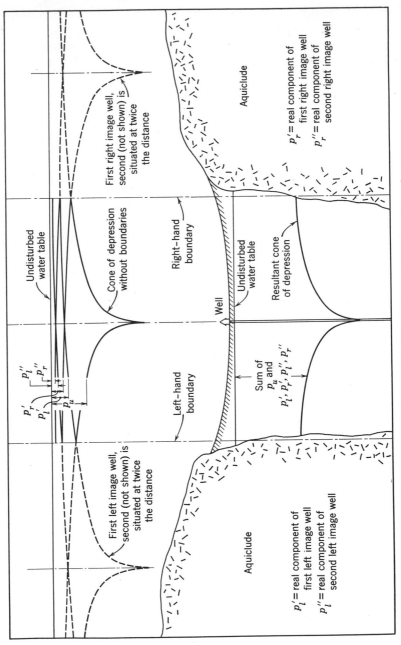

Fig. 10-7. Application of the method of images to a well between impervious outcrops.

where $y \times 1$ is the area of unit width through which the groundwater flows with velocity $K(dy/dx)$. By integration

$$qx = \tfrac{1}{2}Ky^2 + c \qquad (10\text{-}2)$$

and if $y = H$ at $x = L$, and it is assumed that $y = h$ at $x = 0$, it follows that

$$q = \tfrac{1}{2}K(H^2 - h^2)/L \qquad (10\text{-}3)$$

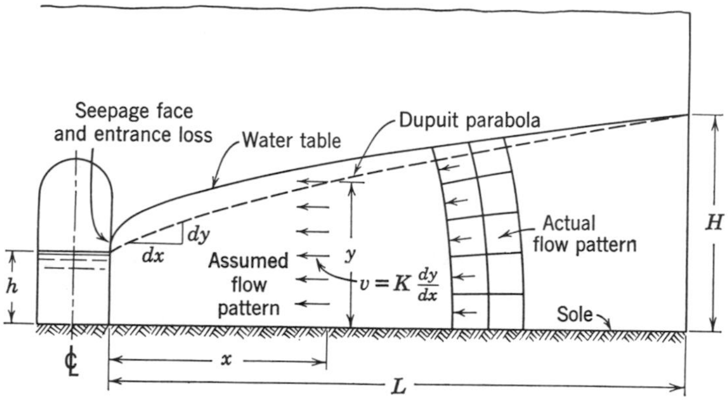

Fig. 10-8. Flow into an infiltration gallery.

Equation 10-1 traces a parabolic water table that departs, often significantly, from the true water table and continues to rise beyond any finite boundary. What the line of seepage should be, in order to meet the requirements at entrance and discharge laid down in Fig. 9-15, is indicated in Fig. 10-8. The capillary fringe is not taken into account. The greater the ratio L/H, the closer is the agreement between the calculated and true flow systems except at the discharge face.

Example 10-3. A stratum of clean sand and gravel 20 ft deep has a coefficient of permeability $K = 10^{-1}$ cm/sec (3.28×10^{-3} fps) and is supplied with water from a diffusion ditch penetrating to the bottom of the stratum. If the water surface in an infiltration gallery lies 2 ft above the sole of the stratum, and its distance to the diffusion ditch is 30 ft, what is the flow into a foot of gallery?

In accordance with Eq. 10-3, $q = \tfrac{1}{2}(3.28 \cdot \times 10^{-3})(20^2 - 2^2)/30 = 2.2 \times 10^{-2}$ cfs or 14,000 gpd.

10-12   Groundwater Recharge

Water may be forced into the ground for the following purposes: (1) to dispose of wastewater, (2) to dispose of heat without depleting available groundwater, (3) to replenish overpumped groundwater basins, (4) to form a freshwater barrier against intrusion of salt water into heavily pumped groundwater basins along the coast, and (5) to complement or replace surface storage by ground storage in increasing the safe yield of surface supplies.

Water is recharged or recycled to the ground through *spreading grounds*, check dams in streams, seepage ponds, pits, or ditches, underground leaching systems, and recharge wells. These may be the reverse of collection works. With appropriate adjustments, they can then be treated analytically by similar procedures.[7] Their hydraulic and economic success depends upon available storage space, transmissibility of the soil, and keeping the soil from being clogged by suspended solids, slime growths, or chemical reactions. Because some clogging is inevitable, recharge works generally require more maintenance and pass less water than do corresponding discharge and collection works.

Off-channel spreading grounds or recharge basins have been introduced extensively in Southern California to capture flood flows otherwise wasted to the ocean.[8] On Long Island, N.Y., hundreds of recharge basins serve the dual purpose of runoff disposal from urban areas and groundwater replenishment.[9] In the high plains of western Texas, water is mined at rates many times its natural replenishment, while surface runoff collects in myriads of playa lakes (about 37,000) from which it subsequently evaporates.[10] Efforts to recharge the otherwise wasted surface water led to the discovery that unfiltered surface water would enter the Ogallala aquifer through recharge or multipurpose wells without serious clogging. However, the wells had to be pumped at rates higher than the recharge rate, and they had to be surged by being turned on and off every 30 min for 2 hr out of each 24-hr recharge period. Throughout the United States, it has become common practice to keep groundwater used only for cooling in tight systems and return it to the ground through recharge wells.

10-13   Freshwater Barriers[8,11]

Where groundwater naturally finds its way into the ocean or other brackish waters, heavy inland pumping may reverse the flow direction and

[7] Leonard Schiff, Ground Water Recharge Hydrology, *Ground Water*, **2**, 3, 16 (1964).
[8] Paul Bauman, Groundwater Movement Controlled through Spreading, *Trans. Am. Soc. Civil Engrs.*, **117**, 1024 (1952); also Basin Recharge, *ibid*, **122**, 458 (1957).
[9] The highly permeable glacial material is counted on to accept about 11 gal/sq ft/day. Domestic and other wastewaters are also recharged through cesspools or seepage pits and the like.
[10] James Valliant, Artificial Recharge of Surface Water to the Ogallala Formation in the High Plains of Texas, *Ground Water*, **2**, 2, 42 (1964).
[11] N. J. Lusczynski, Head and Flow of Ground Water of Variable Density, *J. Geophys. Res.*, **66**, 4247 (1960). R. J. M. DeWiest, Dispersion and Salt Water Intrusion, *Ground Water*, **2**, 3, 39 (1964); and J. A. Harder, and F. L. Hotes Report on Laboratory and Model Studies of Sea Water Intrusion, *Tech. Bull.* No. 11, Sanitary Engineering Research Laboratory, University of California (May 1955).

draw a saltwater wedge landward. Ultimately, this would destroy the freshwater resource. Salination of this kind can be delayed or arrested by recharge wells or trenches that create a freshwater barrier between sea and land.

To hold the saltwater wedge stationary, the potential within the wedge, expressed as feet head of salt water, must be the same everywhere. For equilibrium, the Ghyben-Herzberg principle (Sec. 9-8) requires that the freshwater potential along the sloping saltwater-freshwater interface decrease in the direction of the ocean. This will be so only if fresh water flows

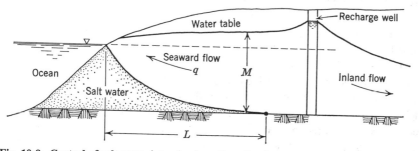

Fig. 10-9. Control of salt-water intrusion by a line of recharge wells forming a freshwater barrier.

towards the ocean. Model studies as well as theoretical considerations produce the following relationship between freshwater flow and the geometric parameters shown in Fig. 10-9:

$$q = \tfrac{1}{2}(s_s - 1)(M/L)T \qquad (10\text{-}4)$$

where q is the freshwater discharge per foot of ocean front, s_s is the specific gravity of sea water, M is the thickness of the saturated aquifer, L is the length of the wedge, and T is the coefficient of transmissibility at unit gradient. To erect an effective freshwater barrier against saltwater intrusion, inland pumping having lowered the freshwater below sea level, the recharge parallel to the ocean front must equal the sum of the flows towards the ocean and the land. The longer the wedge, or length L in Fig. 10-9, the less is the seaward loss. However, moving the barrier inland would be expected to increase the landward flow of recharged water. If the barrier were generated in an already salinized portion of the aquifer, a wave of salty water would be driven inland as the barrier forms. Well spacing is determined (1) by limitations on recharge head and thus on well capacity, and (2) by the need to elevate the water table saddle between wells enough to prevent incursion of the wedge between two adjacent wells.

10.14   Groundwater Management[12]

As shown in Chap. 9, the behavior of surface and groundwaters is inextricably interrelated. All groundwater not returning to the atmosphere or escaping into the oceans eventually contributes to the surface supply. Underground water storage and its escape or withdrawal differ little from storage, escape, and withdrawal of water in surface lakes and reservoirs. It follows that integrated management of underground and surface sources provides many opportunities for improved use of the total water resource. The principal objectives of management may be to minimize cost or maximize yield. Cost minimization is generally the objective in well-watered humid regions; yield maximization is more important in water-short, arid regions.

The feasibility of conjunctive water management depends on geologic, hydrologic, economic, and legal factors and on alternatives that bear on each particular situation. In the humid east of the United States, for example, where surface waters are abundant and widely distributed, but surface storage may be expensive, heavy seasonal pumping of groundwaters to satisfy demands during periods of deficient surface flows may be alternated with drafts upon surface sources during periods of ample runoff. This would convert the ground into a naturally replenished reservoir heavily drawn on during the summer and allowed to recuperate during the remainder of the year. Costs of such schemes should be compared with alternative methods of providing equivalent supplies.

In arid climates, conjunctive use would ordinarily seek to minimize overall losses and stretch the limited supplies over as wide an area as possible. Groundwater-basin recharge, either for local use or later export, would normally be made a part of the system. Water levels would be reduced to prevent consumption by phreatophytes, and water would be pumped at basin outlets to cut off underflow from the area. The volume of underground storage is often so large that it can even out year-to-year variations in available supply. Assuring passage of dissolved minerals through surfacewater-groundwater systems with minimum economic loss is another important aspect of resource planning in arid climates.

[12] R. O. Thomas, Planned Utilization, Groundwater Development, A Symposium, *Trans. Am. Soc. Civil Engrs.*, **122,** 422 (1957); and M. W. Bettinger, The Problem of Integrating Groundwater and Surface Water Use, *Ground Water*, **2,** 3, 33 (1964).

CHAPTER 11

Surface-Water Collection

11-1 Scope of Discussion

The present chapter is a continuation of Chaps. 7 and 8 in which important hydrological aspects of surface-water sources have been discussed: stream flow and the yield of natural catchment areas; storage to be provided in impounding reservoirs; and the routing of floods through stream-diversion conduits and over the spillways of dams. The chapter is likewise a continuation of Chaps. 9 and 10, because groundwater flows may reach surface-water courses in substantial amounts, and seepage through soils is an element—often a controlling element—in constructions for surface-water supplies.

The comparative advantage of working in the open in the collection of information on surface waters rather than groundwaters and of building surface rather than underground structures is offset, in large measure, by the unsteadiness of surface runoff, both in quantity and quality, and the recurrence of extremes in flow. That hydrological factors enter strongly into the development of surface-water supplies must, therefore, be kept clearly in mind in their design and operation, with special reference to (1) the principles of selecting, preparing, and controlling catchment areas; (2) the choice and treatment of reservoir areas and the management of natural ponds and lakes as well as of impoundages; and (3) the siting, dimensioning, construction, and maintenance of necessary engineering works, including dams and dikes, intake structures, spillways, and diversion works. It should also be kept in mind that river systems must be developed for multiple purposes, not just for municipal uses.

11-1

11-2 Catchment Areas

The gathering grounds for public water supplies vary *in size* from a few hundred acres to thousands of square miles; *in character*, from sparsely inhabited uplands to densely populated river valleys. The smaller they are and the less developed, the better do they lend themselves to exploitation for large and steady yields and to the production of water of high quality.

Upland Areas. Occasionally, yet seldom, a water utility can, with economic justification, acquire the entire watershed of its source and manage it solely for water-supply purposes; excluding habitations and factories to keep the water safe and attractive; letting arable lands lie fallow to prevent wasteful runoff and high turbidities; draining swamps to reduce evaporation and eliminate odors, tastes, and color; and cultivating woodlots to hold back winter snows and storm runoff and help to preserve the even tenor of stream flow. As competition for water and land increases, land holdings of water utilities are understandably confined to the marginal lands of water courses, especially those closest to water intakes themselves. Yet water-quality management need not be neglected. Scattered habitations can be equipped with acceptable sanitary facilities; sewage and industrial wastes can be adequately treated or, possibly, diverted into neighboring drainage areas not used for water supply; swamps can be drained; and soil erosion can be controlled—by intelligent land management.

Situations like this are encountered most often when water is drawn from upland sources where small streams traverse land of little value and small area. However, some upland watersheds are big enough to satisfy the demands of great cities.[1]

Lowland Areas. When water is drawn from large lakes and wide rivers that, without additional storage, yield an abundance of water, management of their catchments ordinarily becomes the concern of more than one community;[2] sometimes of more than a single state;[3] even of a single country.[4] Regional, interstate, and international authorities must be set up to manage and protect land and water resources of this kind.

Quality Control. To safeguard their sources, water utilities can fence and post their lands, patrol watersheds, and obtain legislative authority for enforcing reasonable rules and regulations for the sanitary management of the catchment area. When the cost of policing the area outweighs the

[1] The water supplies of Boston, Mass., New York, N.Y., and San Francisco, Calif., are examples.
[2] Examples are many on the Ohio and Mississippi rivers.
[3] Allocation of the waters of the Colorado River to the states of Colorado, Arizona, and California is a notable example.
[4] This is true for the Great Lakes shared with Canada.

cost of purifying its waters in suitable treatment works, purification is often preferred. It is likewise preferred when lakes, reservoirs, and streams become important recreational assets and their enjoyment can be encouraged without endangering their quality. That recreation must be properly supervised and recreational areas suitably located and adequately equipped with sanitary facilities needs no special plea.

Swamp Drainage.   Three types of swamps may occur on catchment areas: (1) rainwater swamps where precipitation accumulates on flat lands, or rivers overflow their banks in times of flood; (2) backwater swamps or reaches of shallow flowage in sluggish, often meandering,[5] streams and at bends or other obstructions to flow; and (3) seepage-outcrop swamps where hillside meets the plain or sand and gravel overlie clay or other impervious formations.

Rainwater swamps can be drained by ditches cut into the flood plain; backwater swamps by channel regulation; and seepage-outcrop swamps by marginal interception of seepage waters along hillsides sometimes supplemented by central surface and subsurface drains.

11-3   Reservoir Siting

In the absence of natural ponds and lakes, intensive development of upland waters requires the construction of impounding reservoirs. Suitable siting is governed by interrelated considerations of adequacy, economy, safety, and palatability of the supply. Desirable factors include:

1. Surface topography that generates a low ratio of dam volume to volume of water stored; for example, a narrow gorge for the dam, and a broad and branching upstream valley for the reservoir. In addition, a favorable site for a stream-diversion conduit and a spillway; and a suitable route for an aqueduct or pipeline to the city.

2. Subsurface geology that ensures (*a*) safe foundations for the dam and other structures, (*b*) tightness against seepage through abutments and beneath the dam, and (*c*) materials, such as sand, gravel, and clay, for construction of the dam and appurtenant structures.

3. A reservoir valley that is sparsely inhabited, neither marshy nor heavily wooded, and not traversed by important roads or railroads; the valley being *so shaped* that waters pouring into the reservoir are not short-circuited to the outlet, and *so sloped* that there is little shallow flowage around the margins. Natural purification by storage can be an important asset. Narrow reservoirs stretching in the direction of prevailing winds are easily short-circuited and may be plagued by high waves. Areas of shallow flowage often support a heavy growth of water plants while they are submerged, and of land plants while they are uncovered. Shore-line vegetation encourages mosquito breeding; decaying vegetation imparts odors, tastes, and color to the water.

[5] After the river *Maiandros* in Asia Minor, proverbial for its windings.

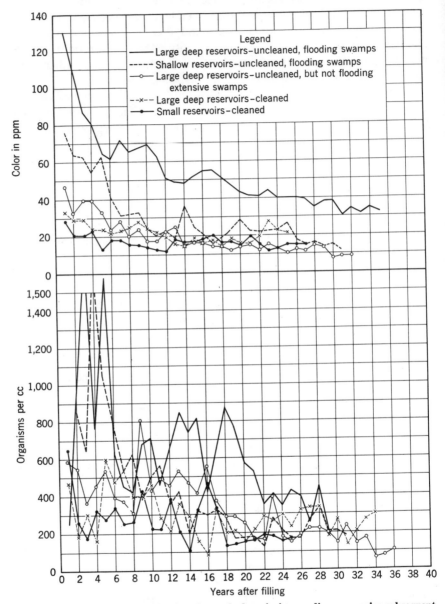

Fig. 11-1. Progressive reduction in color and algae in impounding reservoirs subsequent to their filling. (From *Microscopy of Drinking Water*, Whipple, Fair, and Whipple, John Wiley & Sons, Fourth Edition, 1927.)

4. Reservoir flowage that interferes as little as possible with established property rights, close proximity of the intake to the community served, and location at such elevation that supply can be by gravity.

11-4   Site Preparation

Large reservoirs may inundate a village or two, their dwellings, stores, and public buildings; mills and manufacturing establishments; farms and farmlands, stables, barns, and other outhouses; gardens, playgrounds, and graveyards. Although such properties can be seized by *right of eminent domain*, a wise water authority will proceed with patience and understanding. To be humane and foster good will, the authority will transport dwellings and other wanted and salvable buildings to favorable new sites, establish new cemeteries or remove remains and headstones to grounds chosen by surviving relatives, and assist in reconstituting civil administration and the regional economy.

Initial Stabilization Rates.   When reservoir sites are flooded, land plants die and organic residues of all kinds begin to decompose below the rising waters; nutrients are released; algae and other microorganisms flourish in the eutrophying environment; and odors, tastes, and color are intensified. Ten to 15 years normally elapse before the biodegradable substances are minimized and the reservoir is more or less stabilized. A steady state would be reached if the water within the reservoir became substantially like the incoming water. Although the minimum may be transient, reductions in color and plankton are useful measures of initial stabilization trends. Their course is illustrated in Fig. 11-1. Referred to minimum conditions, rates of improvement approximate 15% annually, implying that 90% improvement is accomplished in less than 15 years.[6] The processes of initial stabilization, although slow, are quite like the processes responsible for the natural purification of polluted waters and can be formulated in much the same terms (Vol. 2).

Site Clearance.   In modern practice, reservoir sites are cleared only in limited measure as follows:

1. Within the entire reservoir area:
   - *a.* Dwellings and other structures are removed or razed.
   - *b.* Barnyards, cesspools, and privies are cleaned; ordure and manure piles are carted away.
   - *c.* Trees and brush are cut close to the ground, usable timber is salvaged, and slash, weeds, and grass are burned.
   - *d.* Swamp muck is dug out to reasonable depths; and residual muck is covered with clean gravel, and the gravel, in turn, with clean sand.

[6] Because the proportion of degradable substances left at the end of each year is $(1 - 0.15) = 0.85$ that at the beginning, $0.85^t = (1 - 0.90)$, and $t = \log 0.10/\log 0.85 = 14.2$ years.

      e. Channels are cut to pockets that would not drain when the water level of the reservoir is lowered.

  2. Within a marginal strip between the high-water mark reached by waves and a contour line about 20 ft below reservoir level:

      a. Stumps, roots, and topsoil are removed.

      b. Marginal swamps are drained or filled.

      c. Banks are steepened to produce shore-water depths close to 8 ft during much of the growing season of aquatic plants. To do this, upper reservoir reaches may have to be improved by excavation or fill or by building auxiliary dams across shallow arms of the impoundage.

Soil stripping, namely, the removal of all topsoil containing more than 1 or 2% organic matter from the entire reservoir area, is no longer economical. The stored waters can be purified more cheaply. A more uniformly satisfactory product water is obtained as an incidental advantage. Moreover, benefits of stripping are confined, in any case, only to the first decade and a half of reservoir life (Fig. 11-1). Unstripped reservoirs catch up with stripped ones in that time, but see Vol. 2 for lake eutrophication.

In malarious regions, impounding reservoirs should be so constructed and managed that they will not breed dangerous numbers of anopheline mosquitoes. To this purpose, banks should be clean and reasonably steep. To keep them so, they may have to be protected by riprap.

11-5 Reservoir Management

The introduction of impounding reservoirs into a river system or the existence of natural lakes and ponds within it raise questions of quality control that are best discussed by themselves under the general title of limnology. This is done in Vol. 2, rather than here. What should be said here, however, is that some limnological factors are important not only in the management of ponds, lakes, and reservoirs but also in reservoir design.

Quality Control. Of concern in the quality management of reservoirs is the control of water weeds and algal blooms; the bleaching of color; the settling of turbidity; and the selection of water of optimal quality and temperature by shifting intake depths in accordance with water conditions at different horizons.

In times of storm, gulls often seek shelter on bodies of fresh water within flight range from the ocean. As scavengers of the sea, they may transfer pollutants both mechanically and through droppings to the waters on which they come to rest. Firing blank cartridges and, if necessary, live ammunition may frighten invading shore birds away and delay their return for acceptable lengths of time. Roosting mud hens and some varieties of duck are more difficult to control. Some small reservoirs have been cleared of large birds by stretching wires to form 200- to 500-ft grids over them, about 10 to 20 ft above high-water mark, or by covering about half the surface area with well-timed water spray. Song birds are not affected by wires; they are too small and quick.

Evaporation Control. The thought that oil spread on water will suppress evaporation is not new. Yet the threshold of its realization has only just been crossed, thanks largely to Irving Langmuir's Nobel Prize winning work.[7] What has been learned is (1) that certain chemicals spread spontaneously on water as layers no more than a molecule thick; (2) that these substances include alcohol (hydroxyl) or fatty acid (carboxyl) groups attached to a saturated paraffin chain of carbon atoms; (3) that the resulting *monolayers* consist of molecules oriented in the same direction and thereby offer more resistance to the passage of water molecules than do thick layers of oil composed of multilayers of haphazardly oriented molecules; and (4) that the hydrophilic radicals (OH or COOH) at one end of the paraffin chain move down into the water phase while the hydrophobic paraffin chains, themselves, stretch up into the gaseous phase. Examples of suitable chemicals are the following alcohols and corresponding fatty acids: cetyl alcohol, in technical language hexadeconal, with $C_{16}OH$ as its abbreviated symbol; stearyl alcohol or octadeconal, $C_{18}OH$; palmitic acid, $C_{15}COOH$; and stearic acid, $C_{17}COOH$. Of these, hexadeconal spreads spontaneously; octadeconal does not. Yet a mixture of the two does, because the shorter chain presumably drags the longer chain along. Moreover, all long-chain, nonspreading compounds can form monolayers if they are applied as solutions in volatile solvents. However, the solvent must evaporate completely; otherwise, molecules left behind become molecular holes in the film and reduce its effectiveness.

The principles governing evaporation control are discussed further in connection with transport processes by which gases or vapors enter or leave water (Vol. 2). A satisfactory technology of applying monolayers to large water surfaces and keeping them there remains to be worked out. There may be bacterial degradation of the films as well as destruction by wind and wave and adsorption onto shore and vegetation.

11-6 Dams and Dikes

Generally speaking, the great dams and barrages of the world are the most massive structures built by man. To block river channels carved through mountains in geological time periods, many of them are wedged

[7] V. K. La Mer, Editor, *Retardation of Evaporation by Monolayers: Transport Processes,* Academic Press, New York, 1962. Langmuir (1881–1957) received the Nobel Prize in chemistry in 1932 for his work on the structure of matter and surface chemistry. He is known to hydrologists also for his experiments on seeding clouds with silver iodide to start rainfall.

between high valley walls and impound days and months of flow in deep reservoirs. Occasionally, impoundages reach such levels that their waters would spill over low saddles of the divide into neighboring watersheds if saddle dams or dikes were not built to complement the main structure. In other ways, too, surface topography and subsurface geology are of controlling influence. Hydraulically, they determine the siting of dams; volumes of storage, including subsurface storage in glacial and alluvial deposits; and spillway and diversion arrangements. Structurally, they identify the nature and usefulness of foundations and the location and economic availability of suitable construction materials. Soils and rock of many kinds can go into the building of dams and dikes. Timber and steel have found more limited application. Like most other civil engineering constructions, therefore, dams and their reservoirs are derived largely from their own environment.

Structurally, dams resist the pressure of waters against their upstream face by gravity, arch action, or both. Hydraulically, they stem the tides of water by their tightness as a whole and the relative imperviousness of their foundations and abutments. Coordinately, they combine hydraulic and structural properties to keep seepage within tolerable limits and so channeled that the working structures are and remain safe.

Materials and methods of construction create dams of many types. The following are most common: (a) embankment dams of earth, rock, or both; and (b) masonry dams (today largely concrete dams) built as gravity, arched or buttressed structures.

Embankment Dams. Rock, sand, clay, and silt are the principal materials of construction for rock and earth embankments. Permeables provide weight, impermeables water tightness. Optimal excavation, handling, placement, distribution, and compaction in special reference to selective placement of available materials challenge the ingenuity of the designer and constructor. Permeables form the shells or shoulders, impermeables the core or blanket of the finished embankment. Depending in some measure on the abundance or scarcity of clays, relatively thick cores are centered in substantially vertical position, or relatively thin cores are displaced towards the upstream face in inclined position. Common features of an earth dam with central clay core wall are illustrated in Fig. 2-3. Concrete walls can take the place of clay cores, but they do not adjust well to the movements of newly placed, consolidating embankments and foundations; by contrast, clay is plastic enough to do so. If materials are properly dispatched from borrow pits, earth shells are ideally graded from fine at the watertight core to coarse and well-draining at the upstream and downstream faces. In rock fills, too, there must be effective transition from core to shell, the required change in particle size ranging from a fraction of a millimeter for fine sand through coarse sand (about 1 mm) and gravel (about 10 mm) to rock of appreciable size.

Within the range of destructive wave action, stone placed either as paving or as riprap wards off erosion of the upstream face. Concrete aprons are not so satisfactory, sharing as they do most of the disadvantages of concrete core walls. A wide berm at the foot of the protected slope helps to keep riprap in place. To save the downstream face from washing away, it is commonly seeded to grass or covering vines and provided with a system of surface and subsurface drains. Berms break up the face into manageable drainage areas and give access to slopes for mowing and maintenance. Although they are more or less horizontal, berms do slope

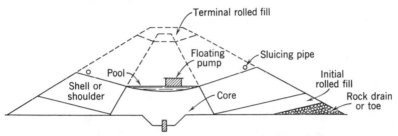

Fig. 11-2. Construction of earth dam by hydraulic fill method.

inward to gutters; moreover, they are pitched lengthwise for the gutters to conduct runoff to surface or subsurface main drains and through them safely down the face or abutment of the dam, eventually into the stream channel.

Earth embankments are constructed either as *rolled fills* or *hydraulic fills*; rock embankments are built as *uncompacted* (dumped) or *compacted* fills. In *rolled earth fills*, successive layers of earth 4 to 12 in. thick are spread, rolled, and consolidated. Sheep's-foot rollers do the compacting, but they are helped in their work by heavy earth-moving vehicles bringing fill to the dam or bulldozing it into place. Portions of embankment that cannot be rolled in this way are compacted by hand or power tampers. Strips adjacent to concrete core walls, the walls of outlet structures, and the wingwalls of spillway sections are examples.

In *hydraulic fills* water-carried soil is deposited differentially to form an embankment graded from coarse at the two faces of the dam to fine in the central core. In favorable situations, materials are washed from side-hill borrow pits by water jets (giants or monitors), passed through horizontal racks (grizzlies) ahead of sluiceways or pipes to remove oversized boulders, and transported to the shoulders of the dam. There, the mixture of earth and water is discharged inward over beaches towards a central pool (Fig. 11-2). As the water gushes from the openings, it spreads and loses

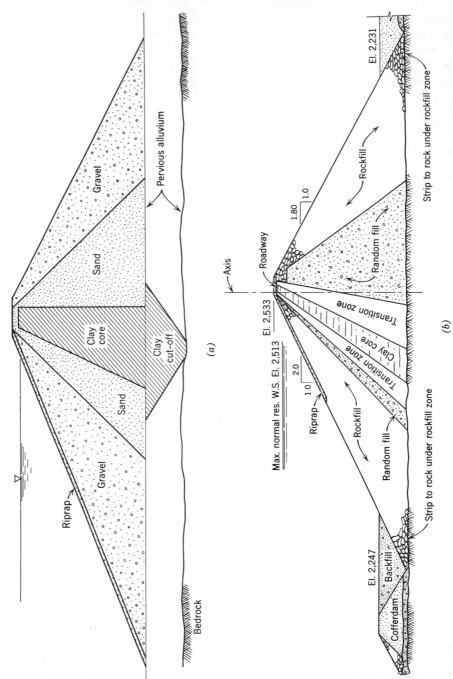

Fig. 11-3. Zoned earth-fill and rock-fill dams. *Kindness of Arthur Casagrande.* (*a*) Earth-fill dam on pervious alluvium. (*b*) Rock-fill dam on

much of its speed and carrying power. Coarse components of its soil burden drop out first, fine components last. The finest grains do not settle before they reach the quiescent, central pool maintained for this purpose. Water relieved of wanted fines is wasted downstream, possibly after treatment, or it is repumped to the borrow area. Grain-size distribution of available media (Sec. 9-4), pool width, and detention time are regulated by pumping so as to govern the composition of the core. If grain size is carefully controlled and the component sizes permit it, the core will solidify substantially in a short time; more often there are too many fines, and the core remains fluid and unstable and takes much time to consolidate. Pore water drains away from the core through the surrounding permeable shell. In practice, the pool has often been kept as wide as the remaining height of the dam.

Where it is more convenient or economic to transport fill to the dam site by truck, tractor, train, or belt, embankment fill can still be delivered from sluiceways or pipes if constituent materials are first discharged into a head chamber (hog box) along with enough water to *fluidize* the component solids. Fill dumped onto the dam itself and washed into place by jets of water (hydraulic placement) is, understandably, not so well graded as *true* hydraulic fill. Failure of some hydraulic fills and improved economy of rolled-fill operations have tipped the scales in favor of rolled fills for the present.

Methods as well as materials of construction determine the strength, tightness, and stability of embankment dams. Whether their axis should be straight or curved depends largely upon topographic conditions. Whether upstream curves are in fact useful is open to question. Intended is axial compression in the core and prevention of cracks as the dam settles. Spillways are incorporated into some embankment dams; divorced from others in separate constructions (Sec. 11-11).

Where rock outcrops on canyon walls and can be blasted into the stream bed or where spillways or stream-diversion tunnels are constructed in rock, rock embankment becomes particularly economic. In modern construction, rock fills are given internal clay cores or membranes in somewhat the same fashion as earth fills (Fig. 11-3). Concrete slabs or timber sheathing once much used on the upstream face can be dangerously stressed and fail as the fill itself, or its foundation, settles. They are no longer in favor.

Masonry Dams.   A gravity masonry dam with a central gate-controlled spillway is shown in some detail in Fig. 11-4; arched and buttressed dams are outlined in Fig. 11-5. In the construction of gravity dams, cyclopean masonry and mass concrete embedding great boulders have, in the course of time, given way to poured concrete; in the case of arched dams rubble

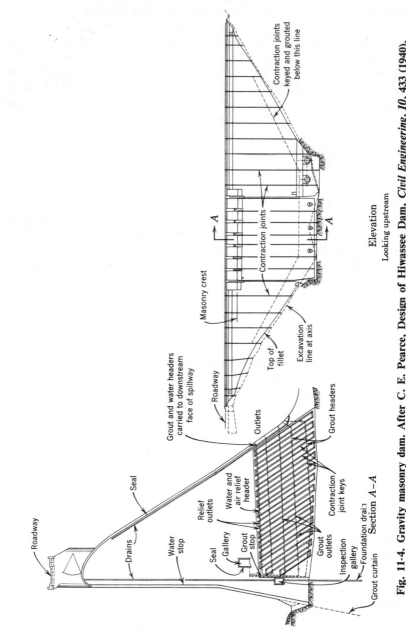

Elevation

Looking upstream

Contraction joints keyed and grouted below this line

Contraction joints

Masonry crest

Top of fillet

Excavation line at axis

Roadway

Grout and water headers carried to downstream face of spillway

Outlets

Seal

Grout headers

Roadway

Drains

Water stop

Seal

Gallery

Grout stop

Relief outlets

Water and air relief header

Contraction joint keys

Grout outlets

Inspection gallery

Foundation drain

Grout curtain

Section A-A

Fig. 11-4. Gravity masonry dam. After C. E. Pearce, Design of Hiwassee Dam, *Civil Engineering, 10*, 433 (1940).

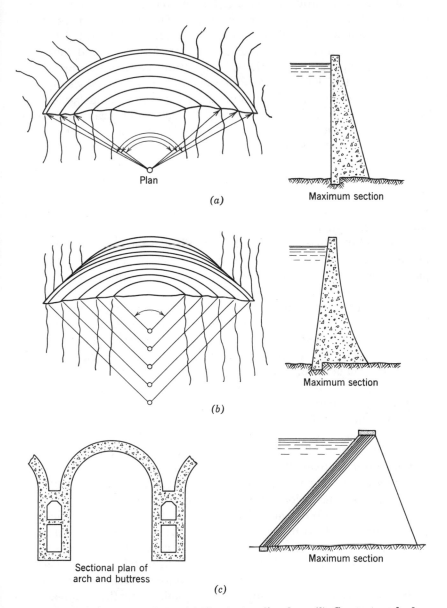

Plan

(a)

Maximum section

(b)

Maximum section

Sectional plan of
arch and buttress

(c)

Maximum section

Fig. 11-5. Arched masonry dams. (a) Constant radius dam. (b) Constant angle dam. (c) Multiple arch (hollow buttress) dam.

has also ceded the field to concrete. Gravity dams are designed to be in compression under all conditions of loading. They will fit into almost any site with suitable foundation. Some arched dams are designed to resist water pressures and other forces as vertical cantilevers and horizontal arches simultaneously; for others, arch action alone is assumed, thrust being transmitted laterally to both sides of the valley, which must be strong enough to serve as abutments. In constant-radius[8] dams, the upstream face is vertical or, at most, slanted steeply near the bottom; the downstream face is projected as a series of concentric, circular contours in plan. Dams of this kind fit well into U-shaped valleys, where cantilever action is expected to respond favorably to the high-intensity bottom loads. In constant-angle[8] dams, the upstream face bulges up-valley; the downstream face curves inward like the small of a man's back. Dams of this kind fit well into V-shaped valleys where arch action becomes their main source of strength at all horizons.

Concrete buttresses are designed to support flat slabs or multiple arches in buttress dams. Here and there, wood and steel structures have taken the place of reinforced concrete. Their upstream face is normally sloped 1 on 1 and may terminate in a vertical cut-off wall.

All masonry dams must rest on solid rock. Foundation pressures are high in gravity dams, abutment pressures intense in arched dams. Buttress dams are light on their foundations. Making foundations tight by sealing contained pockets or cavities and seams or faults with cement or cement-and-sand grout under pressure is an important responsibility. Low-pressure grouting (up to 40 psig) may be followed by high-pressure grouting (200 psig) from permanent galleries in the dam itself, and a curtain of grout may be forced into the foundation at the heel of gravity dams to obstruct seepage and reduce uplift.

Concrete is generally cast in place in blocks no more than 50 ft wide and lifts no more than 10 ft high (5 ft for gravity dams). The heat output of setting cement is controlled in various ways: (1) by allowing it to be dissipated before new blocks are cast; (2) by including a system of cooling pipes in the dam; (3) by employing a lean mix for the interior concrete of gravity dams; and (4) by resorting to low-heat cements. The damage is done when the dam contracts on cooling. Keyways are cast into adjacent blocks to increase their resistance to shear, and metal water stops are let into them to reduce seepage through vertical joints between them. At the same time asphaltic paint is applied to adjoining lateral interior faces to leave blocks free to move as individual units in response to temperature changes.

[8] Constant-radius dams are also called constant-center or single-center dams; constant-angle dams are also called variable-center dams. Figure 11-5 shows why.

11-7   Structural Design

The external forces shown in Fig. 11-6 act upon all dams regardless of materials and methods of construction. Understandably, however, design procedures are quite different for the two main constructional categories: gravity or arched masonry dams on the one hand; earth or rock embankments on the other. In the design of masonry dams, resistance to external forces is of primary concern; in the design of embankment dams, control of internal seepage is the dominant consideration.

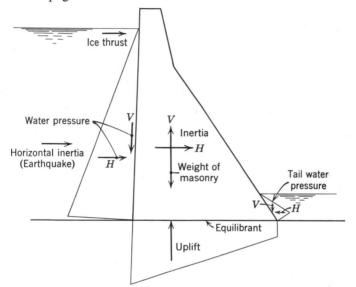

Fig. 11-6. Forces acting on masonry dams. V = vertical component of force, H = horizontal component of force.

The nature, magnitude, and line of action of external forces are summarized below.

Water Pressure.   For a unit width of dam, the horizontal component of hydrostatic pressure is $wh^2/2$, where w is the specific weight of water (62.4 lb/cu ft) and h is its depth on the upstream face. There is an opposite but smaller horizontal component of hydrostatic pressure on parts of the downstream face below tail-water level. In each instance, pressure distribution increases uniformly from zero at the top to h at the bottom, and the resultant is centered at a distance $\frac{1}{3}h$ above the base. The vertical component of hydrostatic pressure is wh; it acts through the center of gravity of the water column overlying the face (upstream or downstream). In some instances, fluidized silt rather than clear water exerts the pressure; its weight may be as much as 90 lb/cu ft.

Uplift Pressure. For a unit width of dam, vertical uplift is *wht*, where *h* is the average head of water (ft) and *t* is the width of the base subjected to uplift. The resulting uplift acts through the center of area of the assumed pressure triangle or trapezoid. A linear decrease from full or two-thirds hydrostatic pressure at the heel to tailwater or atmospheric pressure at the toe and extending over the full or the upstream half or two-thirds of the base has been postulated in many designs, depending, among other things, upon the extent of internal drainage for which provisions have been made.[9] Uplifts of similar nature are assumed to be generated at other than base levels.

Ice Thrust. Three types of ice are encountered in cold climates: sheet, frazil,[10] and anchor ice. Of the three, sheet ice is of concern in the design of dams and similar structures; frazil and anchor ice are of concern in the design and operation of water intakes (Sec. 11-12). Sheet ice expands as its temperature is raised by the warmth of the sun and ambient air. As shown by Rose,[11] the resulting thrust varies with the rate of temperature rise, thickness of sheet, and degree of lateral restraint. Experimental investigations by the Bureau of Reclamation and reported by Monfore[12] show field measurements of ice thrusts as high as 20,000 lb/lin ft on the 445-ft long, 125-ft high concrete arch dam impounding Eleven Mile Canyon Reservoir, part of the municipal water supply of Denver, Colorado. The values obtained are supported by the results of laboratory investigations.

Earthquake Inertia and Oscillatory Hydrostatic Forces. Earthquakes create both horizontal and vertical inertia forces. Horizontal inertia equals *kmg*, where *k* is the ratio of the acceleration caused by the earthquake to that of gravity, *g*, and *m* is the mass of the dam. For earth foundations, *k* is often assumed to be as little as 0.1 or 0.2; for rock foundations, as much as 0.75. Vertical inertia reduces the effective weight of the dam only momentarily. Like the weight of the structure itself, inertia forces act at the center of area of the cross-section. Oscillatory variation in hydrostatic pressure, earthquake induced, is assumed to equal $0.555kwh^2$ and act at a distance $4h/3\pi$ above the bottom of the reservoir.[13]

[9] Committee Report, Uplift in Masonry Dams, *Trans. Am. Soc. Civil Engrs.*, **117**, 1218 (1952).
[10] A French-Canadian term derived from the French and applied to ice that resembles fine spicular forge cinders.
[11] Edwin Rose, Thrust Exerted by Expanding Ice Sheet, *Trans. Am. Soc. Civil Engrs.*, **112**, 871 (1947).
[12] G. E. Monfore, Ice pressure against Dams, a Symposium, *Trans. Am. Soc. Civil Engrs.*, **119**, 26 (1954).
[13] Theodor von Kármán (1881–1963), Hungarian-American Professor and Director, Aeronautical Laboratory, California Institute of Technology, *Trans. Am. Soc. Civil Engrs.*, **98**, 434 (1933).

Foundation Pressure.   This pressure is the vectorial sum of the external forces and the weight of the dam itself (150 lb per cu ft for mass concrete, about 125 lb per cu ft for dumped rock, or 135 lb per cu ft for rock compacted in 2-ft lifts by 10-ton vibratory rollers; and 100 lb per cu ft for sand and gravel or up to 140 lb per cu ft for glacial till). The weight acts through the center of area of the cross-section whether the reservoir is empty or full. In gravity masonry dams, the equilibrant to the foundation pressure is kept within the middle third of the base to avoid tensile stresses, and similar requirements are made for all other levels of the structure.

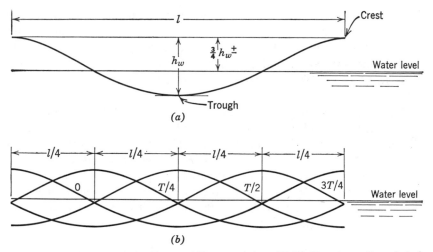

Fig. 11-7. Surface waves. (*a*) **Wave profile at zero time,** (*b*) **Profiles at zero time, $\frac{1}{4}$, $\frac{1}{2}$, $\frac{3}{4}$, and 1 T (period) when wave has advanced zero, $\frac{1}{4}$, $\frac{1}{2}$, $\frac{3}{4}$, and 1 l (length).**

Wave Action.   Wind waves are born and grow when wind sweeping over a water surface drags the water along and pushes against the wave crests formed. As shown in Fig. 11-7, the profile of shallow surface waves is sinusoidal. Each wave is characterized by a length, l_w, from crest to crest, a height, h_w, from trough to crest, a period, t_w, or time interval between the passage of successive crests past a reference point, and a velocity, $v_w = l_w/t_w$. The wave crest rises above mean water level by about three-fourths of the wave height.[14]

In water of constant depth, d,

$$v_w = [(gl_w/2\pi) \tan h(2\pi d/l_w)]^{\frac{1}{2}} \qquad (11\text{-}1)$$

[14] D. DuB. Gaillard, Wave Action in Relation to Engineering Structures, U.S. Corps of Engineers, *Prof. Paper* 31 (1904). Gaillard's name is attached to the deepest cut of the Panama Canal constructed under his supervision.

g being the gravity constant. In deep waters, wave velocities eventually catch up with wind speeds. If d/l_w is large, $\tan h(2\pi d/l_w)$ approaches unity, and the velocity of deep-water waves ($d > l_w/2$) is obtained as

$$v_w = (gl_w/2\pi)^{\frac{1}{2}} \qquad (11\text{-}2)$$

If d/l_w is small, $\tan h(2\pi d/l_w)$ approaches $2\pi d/l_w$ and the velocity of shallow-water waves ($d < l_w/25$) becomes

$$v_w = (gd)^{\frac{1}{2}} \qquad (11\text{-}3)$$

The water particles in low deep-water waves move in circles and complete one revolution in time $t_w = l_w/v_w = (l_w/2\pi g)^{\frac{1}{2}}$. In low shallow-water waves, particles move back and forth more or less horizontally. For v_w in miles per hour, l_w in feet, and t_w in seconds, Eq. 11-2 states that numerically $v_w = 1.542l_w^{\frac{1}{2}} = 3.49t_w$; whence $l_w = 0.422v_w^2 = 5.12t_w^2$, and $t_w = 0.433l_w^{\frac{1}{2}} = 0.287v_w$.

Wave height, as shown by Stevenson,[15] is governed by the length of the *fetch* or maximum clear sweep of the wind. Understandably, it is also a matter of wind velocity and duration of blow. Stevenson's classical formulation is $h_N = 1.5F_N^{\frac{1}{2}} + (2.5 - F_N^{\frac{1}{4}})$, where F_N is the fetch in nautical miles. The term in parentheses is dropped when $2.5 = F_N^{\frac{1}{4}}$ or $F_N = 39$ nautical miles. Observations on inland reservoirs have suggested the following formulations[16] for the range $0 < (gF/w^2) < 4000$, or $0.1 < F < 25$ and $10 < w < 80$:

$$h_s = 0.22(w^2/g)^{0.53}F^{0.47} \qquad (11\text{-}4)$$

and

$$t_s = 6.0(w/g)^{0.44}(F/g)^{0.28} \qquad (11\text{-}5)$$

where h_s is the average or *significant wave height* of the highest one-third of the waves, w the wind velocity in mph about 25 ft above the water surface, F the effective fetch in statute miles, g the gravity constant, and t_s the wave period in seconds.

In contrast to the free sweep of the open sea, the fetch of inland waters is restricted by proximate shores. A procedure for determining the effective fetch, based upon the assumption that the effectiveness of the wind is proportional to the cosine of the angle from the average wind

[15] Thomas Stevenson, *Design and Construction of Harbors*, 2nd Ed., A. J. Black, Edinburgh, 1874. Thomas Stevenson (1818–1887), engineer and meteorologist, was the father of Robert Louis Stevenson.
[16] Thorndike Saville, Jr., E. W. McClendon, and A. L. Cochran, Freeboard Allowances for Waves in Inland Reservoirs, *J. Waterways and Harbors Div., Am. Soc. Civil Engrs.,* **93**, 1962.

direction, is exemplified in Fig. 11-8. The minimum duration of wind required to produce given wave heights is

$$t_d = 1100F/(gt_s) \qquad (11\text{-}6)$$

where t_d is the duration in minutes. The wind velocity over the clear sweep of water is 8% greater than its velocity over land when the fetch is 0.5 mile and reaches 31% at and above 6 miles with intermediate values of 13, 21, and 28% for 1, 2, and 4 miles of fetch respectively.

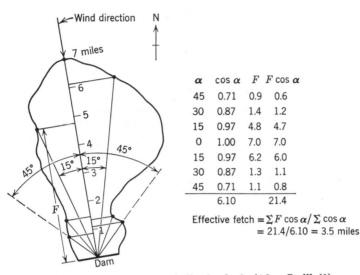

α	$\cos \alpha$	F	$F \cos \alpha$
45	0.71	0.9	0.6
30	0.87	1.4	1.2
15	0.97	4.8	4.7
0	1.00	7.0	7.0
15	0.97	6.2	6.0
30	0.87	1.3	1.1
45	0.71	1.1	0.8
		6.10	21.4

Effective fetch $= \Sigma F \cos \alpha / \Sigma \cos \alpha$
$= 21.4/6.10 = 3.5$ miles

Fig. 11-8. Computation of effective fetch. (After *Saville*.[16])

The run-up, h_r, on the face of a dam or other embankment is a function of the wave height and length and the steepness and nature of the surface. Generalized values of the relative run-up h_r/h_w for different embankment slopes and ratios of wave height and length h_w/l_w are shown in Fig. 11-9 for deepwater waves ($l_w = 5.12t_w^2$).

Measurement of *wind tide set-up* (or rise in water level at the leeward shore) for the Zuider Zee dams and dikes in Holland are approximated by the relationship

$$h_s' = w^2F \cos \alpha/(1400d) \qquad (11\text{-}7)$$

where h_s' is the wind set up above pool (or still-water) level in feet, w is the wind velocity in miles per hour, F is the fetch in miles, d is the mean depth of water in feet, and α is the angle between the wind direction and a normal to the structure or shoreline. After the wind subsides, the water at the leeward shore falls while that at the windward shore rises. This rhythmic rising and falling repeats itself and is called a *seiche*, a French word pronounced sāsh (Vol. 2). Like winds themselves, seiches are caused also by barometric pressure differences between opposite shores.

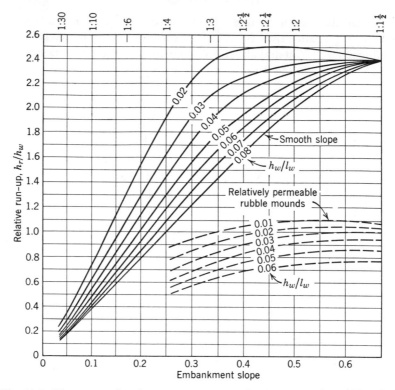

Fig. 11-9. Wave run-up for given wave steepness and embankment slope. (After *Saville*.[16])

Example 11-1. The overland travel of winds at right angles to a proposed dam[17] has been clocked at a speed of 20 mph for 90 min. The effective fetch of the wind is 7.5 miles. The slope of the dam at full reservoir level (elevation 173.0) is to be $1:2\frac{1}{2}$, and the average elevation of the reservoir bottom over a 5-mile stretch in advance of the dam is 100 ft above mean sea level. The wind-tide fetch is 31 miles.

Find: (1) the overwater wind speed; (2) the significant wave height; (3) the significant wave period; (4) the minimum wind duration required to reach the significant wave height; (5) the significant wave length and steepness; (6) the (reservoir-depth): (wave-length) ratio; (7) the wind tide or set-up; (8) the run-up; and (9) the maximum elevation reached by the waves (including set-up).

1. Overwater wind speed, $w = 20 \times 1.31 = 26$ mph.
2. By Eq. 11-4, $h_s = 0.22[(26)^2/32.2]^{0.53} \times 7.5^{0.47} = 2.8$ ft.

[17] The basic information for this example is taken from Reference 16 with but slight modification.

3. By Eq. 11-5, $t_s = 6.0(26/32.2)^{0.44} \times (7.5/32.2)^{0.28} = 3.6$ sec.
4. By Eq. 11-6, $t_d = 1100 \times 7.5/(32.2 \times 3.6) = 71$ min.
5. $l_s = 5.12 \times (3.6)^2 = 66$ ft; $h_s/l_s = 2.8/66 = 0.042$.
6. $d/l_s = 73/66 = 1.1$.
7. By Eq. 11-7, $h_t = (26)^2 \times 7.5 \times 1/(1400 \times 73) = 0.2$ ft.
8. From Fig. 11-9, $h_r/h_s = 2.06$ for $h_s/l_s = 0.042$ and a slope of $1:2\frac{1}{2}$. Hence $h_r = 2.06 \times 2.8 = 5.8$ ft.
9. Maximum water level: $173.0 + 0.2 + 5.8 = 179.0$ ft.

Other External Forces.   If the nappe of water falling over the crest or spillway of a dam is not well ventilated, dangerous vibrational pulsations may be generated. Responsible for them is the following sequence of events and its repetition: the air between the falling sheet of water and the structure is sucked away; a partial vacuum is created; the nappe is pulled back against the dam; the sheet of water breaks; and air is re-admitted to the nappe. Wind pressures are seldom large enough to be taken into account.

Gravity dams and embankments may fail by sliding or shear along any horizontal plane (1) at foundation level, (2) in the dam proper, or (3) in the foundation itself. The factor of safety against sliding is commonly made 1.25. In gravity masonry dams, allowable working stresses are placed at about 600 psi for compression and 250 psi for shear; the coefficient of friction between blocks of masonry is assumed to be 0.65, and a factor of safety of 2.0 against overturning (by rotation about the toe) is not an unusual working assumption.

11-8   Drainage Design

Dams and their foundations are seldom perfectly tight. Some water is bound to make its way into and through them: little through masonry and rock foundations; more through embankments and earth foundations. The resulting losses are not reprehensible in themselves; not enough water is lost in these ways. What is objectionable is that seepage will endanger the structure unless it is placed under control.

Seepage Dangers.   Earth embankments will fail, when water escapes at their downstream face sufficiently fast (1) to erode the surface and cause it to slough,[18] or (2) to dislodge soil grains along a passage or *pipe* opened up within the earthwork. Piping may occur also in earth foundations. When it does, the drag force of upward flow actually exceeds the weight in water of the grains removed. This inequality can be expressed as follows:

$$s > (1 - f)(\gamma_s - \gamma) \quad \text{or, closely,} \quad s > (1 - f)(s_s - 1) \quad (11\text{-}8)$$

---

[18] The upstream face may slough, too, if pore water is not released fast enough to relieve pore pressure when the water surface is lowered rapidly.

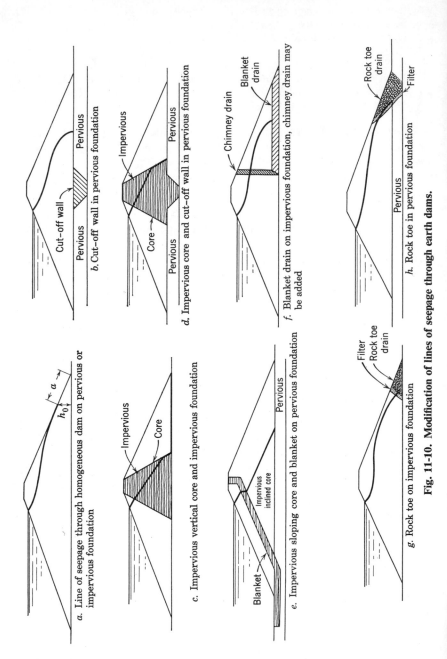

Fig. 11-10. Modification of lines of seepage through earth dams.

where s is the hydraulic gradient through the soil or foundation, γ the specific weight of water and γ_s the specific weight of the soil or foundation material, s_s its specific gravity, and f its porosity. Moreover, the velocity of flow must exceed the settling velocity of the grains washed away by upward flow (Vol. 2).

Example 11-2. Find the hydraulic gradient and seepage velocity at which grains of specific gravity 2.64 (quartz) in soil with a porosity of 39% are subject to removal by piping.

From Eq. 11-8, $s = (1-0.39)(264-1) = 1.00$. In this case, therefore, the critical seepage velocity happens to equal the Darcy coefficient of permeability because in accordance with Darcy's law (Eq. 9-4) $v = Ks$ and $v = K$ for $s = 1.00$.

Creation of a path of least resistance through earth embankments by the chance alignment of gravel and small stones into the equivalent of a French or blind drain must be carefully avoided.

Seepage Control.   As shown in Fig. 11-10 the free water surface or line of seepage in embankment dams can, by selective construction, be moved up or down vertically and upstream or downstream horizontally. Controls are given two forms in particular:

1. Earth or masonry cores are introduced to deflect seepage from the downstream face. They do so by interposing resistance to flow and producing a high loss of head (c and d in Fig. 11-10).

2. Paths of least resistance are provided by constructing (a) toe drains, (b) horizontal blanket drains (as continuous blankets or interior continuous strips with intermittent strip drains leading to the downstream toe), and (c) chimney drains. These deflect the line of seepage by the opposite expedient of drawing the escaping waters into themselves (f and g in Fig. 11-10). Rock-fill embankments are self-controlled in the second sense. For control of seepage through earth foundations (1) a clay or masonry cut-off wall or a clay blanket obstructs underflow (b and e in Fig. 11-10), and (2) a rock toe provides safe drainage while weighting down the foundation (h in Fig. 11-10). To keep soil from washing into rock toes, the rock must grade into the embankment and foundation. The principles of filtration enunciated in Vol. 2 apply in this connection. Where necessary, similar transitions are provided between core and shoulder materials.

As shown in Fig. 11-4 seepage through gravity masonry dams can be bled away effectively through drainage channels terminating in drainage and inspection galleries running the length of the dam just above tail-water height. Water removed through systems of this kind cannot exert uplift on any horizon unless it is placed under pressure by obstructions of one kind or another.

Generally speaking, modern dam construction is distinguished from earlier practice by giving as much thought and expression to the safe removal of seepage as to its prevention.

11-9 Flow Nets and Seepage Calculations

When water seeps through an embankment dam of homogeneous material, the cross-sectional area of flow diminishes as the line of seepage drops. Accordingly, flow, though steady, is nonuniform, and the line of seepage can be determined by analytical methods only if pertinent boundary conditions can be established. This is possible in certain simple cases. Otherwise, the designer must resort to (1) graphical methods of flow-net construction, (2) models in which dyes trace flow lines in a thin section

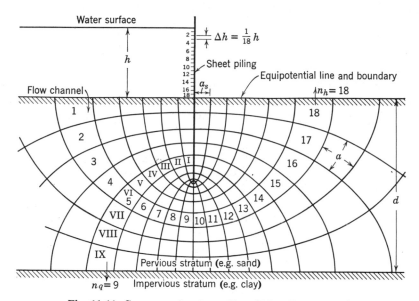

Fig. 11-11. Seepage under sheet piling. (After *Forchheimer*.)

between glass or plastic plates, or (3) electrical analogies. The flow nets in Figs. 9-8 and 11-11 have been prepared in accordance with the principles laid down in Sec. 9-20.

Figure 11-11 depicts Forchheimer's[19] classical solution of a flow net centered around sheet piling driven into a foundation. In this example, possibly that of a coffer dam, the boundary conditions are clearly demarked. The ground surface at either side of the sheet piling is the locus of horizontal equipotential lines; the pressure on the water side equals the head of water h above the ground surface; the pressure on the opposite side is atmospheric or zero in terms of head of water; the bottom of the homogeneous and pervious foundation stratum and the sides of the sheet

[19] Philip Forchheimer, *Hydraulik*, B. Teubner, Leipzig, 1930.

piling constitute the boundaries of the flow lines. The flow net of Figure 11-11 includes $n_h = 18$ equal drops in head Δh or fields, and $n_q = 9$ flow channels. If we call the average dimension of any one of the four-sided figures within the network a, it follows that the hydraulic gradient $s = \Delta h / a$, where $\Delta h = h / n_h$. In accordance with Eq. 9-46, therefore, the quantity of water flowing through a unit width of foundation becomes $q = K h n_q / n_h$.

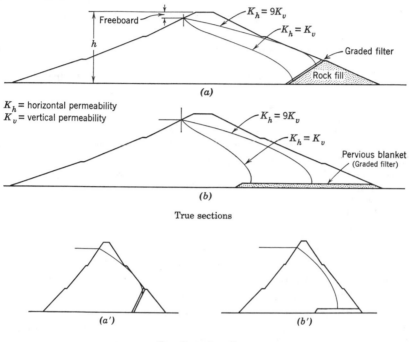

Fig. 11-12. Seepage through stratified dam sections. (After *Arthur Casagrande.*)

In constructing flow nets, it is well to recall that, in nature, soils are seldom *isotropic*, i.e., they do not possess the same properties in all directions. Granular materials laid down in water, for example, are generally stratified horizontally and offer more resistance to flow in a vertical direction ($K = K_{min}$) than in a horizontal direction ($K = K_{max}$). As illustrated in Fig. 11-12, the flow net for such an anisotropic medium can be developed from a transformed cross-section in which all dimensions in the direction of maximum permeability, K_{max}, are foreshortened in proportion to $(K_{min} / K_{max})^{1/2}$. The flow net for the transformed cross-section is then projected back into the true cross-section by multiplying all dimensions, including those of the flow net, by the reciprocal of this factor. In computing the quantity of seepage, the geometric mean of the maximum and minimum permeabilities, namely, $(K_{max}K_{min})^{1/2}$, is substituted for K in Eq. 9-46.

The seepage pressure at any point within the soil is tangent to the flow-line through the point and equal to $s\gamma$, where γ is the specific weight of water. The head remaining within the soil at any point such as equipotential line k is $[(n_h - k)/n_h]h$, and the excess hydrostatic pressure p is

$$p = (1 - k/n_h)\gamma h \qquad (11-9)$$

Example 11-3. If the height of water in Fig. 11-11 is 40 ft and the foundation material has a coefficient of permeability $K = 2 \times 10^{-3}$ cm/sec, what are (1) the seepage through each foot width of the foundation, (2) the intensity of the excess hydrostatic pressure on the upstream side of the bottom of the sheet piling, and (3) the maximum hydraulic gradient and its relation to the coefficient of permeability?

1. From Eq. 9-46, $q = 2 \times 10^{-3} \times 3.28 \times 10^{-2} \times 40 \times \frac{9}{18} = 1.31 \times 10^{-3}$ cfs. This equals $1.31 \times 10^{-3} \times 6.47 \times 10^5 = 850$ gpd/ft width.

2. From Eq. 11-9, $p = (1 - \frac{8}{18})40 \times 0.433 = 9.62$ psig.

3. The maximum hydraulic gradient occurs in the flow channel adjacent to the piling. If this measures 9 ft at the ground surface, $s = \Delta h/a_s = 40/(18 \times 9) = 0.25$. In accordance with Example 11-2, therefore, there is no danger of piping if the medium has a porosity close to 40% and a specific gravity of 2.65. The associated velocity v equals Ks; or it is found from (1) as $q/(n_q a_s) = 1.31 \times 10^{-3}/(9 \times 9) = 1.62 \times 10^{-5}$ fps, or $1.62 \times 10^{-5}/(3.28 \times 10^{-2}) = 4.94 \times 10^{-4}$ cm/sec. Hence $v/K = 4.94 \times 10^{-4}/(2 \times 10^{-3}) = 0.25$, as is to be expected.

To trace the line of seepage through an embankment, one boundary condition, namely, the point, or line, of intersection of the free water surface with the downstream face, with a filter or rock toe, or with the foundation itself, remains to be established. An exact solution of this problem is not always possible. However, approximations can be made, and, in view of the normal variation in the permeability of soils from point to point, they generally fall within the limits of error inherent in stating the problem.[20]

11-10 Common Dimensions of Dams

There is much to be said both for and against reporting a set of common dimensions or rules of thumb for the design of dams. What can be advanced in their favor is that they are generalizations of tested decisions in an otherwise uncertain area of design; what must be said against them is that they stultify the imagination of the designer and obstruct progress. Both statements are invalidated, however, if the fundamental reason for the citation of common dimensions is that they provide useful starting points—no more.

[20] For numerous solutions, see Arthur Casagrande, Seepage through Dams, *J. New Eng. Water Works Assoc.*, **51**, 131 (1937).

Embankment Dams. The detailed design of modern earth and rock fills has become the responsibility of specialists in soil mechanics. However, because detailed design is not the objective of this discussion, first estimates of the order of magnitude of needed structures should be enough. Only to this purpose are common dimensions shown in Fig. 11-13 and explained in the following.

Theoretically, the slope of a cohesionless material could be as steep as the angle of internal friction of its grains. In practice, the slope[21] is reduced for earth but not necessarily for rock fills by a factor of safety of 1.3 to 1.5. Maximum slopes of 1 on 2, for example, are flattened out to 1 on 2.6 to 3.0. The stability of cohesionless materials, such as sand, depends almost entirely on the friction between their grains. In a loose fill, voids are large, points of contact between grains few, and internal friction small. Accordingly, a loose fill is weak and easily disturbed by vibration or shock. If the material is dry, it will gradually shake down into a stabler, denser form and reach its *critical density* when its grains become so interlocked that there can be further movement within the material only if it expands in volume to allow particles to roll over one another. This makes the critical density the *maximum density* of cohesionless materials undergoing shear failure. However, if the material is full of water, the relative incompressibility of this fluid will force it out of the pores as the void space is reduced. In the instant before the water escapes, because of the collapsing movement of the grains therefore, the soil particles are actually suspended in the water, the material is deprived of its resistance to shear, and the entire mass can flow almost like a liquid. This explains the importance of compacting cohesionless materials in earth dams to more than critical density. In rolled fill, as has been shown, this is done by the travel of heavy equipment over successive layers of earth. In hydraulic fill, control is less certain. The fine-grained core substance is often quite loose, and its stability depends primarily on cohesion by molecular attraction. If the core does not drain, the shoulders must, indeed, be heavy enough to resist the fluid pressure not only of the stored water but also of the core so long as it remains liquid. A fluid core weighs about 110 lb per cu ft: therefore, nearly twice as much as water.

The length l (Fig. 11-13) of a clay blanket beneath the upstream shell of an embankment dam is a function of permissible seepage. For example, if the blanket is to offer, within its own thickness y, as much resistance as a depth d of the foundation material beneath the blanket, it follows from Darcy's law that

$$Q = K_1(h/l)\, d = K_2(h/y)x$$

[21] By convention, but also for ease of measurement in the field, the slope of embankments is reported as the tangent of the angle between the slope and its horizontal projection, namely, 1 (vertical) on x (horizontal); or as the cotangent, namely, $x{:}1$.

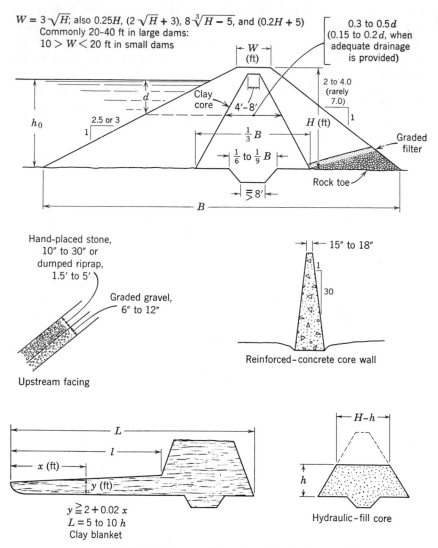

Fig. 11-13. Common dimensions of earth dams.
Upstream slope 2.5 on 1, downstream slope 2 to 4 (rarely 7) on 1 for homogeneous well-graded material; homogeneous silty clay, or clay when $H \lesssim 50$ ft; and sand, or sand and gravel, with reinforced concrete wall.
Upstream slope 3 on 1, downstream slope 2.5 on 1 for homogeneous coarse silt; homogeneous silty clay, or clay, when $H > 50$ ft; and sand, or sand and gravel, with clay core.

and that

$$(y/x) = (K_2/K_1)(l/d) \qquad (11\text{-}10)$$

Here Q is the seepage rate, h the frictional resistance as lost head, and K_1 and K_2 are the coefficients of permeability of the foundation medium and the clay blanket respectively. As shown in Fig. 11-13, y is given a minimum thickness of $(2 + 0.02x)$ feet for practical reasons of construction, and the total length, L, of blanket and core material is made five or ten times the head of water in the reservoir to ensure safety against piping.

In time, even well-constructed embankments shrink in volume or height, internally by consolidation of the embankment material, externally by consolidation of the foundation. Additional fill must be provided in compensation either then or, better, at the time of construction by sloping the crest of the embankment inward and upward from the abutments to the point of maximum height. Depending upon soil type, long-time compression is generally measured at 0.2 to 0.4%. Understandably, dumped rock settles more than compacted rock.

Embankment volumes are computed in accordance with earthwork practice by averaging end areas, applying the prismoidal formula, or combining the two as follows:

$$V = \tfrac{1}{2}l[(a_1 + a_2) - \tfrac{1}{6}(c_1 - c_2)(b_1 - b_2)] \qquad (11\text{-}11)$$

where V is the volume of earthwork between two parallel cross-sections of the dam, l is the distance between these sections, and a_1 and a_2 are the end areas with center heights c_1 and c_2 and base width b_1 and b_2 as shown in Fig. 11-14. For computation of reservoir volumes, see Sec. 8-7.

The upstream shoulder of embankment dams is usually saturated with water—up to the flowline of the reservoir by entrant water and above it by capillary rise. This reduces the stability of the upstream shoulder and re-quires that the upstream slopes of earth dams be flatter than their down-stream slopes. The slopes of embankments that rest on soft foundations or that include cohesive materials, clay for instance, must be flatter than normal. Embankments in narrow rock canyons can be given slopes that are steeper than normal.

The full weight of the central vertical core often used in earth dams is transmitted to its foundation. This keeps leakage at contact with the foundation small. Because the full weight of the sloping core common to rock-fill dams is not transmitted to the contact area with the foundation, more leakage must be expected. An advantage of rock-fill over earth-fill is that the bulky rock-fill can be placed in the wet as well as the dry season. This leaves only the core and upstream portion and the grouting of the foundation to be completed during the dry season.

Berms on the downstream face of embankment dams are about 30 ft apart vertically and wide enough to accommodate gutters and other drainage appurtenances as well as maintenance vehicles such as mowers. In practice berms often cut into the dam as set-backs without increasing the volume of earthwork. To accomplish this, the slopes between berms must be some-what steeper than they would be if there were no berms. As stated before,

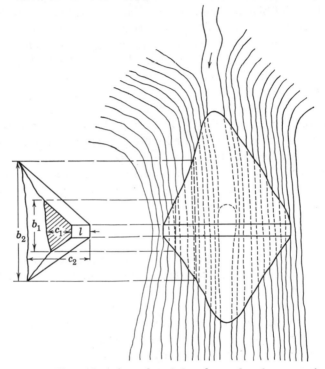

Fig. 11-14. Plan and sections of earth dam for earthwork computations.

a single berm on the upstream face supports needed riprap. The average depth and size of riprap may vary[22] from 12 in. of 10-in. rock for waves expected to be as high as 2 ft up to 30 in. of 18-in. rock for wave heights up to 8 ft. Transition from riprap to embankment material is by graded filters 6 to 12 in. deep.

Masonry Dams.   For gravity dams, first estimates of the amount of masonry needed at a given site can be based on *practical profiles* developed for this purpose and in agreement with common assumptions. Wegmann's

[22] J. L. Sherard, R. J. Woodward, S. F. Gizienski, and W. A. Clevenger, *Earth and Earth-Rock Dams*, New York, John Wiley & Sons, 1963, p. 456.

Practical Type No. 2 is shown in Fig. 11-15. This cross-section was designed by him[23] for zero uplift, masonry weighing 145.8 lb/cu ft, and zero ice pressure. However, the top was made 20 ft wide. To obtain the profile of a dam with this top width but less than 200 ft high, the unwanted lower

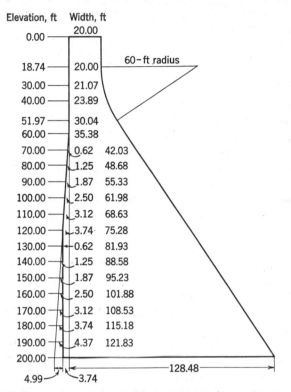

Fig. 11-15. Dimensions of masonry dams; Wegmann's Practical Type 2.

portion is simply cut off. For a smaller top width, every dimension shown in Fig. 11-15 is reduced in the ratio of the desired width to 20 ft before lopping off the lower part of the modified structure.

Example 11-4. Estimate the principal dimensions of a dam 120 ft high with a top width of 16 ft.

Calculated from Wegmann's Practical Type No. 2 for a ratio of $\frac{16}{20} = 0.8$, the

[23] Edward Wegmann, *The Design and Construction of Dams*, 8th Ed., New York, John Wiley & Sons, 1927. Edward Wegmann (1850–1935) was the designer of the New Croton Dam, a lofty and lovely structure, in the Croton Water Supply System of the City of New York, with which he was long associated.

dimensions for a 120-ft dam are read from the top $120/0.8 = 150$ ft of Fig. 11-15 and corrected as follows:

Upstream face: From the top down vertical for $60 \times 0.8 = 48$ ft; next sloping outward to a depth of $60 \times 0.8 = 48$ ft and a width of $3.74 \times 0.8 = 2.99$ ft; and finally vertical again for $120 - 2 \times 48 = 24$ ft.

Downstream face: From the top down vertical for $18.74 \times 0.8 = 14.99$ ft; next curved to a depth of $51.97 \times 0.8 = 41.58$ ft with a radius of curvature of $60 \times 0.8 = 48$ ft; finally slanted to the toe.

Base: In succession from the intersection of the upstream slope and the base $1.87 \times 0.8 = 1.50$ ft; $3.74 \times 0.8 = 2.99$ ft; and $95.23 \times 0.8 = 76.18$ ft.

11-11 Spillways

Spillways have been built into the immediate structure of both embankment and masonry dams; in each instance as masonry sections. Masonry dams may indeed serve as spillways over their entire length. In general, however, spillways are placed at a distance from the dam itself to divert flow and direct possible destructive forces—generated, for example, by ice and debris, wave action, and the onward rush of waters—away from the structure rather than towards it. Saddle dams or dikes may be built to lower elevation than the main impounding dam in order to serve as emergency flood ways.

The head on the spillway crest at time of maximum discharge is the principal component of the *freeboard*, namely, the vertical distance between maximum reservoir level and elevation of dam crest. Other factors are wave height (trough to crest), wave run-up on sloping upstream faces, wind set-up or tilting of the reservoir surface by the drag exerted in the direction of persistent winds in common with differences in barometric pressure, and (for earth embankments only) depth of frost. These factors and their magnitudes, which are not necessarily additive *in toto*, are discussed and evaluated in Sec. 11-7.

Overflow sections of masonry and embankment dams are designed as masonry structures; separate spillways as *saddle, side channel,* and *drop inlet* or *shaft* structures. Spillways constructed through a *saddle* normally discharge into a natural flood way leading back to the stream below the dam. Usually they take the form of open channels and may include a relatively low overflow weir in the approach to the flood way proper. Overflow sections and overflow weirs must be calibrated if weir heads are to record flood discharges accurately; but their performance can be approximated from known calculations of similar structures. If their profile conforms to the ventilated lower nappe of a sharp-crested weir of the same relative height d/h (Fig. 11-16), under the design head, h, the rate of discharge, Q, becomes

$$Q = \tfrac{2}{3}c\sqrt{2g}\,lh^{3/2} = clh^{3/2} \tag{11-12}$$

where $C = \frac{2}{3}c\sqrt{2g}$ is the coefficient of discharge, g the gravity constant, and l the unobstructed crest length of the weir. For a crest height d above the channel bottom, the magnitude of C is approximately[24] $4.15 + 0.65\ h/d$ for $h/d < 4$ or $C = 4.15$ to 6.75. Under heads h' other than the design head h, C approximates[24] $4.15(h'/h)^{\frac{2}{5}}$ up to a ratio of $h'/h = 3.0$.

If the entrance to the flood way is streamlined, little if any energy is lost; certainly no more than $0.05v^2/2g$. Otherwise, too, losses are presumably of the same relative magnitude as for entrances to pipes (Sec. 12-2).

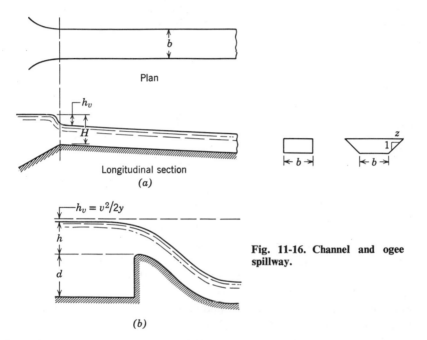

Plan

Longitudinal section
(a)

$-h_v = v^2/2y$

Fig. 11-16. Channel and ogee spillway.

(b)

As suggested in Fig. 11-16, substantial quiescence within the reservoir must be translated into full channel velocity. Discharge is greatest when flow becomes critical (Sec. 14-6). The velocity head h_v then equals one-third the height H of the reservoir surface above the entrance sill to a rectangular channel, and the rate of discharge Q becomes

$$Q = \frac{2}{3}CbH\sqrt{2gH/3} = 3.087CbH^{\frac{3}{2}} \qquad (11\text{-}13)$$

where b is the width of the channel and C is an entrance coefficient varying from 1.0 for a smooth entrance to 0.8 for an abrupt one. In accordance with

[24] A. T. Ippen, Channel Transitions and Controls, in *Engineering Hydraulics*, edited by Hunter Rouse, New York, John Wiley & Sons, 1950, pp. 534 and 535 (approximations of curves in Figs. 15 and 16 respectively).

Sec. 14-6. a trapezoidal channel with side slopes of $1:2$ discharges

$$Q = 8.03Ch_v^{\frac{1}{2}}(H - h_v)[b + z(H - h_v)] \qquad (11\text{-}14)$$

where

$$h_v = \frac{3(2zH + b) - (16z^2H^2 + 16zbH + 9b^2)^{\frac{1}{2}}}{10z} \qquad (11\text{-}15)$$

Best hydraulic but, not necessarily, best economic efficiency is obtained when a semicircle can be inscribed in the cross-section. (Sec. 12-5).

Flow is uniform below the entrance when friction and channel slope are in balance. Otherwise, flow becomes nonuniform and channel cross-section must be adjusted accordingly. A weir within the channel produces a backwater curve (Sec. 14-7).

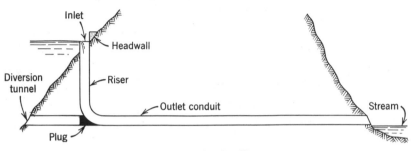

Fig. 11-17. Shaft spillway.

Side-channel spillways occupy relatively little space in the cross-section of a valley. The crest more or less parallels one abutting hillside and can be made as long as wanted. The channel, into which the spillway pours its waters, skirts the end of the dam and delivers its flows safely past the toe. If it is blasted out of tight rock, the channel can be left unlined. Crest length and channel size are determined in much the same way as for wash-water gutters in rapid sand filters (Vol. 2).

As shown in Fig. 11-17, *shaft* or *drop-inlet spillways* consist of an over-flow lip supported on a shaft rising from an outlet conduit, often the original stream-diversion tunnel. The lip can be of any wanted configuration. A circular lip and trumpet-like transition to the shaft form a *morning-glory*[25] *spillway* that must lie far enough from shore to be fully effective. By contrast, a three-sided semicircular lip can be placed in direct contact, with the shore; accessibility is its advantage. The capacity of shaft spill-ways is governed by their constituent parts and by flow conditions including air entrainment and hydraulic submersion. Hydraulic efficiency and capacity are greatest when the conduit flows full. Model studies are useful in arriving at suitable dimensions.

[25] J. N. Bradley, W. E. Wagner, and A. J. Peterka, Morning-Glory Shaft Spillways—A Symposium, *Trans. Am. Soc. Civil Engrs.*, **121**, 312 (1956).

Flashboards or stop logs and gates of many kinds are added to spillways to take advantage of storage above crest level. They must be so designed and operated that the dam itself is not endangered in times of flood.

11-12 Intakes

Depending on size and nature of the installation, water is drawn from rivers, lakes, and reservoirs through relatively simple submerged intake pipes, or through fairly elaborate tower-like structures that rise above the water surface and may house intake gates; openings controlled by stop logs; racks and screens, including mechanical screens, pumps, and compressors; chlorinators and other chemical feeders; venturi meters and other measuring devices; yes, even living quarters and shops for operating personnel (Fig. 2-2). Important in the design and operation of intakes is that the water they draw is as clean, palatable, and safe as the source of supply can provide.

River Intakes. Understandably, river intakes are constructed well upstream from points of discharge of sewage and industrial wastes. Optional location will take advantage of deep water, a stable bottom, and favorable water quality (if pollution hugs one shore of the stream, for example), all with proper reference to protection against floods, debris, ice, and river traffic (Fig. 11-18). Small streams may have to be dammed up by *diversion* or *intake dams* to keep intake pipes submerged and preclude hydraulically wasteful air entrainment. The resulting intake pool will also work usefully as a settling basin for coarse silt and allow protective sheet ice to form in winter (Sec. 11-7). Where the river bed shifts or depth of flow varies greatly, intake pumps may be mounted on carriages that are moved up and down an incline on the river bank to stay within wanted suction lift as flows rise and fall.

Lake and Reservoir Intakes. Lake intakes are sited with due reference to sources of pollution, prevailing winds, surface and subsurface currents, and shipping lanes. As shown in Fig. 11-19, shifting the depth of draft makes it possible to collect clean bottom water when the wind is off-shore and, conversely, clean surface water when the wind is onshore (Sec. 15-12). If the surrounding water is deep enough, bottom sediments will not be stirred up by wave action and ice troubles will be few.

Reservoir intakes resemble lake intakes but generally lie closer to shore in the deepest part of the reservoir. They are often incorporated into the impounding structure itself (Fig. 2-3). Where a reservoir serves many purposes, the intake structure is equipped with gates, conduits, and machinery not only for water supply but also for regulation of low-water flows (including compensating water); development of hydroelectric power; release of irrigation waters; and control of floods. Navigation

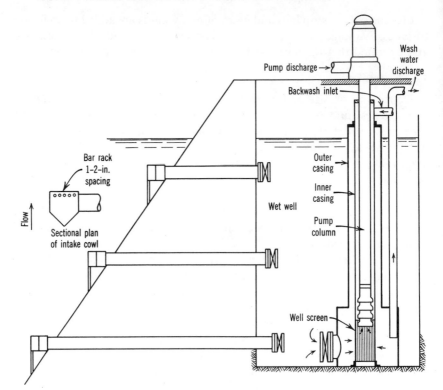

Fig. 11-18. River or lake intake with vertical pump and backwashed well-type screen.

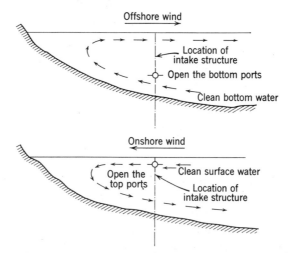

Fig. 11-19. Effect of onshore and offshore winds on water quality at intake.

locks and fish ladders or elevators complete the list of possible control works.

Submerged and Exposed Intakes.   Submerged intakes are constructed as *cribs* or screened *bellmouths*. Cribs are built of heavy timber weighted down with rocks to protect the intake conduit against damage by waves and ice and to support a grating that will keep large objects out of the central intake pipe.

Exposed intake gatehouses, often still misnamed cribs, are tower-like structures built (1) into dams, (2) on banks of streams and lakes, (3) sufficiently near the shore to be connected to it by bridge or causeway, and (4) at such distance from shore that they can be reached only by boat. In *dry* intakes, ports in the outer wall admit water to gated pipes that bridge a circumferential dry well and open into a central wet well comprising the entrance to the intake conduit. In *wet* intakes, water fills both wells. Open ports lead to the outer well, whence needed flows are drawn through gated openings into the inner well.

Intake Velocities and Depths.   In cold climates, ice troubles are reduced in frequency and intensity if intake ports lie as much as 25 ft below the water surface and entrance velocities are kept down to 3 or 4 in. a sec. At such low velocities, frazil ice, leaves, and debris are not entrained in the flowing water and fish are well able to escape from the intake current.

Of the three types of ice encountered in cold climates, sheet ice is seldom troublesome at intakes, but frazil[10] and anchor ice often are (Sec. 11-7). Depending upon the conditions of its formation, frazil ice takes the shape of needles, flakes, or formless slush. According to Barnes,[26] it is a surface-formed ice that does not freeze into a surface sheet. Carried to intakes or produced in them from supercooled water, it obstructs flow by attaching itself to metallic racks, screens, conduits, and pumps or being held back by them. Anchor ice behaves like frazil ice but is derived from ice crystals formed on the bottom of lakes and reservoirs and on submerged objects in much the same way that frost forms on vegetation during a clear night. Frazil and anchor ice are seldom encountered below sheet ice. Their generation can be prevented by heating metallic surfaces or raising the temperature of supercooled water by about 0.1 F, the common order of magnitude of maximum supercooling. Compressed air, backflushing, and light explosives ($\frac{1}{4}$ lb of 60% dynamite) have successfully freed ice-clogged intakes. Telltale chains hung in front of ports will give warning of impending trouble.

Bottom sediments are kept out of intakes by raising entrance ports 4 to 6 ft above the lake or reservoir floor. Ports controlled at numerous horizons permit water-quality selection and optimization. A vertical interval

[26] H. T. Barnes, *Ice Formation*, John Wiley & Sons, New York, 1906.

of 15 ft is common. Submerged gratings are given openings of 2 to 3 in. Specifications for screens commonly call for 2 to 8 meshes to the inch and face (approach) velocities of 3 or 4 in. a sec (Sec. 16-7). Wet wells should contain blow-off gates for cleaning and repairs.

Intake Conduits and Pumping Stations. Intakes are connected to the shores of lakes and reservoirs (1) by pipe lines (often laid with flexible joints) or (2) by tunnels blasted through rock beneath the floor. Pipe lines are generally laid in a trench on the lake or reservoir floor and covered after completion. This protects them against disturbance by waves and ice. Except in rock, conduits passing through the foundations of dams are subjected to heavy loads and to stresses caused by consolidation of the foundation.

Intake conduits are designed to operate at self-cleansing velocities; at 3 to 4 fps, therefore. Flow may be by gravity or suction. Pump wells are generally located on shore. Suction lift, including friction, should not exceed 15 to 20 ft. Accordingly, pump wells or rooms are often quite deep. The determining factor is the elevation of the river, lake, or reservoir in times of drought. Placing pumping units in dry wells introduces problems of hydrostatic uplift and seepage in times of flood. Wet wells and deep-well pumps may be used instead.

11-13 Diversion Works

Depending upon the geology and topography of the dam site and its immediate surroundings, streams are diverted from the construction area in two principal ways:

1. The entire flow is carried around the site in a diversion conduit or tunnel. An upstream cofferdam and, if necessary, a downstream cofferdam lay the site dry. After fulfilling its duty of by-passing the stream and protecting the valley during construction, the diversion conduit is usually incorporated in the intake or regulatory system of the reservoir (Figs. 2-3 and 11-16).

2. The stream is diverted to one side of its valley, the other side being laid dry by a more or less semicircular cofferdam. After construction has progressed far enough in the protected zone, stream flow is rediverted through a sluiceway in the completed section of the dam, and a new cofferdam is built to pump out the remaining portion of the construction site.

Diversion conduits are built as grade aqueducts and tunnels, or as pressure conduits and tunnels (Sec. 12-1). As a matter of safety, however, it should be impossible for any conduit passing through an earth embankment dam to be put under pressure; a leak might bring disaster. Accordingly, gates should be installed only at the inlet portal, never at the outlet portal. If a pipe must work under pressure, it should be laid within a larger access conduit. To discourage seepage along their outer walls, conduits passing through earth dams or earth foundations are often given pro-jecting fins or collars that increase the length of path of seepage (by say 20% or more) and force flow in the direction of minimum, not only maxi-mum, permeability. At their terminus near the toe of the dam, moreover, emerging conduits should be surrounded by rock through which residual seepage waters can escape safely.

The capacity of diversion conduits is determined by flood-flow require-ments (Sec. 8-8). Variations in head and volume of flood water impounded behind the rising dam are important factors in this connection. Rising heads normally increase the capacity of diversion conduits, and increasing storage reduces the intensity of floods. At the same time, however, dangers to the construction site and the valley below mount higher.

CHAPTER 12

Water Transmission

12-1 Transmission Systems

Water is transported from source to community in open or closed conduits, the necessary energy being provided by gravity or pumping. Topography and available materials are primary considerations in selecting suitable conduits and routes. Figure 2-6 shows (1) canals, grade aqueducts, and grade tunnels in illustration of free flow; (2) pipe lines, sag pipes, pressure aqueducts, and pressure tunnels in illustration of flow under pressure. When flow is free, the *hydraulic grade line* coincides with the water surface and parallels the invert of the conduit. When flow is under pressure, as in Fig. 12-6, the hydraulic grade line could be defined by the menisci of piezometric tubes inserted along the conduit itself as it follows the ground surface up and down hill or dips beneath valley or mountain. For both grade and pressure conduits, *the hydraulic gradient* or slope of the hydraulic grade line is a function of the frictional resistance to flow in a given length of conduit. The *energy grade line* lies above the hydraulic grade line by a distance equal to the velocity head or mean kinetic energy per unit weight of flowing water.

Generally speaking, water is transported from place to place more often than not under pressure, whereas flow in wastewater systems and other drainage schemes is quite generally free.

Canals and Flumes. Because *canals* are constructed so far as possible in balanced cut and fill, they are cheap to build in suitable soils. Whether they are lined or left unlined depends upon the nature of the ground, available slopes, design velocities, and the value of water. Other factors of importance are loss of water by infiltration and evaporation, ice troubles, injury by cattle and burrowing animals, pollution by surface wash and seepage, and the proliferation of water weeds. For structural reasons, canals in earth are generally trapezoidal in cross-section; canals in rock often rectangular. That there are hydraulically optimal cross-sections will be shown later (Sec. 12-5).

Open channels supported above ground to transport water across valleys and minor depressions or over obstructions in their path are called *flumes*. When they follow steep or rocky hillsides, they become bench flumes. Built of wood, masonry, or metal, they are usually rectangular or circular in cross-section. Understandably, bench flumes possess many of the drawbacks of canals.

Grade Aqueducts and Tunnels. *Grade aqueducts* wind through the landscape like highways or railroads. Today they are built of concrete; formerly they were made also of brick and stone. Steel reinforcing is usually confined to the invert of those portions of the aqueduct that rest on deep fill or unstable soil. For structural, not for hydraulic, reasons, grade aqueducts and tunnels are generally horseshoe shaped. Usually quite large, they must be built to the full capacity of the supply in most circumstances. Although they are closed, pollution can seep into their waters through cracks and leaky joints. Like canals, grade aqueducts interfere with normal development of the countryside. Moreover, they obstruct natural drainage channels unless suitable culverts are carried below their inverts. When dams are constructed in wide valleys, the stream to be impounded is often diverted through a grade aqueduct which is later put to use in the hydraulic management of the completed reservoir (Fig. 2-3).

Grade tunnels are built either to shorten the route, conserve the head, and reduce the cost of aqueducts traversing broken country; or they lead out of difficult terrain such as deep river gorges to more accessible or more convenient ground in neighboring valleys or watersheds. When they are blasted through stable rock, they may be left unlined, but they are usually lined with concrete to conserve head and reduce entrant seepage. In soils and unstable rock, lining is essential. Working requirements set the minimum size of tunnels at heights of 6 or 7 ft and widths of about 5 ft for hand excavation and at 8 by 8 ft for machine excavation. Where tunnels of smallest workable size would carry more water than needed, the invert alone may be lined or a pipe laid through the unlined tunnel. Grade tunnels, too, find use in the diversion of streams during dam construction, however, in narrow rather than broad valleys (Fig. 11-18).

Pipelines. *Pipelines* usually follow the profile of the ground surface quite closely. Constituent units are cast-iron, steel, cement-asbestos, or precast reinforced concrete pipes. However, they may be built in place of wood with steel bands or of reinforced concrete. Plastic pipe is a newcomer to the field for small-diameter lines. Cast-iron and steel pipes are protected against corrosion either by bituminous surface coatings or linings of bitumen or cement. Water may be supplied to pipelines by gravity or by pumps, making of them *gravity mains* or *force mains* respectively.

Where a pipeline drops beneath a valley, stream, tidal estuary, or other depression in the earth's surface or where it passes beneath some other obstruction in its path, it is referred to as a *sag* or *depressed pipe;* it is also called an *inverted siphon*, but with no justification other than its being the mirrored image of a true siphon.

Pressure Aqueducts and Tunnels.   For structural as well as hydraulic reasons, *pressure aqueducts* and *tunnels* are ordinarily circular in cross-section. Pressure aqueducts, however, are not necessarily circular in outer form. Built in place in balanced cut and cover, they share some of the disadvantages of grade aqueducts but are not normally exposed to pollution by seepage flows.

Pressure tunnels are constructed to cross rivers and valleys. In large works and suitable geological formations, the entire conduit may be built in tunnel, especially where it would otherwise have to traverse broken country and cross numerous divides. Large intakes in lakes, reservoirs, and rivers and the main feeders of important distribution systems may also be built as tunnels. The weight of overlying rock and other natural cover is usually relied upon to resist internal pressures that build up as tunnel elevations drop below the surface of the ground. Like grade tunnels, pressure tunnels are normally lined. Where there is not enough cover to balance internal pressures—near tunnel portals, for example—steel cylinders and other reinforcing provide necessary tightness and strength. Where tunnels are constructed at great depth, construction shafts may become useful components of the conduit for downdraft or upflow.

12-2   Fluid Transport

The hydraulic design of supply conduits is concerned chiefly (1) with resistance to flow in relation to available and needed heads or pressures and (2) with required and allowable velocities of flow relative to cost, scour, and sediment transport. In long supply lines, *frictional* or *surface resistance* offered by the pipe interior is the dominant element. *Form resistance* responsible for losses in transitions and appurtenances is often negligible. In short transport systems, on the other hand, form resistance may be of controlling importance.

A Rational Equation for Surface Resistance.   The most nearly rational relationship between velocity of flow and head loss in a conduit is also one of the earliest. Generally referred to as the Darcy-Weisbach formula,[1] it is actually written in the form suggested by Weisbach, rather than Darcy, namely:

$$h_f = f(l/d)(v^2/2g) \tag{12-1}$$

where h_f is the head loss[2] in a pipe of length l and diameter d through which a fluid is transported at a mean velocity v; g is the acceleration of gravity and f is a dimensionless friction factor. In the more than 100 years of its existence, use, and study, this formulation has been foremost in the minds of engineers concerned with the transmission of water as well as other fluids. That this has often been so in a conceptual rather than a practical sense does not detract from its importance. As will appear in other parts of this book, it is imperative again and again to relate flows of fluids other than water as well as flows of water and other fluids through structures other than pipes back to the Weisbach equation.

Within Eq. 12-1, the dimensionless friction factor f is both its strength and its weakness in applications—its strength as a function of the Reynolds[3] number $\mathbf{R}$; its weakness as a function of relative roughness ϵ/r, where ϵ is a measure of absolute roughness and r is the inside radius of the pipe ($2\epsilon/d = \epsilon/r$). The $f:\mathbf{R}$ relationship is shown in Fig. 12-1, a Hunter Rouse[4] general resistance diagram for flow in uniform conduits. This diagram evolves from a logarithmic plot of $1/\sqrt{f}$ against $\mathbf{R}\sqrt{f}$ with scales for f and $\mathbf{R}$ added for convenience in finding f for use in Eq. 12-1.

In reference to $\mathbf{R}$ and ϵ/r, Fig. 12-1 shows the following:

1. Laminar flow persists until $\mathbf{R} = 2000$, and the $f:\mathbf{R}$ relationship is quite simply $f = 64/\mathbf{R}$.

[1] H. P. G. Darcy, *Recherches expérimentales rélatives au mouvement de l'eau dans les tuyaux* (Experimental Investigations on the Flow of Water in Pipes), Paris 1857. Julius Weisbach, *Lehrbuch der Ingenieur- und Machinen-Mechanik* (Manual of Engineering and Machine Mechanics), Brunswick, Germany, 1845. Darcy's name has appeared before in footnote 16, Chap. 9. Weisbach (1806–1871) taught engineering mechanics at the School of Mines in the Erzgebirge city of Freiberg near Dresden, Germany.
[2] What engineers call head loss or lost head is more specifically the energy lost by a unit weight of water because of surface resistance within the conduit, mechanical energy being converted into nonrecoverable heat energy.
[3] Named after Osborne Reynolds (1842–1912), English mathematician and engineer, first in a succession of eminent teachers of hydraulics at Owens College, later Victoria University, Manchester, England. The nondimensional ratio $\mathbf{R}$ of inertial to viscous parameters of flow $vd\rho/\mu = vd/\nu$, where μ is the absolute viscosity, $\nu = \mu/\rho$ is the kinematic viscosity of the fluid, and ρ is its density. See Osborne Reynolds, An Experimental Investigation of the Circumstances Which Determine Whether the Motion of Water Shall Be Direct or Sinuous and of the Law of Resistance in Parallel Channels, *Philosophical Transactions of the Royal Society*, **174**, 1883.
[4] Hunter Rouse, *Evaluation of Boundary Roughness, Proceedings of the Second Hydraulics Conference*, University of Iowa Studies in Engineering, Bull. 27 (1943); or *Engineering Hydraulics*, John Wiley & Sons, New York, 1950, p. 405.

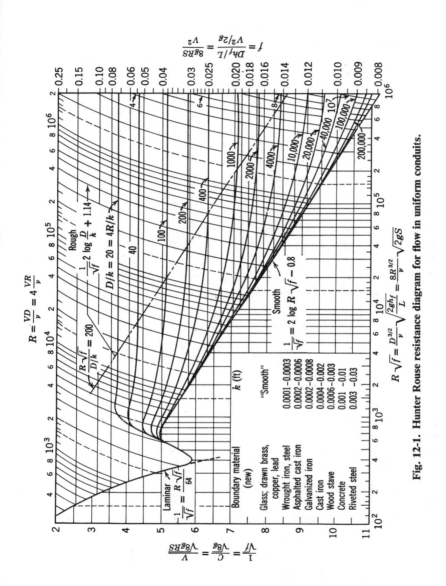

Fig. 12-1. Hunter Rouse resistance diagram for flow in uniform conduits.

2. Above $\mathbf{R} = 4000$, turbulent flow is fully established, and the single trace for laminar flow branches into a family of curves for increasing values of ϵ/r above a lower boundary that identifies the $f:\mathbf{R}$ relationship for smooth pipes as $1/\sqrt{f} = 2 \log \mathbf{R}\sqrt{f} - 0.8$.

3. For rough pipes, the relative roughness ϵ/r takes command and $1/\sqrt{f} = 2 \log r/\epsilon + 1.74$.

4. In the critical zone between $\mathbf{R} = 2000$ and $\mathbf{R} = 4000$, both $\mathbf{R}$ and ϵ/d make their appearance in the semi-empirical equation of Colebrook and White:[5] $1/\sqrt{f} = 1.74 - 2 \log (\epsilon/r + 18.7/\mathbf{R}\sqrt{f})$. Common magnitudes of ϵ/r have been evaluated for large pipes by Bradley and Thompson.[6]

The magnitude of absolute roughness ϵ in the $f:\mathbf{R}$ and $f:(\epsilon/r)$ relationships depends upon the angularity, height, and other geometrical properties of the roughness element and its distribution. The effect of roughness on energy loss has been studied successfully by Nikuradse[7] and others, and the expressions for $1/\sqrt{f}$ included in the preceding paragraph of this chapter are in agreement with Nikuradse's findings.

Despite the logic and inherent conceptual simplicity of the combination of friction-factor diagram and Weisbach formulation, there are important reasons why water engineers do not make use of them for the routine solution of fluid transport problems encountered in water transmission lines and pipe networks. Among the reasons are the following:

1. Because the relative roughness ϵ/r is a key to f, it is not possible to find r (or d) directly when h_f, v or Q, ϵ and water temperature (or ν) are given. A trial-and-error solution is required.

2. Because transmission lines may include noncircular as well as circular conduits, additional $f:\mathbf{R}$ diagrams are needed.

3. Because what has been said in (2) applies often also to partially filled sections, additional diagrams are necessary also for them. For such sections, moreover, trial-and-error solutions must be performed whenever the depth of flow is unknown.

An Exponential Equation for Surface Resistance. Because of practical shortcomings of the Weisbach formula, engineers have resorted to so-called exponential equations in flow calculations. Among them, the Hazen-Williams formula is most widely used in the United States to express flow

[5] C. F. Colebrook, Turbulent Flow in Pipes, and C. F. Colebrook and C. M. White, The Reduction of Carrying Capacity of Pipes with Age, *J. Inst. Civil Engrs.*, **11**, 133 (1938–1939) and **7**, 99 (1937–1938) respectively.
[6] J. N. Bradley and L. R. Thompson, Friction Factors for Large Conduits Flowing Full, *Bur. Reclamation Eng. Monograph* 7, Denver (1951).
[7] J. Nikuradse, Gesetzmässigkeiten der turbulenten Strömung in glatten Rohren (Laws governing turbulent flow in smooth pipes) and Strömungsgesetze in rauhen Rohren (Laws of flow in rough pipes), *Verein Deutscher Ingenieure, Forschungsheft* 356 (1932) and 361 (1933) respectively.

relations in pressure conduits or conduits flowing full, the Manning formula in free-flow conduits or conduits not flowing full.

The Hazen-Williams formula,[8] which was proposed in 1905, will be discussed in this chapter; Manning's formula is taken up in Chap. 14.

The following notation is used:

Q = rate of discharge, in gpm, gpd, mgd, or cfs as needed.

d = diameter of small circular conduits, in in.

D = diameter of large circular conduits, in ft.

v = mean velocity, in fps.

$a = \pi D^2/4 = \pi d^2/576$ = cross-sectional area of conduit in sq ft.

$r = a$/wetted perimeter $= D/4 = d/48$ = hydraulic radius, in ft.

$s = h_f/l$ = hydraulic gradient, or loss of head h_f, in ft, in a conduit of length, l, in ft.

As written by its authors, the Hazen-Williams formula is

$$v = Cr^{0.63}s^{0.54}(0.001^{-0.04}) \qquad (12\text{-}2)$$

where C is a coefficient, known as the Hazen-Williams coefficient, and the factor $(0.001^{-0.04}) = 1.32$ makes C conform in general magnitude[9] with established values of a similar coefficient in the more than a century older Chezy[10] formula

$$v = C\sqrt{rs} \qquad (12\text{-}3)$$

It is of interest that the exponents of r and s, respectively $a = 0.63$ and $b = 0.54$, fail by very little to obey the requirement that $3b = a + 1$, namely, $1.62 \approx 1.63$, for dimensional homogeneity,[11] and that it is possible to make the Hazen-Williams equation dimensionally consistent by writing it

$$v = \nu^{-0.067}(8g/k)^{0.543}r^{0.63}s^{0.543} \qquad (12\text{-}4)$$

where ν is the kinematic viscosity, g the gravity constant, and k a coefficient such that $1.32C = \nu^{-0.067}(8g/k)^{0.543}$. For $C = 100$ and a temperature of 50 F (10 C), $k = 0.12$.

[8] This formula carries the names of its proponents Allen Hazen (1870–1930), intellectually the most productive water-supply engineer of his day, and Gardner S. Williams (1866–1931), professor of hydraulics at Cornell University and the University of Michigan.

[9] Specifically for $r = 1$ ft and $s = 1$ ft/1000 or $1‰$.

[10] Antoine Chézy (1718–1798) was a teacher in and later director of the Ecole des Ponts et Chaussées. This first professional school of civil engineering was founded in Paris in 1747 to supply qualified engineers to the ministry of works which was engaged in constructing roads, bridges, and canals for expediting communications and improving the economy of a France weakened by the wars and extravagances of Louis XIV.

[11] L. C. Neal and R. E. Price, Flow Characteristics of PVC Sewer Pipe, *J. Sanitary Eng. Div.*, Am. Soc. Civil Engrs., **90**, 109 (June 1964) and 133 (Dec. 1964).

Actually, Chézy related the hydraulics of channels to one another by the ratios $v^2/rs = V^2/RS$ (in our notation), the conditions of flow being well established in the channel characterized by capital letters. It follows that $v = (V/\sqrt{RS})\sqrt{rs} = C\sqrt{rs}$ where C^2 has the dimensions of an acceleration,[12] and the exponents of r and s meet the requirement: $3b = a + 1$.

For circular conduits; the Hazen-Williams formulation can take one of the following forms:

$$v = 0.115Cd^{0.63}s^{0.54} = 0.550CD^{0.63}s^{0.54} \tag{12-5}$$

$$h_f = 5.47(v/C)^{1.85}l/d^{1.17} = 3.02(v/C)^{1.85}l/D^{1.17} \tag{12-6}$$

$$Q_{(gpd)} = 405Cd^{2.63}s^{0.54}; \quad Q_{(mgd)} = 0.279CD^{2.63}s^{0.54};$$

$$Q_{(cfs)} = 4.32CD^{2.63}s^{0.54} \tag{12-7}$$

$$h_f = 1.50 \times 10^{-5}(Q_{gpd}/C)^{1.85}l/d^{4.87} = 10.6(Q_{mgd}/C)^{1.85}l/D^{4.87}$$

$$= 0.667(Q_{cfs}/C)^{1.85}l/D^{4.87} \tag{12-8}$$

Solution of Eqs. 12-2 and 12-5 through 12-8 for Q, v, r, D, d, s, h_f, l, or C requires the use of logarithms, a log-log slide rule, tables,[13] a diagram with logarithmic scales (such as the diagram at the end of this volume), or an alignment chart.

The weakest element in the Hazen-Williams formula is the estimate of C in the absence of measurements of loss of head and discharge or velocity. It should be noted that C is a coefficient of hydraulic capacity and not a friction factor[14] like f.

Values of C vary for different conduit materials and their relative deterioration in service. They vary somewhat also with size and shape. The values listed in Table 12-1 reflect more or less general experience.

For purposes of comparison, the size of a noncircular conduit can be stated in terms of the diameter of a circular conduit of equal carrying capacity. For identical values of C and s, multiplication of Eq. 12-2 by the conduit area a in square feet and equating the resulting expression to Eq. 12-6, the diameter of the equivalent conduit becomes

$$D = 1.53a^{0.38}r^{0.24} \tag{12-9}$$

Variation in the hydraulic elements of circular and noncircular conduits with depth of flow is discussed in Chap. 14.

[12] Hunter Rouse and Simon Ince, *History of Hydraulics*, Iowa Institute of Hydraulic Research, 1959, p. 119.
[13] Gardner S. Williams and Allen Hazen, *Hydraulic Tables*, John Wiley & Sons, New York, 3rd ed., 1933.
[14] Specifically $C = \text{constant}/(f^{0.5}d^{0.13}s^{0.04})$.

Table 12-1 Values of the Hazen-Williams Coefficient C for Different Conduit Materials and Age of Conduit

Conduit Material	Age	
	New	Uncertain
Cast-iron pipe, coated (inside and outside)	130	100
Cast-iron pipe, lined with cement or bituminous enamel	130*	130*
Steel, riveted joints, coated	110	90
Steel, welded joints, coated	140	100
Steel, welded joints, lined with cement or bituminous enamel	140*	130*
Concrete	140	130
Wood stave	130	130
Cement-asbestos and plastic pipe	140	130

* For use with the nominal diameter, i.e., diameter of unlined pipe.

Example 12-1. The pipe-flow diagram at the end of this volume establishes the numerical relationships between Q, v, d, and s for a value of $C = 100$. Conversion to other magnitudes of C is simple because both v and Q vary directly as C. Show the mathematical and graphical basis of this diagram.

1. Written in logarithmic form, Eq. 12-7 is (a) $\log Q = 4.61 + 2.63 \log d + 0.54 \log s$, or (b) $\log s = -8.54 - 4.87 \log d + 1.85 \log Q$.

A family of straight lines of equal slope is obtained, therefore, when s is plotted against Q on log-log paper for specified diameters d. Two points define each line. Pairs of coordinates for a 12-in. pipe, for example, are: (a) $Q = 100,000$ gpd, $s = 0.028\%_0$; and (b) $Q = 1,000,000$ gpd, $s = 2.05\%_0$.

2. Written in logarithmic form, Eq. 12-5 is: $\log v = 1.0607 + 0.63 \log d + 0.54 \log s$. If the diameter d is eliminated from the logarithmic transforms of Eqs. 12-7 and 12-5: (a) $\log Q = 0.180 + 4.17 \log v - 1.71 \log s$; and (b) $\log s = 0.105 + 2.43 \log v - 0.585 \log Q$.

A family of straight lines of equal slope is obtained when s is plotted against Q on log-log paper for specified velocities v. Two points define each line. Pairs of coordinates for a velocity of 1 fps, for example, are: (a) $Q = 100,000$ gpd, $s = 1.5\%_0$; and (b) $Q = 10,000,000$ gpd, $s = 0.10\%_0$.

3. If the discharge were read in cubic feet per second (instead of thousands of gallons per day), by what factor F would the diameter have to be multiplied if it were to be read in feet (instead of inches)?

From Eq. 12-7, because 1 cfs = 646,000 gpd, $646Q = 405C(12FD)^{2.63}s^{0.54}$, whence $(12F)^{2.63} = 646$, and $F = 0.976$.

To carry 1000 cfs on a gradient of $5.0\%_0$, for example, a circular conduit would have to be $10 \times 0.976 = 9.76$ ft in diameter.

Example 12-2. A tunnel of horseshoe shape has a cross-sectional area of 27.9 sq ft and a hydraulic radius of 1.36 ft. Find the diameter, hydraulic radius, and area of the hydraulically equivalent circular conduit.

1. By Eq. 12-9, the diameter $D = 1.53 \times (27.9)^{0.38} \times (1.36)^{0.24} = 5.85$ ft.
2. The hydraulic radius $r = D/4 = 1.46$ ft.
3. The area $a = (\pi D^2)/4 = 26.8$ sq ft.

It should be noted that neither the cross-sectional area nor the hydraulic radius of this equivalent circular conduit is the same as that of the horseshoe section proper.

Form Resistance. Pipeline transitions and appurtenances add form resistance to surface resistance. Head losses are stepped up by changes in cross-sectional geometry and changing directions of flow. Expansion and contraction exemplify geometric change; elbows and branches directional change. Valves and meters as well as other appurtenances may create both geometrical and directional change. With rare exceptions, head losses are expressed either in terms of velocity heads, as $kv^2/2g$, or as equivalent lengths of straight pipe, $l_e = kv^2/2gs = kD/f$. The outstanding exception is the loss on sudden expansion or enlargement called the Borda[15] loss $(v_1 - v_2)^2/2g$, where v_1 is the velocity in the original conduit and v_2 the velocity in the expanded conduit; even it, however, is sometimes converted, for convenience, into $kv^2/2g$. Because continuity as $a_1v_1 = a_2v_2$ equates $k_1v_1^2/2g$ to $(v_1^2/2g)(1 - a_1/a_2)^2$, the loss at the point of discharge of a pipeline into a reservoir (making a_2 very large in comparison with a_1) closely equals $v_1^2/2g$; consequently, there is no recovery of energy. In all but special cases like this, k must be determined experimentally. When there is no experimental information, the following values of k give useful first approximations on likely losses:

	Value of k		Value of k
Sudden contraction*	0.3–0.5	Valve (open), gate	0.2
Entrance, sharp	0.5	with reducer and	
well-rounded	0.1	increaser	0.5
Elbow,† 90°	0.5–1.0	globe	10
45°	0.4–0.75	angle	5
22.5°	0.25–0.5	swing check	2.5
Tee, 90° take-off	1.5	Meter, venturi	0.3
straight run	0.3	orifice	1.0
Coupling	0.3		

* Varying with area ratios.   † Varying with radius ratios.

Hydraulic Transients. Transmission lines are subjected to transient pressures when valves are opened or closed or when pumps are started or stopped (Sec. 12-6). Water hammer and surge are among such transient phenomena.[16]

[15] Named after Jean Charles Borda (1733–1799), French military engineer.
[16] G. R. Rich, *Hydraulic Transients*, McGraw-Hill Book Co., New York, 1951.

Water hammer is the pressure rise accompanying a sudden change in velocity. When velocity is decreased in this way, energy of motion must be stored by elastic deformation of the system. The sequence of phenomena that follows sudden closure of a gate, for example, is quite like what would ensue if a long, rigid spring, traveling at uniform speed, were suddenly stopped and held stationary at its forward end. A pressure wave would travel back along the spring as it compressed against the point of stoppage. Kinetic energy would change to elastic energy. Then the spring would vibrate back and forth. In a pipe, compression of the water and distention of the pipe wall replace the compression of the spring. The behavior of the pressure wave and the motion of the spring and the water are identically described by the differential equations for one-dimensional waves. Both systems would vibrate indefinitely, were it not for the dissipation of energy by internal friction.

Water hammer is held within bounds in small pipelines by operating them at moderate velocities, because the pressure rise in pounds per square inch cannot exceed about fifty times the velocity expressed in feet per second. In larger lines the pressure is held down by arresting flows at a sufficiently slow rate to allow the relief wave to return to the point of control before pressures become excessive. If this is not practicable, pressure-relief or surge valves are introduced.

Very large lines, 6 ft or more in equivalent diameter, operate economically at relatively high velocities. However, the cost of making them strong enough to withstand water hammer would ordinarily be prohibitive if the energy could not be dissipated slowly in surge tanks. In its simplest form, a surge tank is a standpipe at the end of the line next to the point of velocity control. If this control is a gate, the tank accepts water and builds up back pressure when velocities are regulated downward. When demand on the line increases, the surge tank supplies immediately needed water and generates the excess hydraulic gradient for accelerating the flow through the conduit. Following a change in the discharge rate, the water level in a surge tank oscillates slowly up and down till excess energy is dissipated by hydraulic friction in the system.

12-3   Capacity and Size of Conduits

With rates of water consumption and fire demand known, the capacity of individual supply conduits depends upon their position in the water-works system and the choice of the designer for (1) a structure of full size or (2) duplicate lines staggered in time of construction.

Minimum workable size, as already stated, is one controlling factor in the design of tunnels. Otherwise, size is determined by hydraulic and economic considerations. Controlling hydraulic factors are available heads and allowable velocities. Head requirements include proper allowances for drawdown of reservoirs and maintenance of pressures in the various parts of the community, under conditions of normal as well as fire demand. Heads greater than necessary to transport water at normal velocities may be turned into power when it is economical to do so.

Allowable velocities are governed by the characteristics of the water carried and the magnitude of the hydraulic transients. For silt-bearing waters, there are both lower and upper limits of velocity; for clear waters, only an upper limit. The minimum velocity should prevent deposition of silt; it lies in the vicinity of 2 to 2.5 fps. The maximum velocity should not cause erosion or scour, nor should it endanger the conduit by excessive water hammer when gates are closed quickly. Velocities of 4 to 6 fps are common, but the upper limit lies between 10 and 20 fps for most materials of which supply conduits are built and for most types of water carried. Unlined canals impose greater restrictions. Silting and scouring are discussed in connection with self-cleansing velocities in sewers (Sec. 14-3) and with the design of grit chambers (Vol. 2). Some of the formulations advanced there are applicable also here.

The size of force mains and of gravity mains that include power generation is fixed by the relative cost or value of the conduit and the cost of pumping or power.

When aqueducts include more than one kind of conduit, the most economical distribution of the available head among the component classes is effected when the change in cost Δc for a given change in head Δh is the same for each kind. The proof for this statement is provided by Lagrange's method[17] of undetermined multipliers described in Sec. 17-10. As shown in Fig. 12-2 for three components of a conduit with an allowable, or constrained, head loss H, the Lagrangian requirement of $\Delta c_1/\Delta h_1 = \Delta c_2/\Delta h_2 = \Delta c_3/\Delta h_3$ is met when parallel tangents to the three $c:h$ curves identify, by trial, three heads h_1, h_2, and h_3 that satisfy the constraint $h_1 + h_2 + h_3 = H$.

Example 12-3.   Given the costs and losses of head shown in Fig. 12-2 for three sections of a conduit, find the most economical distribution of the available head $H = 60$ ft between the three sections:

By trial
$$h_1 = 13.5 \qquad c_1 = 2.0 \times 10^4$$
$$h_2 = 19.0 \qquad c_2 = 2.1 \times 10^4$$
$$h_3 = 27.5 \qquad c_3 = 2.2 \times 10^4$$
$$\overline{}$$
$$H = 60.0 \qquad C = 6.3 \times 10^4$$

[17] Developed by the French mathematician Joseph-Louis Lagrange (1736–1813).

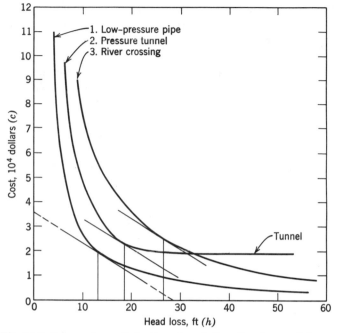

Fig. 12-2. **Lagrangian optimization of conduit sections by parallel tangents.**

12-4 Multiple Lines

As has been said before, masonry aqueducts and tunnels of all kinds are best designed to the full projected capacity of the system. This is not necessarily so for pipelines. Parallel lines built a number of years apart may prove to be more economical. Cost, furthermore, is not the only consideration. It may be expedient to lay more than one line under the following conditions:

1. When the maximum pipe size of manufacture is exceeded; 36 in. in the case of centrifugal cast-iron pipe, for example.

2. When possible failure would put the line out of commission for a long time; collapse of steel pipe under a vacuum is a case in point.

3. When pipe location presents special hazards; floods, ice, and ships' anchors endangering river crossings or submarine pipes and cave-ins rupturing pipelines in mining areas are examples.

Twin lines cost 30 to 50% more than a single line of equal capacity. If they are close enough to be interconnected at frequent intervals, gates should be installed in the bridging pipes to keep most of the system in operation during repairs to affected parts. However, if failure of one line will endanger the other, twin lines should not be laid in the same trench.

Thus cast-iron pipe can fail so suddenly that a number of pipe lengths will be undermined and pulled apart before the water can be turned off. Another reason for having dual lines traverse different routes is to have them feed water into opposite ends of the distribution system. This permits the normally central, high-value district to draw water from two rather than a single direction at consequently lower pressure gradients or in larger amounts at the same gradient.

12-5   Cross-sections

Both hydraulic performance and structural behavior enter into the choice of cross-section. Because hydraulic capacity is a direct function of

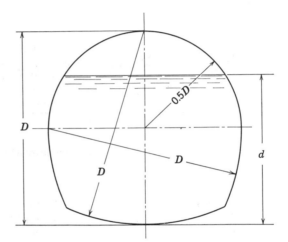

Fig. 12-3. Common proportions of horseshoe sections.

the hydraulic radius, and circle and half circle possess the largest hydraulic radius, or smallest (frictional) surface for a given volume of water, the circle is the cross-section of choice for closed conduits and the semicircle for open conduits whenever structural conditions permit. Next best are cross-sections in which circles or semicircles can be inscribed. Examples are:

1. For canals in earth—trapezoids approaching half a hexagon as nearly as maintainable slopes permit.

2. For canals in rock and flumes of masonry or wood—rectangles twice as wide as they are deep.

3. For flumes of wood staves or steel—semicircles.

4. For pressure aqueducts, pressure tunnels, and pipelines—circles.

5. For grade aqueducts and grade tunnels—horseshoe sections.

Internal pressures are best resisted by cylindrical tubes and materials strong in tension; external earth and rock pressures (not counterbalanced by internal pressures) by horseshoe sections and materials strong in compression. By design, the hydraulic properties of horseshoe sections are only slightly poorer than those of circles. Moreover, their relatively flat *invert* makes for easy transport of excavation and construction materials in and out of the aqueduct. As shown in Fig. 12-3, four circular arcs are struck to form the section: a circular arc rising from the *springing line* of the arch at half depth, two lateral arcs struck by radii equaling the height of the *crown* above the invert, and a circular arc of like radius establishing the bottom.

12-6 Structural Requirements

Structurally, closed conduits must resist a number of different forces singly or in combination:

1. Internal pressure equal to the full head of water to which the conduit can be subjected.
2. Unbalanced pressures at bends, contractions, and closures.
3. Water hammer or increased internal pressure caused by sudden reduction in the velocity of the water; by the rapid closing of a gate or shutdown of a pump, for example.
4. External loads in the form of backfill, traffic, and their own weight between external supports (piers or hangers).
5. Temperature-induced expansion and contraction.

Internal pressure, including water hammer, creates transverse stress or *hoop tension*. Bends and closures at dead ends or gates produce unbalanced pressures and *longitudinal stress*. When conduits are not permitted to change length, variations in temperature likewise create longitudinal stress. External loads and foundation reactions (manner of support), including the weight of the full conduit, and atmospheric pressure (when the conduit is under vacuum) produce *flexural stress*.

For convenience of reference, the equations describing most of these relations are summarized here, using the following notation:

w = weight of unit volume of water: 62.4 lb/cu ft
g = acceleration of gravity: 32.2 ft/sec^2 at middle latitudes
P = total force, lb
p = intensity of pressure, psi or psig
d = diameter of conduit, in.
t = thickness of conduit shell, in.
s = allowable stress, psi
E = modulus of elasticity of pipe walls, psi: 29.4×10^6 for steel; 15×10^6 for cast iron; and 2.5×10^6 for concrete

K = volume modulus of compression of water: 29.4×10^4

v = velocity of flow, fps

u = velocity of pressure wave; velocity of sound: $u_s = 4700$ fps for water

l = length of conduit, ft

t = time of closure of a gate or shut down of pump at end of line, sec

α = angular change in direction, or angle of a bend

θ = change in temperature, F

c = coefficient of expansion of conduit shell/deg F: 6.5×10^{-6} for steel; 6.2×10^{-6} for cast iron; and 5.5×10^{-6} for concrete

Δ = change in length of conduit, ft

Hoop tension per linear inch of length: $P/2 = pd/2$

and resulting transverse stress: $s = pd/2t$

Longitudinal tension: $P = (\pi/4)d^2p$

and resulting longitudinal stress: $s = pd^2/[4t(d + t)]$
$= pd/(4t)$ closely

Velocity of pressure wave in rigid pipe: $u_s = \sqrt{K/(w/g)}$ = velocity of sound
$= 4700$ fps

and in elastic pipe: $u = u_s/\sqrt{1 + (K/E)(d/t)}$

Critical time of gate closure: $t_c = 2\, l/u$

Maximum water hammer: $p = (w/g)uv$ for closures in time t_c
or less

Unbalanced static pressure at bends: $P = \frac{1}{2}\pi d^2 p \sin \frac{1}{2}\alpha$

Unbalanced dynamic pressure at bends: $P = \frac{1}{2}\pi (d^2/144)(w/g)v^2 \sin \frac{1}{2}\alpha$

Change in pipe length with temperature: $\Delta = c\theta l$, commonly at the prevailing water temperature

and resulting longitudinal stress: $s = c\theta E$, for pipeline with fixed ends

or resulting longitudinal force: $P = \pi(d + t)ts = \pi dts$ closely

Collapsing pressure for cylindrical steel shells, plain: $p = 50.2 \times 10^6 (t/d)^3$

and with stiffener rings: $p = 6.12 \times 10^6 (t/d)^{5/2}/(l/d)$

For longer times of closure t, water hammer is reduced about in proportion to t_c/t; t is naturally longer for large gates than small ones even when large gates are closed by machine. However, it is possible to reduce water hammer in small lines by designing them for lower velocities of flow.

In jointed pipes, such as bell-and-spigot cast-iron pipes, the longitudinal stresses must either be resisted by the joints or relieved by motion. Mechanical joints offer much resistance. The resistance of lead and lead-substitute joints in bell-and-spigot cast-iron pipe to being pulled apart can be estimated from Prior's observational equation:[18]

$$p = \frac{3800}{(d + 6)} - 40; \qquad P = \left(\frac{3000}{d + 6} - 31\right)d^2 \qquad (12\text{-}10)$$

[18] J. C. Prior, Investigation of Bell-and-Spigot Joints in Cast-Iron Water Pipes, *Ohio State Univ. Eng. Exp. St. Bull.* 87 (1935).

Tables of standard dimensions and laying lengths are found in professional manuals, specifications of the American Water Works Association, and publications of manufacturers and trade associations.

The magnitude of external loads imposed upon conduits laid in trench or otherwise surrounded with earth depends upon many things, among them: (1) the nature of the covering and bedding material, (2) the method of supporting the conduit, (3) the relative width and depth of the trench, (4) the method of backfilling, and (5) the rigidity of the conduit. Marston, Schlick, and their coworkers[19] have shown that the vertical external load, w, in pounds per foot (length) of pipe is approximated by the following products: cwD^2 for pipes on, or projecting above, ground in cohesionless cover; $(c_0 - c')wBD$ for flexible pipes in trenches and thoroughly compacted side fills; and $(c_0 - c')wD^2$ for rigid pipes in trenches, with ordinary bedding and $B < 1.5D$. Here c, c_0, and c' are experimental coefficients; w is the unit weight of backfill (lb/cu ft); B is the width of the trench at the top of the pipe (ft); and D is the external diameter of the pipe (ft).

Characteristic values of the experimental coefficients for different soils and methods of laying are shown in Fig. 12-4. In all but narrow trenches, some relief of stress is obtained by horizontal earth pressure, which ordinarily is 20 to 30% of the vertical pressure.

12-7 Location

Supply conduits are located in much the same way as railroads and highways.

Line and Grade. The invert of a grade aqueduct or grade tunnel is placed on the same slope as the hydraulic grade line. Cut and fill, as well as cut and cover, are balanced to maintain a uniform gradient and reduce haul. Valleys and rivers that would be bridged by railroads and highways may be bridged also by aqueducts. Such indeed was the practice of ancient Rome; but modern aqueducts no longer rise above valley, stream, and hamlet except where a bridge is needed primarily to carry road or railway traffic. Pressure conduits have taken their place. Sometimes they are laid in trenches as sag pipes to traverse valleys and pass beneath streams; sometimes they strike deep below the earth's surface in pressure tunnels for which geological exploration fixes both line and grade.

Pressure aqueducts and pipelines move freely up and down slopes. For economy they should hug the hydraulic grade line in profile and a straight

[19] Anson Marston, The Theory of External Loads on Closed Conduits in the Light of the Latest Experiments, *Iowa State Coll. Eng. Exp. St. Bull.* 96 (1930); W. J. Schlick, Loads on Pipes in Wide Trenches, *Iowa State Coll. Eng. Exp. St. Bull.* 108 (1932); and M. J. Spangler, Underground Conduits—An Appraisal of Modern Research, *Trans. Am. Soc. Civil Engrs.*, **112**, 316 (1948). Anson Marston (1864–1949) was dean of engineering at Iowa State University for many years.

line in plan. Size and thickness of conduit and difficulty of construction must be kept in balance with length. The shortest route is not necessarily the cheapest.

True siphons should be avoided if possible. Air released from the water

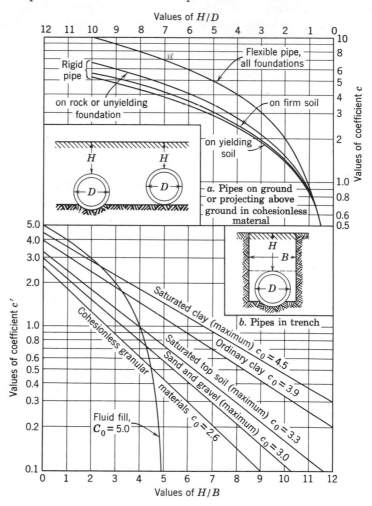

Fig. 12-4. Determination of vertical external loads on circular conduits. (After *Marston and Schlick*.)

and trapped at high points reduces the waterway, increases friction, and may interrupt flow unless an air ejector or vacuum pump is installed. However, if the height of rise above the hydraulic grade is confined to less than 20 ft and the velocity of flow is kept above 2 fps, operating troubles will be few. For best results, the line should leave the summit at a slope less than that of the hydraulic gradient.

In practice, possible locations of supply conduits are examined on available maps of the region; the topographic and geologic sheets of the U.S. Geological Survey are useful examples. Route surveys are then carried into the field. Topography and geology are confirmed and developed in needed detail, possibly by aerial surveys. Rights of way, accessibility of proposed routes, and the nature of obstructions are also identified.

Vertical and Horizontal Curves. In long supply lines, changes in direction and grade are effected gradually in order to conserve head and avoid unbalanced pressures. Masonry conduits built in place can be brought to any desired degree of curvature by proper form work. Cast-iron and other sectional pipelines are limited in curvature by the maximum angular deflection of standard lengths of pipe at which joints will remain tight. The desired curve is built up by the necessary number of offsets from the tangent. Sharper curves can be formed by shorter or shortened pipes. The smaller the pipe, the sharper can be the deflection. Welded pipelines less than 15 in. in diameter are sufficiently flexible to be bent in the field after several joints have been welded together for leverage. The ends of larger steel pipe must be cut at an angle which depends upon the type of transverse joint, the thickness of the steel plate, and the size of the pipe. Continuous-stave pipe is built in place on curves with a minimum radius about fifty times the diameter of the pipe.

For sharp curves, transitions, and branches, special fittings are often built up or manufactured of the same materials as the main conduit.

Depth of Cover. Conduits that follow the surface of the ground are generally laid below the frost line, although the thermal capacity and latent heat of water are so great that there is little danger of freezing so long as the water remains in motion. To reduce the external load on large conduits, only the lower half may be laid below frost. Along the forty-second parallel of latitude, which describes the southern boundaries of Massachusetts, upper New York, and Michigan in the United States, frost seldom penetrates more than 5 ft beneath the surface; along the forty-fifth parallel the depth increases to 7 ft. The following equation approximates Shannon's[20] observations of frost depth;

$$d = 1.65F^{0.468} \qquad (12\text{-}11)$$

where d is the depth of frozen soil in inches and F, the freezing index, is the algebraic difference between the maximum positive and negative cumulative departures, $\Sigma(T_d - 32)$, of the daily mean temperatures (T_d)

[20] W. L. Shannon, Prediction of Frost Penetration, *J. New Eng. Water Works Assoc.*, **59**, 356 (1945).

from 32 F. Accumulation, as shown in Fig. 12-5, begins with the first day on which a freezing temperature is recorded. In concept, the freezing index is analogous to the *degree day* which describes the heat requirements of buildings during the heating season. In the absence of daily readings, the value of F may be approximated, in North America, from the mean monthly temperatures as follows:

$$F = (32n - \Sigma T_m)30.2 \qquad (12\text{-}12)$$

Here n is the number of months during which the temperature is less than 32 F, ΣT_m is the sum of the mean temperatures during each of these

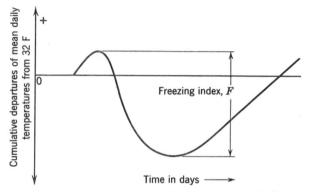

Fig. 12-5. Determination of the freezing index of soils as the cumulative departure of the mean daily temperature from 32 F. (After *Shannon*.)

months, and 30.2 is the mean number of days in December, January, February, and March.

Pipes laid at depths of 2 to 3 ft are safe from extremes of heat and ordinary mechanical damage, but it is wise to go to 5 ft in streets or roads open to heavy vehicles. Otherwise, structural characteristics of conduits determine allowable depth of cover or weight of backfill. Some conduits may have to be laid in open cut to keep the depth of backfill below the maximum allowable value.

12-8   Materials of Construction

Selection of pipeline materials must be based on the following considerations:

1. The initial carrying capacity of the pipe and its reduction with use, defined, for example, by the Hazen-Williams coefficient C (Sec. 12-2).
2. The strength of the pipe, as measured by its ability to resist internal pressures and external loads (Sec. 12-6).

3. The life or durability of the pipe, as determined by the resistance of cast-iron and steel pipe to corrosion; of steel-banded wood-stave pipe to rotting and corrosion; of concrete and asbestos-cement pipe to erosion and disintegration; and of plastic pipe to crackling and disintegration.

4. The ease or difficulty of transporting, handling, and laying the pipe under different conditions of topography, geology, and communication.

5. The safety, economy, and availability of manufactured sizes (Sec. 12-4 and footnote 22).

6. The availability of labor skilled in the construction of pipelines of different kinds.

7. The requirements of maintenance and repair, losses of water by leakage, and other matters of pipe behavior and suitability.

Carrying Capacity.   The initial value of the Hazen-Williams coefficient C hovers around 140 for all types of well-laid pipelines, but the coefficient tends to be somewhat higher for reinforced-concrete and asbestos-cement lines and to drop to a normal value of about 130 for unlined cast-iron pipe unless the line is laid with more than ordinary care. Double-riveted steel pipe loses about twenty points in addition; but riveted longitudinal joints are seldom used today. Their place has been taken in succession by lock-bar and welded joints. Riveted transverse joints, too, have given way to welded joints or mechanical couplings. Unlined, welded-steel pipe has an initial coefficient C close to 140. Spiral-riveted pipe is no longer used in long lines; its coefficient is low. Cast-iron and steel pipes lined with cement or with bituminous enamel possess coefficients of 130 and over on the basis of their nominal diameter; improved smoothness offsets the reduction in cross-section.

Loss of capacity with age or, more strictly, with service depends (1) upon the properties of the water carried and (2) upon the characteristics of the pipe. Modern methods for controlling aggressive water (Vol. 2) promise that the corrosion of metallic pipes and the disintegration of cement linings and of reinforced-concrete and asbestos-cement pipe will be held in check very largely, if not fully, in the future. In the present state of the art, however, it is not yet possible to estimate how C will change with length of service. The values shown in Table 12-2 represent background information only for times when corrective treatment was still uncommon.[21] An examination of Table 12-2 will show that the following observations are pertinent:

1. Loss of capacity is relatively more rapid for small than for large pipes; in iron and steel pipes, because rust and other deposits restrict the waterway and increase the roughness of the pipe walls; in cement-lined pipes and asbestos-cement pipes because the smoothness of the walls is destroyed.

[21] *J. New Eng. Water Works Assoc.*, **49**, 241 (1935).

2. Before extensive corrective treatment was introduced, loss of capacity was often more pronounced in purified than in raw waters. Then probably purification rendered the water more aggressive by removing protective slime coatings, adding oxygen and carbon dioxide, and otherwise affecting the physical and electrochemical properties of the water.

3. Discharge capacity is greater for supply than for distribution lines, because there are many more fittings, valves, and other appurtenances in distribution systems.

Table 12-2 Reduction in the Capacity of Pipes with Length of Service in Terms of the Hazen-Williams Coefficient C

Number and Material	Water Quality	Diameter, in.	Age, years				
			0	10	20	30	40
1. Steel	Inactive	...	135	128	121	115	108
2. Steel	Eastern	...	135	125	115	106	97
3. Cast iron	Average, soft, unfil-	48	130	112	100	90	83
	tered river water	36	130	112	100	90	82
	(Hazen-Williams)	24	130	111	99	89	81
		12	130	110	96	86	77
		6	130	107	93	80	72
4. Cast iron (tar-coated)							
a. Supply lines, 9 cities		28 (ave)	135	106	93	85	...
b. Supply and distribution, 19 cities		25 (ave)	130	90	74	65	...
c. Distribution, 10 cities		6.85 (ave)	125	77	55	45	...

Cement and bituminous-enamel linings and reinforced-concrete and asbestos-cement pipes do not, as a rule, deteriorate significantly with service.

Strength. Steel pipes can resist high internal pressures, but large lines cannot withstand heavy external loads when they are emptied or placed under partial vacuum. Accordingly, their depth of cover must be kept small, or they must be surrounded with concrete. Cast-iron and asbestos-cement pipes are good for moderately high water pressures and appreciable external loads, provided that they are properly bedded. Reinforced-concrete and wood-stave pipe are satisfactory for moderate water pressures. Reinforced-concrete pipes can support high external loads.

Durability. Experience with all but coated, cast-iron pipe has been too short and changes in water treatment have been too many to give us reliable values on the length of life of different pipe materials. The following estimates are on the safe side:

Cast-iron pipe, coated	100 years
Steel pipe, coated	25 to 50 years
Reinforced-concrete pipe	75 years
Wood-stave pipe	25 to 50 years

Wood-stave pipe must be kept under pressure if the wood is not to rot. External corrosion (soil corrosion) and disintegration of metallic pipes are important along with internal corrosion. Acid soils, sea water, and cinder fills should be avoided. Metallic pipes and the banding of wood-stave pipes are more rapidly destroyed than reinforced-concrete and asbestos-cement pipes. Moreover, metallic pipes are better conductors of electricity and so more exposed to damage by electrolysis (Vol. 2). Cathodic protection is of much promise.

Transportation.   When pipelines must be built in rugged and inaccessible locations, their size and weight become important. Cast-iron pipe is heavy in the larger sizes; steel pipe relatively much lighter but longer. The normal laying length of cast-iron pipe is 12 ft;[22] that of steel pipe is 20 to 30 ft. Wood-stave pipe is machine made or prefabricated in sizes up to 24 in. and lengths up to 20 ft. Beyond 24 in., it is built in place from staves and bands. This simplifies transportation. Reinforced-concrete pipe is generally precast in the vicinity of the pipeline. The sections are 12 and 16 ft long and very heavy in the larger sizes. A diameter smaller than 24 in. is unusual. Asbestos-cement pipe comes in laying lengths of 18 ft. Its weight is about one-quarter that of cast-iron pipe of like diameter.

Safety.   As stated before, breaks in cast-iron pipes are often quite destructive. By contrast, steel pipe fails slowly, chiefly by corrosion. The shell is perforated at scattered points, and repairs are simple. However, steel pipelines may collapse under vacuum while they are being drained. With proper operating procedures, this is a rare occurrence. Wood-stave pipe, and reinforced-concrete pipe fail gradually. Asbestos-cement pipe fails suddenly, much like cast-iron pipe.

Skilled Labor.   Modern mechanical and preformed pipe joints have simplified pipe laying. Before their introduction, welded and poured joints placed heavy demands upon skilled labor.

Maintenance.   Pipelines large enough to be entered should be inspected regularly and well maintained. All sizes and kinds must be watched for leakage or loss of pressure—outward signs of failure. There is little choice between materials in this respect. Repairs to precast concrete pipe are perhaps most difficult, but they are rarely required. Cast-iron and small welded-steel pipes can be cleaned by scraping machines and lined in place with cement to restore their capacity. New lines and repaired lines should be disinfected before they are put into service (Vol. 2).

Leakage.   All pipelines should be tested for tightness as they are constructed. Observed leakage is often expressed in gallons per day per inch diameter (nominal) and mile of pipe; but gallons per day per foot of

---

[22] Lengths of 16 ft, 5 m (16.4 ft), 18 ft, and 20 ft are also available in different types of bell-and-spigot pipe.

joint is a more rational concept. The test pressure must naturally be stated. To make a leakage test, the line is isolated by closing gates and placing a temporary header or plug at the end of the section to be tested. The pipe is then filled with water and placed under pressure, the water needed to maintain the pressure being measured by an ordinary household meter. Where there is no water, air may be substituted. Losses are assumed to vary with the square root of the pressure, as in orifices.

The allowable leakage of bell-and-spigot cast iron, and cement-asbestos pipe that has been carefully laid and well tested during construction is often set at

$$Q = nd\sqrt{p}/1850 \qquad (12\text{-}13)$$

where Q is the leakage in gallons per hour, n is the number of joints in the length of line tested, d is the nominal pipe diameter in inches, and p is the average pressure during test in pounds per square inch, gage. A mile of 24-in. cast-iron pipe laid in 12-ft lengths and tested under a pressure of 64 psig, for example, can be expected to show a leakage of $Q = (5280/12) \times 24 \times \sqrt{64}/1850 = 46$ gal/hr. Considering that the pipe has a carrying capacity of 250,000 gal/hr at a velocity of 3 fps, the expected leakage from joints is quite small. Preformed joints reduce leakage still further.

Steel and precast concrete pipe should be made tight by calking. When steel pipe is laid under water with mechanical couplings, small leaks are hard to detect, and allowances as high as 6 gpd per foot of transverse joint may have to be made.

12-9 Appurtenances

To isolate and drain pipeline sections for test, inspection, cleaning, and repairs, a number of appurtenances, or auxiliaries, are generally installed in the line (Figs. 12-6 and 7 and 13-3, and Sec. 16-15).

Gates. Gate valves are usually placed at major summits of pressure conduits (1) because summits identify the sections of line that can be drained by gravity and (2) because pressures are least at these points, making for cheaper valves and easier operation. For the sake of economy, valves smaller in diameter than the conduit itself are generally installed together with necessary reducers and increasers. Gates 8 in. in diameter or larger commonly include a 4-in. or 6-in. gated by-pass. When the larger gate is seated under pressure, water admitted through the by-pass can then equalize the pressure on both sides and make it easier to lift the main gate.

Gravity conduits are commonly provided with gate chambers, (1) at points strategic for the operation of the supply conduit, (2) at the two ends of sag pipes and pressure tunnels, and (3) wherever it is convenient to drain given sections. Sluice gates are normally installed in grade conduits,

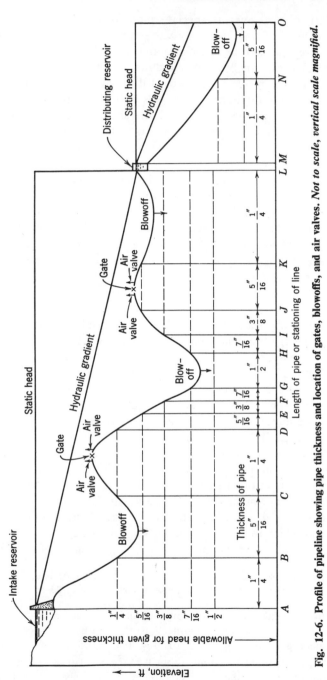

Fig. 12-6. Profile of pipeline showing pipe thickness and location of gates, blowoffs, and air valves. *Not to scale, vertical scale magnified.*

particularly in large ones. In special situations, needle valves are preferred for fine control of flow, butterfly valves for ease of operation, and cone valves for regulating time of closure and controlling water hammer.

Blowoff Valves. In pressure conduits, small, gated take-offs, known as *blowoff* or *scour valves*, are provided at low points in the line. They discharge into natural drainage channels or empty into a sump from which the water can be pumped to waste. There should be no direct connection to sewers or polluted water courses. For safety, two blowoff valves are placed in series. The chance of both failing to close is thus reduced greatly. Their size depends upon local circumstances, especially upon the time in which a given section of line is designed to be emptied and upon the resulting velocities of flow (see next paragraph of this section). Calculations are based upon orifice discharge under a falling head, equal to the difference in elevation of the water surface in the conduit and the blowoff, minus the friction head. Frequency of operation depends upon the quality of the water carried, especially on silt loads. The drainage gates of gravity conduits are placed in gate chambers.

Air Valves. Cast-iron and other rigid pipes and pressure conduits are equipped with air valves at all high points. The valves automatically remove (1) air displaced while the line is being filled and (2) air released from the flowing water when the pressure decreases appreciably or summits lie close to the hydraulic grade line. A manually operated cock or gate can be substituted if the pressure at the summit is high. Little, if any, air will then accumulate, and air needs to escape only while the line is being filled.

Steel and other flexible conduits are equipped with automatic air valves that will also admit air to the line and prevent its collapse under negative pressure (Fig. 12-7). Pressure differences are generated when a line is being drained on purpose or when water escapes accidentally through a break at a low point. Locations of choice are both sides of gates at summits, the downstream side of other gates, and changes in grade to steeper slopes in sections of line not otherwise protected by air valves.

The required valve size is related to the size of the conduit, and to the velocities at which the line is emptied. The following ratios of air valve to conduit diameter provide common but rough estimates of needed sizes.

For release of air only	1:12 or 1 in. per ft
For admission as well as release of air	1:8 or $1\frac{1}{2}$ in. per ft

An approximate calculation will show that under a vacuum of 48 in. of water, an automatic air valve, acting as an injection orifice with a coefficient of discharge of 0.5 under a head of $4/(1.3 \times 10^{-3}) = 3080$ ft of air of specific gravity 1.3×10^{-3}, is expected to admit about $0.5\sqrt{2g \times 3080} = 220$ cfs of air per square foot of valve. If the diameter ratio is 1:8, the displacement velocity in the conduit can be as high as 220/64 = 3.5 fps without exceeding a vacuum of 48 in. of water. A similar calculation will show the rate of release of air. The amounts of air that can be dissolved by water at atmospheric pressure are about 2.9% by volume at 32 F and 1.9% at 77 F, changing in direct proportion to the pressure. Accordingly, they are doubled at two atmospheres or 14.7 psig.

An analysis of air-inlet valves for steel pipelines by Parmakian[23] takes the compressibility of air into account (Sec. 16-8) and combines equations

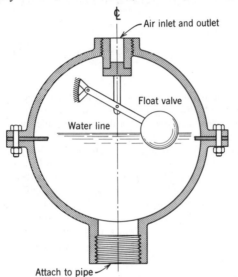

Fig. 12-7. Air inlet and release valve.

for safe differential pressures of cylindrical steel pipe (Sec. 12-6), pipe flow, and air flow, in the following approximate relationships:

$$d_a/d = 1.99 \times 10^{-2}\sqrt{\Delta V/C}\,[1 - (p_2/p_1)^{0.288}]^{-0.25} \qquad (12\text{-}14)$$

for $p_2 > 0.53p_1$, and as

$$d_a/d = 3.91 \times 10^{-2}\sqrt{\Delta V/C}\,(p_2/p_1)^{0.356} \qquad (12\text{-}15)$$

for $p_2 \leq 0.53p_1$, because air flow cannot increase beyond a critical pressure differential of 6.94 psi.

In these equations, d_a and d are respectively the diameter of the air orifice and pipe in inches, ΔV is the difference in the velocities of flow on each side of the inlet valve, C is the coefficient of discharge of the valve, and p_2 and p_1 are the pressures inside and outside the pipe respectively, with $p_1 - p_2$ not exceeding one half the collapsing pressure as a matter of safety.

[23] John Parmakian, Air-inlet Valves for Steel Pipe Lines, *Trans. Am. Soc. Civil Engrs.*, **115**, 438 (1950). More exact equations are also derived in this paper.

The equations apply strictly only to elevations of 1000 ft above mean sea level at 40 degrees latitude ($g = 32.2$ fps/sec), temperatures of 75 F, 20% humidity, and adiabatic expansion for which $pv^n = pv^{1.40}$, the air occupying a volume of 13.97 cu ft/lb.

For significantly different conditions, the weight of air W in pounds per second flowing through the inlet valve should be calculated as:

$$W = C[\pi d_a^2/(4 \times 144 v_2)]\sqrt{2g(144 p_1 v_1)[n/(n-1)][1 - (p_2/p_1)^{(n-1)/n}]}$$

(12-16)

for $p_2 > 0.53 p_1$, and as

$$W = C[\pi d_a^2/(4 \times 144)][2/(n+1)]^{1/(n-1)}\sqrt{2g[n/(n+1)]144 p_1/v_1} \quad (12\text{-}17)$$

for $p_2 \leq 0.53 p_1$.

Example 12-4. In a 60-in. steel pipeline $\frac{3}{8}$ in. thick leading from a reservoir, 2000 ft of steel pipe with hydraulic slope of 20‰ are followed by 1000 ft with a slope of 40‰. Find the size of an air valve with a discharge coefficient $C = 0.5$ to be placed at the change in slope.

From Sec. 12-6, the collapsing pressure for cylindrical shells is $p = 50.2 \times 10^6(t/d)^3 = 50.2 \times 10^6[(\frac{3}{8})/60]^3 = 12.2$ psi. Hence $p_1 - p_2 = 12.2/2 = 6.1$ psi and $p_2/p_1 = 6.1/14.3 = 0.426$, where 14.3 is the atmospheric pressure at elevation 1000 ft.

By the Hazen-Williams formula the difference in the velocities of flow is $\Delta V = 26.7 - 18.3 = 8.4$ fps. Because $p_2/p_1 \leq 0.53$, Eq. 12-14 establishes the ratio of the air inlet valve d_a to the pipe diameter d. Assuming $C = 0.5$, $d_a/d = 3.9 \times 10^{-2}\sqrt{\Delta p/C}(p_2/p_1)^{0.356} = 3.9 \times 10^{-2}\sqrt{8.4/0.5}(0.426)^{0.356} = 11.7 \times 10^{-2}$ or $1:8.5$, and $d_a = 60 \times 11.7 \times 10^{-2} = 7.02$ in. Either a single stock-item 8-in. valve or a pair of 6-in. valves would probably be chosen.

Manholes.   Access manholes are spaced 1000 to 2000 ft apart on large conduits. They are helpful during construction and serve later on for inspection and repairs. They are less common on cast-iron and asbestos-cement lines than on steel and concrete lines.

Insulation Joints.   Insulation joints control electrolysis by introducing resistance to the flow of stray electric currents along pipelines. Modern insulation joints make use of rubber gaskets or rings and of rubber-covered sections of pipe sufficiently long to introduce appreciable resistance.

Expansion Joints.   The effect of temperature changes, formulated in Sec. 12-6, is small if pipe joints permit adequate movement. Steel pipe laid with rigid transverse joints must either be allowed to expand at definite points or be rigidly restrained by anchoring the line.

Anchorages.   Anchorages are employed for one or more of the following reasons:

1. To resist the tendency of pipes to pull apart at bends and other points of unbalanced pressure when the resistance of their joints to longitudinal (shearing) stresses is exceeded.

2. To resist the tendency of pipes laid on steep gradients to pull apart when the resistance of their joints to longitudinal (shearing) stresses is inadequate.

3. To restrain or direct the expansion and contraction of rigidly joined pipes under the influence of temperature changes.

The following examples will give some concept of the magnitude of the forces to be resisted by anchorages.

Example 12-5.   In accordance with Sec. 12-6, unless otherwise stated:

1. The unbalanced pressure at a 90-deg bend in a 48-in. pipeline that carries water under a pressure of 100 psig is $P = \frac{1}{2}\pi \times (48)^2 \times 100 \times 0.7071 = 256,000$ lb or 128 tons, the two component pressures in the direction of each pipe leg being $\frac{1}{4}\pi \times (48)^2 \times 100 = 182,000$ lb or 91 tons.

2. If the line is constructed of cast-iron pipe, the resistance offered by lead joints between pipe and bend (even before applying a factor of safety), namely, $P = [(3,000/54) - 31](48)^2 = 56,000$ lb or 28 tons, is inadequate, and the line must be tied together or suitably anchored.

3. If the line is constructed of butt-welded steel plates, $\frac{1}{4}$ in. thick, the temperature stress created by a possible range in water temperature from 32 to 75 or 80 F, a difference of about 46 F, is $s = 6.5 \times 10^{-6} \times 46 \times 30 \times 10^6 = 9000$ psi, and $P = \pi \times 48 \times \frac{1}{4} \times 9000 = 340,000$ lb or 170 tons. The magnitude of this stress may be halved by closing the pipeline at the average water temperature, say 55 F, instead of the highest or lowest temperature. An anchor that will resist a force of $\frac{1}{2} \times 170 = 85$ tons must, therefore, be provided.

4. The expansion and contraction of the steel line, if unrestrained, might be as great as $\Delta = 6.5 \times 10^{-6} \times 46 \times 1000 = 0.3$ ft per 1000 ft of length.

Anchorages take many forms as follows:

1. For bends—both horizontal and vertical—concrete buttresses or *kick blocks* resisting the unbalanced pressure by their weight, much as a gravity dam resists the pressure of the water behind it. The resistance offered by the pipe joints themselves, by the friction of the pipe exterior, and by the bearing value of the soil in which the block is buried may be taken into consideration.

2. Steel straps attached to heavy boulders or to bed rock.

3. Lugs cast on cast-iron pipes and fittings to hold tie rods that prevent movement of the pipeline.

4. Anchorages of mass concrete on steel pipe to keep it from moving, or force motion to take place at expansion joints inserted for that purpose. The pipe must be well bonded to the anchors, for example, by angle irons welded onto the pipe. In the absence of expansion joints, steel pipe must be anchored at each side of gates and meters in order to prevent their destruction by pipe movement.

5. Gate chambers so designed of steel and concrete that they hold the two ends of steel lines rigidly in place.

In the absence of anchors, flanged gates are sometimes bolted on one side to the pipe—usually the upstream side—and on the other side to a cast-iron nipple connected to the pipe by means of a sleeve or expansion joint.

Other Appurtenances.   These may include (Sec. 16-15):

1. Air-relief towers at the first summit of the line to remove air mechanically entrained as water flows into the pipe entrance.

2. Surge tanks at the end of the line to reduce water hammer created by rapid closing of a valve at the end of the line.

3. Pressure-relief valves or overflow towers on one or more summits to keep the pressure in the line below a given value by letting water discharge to waste when the pressure builds up beyond the design value.

4. Check valves on force mains to prevent backflow when pumps shut down.

5. Self-acting shut-off valves triggered to close when the pipe velocity exceeds a predetermined value as a result of an accident.

6. Altitude-control valves that will shut off the inlet to service reservoirs, elevated tanks, and standpipes before overflow levels are reached (Fig. 13-14).

7. Venturi or other meters and recorders to measure the flow.

CHAPTER 13

Water Distribution

13-1 Systems of Distribution

Apart from a few scattered taps and take-offs along their feeder conduits, distribution systems for public water supplies are networks of pipes within networks of streets. As pointed out in Sec. 2-9, street plan, topography, and location of supply works, together with service storage, therefore determine the type of distribution system and the type of flow through it. Although service reservoirs are often placed along lines of supply, where they may usefully reduce conduit pressures (Fig. 12-6), their principal purpose is to satisfy network requirements. Accordingly they are, in fact, components of the distribution system, not of the transmission system.

One- and Two-Directional Flow.   Type of flow creates the four systems, sketched in Fig. 13-1. Hydraulic grade lines and residual pressures within the areas served, together with the volume of distribution storage, govern pipe sizes within the network. It is plain that flows from opposite directions increase system capacity. There is two-directional flow in the main arteries when a pumped or gravity supply, or service reservoir, feeds into opposite ends of the distribution system; or through the system to elevated storage in a reservoir, tank, or standpipe situated at the far end of the area of greatest water demand. Volume and location of service storage depend upon topography and water needs (Sec. 13-12).

Types of Service.   As explained in Sec. 2-9, parts of communities at different elevations may be supplied through separate, though commonly interconnected, distribution systems, each with its own service storage: high-lying areas in a *high service system*, low-lying areas in a *low-service* *system.* Areas of intermediate elevation, too, may be set apart. Hydraulic analysis must take cognizance of the independence as well as the interdependence of the component networks. High-service draft from low-service arteries, for example, must be planned for. Because high-service areas are commonly small and low-service areas commonly large, support from high-service storage, during breakdowns in the main supply, is generally disappointing.

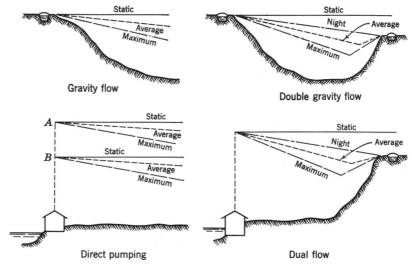

Fig. 13-1. One- and two-directional flow in distribution systems.

Independent high-pressure *fire-supply systems* within high-value districts of some communities (Sec. 2-9) occupy much the same hydraulic status as high-service supplies. They are independent in their larger functions of water distribution but depend upon the general water works for supply. However, high-capacity fire engines have made separate fire-supply systems unnecessary. Emergency connections to other water sources must be properly safeguarded.

13-2 Pipe Grids

The gridiron system of pipes stretching over all but the outlying sections of a community (Fig. 2-8) may consist of *single mains* or *dual mains* (Fig. 13-2). In the northern hemisphere, single mains are customarily laid on the north and east sides of streets for protection against freezing. In the southern hemisphere, the south and east sides are used. Valves are generally installed as follows: three at crosses, two at tees, and one on single-hydrant branches. In dual-main systems, *service headers* are added

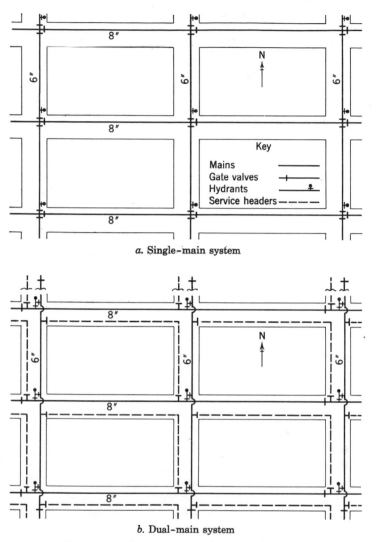

a. Single-main system

b. Dual-main system

Fig. 13-2. Gridiron system of single and dual mains.

on the south (north in southern hemisphere) and west sides of streets, and piping is generally placed beneath the sidewalks. In a scheme suggested by Ballou,[1] valves are installed as follows: one on each main at intervals of two blocks, one at the junction of the service header with its main, and one on each of two hydrant branches. Service operations and conditions

[1] A. F. Ballou, Hydrant Connections and the Control of Dual Mains, *J. New Eng. Water Works Assoc.,* **52,** 81 (1938).

in breakdowns can then be compared as follows:

Breakdown of	Single-Main System	Dual-Main System
(1) Hydrant	Close one hydrant valve.	Close two hydrant valves.
(2) East-west main	Close four valves on main. This dead-ends supply to one hydrant and cuts out intermediate service taps; it also dead-ends supply to eastern intersection.	Close two valves on main and one valve on each of the connected hydrants and service headers. Hydrants and service headers remain in commission; house service taps on main are placed out of commission; service headers are dead-ended.
(3) North-south main	Close two valves on main. One hydrant and intermediate house taps are placed out of commission.	Same as for east-west main.

The hydraulic advantages of dual-main systems over single-main systems are more or less local, because service headers do not contribute to flow outside their own blocks. The important fact is that breaks in mains do not impair the usefulness of hydrants; nor do they dead-end mains. Dual-main systems must not be confused with dual water supplies: a high-grade supply for some purposes and a low-grade supply for others.

13-3 System Capacity and Pressure

The capacity of distribution systems must comprehend *stand-by* or *ready-to-serve* requirements for fire fighting as well as fluctuations in domestic, industrial, and other normal water demands. However, capacity to serve is not merely a function of available rate of draft; it is also a function of available pressure. The water must rise to the upper stories of buildings of normal height and must flow from hydrants, directly or through pumpers, to deliver needed fire streams issuing through fire hose long enough to reach the fire.

Capacity. If there was no fire hazard, the hydraulic capacity of distribution systems would have to equal the maximum demand for domestic, industrial, and other general uses. For absolute safety, fire demand would be added. Ordinarily, this is not done: (1) because maximum draft will probably not coincide with a serious conflagration; (2) because systems are dimensioned for the future, and new construction is generally completed, in a reasonably foresighted community, before the designed capacity of the original system has been reached. In the absence of unusual hazards, such as flammable structures or storage of flammable raw or manufactured materials, a coincident draft of 40 to 50 gpcd in excess of the average annual consumption is often assumed. In the presence of unusual hazards, allowances should be higher. Determination of requisite system capacity for different areas of the community becomes simpler if the municipality has been *zoned*, and well-drawn ordinances regulate both the allowable *use* of properties in different zones and the allowable *bulk* of buildings erected.

The general fire-fighting requirements of the National Board of Fire Underwriters have been stated in Sec. 5-9. In part they are briefed, in part elaborated, in the following schedule.

1. Within the central, congested, or high-value, district of North American communities:
   (a) For communities of 200,000 people or less, $Q = 1020 \sqrt{P}(1 - 0.01 \sqrt{P})$, according to Eq. 5-10, Q being the fire draft in gpm and P the population in thousands.
   (b) For populations in excess of 200,000, $Q = 12,000$ gpm with 2000 to 8000 gpm in addition for a second fire.
2. For residential districts with:
   (a) Small, low buildings—$\frac{1}{3}$ of lots in block built upon, $Q = 500$ gpm.
   (b) Larger or higher buildings, $Q = 1000$ gpm.
   (c) High-value residences, apartments, tenements, dormitories, and similar structures, $Q = 1500$ to 3000 gpm.
   (d) Three-story buildings in densely built-up sections, $Q = $ up to 6000 gpm.
3. Proportion or amount of estimated flow to be concentrated, if necessary, on one block or one very large building:
   (a) In the high-value district, $\frac{2}{3}$.
   (b) In compact residential areas, $\frac{1}{4}$ to $\frac{1}{2}$.
   (c) For detached buildings, 500 to 750 gpm.

Table 13-1, based upon Eq. 5-10, shows the relatively large stand-by capacity prescribed.

Pressure. For normal drafts, water pressure at the street line must be at least 20 psig (46 ft) to let water rise three stories and overcome the frictional resistance of the house-distribution system; but 40 psig is more desirable. Business blocks are supplied more satisfactorily at pressures of 60 to 75 psig. To supply their upper stories, tall buildings must boost water to tanks on their roofs or in their towers, and often, too, on intermediate floors.

Fire demand is commonly gaged by the *standard fire stream*: 250 gpm issuing from a $1\frac{1}{8}$-in. nozzle at a pressure of 45 psig at the base of the tip. When this amount of water flows through $2\frac{1}{2}$-in. rubber-lined hose, the

Table 13-1   Required Fire Flow, Fire Reserve, and Hydrant Spacing Recommended by the National Board of Fire Underwriters

Population	Fire Flow gpm	Fire Flow mgd	Duration, hr	Fire Reserve, mg	Area per Hydrant, sq ft — Engine Streams	Area per Hydrant, sq ft — Hydrant Streams
1,000	1,000	1.4	4	0.2	120,000	100,000
2,000	1,500	2.2	6	0.5	. . .	90,000
4,000	2,000	2.9	8	1.0	110,000	85,000
6,000	2,500	3.6	10	1.5	. . .	78,000
10,000	3,000	4.3	10	1.8	100,000	70,000
13,000	3,500	5.0	10	2.1	. . .	. . .
17,000	4,000	5.8	10	2.4	90,000	55,000
22,000	4,500	6.5	10	2.7	. . .	. . .
28,000	5,000	7.2	10	3.0	85,000	40,000†
40,000	6,000	8.6	10	3.6	80,000	. . .
60,000	7,000	10.1	10	4.2	70,000	. . .
80,000	8,000	11.5	10	4.8	60,000	. . .
100,000	9,000	13.0	10	5.4	55,000	. . .
125,000	10,000	14.4	10	6.0	48,000	. . .
150,000	11,000	15.8	10	6.6	43,000	. . .
200,000*	12,000	17.3	10	7.2	40,000	. . .

* For populations over 200,000 and local concentration of streams, see outline of National Board Requirements.
† For fire flows of 5000 gpm and over.

frictional resistance is about 15 psi per 100 ft of hose. Adding the hydrant resistance and required nozzle pressure of 45 psig then gives the pressure needs at the hydrant shown in Table 13-2.[2] A standard fire stream is effective to a height of 70 ft and has a horizontal carry of 63 ft.

Because hydrants are normally planned to control areas within a radius of 200 ft, Table 13-2 shows that direct attachment of fire hose to hydrants (hydrant streams) calls for a residual pressure at the hydrant of about 75 psig. To maintain this pressure at times of fire, system pressures must approach 100 psig. This has its disadvantages; among them are increased danger of breaks and leakage or waste of water approximately in proportion to the square root of the pressure. Minimum pressures for hydrant

[2] J. R. Freeman, Experiments Relating to Hydraulics of Fire Streams, *Trans. Am. Soc. Civil Engrs.*, **21**, 303 (1889). As a young man, Mr. Freeman (1855–1932) studied the performance of fire nozzles in the hydraulic laboratory of Hiram F. Mills at Lawrence, Mass., and brought order into the operations of fire departments and fire insurance agencies. Eventually, he became one of America's leading hydraulic engineers and a pioneer in the study of hydraulic models.

Table 13-2   Hydrant Pressures for Different Lengths of Fire Hose

Length of hose, ft	100	200	300	400	500	600
Required pressure, psig	63	77	92	106	121	135

streams, commonly set at 50 psig, do not deliver standard fire streams after passing through as little as 50 ft of hose.

Motor pumpers commonly deliver up to 1500 gpm at adequate pressures. Capacities of 20,000 gpm are in sight, with single streams discharging as much as 1000 gpm from 2-in. nozzles. To maintain domestic and industrial draft and keep pollution from entering water mains by seepage or failure under a vacuum, fire engines should not lower pressures in the mains to less than 20 psig. For large hydrant outlets, the safe limit is sometimes set at 10 psig. In a real way, modern fire-fighting equipment has done away with the necessity for pressures much in excess of 60 psig, except in small towns that cannot afford a full-time, well-equipped fire department. Pumpers have increased system capacity in the ratio of $\sqrt{p-20}/\sqrt{p-75}$, where p is the normal dynamic pressure of the network. More closely, the ratio is $[(p-20)/(p-75)]^{0.54}$.

13-4   Distribution-System Components

Pipes, gates, and hydrants are the basic elements of reticulation systems (Fig. 13-3). Their dimensioning and spacing rest upon experience normally precise enough in its minimum standards to permit roughing in all but the main arteries and feeders. Common standards include the following:

Pipes

Smallest pipes in gridiron	6-in.
Smallest branching pipes (dead ends)	8-in.
Largest spacing of 6-in. grid (8-in. pipe used beyond this value)	600 ft
Smallest pipes in high-value district	8-in.
Smallest pipes on principal streets in central district	12-in.
Largest spacing of supply mains or feeders	2,000 ft

Gates

Spacing in single- and dual-main systems	(See Sec. 13-2)
Largest spacing on long branches	800 ft
Largest spacing in high-value district	500 ft

Hydrants

Areas protected by hydrants	(See Table 13-1)
Largest spacing when fire flow exceeds 5,000 gpm	200 ft
Largest spacing when fire flow is as low as 1,000 gpm	300 ft

The choice of large pipe sizes depends upon occupancy of the properties along mains (whether residential, commercial, or industrial), their water uses and fire risks.

Because the *hydrant areas* shown in Table 13-1 are based upon a single fire stream being effective within a radius of 200 ft from the hydrant, the

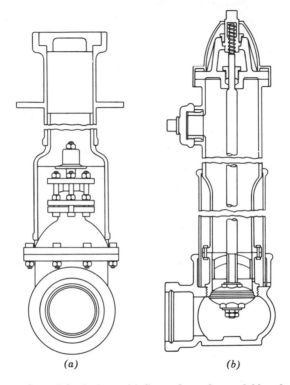

(a)   (b)

Fig. 13-3. Gate valve and fire hydrant. (a) Gate valve and extendable valve box. (b) Post fire hydrant with compression valve.

area served is 120,000 sq ft. In order to attack a fire from all sides, or at least from two hydrants, a minimum of four streams (1000 gpm) must be brought to play upon this area. However, when communities become larger, buildings grow in bulk, and the area served by each hydrant must be reduced. Hydrant streams tax the distribution system more than do engine streams and offer less leeway when pressures drop. The area served by each hydrant must be reduced accordingly. Common standards are based upon needs observed during actual conflagrations.

13-5 Field Studies

The hydraulic performance of existing distribution systems is determined most directly and expeditiously by pressure surveys and hydrant-flow tests. There is no limit to the extent of such tests. They should cover all typical portions of the community: the high-value district, residential neighborhoods and industrial areas of different kinds, the outskirts, and high-service zones. If need be, tests can be extended into every block. The results obtained will establish available pressures and flows and existing deficiencies. These can then be made the basis of hydraulic calculations for extensions, reinforcements, and new gridiron layouts. Follow-up tests can show how nearly the desired changes have been accomplished.

Pressure Surveys. These yield the most rudimentary information about networks. If they are conducted both at night (minimum flow) and during the day (normal demand), they will indicate the hydraulic efficiency of the system in meeting common requirements; but they will not establish the probable behavior of the system under stress, during a serious conflagration, for example.

Hydrant-Flow Tests. As commonly performed, hydrant-flow tests include (1) observation of the pressure at a centrally situated hydrant during the conduct of the test; and (2) measurement of the combined flow from a group of neighboring hydrants. Velocity heads in the jets issuing from the hydrants are usually measured by hydrant pitot tubes. If the tests are to be significant, the following precautions should be observed:

1. The hydrants tested should form a group such as might be called into play in fighting a serious fire in the district under study.
2. Water should be drawn at a rate that will drop the pressure enough to keep it from being measurably affected by normal fluctuations in draft within the system.
3. The time of test should coincide with drafts (domestic, industrial, etc.) in the remainder of the system, reasonably close to *coincident* values.

The requirements of the National Board of Fire Underwriters already outlined are valuable aids in planning hydrant-flow tests. A layout of pipes and hydrants in a typical flow test is shown in Fig. 13-4, and observed values are summarized in Table 13-3.

This table is more or less self-explanatory. The initial and residual pressure was read from a Bourdon gage at hydrant 1. Hydrants 2, 3, 4, and 5 were opened in quick succession, and their rates of discharge were measured simultaneously by means of hydrant pitots. A test such as this does not consume more than 5 min, if it is conducted by a well-trained crew.

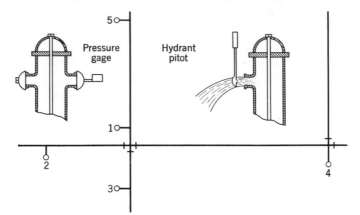

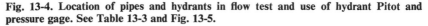

Fig. 13-4. Location of pipes and hydrants in flow test and use of hydrant Pitot and pressure gage. See Table 13-3 and Fig. 13-5.

Hydrant-Flow Calculations. Necessary calculations may be outlined as follows for the flow test recorded in Table 13-3.

Example 13-1. For outlets of diameter d in., the discharge Q in gpm is: $Q = 29.82cd^2\sqrt{p}$, where p is the pitot reading in psig and c is the coefficient of hydrant discharge.[3] For smooth well-rounded $2\frac{1}{2}$-in. outlets, $c = 0.9$ and $Q = 168.2\sqrt{p}$.

Pressure-discharge relations established in this test are illustrated in Fig. 13-5. If the true static pressure is known, a more exact calculation is possible, although the additional labor involved is seldom justified. In accordance with the common hydraulic analysis of Borda's mouthpiece, a pressure gage inserted in a hydrant in juxtaposition to the hydrant

Table 13-3   Record of a Typical Hydrant-Flow Test

(All pressures are expressed in psig)

Conditions of test	Observed Pressure at Hydrant 1	Observed Discharge Pressure (p) (Velocity Head)	Calculated Flow (Q), gpm	Remarks
All hydrants closed	74	...	...	All hydrant outlets are
Hydrant 2 opened, 1 outlet	...	13.2	610	$2\frac{1}{2}$ in. in diameter.
Hydrant 3 opened, 2 outlets	...	9.6	2 × 520	Total Q = 2980 gpm
Hydrant 4 opened, 1 outlet	...	16.8	690	Calculated engine
Hydrant 5 opened, 1 outlet	46	14.5	640	streams = 4200 gpm
All hydrants closed	74	...	...	

[3] Because $Q = cav$, where c is the hydrant discharge coefficient, a is the hydrant outlet area, and v is the discharge velocity ($2.308p = v^2/2g$). Here Q is measured in cfs, a in sq ft, and v in fps. The value of c varies from 0.9 for well-rounded, smooth outlets to 0.7 for sharp outlets projecting into the barrel.

outlet to be opened will also record the discharge pressure otherwise measured by hydrant pitots.

Hydrant tests are sometimes made to ascertain the capacity of individual hydrants and advertise it to firemen (particularly to engine companies summoned from neighboring towns) by painting the bonnet a suitable color. The New England Water Works Association has recommended

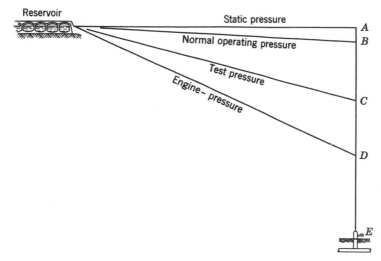

Fig. 13-5. Pressure and discharge relations established by hydrant-flow test. See Fig. 13-4 and Table 13-3.

   A: Static water table.
   B: No hydrant discharge. Pressure = 74 psig; pressure drop p_0 due to coincident draft Q.
   C: Hydrant discharge. Pressure = 46 psig; pressure drop $p_1 = (74 - 46) = 28$ psi accompanies discharge of $Q_1 = 2980$ gpm.
   D: Engine streams. Pressure = 20 psig; pressure drop $p_2 = (74 - 20) = 54$ psi accompanies discharge $Q_2 = 4200$ gpm.
   E: Hydrant 1, recording residual pressure of hydrant groups shown in Fig. 13-4.

painting hydrant barrels chrome yellow for visibility and giving bonnets the following distinguishing colors:

Color	Related Capacity
Red	less than 500 gpm
Yellow	500 to 1000 gpm
Green	more than 1000 gpm

The weakness of this arrangement is the restriction of flow measurements to single hydrants. In fire fighting, groups of hydrants are normally brought into action. Tests of individual hydrants are of limited value; they may be quite misleading.

13-6 Office Studies

No matter how energetically distribution systems are field-tested, needed extensions and reinforcements of old networks and the design of new ones can be adequately identified only by office studies. Necessary analysis presupposes familiarity with processes of hydraulic computation, including analog and high-speed digital computers. Even without large computers, however, the best processes can be so systematized as to make their application a matter of simple arithmetic and pipe-flow tables, diagrams, or slide rules.

Useful methods of analysis are: (1) sectioning; (2) relaxation; (3) pipe equivalence; (4) computer programming; (5) electrical analogy.

13-7 Method of Sections

This is an approximate and, in a sense, an exploratory method, simple in concept and application, and widely useful provided its limitations are clearly understood. Allen Hazen developed it as a quick check of distribution systems. Pardoe's method[4] is somewhat like Hazen's, but more involved. Similar in concept, too, is the circle method, which is usually confined to cutting pipes tributary to a central fire hydrant or group of hydrants at the center of a circle (Example 13-3).

The method of sections is illustrated in Fig. 13-6 and Example 13-2. Needed steps are outlined as follows:

1. Cut the network by a series of lines, not necessarily straight or regularly spaced but chosen with due regard to the varying sequence of pipe sizes and district characteristics. A first series of lines may well cut the distribution piping substantially at right angles to the general direction of flow, i.e., perpendicular to a line drawn from the supply conduit to the high-value district (Fig. 13-6). Further series may be oriented in some other critical direction, for example, horizontally and vertically in Fig. 13-6. For more than one supply conduit, the sections may be curved to intercept the flow from each conduit.

2. Estimate how much water must be supplied to areas *beyond* each section. Base estimates on a knowledge of the population density and the general characteristics of the zone—residential, commercial, and industrial. The water requirements comprise (*a*) the normal, coincident draft, here called the domestic draft, and (*b*) the fire demand (Table 13-1). Domestic use decreases progressively from section to section, as population or industry is left behind; fire demand remains the same until the high-value district has been passed, then it drops to a figure applicable to the type of outskirt area.

3. Estimate the distribution-system capacity at each section across the piping. To do this:

---

[4] W. S. Pardoe, *Eng. News-Rec.*, **93**, 516 (1924).

a. Tabulate the number of pipes of each size cut. Count only pipes that deliver water in the general direction of flow.

b. Determine the average available hydraulic gradient or frictional resistance. This depends upon (1) the pressure to be maintained in the system and (2) the allowable pipe velocity.[5] Ordinarily, hydraulic gradients lie between 1 and 3‰, and velocities range from 2 to 4 fps.

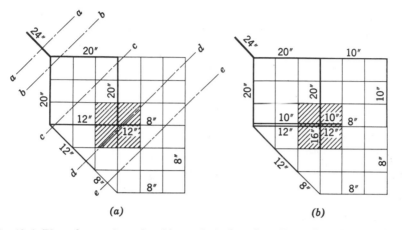

(a)   (b)

Fig. 13-6. Plan of network analyzed by method of sections. Example 13-2. (*a*) Existing System. (*b*) Recommended system. Unless otherwise indicated, pipe diameters are 6 in. The high-value district is cross-hatched.

4. For the available, or desirable, hydraulic gradient, determine the capacities of existing pipes and sum them for total capacity.

5. Calculate the deficiency or difference between required and existing capacity.

6. For the available, or desirable, hydraulic gradient, select the sizes and routes of pipes that will offset the deficiency. General familiarity with the community and studies of the network plan will aid judgment. Some existing small pipes may have to be removed to make way for larger mains.

7. Determine the size of the equivalent pipe for the reinforced system and calculate the velocity of flow. Excessive velocities may make for dangerous water hammer. They should be avoided, if necessary, by lowering the hydraulic gradients actually called into play.

[5] To illustrate, for a level region, a distance of 25,000 ft from the junction of the supply conduit with the network to the high-value district, a pressure of 70 psig at the junction, an available pressure drop to 20 psig for engine streams, a requisite system capacity of 17 mgd, and a variation in pipe sizes from 6 in. to 24 in: the available hydraulic gradient is $(70 - 20) \times 2.308/25 = 4.6‰$, the carrying capacity is that of a 30-in. pipe, and the velocities lie between 1.9 fps for 6-in. pipes and 4.7 fps for 24-in. pipes. If the velocity in 24-in. pipes is to be reduced to 3 fps, the hydraulic gradient must be lowered to 2‰ and the network strengthened by the addition of pipes. The reinforced network must possess the carrying capacity of a 35-in. pipe.

8. Check important pressure requirements against the plan of the reinforced network.

The method of sections is particularly useful (1) in preliminary studies of large and complicated distribution systems; (2) as a check upon other methods of analysis; and (3) as a basis for further investigations and more exact calculations.

Example 13-2. Analyze the network of Fig. 13-6 by the method of sections. The hydraulic gradient available within the network proper is estimated to lie close to 2‰. The value of C in the Hazen-Williams formula is assumed to be 100, and the domestic (coincident) draft, in this case, only 150 gpcd. The fire demand is taken from Table 13-2.

1. Section *a-a*. Population 16,000.
   (*a*) Demands (mgd): domestic, 2.2; fire, 5.6; total, 7.8.
   (*b*) Existing pipes: one 24-in.; capacity, 6.0 mgd.
   (*c*) Deficiency: 7.8 − 6.0 = 1.8 mgd.
   (*d*) If no pipes are added, the 24-in. pipe must carry 7.8 mgd. This it will do with a loss of head of 3.2‰ at a velocity of 3.8 fps (Hazen-Williams diagram).
2. Section *b-b*. Population and flow as in *a-a*.
   (*a*) Total demand, 7.8 mgd.
   (*b*) Existing pipes: 2, 20-in. @ 3.7 mgd = 7.4 mgd.
   (*c*) Deficiency, 7.8 − 7.4 = 0.4 mgd.
   (*d*) If no pipes are added, existing pipes will carry 7.8 mgd with a loss of head of 2.2‰ at a velocity of 2.8 fps.
3. Section *c-c*. Population 14,000.
   (*a*) Demands (mgd): domestic, 2.0; fire, 5.6; total, 7.6.
   (*b*) Existing pipes: one 20-in. @ 3.7 mgd; two 12-in. @ 1.0 mgd = 2.0 mgd; five 6-in. @ 0.16 = 0.8 mgd; total, 6.5 mgd.
   (*c*) Deficiency: 7.6 − 6.5 = 1.1 mgd.
   (*d*) Pipes added: two 10-in. @ 0.6 = 1.2 mgd
        Pipes removed: one 6-in. @ 0.2 mgd
        Net added capacity: 1.2 − 0.2 = 1.0 mgd
   (*e*) Reinforced capacity: 6.5 + 1.0 = 7.5 mgd.
        The reinforced system (equivalent pipe,[6] 26.0 in.) will carry 7.6 mgd with a loss of head of 2.1‰ at a velocity of 3.2 fps.
4. Section *d-d*. Population 8000.
   (*a*) Demands (mgd): domestic, 1.1; fire, 5.6; total, 6.7.
   (*b*) Existing pipes: two 12-in. @ 1.0 = 2.0 mgd; eight 6-in. @ 0.16 = 1.3 mgd; total, 3.3 mgd.
   (*c*) Deficiency: 6.7 − 3.3 = 3.4 mgd.
   (*d*) Pipes added: one 16-in. @ 2.1 mgd; two 10-in. @ 0.6 = 1.2 mgd; total 3.3 mgd.
        Pipes removed: two 6-in. @ 0.16 = 0.3 mgd.
        Net added capacity: 3.3 − 0.3 = 3.0 mgd.
   (*e*) Reinforced capacity: 3.3 + 3.0 = 6.3 mgd.
        The reinforced system (equivalent pipe, 24.4 in.) will carry 6.7 mgd with a loss of head of 2.2‰ at a velocity of 3.2 fps.
5. Section *e-e*. Population 3000.
   (*a*) Demands (mgd): domestic, 0.5; fire, 1.5; total, 2.0.
   (*b*) Existing pipes: two 8-in. @ 0.35 = 0.7 mgd; six 6-in. @ 0.16 = 0.9 mgd; total, 1.6 mgd.

[6] The equivalent pipe will carry 7.5 mgd on a hydraulic gradient of 2‰.

(c) Deficiency: 2.0 − 1.6 = 0.4 mgd.
(d) Pipes added: one 10-in. @ 0.6 mgd.
   Pipes removed: one 6-in. @ 0.16 mgd.
   Net added capacity: 0.6 − 0.2 = 0.4 mgd.
(e) Reinforced capacity: 1.6 + 0.4 = 2.0 mgd.
   The reinforced system (equivalent pipe, 15.8 in.) will carry 2 mgd with a loss of
   head of 2.0‰ at a velocity of 2.3 fps.

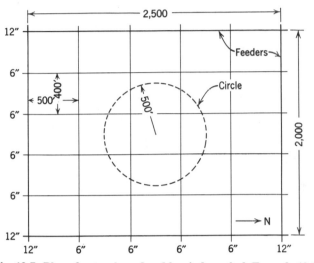

Fig. 13-7. Plan of network analyzed by circle method. Example 13-3.

Example 13-3.   Assuming water is to be delivered to a fire through not more than
500 ft of hose, find, by the circle method, the water available at the circumference of a
500-ft circle placed in the center of the network shown in Fig. 13-7, the pressure in the
12-in. feeders being 40 psig and the residual hydrant pressure not less than 20 psig.

1. The pipes cut by the circle, the average length of these pipes from their feeder
pipes to the hydrants within the circle, and the hydraulic gradients of these pipes are as
follows:
East-West: four 6-in., $[1000 − \frac{1}{2}(500)] = 750$ ft, $(40 − 20) \times 2.308/0.75 = 61.6‰$.
North-South: four 6-in., $[1250 − \frac{1}{2}(500)] = 1000$ ft, $(40 − 20) \times 2.308/1.00 = 46.2‰$.

2. The carrying capacity of these pipes, assuming $C = 100$, is: East-West: 4 @ 700 =
2800 gpm; North-South: 4 @ 600 = 2400 gpm; total: 5200 gpm.

3. The number of standard fire streams is 5200/250 = 20.8.

13-8   Relaxation Method

A method of relaxation, or controlled trial and error, was introduced
by Hardy Cross[7] whose procedures are followed here with only a few
modifications. In applying a method of this kind, calculations become

---

[7] Hardy Cross, Analysis of Flow in Networks of Conduits or Conductors, *Univ.
Illinois Bull.* 286 (1936). Hardy Cross (1885–1959) was Professor of Civil Engineering
(structures) first at the University of Illinois, later at Yale University. The method
discussed here was translated by him from structural to hydraulic analyses.

speedier if pipe flow relationships are expressed by an exponential formula with unvarying capacity coefficient, and notation becomes simpler if the exponential formula is written $H = kQ^n$, where, for a given pipe, k is a numerical constant depending upon C, d, and l, and Q is the flow, n being a constant exponent for all pipes.[8] Two procedures may be involved, depending upon whether (a) the quantities of water entering and leaving the network or (b) the piezometric levels, pressures, or water-table elevations at inlets and outlets are known.

Balancing Heads by Correcting Assumed Flows. In this procedure, necessary formulations are made algebraically consistent by arbitrarily assigning *positive signs* to *clockwise* flows and associated head losses, and *negative signs* to *counterclockwise* flows and associated head losses. For the simple network shown in Fig. 13-8a, inflow Q_i and outflow Q_o are equal and known, inflow being split between two branches in such manner that the sum of the balanced head losses H_1 (clockwise) and $-H_2$ (counterclockwise) or $\Sigma H = H_1 - H_2 = 0$. If the assumed split flows Q_1 and $-Q_2$ are each in error by the same small amount q, $\Sigma H = \Sigma k(Q + q)^n = 0$. Expanding this binomial and neglecting all but its first two terms, because higher powers of q are presumably very small, $\Sigma H = \Sigma k(Q + q)^n = \Sigma k Q^n + \Sigma n k q Q^{n-1} = 0$, whence

$$q = - \frac{\Sigma k Q^n}{n \Sigma k Q^{n-1}} = - \frac{\Sigma H}{n \Sigma (H/Q)} \qquad (13\text{-}1)$$

If a take-off is added to the system as in Fig. 13-8b, both head losses and flows are affected.

Balancing Flows by Correcting Assumed Heads. In this procedure necessary formulations become algebraically consistent when *positive signs* are arbitrarily assigned to *flows towards junctions* other than inlet and outlet junctions (for which water table elevations are known) and *negative signs* to *flows away from* these *intermediate junctions*, the sum of the balanced flows at the junctions being zero. If the assumed water table elevation at a junction, such as the take-off junction in Fig. 13-8b, is in error by a height h, different small errors q are created in the individual flows Q leading to and leaving from the junction. For any one pipe, therefore, $H + h = k(Q + q)^n = kQ^n + h$, where H is the loss of head associated with the flow Q. Moreover, as before, $h = nkqQ^{n-1} = nq(H/Q)$ and $q = (h/n)(Q/H)$. Because $\Sigma(Q + q) = 0$ at each junction, $\Sigma Q = -\Sigma q$ and $\Sigma q = (h/n)\Sigma(Q/H)$, or $\Sigma Q = -(h/n)\Sigma(Q/H)$. Therefore

$$h = - \frac{n \Sigma Q}{\Sigma (Q/H)} \qquad (13\text{-}2)$$

[8] In Eq. 12-7, for example, $Q = 405Cd^{2.63}s^{0.54}$, or $sl = H = kQ^{1.85}$ for pipes with given values of C, d, and l.

In accordance with their derivation, the corrections q and h are only approximate. After they have been applied once to the assumed flows, the network is more nearly in balance than it was at the beginning, but the process of correction must be repeated until the balancing operations are perfected. The work involved is straightforward, but it is greatly facilitated by a satisfactory scheme of bookkeeping such as that outlined for the method of balancing heads in Example 13-4 for the network sketched in Fig. 13-9.

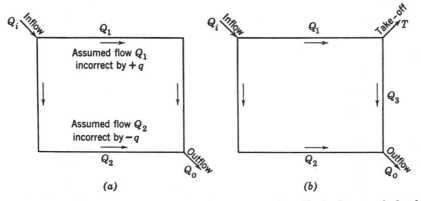

Fig. 13-8. Simple network illustrating (a) the derivation of the Hardy Cross method and (b) the effect of changing flows.

Although the network in Example 13-4 is simple, it cannot be solved conveniently by algebraic methods, because it contains two interfering hydraulic constituents: (1) a crossover (pipe 4) involved in more than one circuit; and (2) a series of take-offs representing water used along the pipe lines, fire flows through hydrants, or supplies through to neighboring circuits.

Example 13-4. Balance the network of Fig. 13-9 by the method of balancing heads. The schedule of calculations (Table 13-4) includes the following:

Columns 1–4 identify the position of the pipes in the network and record their length and diameter. There are two circuits and seven pipes. Pipe 4 is shared by both circuits. One star indicates this in connection with Circuit I; a double dagger does so with Circuit II. This dual pipe function must not be overlooked.

Columns 5–9 deal with the assumed flows and the derived flow correction. For purposes of identification the hydraulic elements Q, S, H, and q are given a subscript zero.

Column 5 lists the assumed flows Q_0 in mgd. They are preceded by positive signs if they are clockwise and by negative signs if they are counterclockwise. The distribution of flows has been purposely misjudged in order to highlight the balancing operation. At each junction the total flow remaining in the system must be accounted for.

Column 6 gives the hydraulic gradients s_0 in ft per 1000 ft (‰) when the pipe is

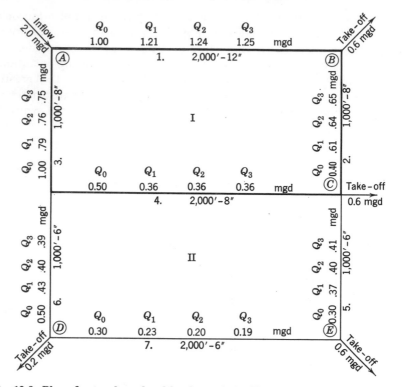

Fig. 13-9. Plan of network analyzed by the method of balancing heads. Example 13-4.

carrying the quantities Q_0 shown in Col. 5. The values of s_0 can be read directly from tables or diagrams of the Hazen-Williams formula.

Column 7 is obtained by multiplying the hydraulic gradients (s_0) by the length of the pipe in 1000 ft; i.e., Col. 7 = Col. 6 × (Col. 3/1000). The head losses H_0 obtained are preceded by a positive sign if the flow is clockwise, by a negative sign if counterclockwise. The values in Col. 7 are totaled for each circuit, with due regard to signs, to obtain ΣH.

Column 8 is found by dividing Col. 7 by Col. 5. Division makes all signs of H_0/Q_0 positive. This column is totaled for each circuit to obtain $\Sigma(H_0/Q_0)$ in the flow-correction formula.

Column 9 contains the calculated flow correction $q_0 = -\Sigma H_0/(1.85 \times \Sigma H_0/Q_0)$. For example: in Circuit I, $\Sigma H_0 = -16.5$, $\Sigma(H_0/Q_0) = 43.1$; and $(-16.5)/(1.85 \times 43.1) = -0.21$; or $q_0 = +0.21$. Because pipe 4 operates in both circuits, it draws a correction from each circuit. However, the second correction is of opposite sign. As a part of Circuit I, for example, pipe 4 receives a correction of $q = -0.07$ from Circuit II in addition to its basic correction of $q = +0.21$ from Circuit I.

Columns 10–14 cover the once-corrected flows. Therefore, the hydraulic elements (Q, s, H, and q) are given the subscript one. Column 10 is obtained by adding, with due regard to sign, Cols. 5 and 9. Columns 11, 12, 13, and 14 are then found in the same manner as Cols. 6, 7, 8, and 9.

Cir-cuit No.(1)	Pipe No.(2)	Length, ft (3)	Diameter, in.(4)	Q_0, mgd (5)	s_0, ‰ (6)	H_0, ft (7)	H_0/Q_0 (8)	q_0, mgd (9)	Q_1, mgd (10)	s_1, ‰ (11)	H_1, ft (12)	H_1/Q_1 (13)	q_1, mgd (14)
				Network		Assumed Conditions			First Correction				
I	1	2,000	12	+1.0	2.1	+4.2	4.2	+0.21	+1.21	3.0	+6.0	5.0	+0.03
	2	1,000	8	+0.4	2.8	+2.8	7.0	+0.21	+0.61	6.1	+6.1	10.0	+0.03
	3	1,000	8	−1.0	15.1	−15.1	15.1	+0.21	−0.79	9.8	−9.8	12.4	+0.03
	4*	2,000	8	−0.5	4.2	−8.4	16.8	+0.21 −0.07†	−0.36	2.3	−4.6	12.8	+0.03 −0.03†
						−16.5 ÷	(43.1) ×	1.85) = −0.21			−2.3 ÷	(40.2) ×	1.85) = −0.03
II	4‡	2,000	8	+0.5	4.2	+8.4	16.8	+0.07 −0.21†	+0.36	2.3	+4.6	12.8	+0.03 −0.03†
	5	1,000	6	+0.3	6.6	+6.6	22.0	+0.07	+0.37	9.8	+9.8	26.5	+0.03
	6	1,000	6	−0.5	16.9	−16.9	33.8	+0.07	−0.43	12.9	−12.9	30.0	+0.03
	7	2,000	6	−0.3	6.6	−13.2	44.0	+0.07	−0.23	4.1	−6.7	35.6	+0.03
						−15.1 ÷	(116.6) ×	1.85) = −0.07			−6.7 ÷	(104.9) ×	1.85) = −0.03

Cir-cuit No.(1)	Pipe No.(2)	Length, ft (3)	Diameter, in.(4)	Q_2, mgd (15)	s_2, ‰ (16)	H_2, ft (17)	H_2/Q_2 (18)	q_2, mgd (19)	Q_3, mgd (20)	s_3, ‰ (21)	H_3, ft (22)	Loss of Head A–E (23)
				Network		Second Correction			Result			
I	1	2,000	12	+1.24	3.1	+6.2	5.0	+0.01	+1.25	3.2	+6.4	1. Via pipes 1, 2, 5, 25.0 ft
	2	1,000	8	+0.64	6.6	+6.6	10.3	+0.01	+0.65	6.8	+6.8	2. Via pipes 3, 4, 5, 25.3 ft
	3	1,000	8	−0.76	9.1	−9.1	12.0	+0.01	−0.75	8.9	−8.9	3. Via pipes 3, 6, 7, 25.5 ft
	4*	2,000	8	−0.36	2.3	−4.6	12.8	+0.01 −0.01†	−0.36	2.3	−4.6	
						−0.9 ÷	(40.1) ×	1.85) = −0.01			−0.3	
II	4‡	2,000	8	+0.36	2.3	+4.6	12.8	+0.01 −0.01†	+0.36	2.6	+4.6	
	5	1,000	6	+0.40	11.3	+11.3	28.2	+0.01	+0.41	11.8	+11.8	
	6	1,000	6	−0.40	11.3	−11.3	28.2	+0.01	−0.39	10.8	−10.8	
	7	2,000	6	−0.20	3.1	−6.2	31.0	+0.01	−0.19	2.9	−5.8	
						−1.6 ÷	(100.2) ×	1.85) = −0.01			−0.2	

* Pipe serves more than one circuit; first consideration of this pipe.
† Corrections in this column are those calculated for the same pipe in the companion circuit; they are of opposite sign.
‡ Second consideration of this pipe.
Q = flow in mgd; s = slope of hydraulic gradient or friction loss in ft per 1000 (‰) by the Hazen-Williams formula for $C = 100$. H = head lost in pipe (ft). q = flow correction in mgd; $q = -\dfrac{\Sigma H}{1.85\Sigma(H/Q)}$. $Q_1 = Q_0 + q_0$; $Q_2 = Q_1 + q_1$; $Q_3 = Q_2 + q_2$.

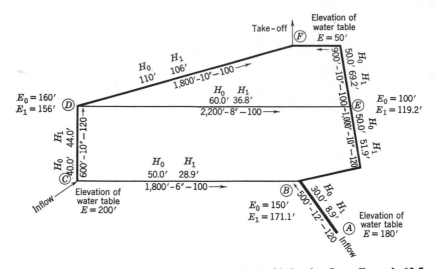

Fig. 13-10. Plan of network analyzed by the method of balancing flows. Example 13-5.

Table 13-5 Analysis of the Network of Figure 13-10 by the Method of Balancing Flows

(Only the first head correction is calculated for purposes of illustration.)

Junction Letter	Pipe	Length, ft	Diam-eter, in.	C	H_0, ft	s_0, %	Q_0, mgd	Q_0/H_0	h_0, ft	H_1, ft
(1)	(2)	(3)	(4)	(5)	(6)	(7)	(8)	(9)	(10)	(11)
B	AB	500	12	120	+30	60.0	+7.33	0.244	−21.1	+8.9
	BE	1000†	10	120	−50	50.0	−4.12	0.082	−21.1 + 19.2	−51.9
	CB	1800	6	100	+50	27.8	+0.66	0.013	−21.1	+28.9
							$1.85 \times (+3.87) \div 0.339 = +21.1$			
D	CD	600	10	120	+40	66.7	+4.8	0.120	+4.01	+44.0
	DE	2200‡	8	100	−60	27.3	−1.37	0.023	+4.01 + 19.2	−36.8
	DF	1800	10	100	−110	61.1	−3.82	0.037	+4.01	−106.0
							$1.85 \times (-0.39) \div 0.180 = -4.01$			
E	BE	1000§	10	120	+50	50.0	+4.12	0.082	−19.2 + 21.1	+51.9
	DE	2200‖	8	100	+60	27.3	+1.37	0.023	−19.2 − 4.01	+36.8
	EF	900	10	100	−50	55.6	−3.64	0.073	−19.2	−69.2
							$1.85 \times (+1.85) \div 0.178 = +19.2$			

* The basic data for this illustrative example are those used by C. E. Carter and Scott Keith, *J. New Eng. Water Works Assoc.*, **59**, 273 (1945).
† First consideration of pipe BE.   ‡ First consideration of pipe DE.
§ Second consideration of pipe BE.   ‖ Second consideration of pipe DE.

Columns 15–19 record the twice-corrected flows, and the hydraulic elements (Q, s, H, and q) carry the subscript two. These columns are otherwise like Cols. 10 to 14.

Columns. 20–23 present the final result, Cols. 20 to 22 corresponding to Cols. 15 to 18 or 10 to 12. No further flow corrections are developed because the second flow corrections are of the order of 10,000 gpd for a minimum flow of 200,000 gpd, or at most 5%. To test the balance obtained, the losses of head between points A and D in Fig. 13-9 via the three possible routes are given in Col. 23. The losses vary from 25.0 to 25.5 ft. The average loss is 25.3 ft and the variation about 1%.

Example 13-5. Balance the network of Fig. 13-10 by the method of balancing flows. Necessary calculations are given in Table 13-5.

The schedule of calculations includes the following:

Columns 1 to 5 identify the pipes at the three *free* junctions.

Columns 6 and 7 give the assumed head loss and the derived hydraulic gradient which determines the rate of flow shown in Col. 8 and the flow-head ratio recorded in Col. 9 = (Col. 8 /Col. 6).

Column 10 contains the head correction h_0 as the negative value of 1.85 times the sum of Col. 8 divided by the sum of Col. 9, for each junction in accordance with Eq. 13-2. A subsidiary head correction is made for *shared* pipes as in Example 13-2.

Column 11 gives the corrected head $H_1 = H_0 + h_0$ and provides the basis for the second flow correction by determining s_1, Q_1, and Q_1/H_1 in that order.

13-9 Method of Equivalent Pipes

In this method, a complex system of pipes is replaced by a single hydraulically equivalent line. The method cannot be applied directly to pipe systems containing crossovers or take-offs. However, it is frequently possible, by judicious skeletonizing of the network, to obtain significant information on the quantity and pressure of water available at important points, or to reduce the number of circuits to be considered. In paring the system down to a workable skeleton, the analyst can be guided by the fact that pipes contribute little to flow: (1) when they are small, 6 in. and under in most systems and as large as 8 or 10 in. in large systems; and (2) when pipes are at right angles to the general direction of flow and there is no appreciable pressure differential between their junctions in the system.

The method of equivalent pipes make use of the two hydraulic axioms: (1) that head losses through pipes in series, such as AB and BD in Fig. 13-11, are additive; and (2) that flows through pipes in parallel, such as ABD and ACD in Fig. 13-11 must be so distributed that the head losses are identical.

Example 13-6. Find an equivalent pipe for the network of Fig. 13-11. Express Q in mgd; s in ‰; H in ft; and assume a Hazen-Williams coefficient C of 100.

1. *Line ABD.* Assume $Q = 1$ mgd   ft
   (a) Pipe AB, 3000 ft, 12 in.; $s = 2.1$; $H = 2.1 \times 3 = 6.3$
   (b) Pipe BD, 4000 ft, 16 in.; $s = 0.52$; $H = 0.52 \times 4 = 2.1$
   (c)   Total $H = 8.4$
   (d) Equivalent length of 12-in. pipe: $1000 \times 8.4/2.1 = 4000$ ft

2. *Line ACD.*   Assume $Q = 0.5$ mgd   ft
   (*a*) Pipe AC, 4000 ft, 10 in.; $s = 1.42$; $H = 1.42 \times 4 =$ 5.7
   (*b*) Pipe CD, 3000 ft, 8 in.; $s = 4.2$; $H = 4.2 \ \times 3 = 12.6$
   (*c*)   Total $H = 18.3$
   (*d*) Equivalent length of 8-in. pipe: $1000 \times 18.3/4.2 = 4360$ ft
3. *Equivalent line AD.*   Assume $H = 8.4$ ft   mgd
   (*a*) Line ABD, 4000 ft, 12 in.; $s = 8.4/4.00 = 2.1$; $Q = 1.00$
   (*b*) Line ACD, 4360 ft, 8 in.; $s = 8.4/4.36 = 1.92$; $Q = 0.33$
   (*c*)   Total $Q = 1.33$
   (*d*) Equivalent length of 14-in. pipe: $Q = 1.33, s = 1.68, 1000 \times 8.4/1.68 = 5000$ ft.
   (*e*) Result: 5000 ft of 14-in. pipe.

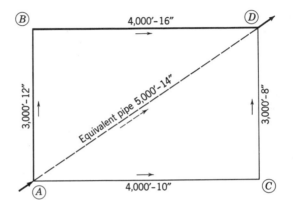

Fig. 13-11. Plan of network analyzed by the method of equivalent pipes. Example 13-6.

Necessary calculations are as follows:

1. Because line *ABD* consists of two pipes in series, the losses of head created by a given flow of water are additive. Find, therefore, from the Hazen-Williams diagram the frictional resistance *s* for some reasonable flow (1 mgd), (*a*) in pipe *AB* and (*b*) in pipe *BD*. Multiply these resistances by the length of pipe to obtain the loss of head *H*. Add the two losses to find the total loss $H = 8.4$ ft. Line *ABD*, therefore, must carry 1 mgd with a total loss of head of 8.4 ft. Any pipe that will do this is an equivalent pipe. Because a 12-in. pipe has a resistance $s = 2.1\%_{0}$ when it carries 1 mgd of water, a 12-in. pipe, to be an equivalent pipe, must be $1000 \times 8.4/2.1 = 4000$ ft long.

2. Proceed in the same general way with line *ACD* to find a length of 4360 ft for the equivalent 8-in. pipe.

3. Because *ABD* and *ACD* together constitute two lines in parallel, the flows through them at a given loss of head are additive. If some convenient loss is assumed, such as the loss already calculated for one of the lines, the missing companion flow can be found from the Hazen-Williams diagram. Assuming a loss of 8.4 ft, which is associated with a flow through *ABD* of 1 mgd,[9] it is only necessary to find from the diagram that the quantity of water that will flow through the equivalent pipe *ACD*, when the loss of head is 8.4 ft (or $s = 8.4/4.36 = 1.92\%_{0}$) amounts to 0.33 mgd. Add this quantity to

[9] It was, therefore, really unnecessary to specify the length and diameter of the equivalent pipe *ABD*.

the flow through line *ABD* (1.0 mgd) to obtain 1.33 mgd. Line *AD*, therefore, must carry 1.33 mgd with a loss of head of 8.4 ft. If the equivalent pipe is assumed to be 14 in. in diameter, it will discharge 1.33 mgd with a frictional resistance $s = 1.68\%_0$, and its length must be $1000 \times 8.4/1.68 = 5000$ ft. Thence, we can replace the network by a single 14-in. pipe 5000 ft long.

No matter what the original assumptions for quantity, diameter, and loss of head, the calculated equivalent pipe will always perform hydraulically in the same way as the network it replaces.

Different in principle is the operational replacement of every pipe in a given network by equivalent pipes with idéntical diameters and capacity coefficients, but variable length. The purpose, in this instance, is to simplify subsequent calculations. For the Hazen-Williams relationship, Eq. 12-8, for example, $l_e = (100/C)^{1.85}(d_e/d)^{4.87}l$, where l_e is the length of a pipe of diameter d_e and discharge coefficient $C_e = 100$ and l, d, and C are the corresponding properties of the existing pipe. Wanted values of l_e can be found readily from a logarithmic plot of l_e/l against d_e/d at given values of C (Fig. 13-12).

13-10   Digital Computer Analysis

High-speed digital computers can be programmed to solve network problems in a number of different ways. Convergence formulas need not be introduced as such. Instead, the computer can be assigned the task of adjusting the water table or pressure at each junction not controlled by a service reservoir until the *circuit laws* discussed in Sec. 13-8 are satisfied throughout the system.[10] These laws can be summarized as follows:

1. At each junction $\Sigma Q_{inflow} = \Sigma Q_{outflow}$
2. In each circuit $\Sigma H = 0$
3. In each pipe $H = kQ^n$ or $Q = (H/k)^{1/n}$

To program the operation, number each pipe and junction and identify pipe ends by junction numbers; then tabulate pipe resistances, junction pressures (including assumed values where pressures are unknown), and net inflows at each junction (zero at all but entrance and exit points of the system), and feed the tabulated information into the computer. The computer instructions are then as follows: Calculate by *circuit law 3* the total flow into the first junction for which the water-table elevation is unknown; adjust the assumed value until the total inflow and outflow are balanced in accordance with *circuit law 1*; proceed in sequence to the remaining junctions; readjust the first water-table elevation. Repeat the cycle of operations until *all circuit laws* are satisfied. Contemplated network changes can be printed on separate tapes to avoid re-input of the entire program.

[10] R. W. Adams, Distribution Analysis by Electronic Computer, *J. Institution Water Engrs.*, **15**, 415 (1961).

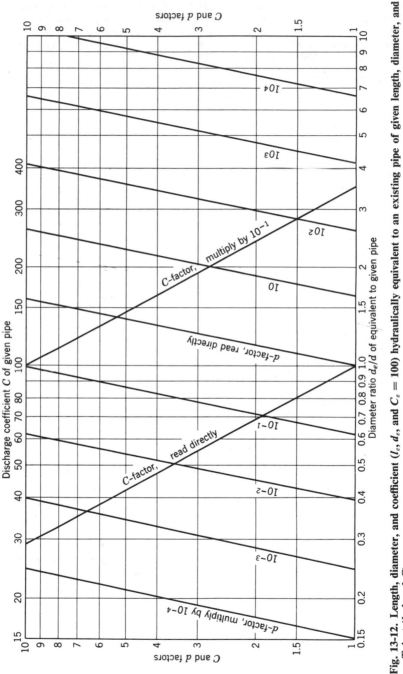

Fig. 13-12. Length, diameter, and coefficient (l_e, d_e, and $C_e = 100$) hydraulically equivalent to an existing pipe of given length, diameter, and coefficient (l, d, and C).

Example: Find the length of a 24-in. pipe, $C_e = 100$, equivalent to a 12-in. pipe, $C = 130$, $l = 2000$ ft. At $C = 130$ read the C-factor 6.2×10^{-1}. At $d_e/d = 2.0$, read the d-factor 2.9 $\times$ 10. Hence $l_e/l = (6.2 \times 10^{-1})(2.9 \times 10) = 18$ or $l_e = 2000 \times 18 = 36,000$ ft.

13-11 Electrical Analogy

Camp and Hazen[11] built the first electric analyzer designed specifically for the hydraulic analysis of water distribution systems. Electric analyzers use non-linear resistors, called fluistors in the McIlroy[12] analyzer, to simulate pipe resistances. For each branch of the system, the pipe equation, $H = kQ^{1.85}$, for example, is replaced by an electrical equation, $V = K_e I^{1.85}$, where V is the voltage drop in the branch, I is the current, and K_e is the nonlinear-resistor coefficient suited to the pipe coefficient k for the selected voltage drop (head loss) and amperage (water flow) scale ratios. If the current inputs and take-offs are made proportional to the water flowing into and out of the system, the head losses will be proportional to the measured voltage drops. Some large, rapidly developing communities have found it economic to acquire electric analyzers suited to their own system.

13-12 Service Storage

The three major components of service storage are: (*a*) equalizing, or operating, storage; (*b*) fire reserve; and (*c*) emergency reserve.

Equalizing, or Operating, Storage.   Required equalizing, or operating, storage can be read from a demand rate curve or, more satisfactorily, from a mass diagram similar in concept to the Rippl diagram (Fig. 8-1). As shown in Fig. 13-13 for the simple conditions of steady inflow, during 12 and 24 hr respectively, the amount of equalizing, or operating, storage is the sum of the maximum ordinates between the demand and supply lines. To construct such a mass diagram proceed as follows:

1. From past measurements of flow, determine the draft during each hour of the day and night for typical days (maximum, average, and minimum).
2. Calculate the amounts of water drawn up to certain times, i.e., the cumulative draft.
3. Plot the cumulative draft against time.
4. For steady supply during 24 hr, draw a straight line diagonally across the diagram, as in Fig. 13-13a. Read the storage required as the sum of the two maximum ordinates between the draft and the supply line.
5. For steady supply during 12 hr, by pumping, for example, draw a straight line diagonally from the beginning of the pumping period to its end; for example, from 6 A.M. to 6 P.M. as in Fig. 13-13b. Again read the storage required as the sum of the two maximum ordinates.

[11] T. R. Camp and H. L. Hazen, Hydraulic Analysis of Water Distribution Systems by Means of an Electric Network Analyzer, *J. New Eng. Water Works Assoc.*, **48**, 383 (1934).
[12] M. S. McIlroy, Direct-Reading Electric Analyzer for Pipeline Networks, *J. Am. Water Works Assoc.*, **42**, 347 (1950); also Water-Distribution Systems Studied by a Complete Electrical Analogy, *J. New Eng. Water Works Assoc.*, **45**, 299 (1953).

Steady supply at the rate of maximum daily use will ordinarily require an equalizing storage between 15 and 20% of the day's consumption. Limitation of supply to 12 hr may raise the operating storage to an amount between 30 and 50% of the day's consumption.

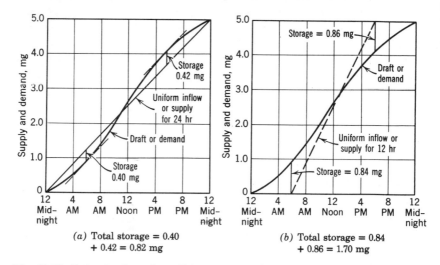

(a) Total storage = 0.40
+ 0.42 = 0.82 mg

(b) Total storage = 0.84
+ 0.86 = 1.70 mg

Fig. 13-13. Determination of equalizing, or operating, storage by mass diagram. See Example 13-7. (a) Uniform inflow, or supply, extending over 24 hr. (e) Uniform inflow, or supply, confined to 12 hr.

Example 13-7. Determine the equalizing, or operating, storage for the drafts of water shown in Table 13-6 (1) when inflow is uniform during 24 hr; (2) when flow is confined to the 12 hr from 6 A.M. to 6 P.M.

1. For steady supply during 24 hr, the draft plotted in Fig. 13-13a exceeds the demand by 0.40 mg by 6 A.M. If this excess is stored, it is used up by 11 A.M. In the afternoon, the demand exceeds the supply by 0.42 mg by 6 P.M. and must be drawn from storage

Table 13-6 Observed Drafts (Example 13-7)

(a) Time	4 A.M.	8 A.M.	noon	4 P.M.	8 P.M.	midnight
(b) Draft, mg	0.484	0.874	1.216	1.102	0.818	0.506
(c) Cumulative draft, mg	0.484	1.358	2.574	3.676	4.494	5.000

that is replenished by midnight. Hence the required storage is the sum of the morning excess and afternoon deficiency, or 0.82 mg. This equals 16.4% of the daily draft.

2. For steady supply during the 12-hr period from 6 A.M. to 6 P.M., the draft plotted in Fig. 13-13b exceeds the supply by 0.84 mg between midnight and 6 A.M. and must be drawn from storage. In the afternoon, the supply exceeds the demand by 0.86 mg by 6 P.M., but this excess is required to furnish water from storage between 6 P.M. and midnight. Total storage, therefore, is 1.70 mg, or 34% of the days' consumption.

Fire Reserve. Basing their recommendations upon observed durations of serious conflagrations, the National Board of Fire Underwriters recommends that distributing reservoirs be made large enough to supply water for fighting a serious conflagration for 10 hr in communities of more than 6000 people and for 8, 6, and 4 hr in places with 4000, 2000, and 1000 people respectively. The resulting fire reserve, shown in Table 13-1, may not always be economically attainable, and design values may have to be adjusted downward to meet local financial abilities. Changing community patterns, moreover, may make for changing requirements in the future.

Emergency Reserve. The magnitude of this storage component depends (1) upon the danger of interruption of reservoir inflow by failure of supply works; and (2) upon the time needed to make repairs. If shutdown of the supply is confined to the time necessary for routine inspections during the hours of minimum draft, the emergency reserve is sometimes made no more than 25% of the total storage capacity, i.e., the reservoir is assumed to be drawn down by one-fourth its average depth. If supply lines or equipment are expected to be out of operation for longer times, higher allowances must be made. The National Board of Fire Underwriters bases its rating system on an emergency storage of 5 days at maximum flow.

Total Storage. The total amount of storage is desirably equal to the sum of the component requirements. In each instance, economic considerations dictate the final choice. In pumped supplies, cost of storage must be balanced against cost of pumping, and attention must be paid to economies effected by operating pumps more uniformly and restricting pumping to a portion of the day only. In all supplies, cost of storage must be balanced against cost of supply lines, increased fire protection, and more uniform pressures in the distribution system.

Example 13-8. For a steady gravity supply equal to the maximum daily demand, a 10-hr fire supply, and no particular hazard to the supply works, find the storage to be provided for a city of 50,000 people using an average of 7.5 mgd of water.

Equalizing storage = 15% of 7.5 mg		1.13 mg
Fire reserve (Table 13-1)		3.90 mg
	Subtotal	5.03 mg

Emergency reserve = one-fourth of total storage.
  Therefore subtotal is three-fourths of total storage,
  and total storage = 5.03/0.75   6.70 mg

If we assume that the maximum daily use is 150% of the average, the emergency storage suggested by the National Board would approximate $5 \times 7.5 \times 1.5 = 56$ mg, instead of $6.70 - 5.03 = 1.67$ mg.

Location of Storage. As shown in Sec. 13-1 and Fig. 13-1, location as well as capacity of service storage is an important factor in the control of distribution systems. A million gallons of elevated fire reserve, suitably sited in reference to the area to be protected, is equivalent, for example, to the addition of a 12-in. supply main. The underlying reasoning is that drawing this volume of water in a 10-hr fire, flow is provided at a rate of $(24/10) \times 1 = 2.4$ mgd. This is the amount of water a 12-in. pipe can carry at a velocity less than 5 fps. Why this must be neighborhood storage is explained by the high frictional resistance of more than 10‰ accompanying such use.

13-13 Types of Distributing Reservoirs

Where topography and geology permit, service reservoirs are formed by impoundage, balanced excavation and embankment, or masonry construction (Fig. 2-7). To protect the water against chance contamination and against deterioration by algal growths stimulated by sunlight, distributing reservoirs should be covered. Roofs need not be watertight if the reservoir is fenced. Open reservoirs should always be fenced. Where surface runoff can drain into them, they should have a marginal intercepting conduit.

Earthen reservoirs, their bottom sealed by a blanket of clay or rubble masonry and their sides by core walls, were widely employed at one time. Today, lining with concrete slabs is more common. Gunite, a sand-cement-water mixture, discharged from a nozzle or gun through and onto a mat of reinforcing steel, has also been employed to line or reline them. Roofs are made of wood or concrete. Beam and girder, flat-slab, arch, and groined-arch construction have been used. Where concrete roofs can be covered with earth, both roof and water will be protected against extremes of temperature.

Inlets, outlets, and overflows are generally placed in a gate house or two. Circulation to ensure more or less continuous displacement of the water and to provide proper detention of water after chlorination may be controlled by baffles or subdivisions between inlet and outlet. Overflow capacity should equal maximum rate of inflow. Altitude-control valves on reservoir inlets (Fig. 13-14) will automatically shut off inflow when maximum water level is reached. An arrangement that does not interfere with draft from the reservoir includes a by-pass with a swing check valve seating against the inflow.

Where natural elevation is not high enough, water is stored in wood, concrete, or steel standpipes and elevated tanks. In cold climates, steel is most suitable. Unless the steel in reinforced-concrete tanks is prestressed, vertical cracks, leakage, and freezing will cause rapid deterioration of the structure. Ground-level storage in reinforced concrete or steel tanks in advance of automatic pumping stations is an alternative.

The useful capacity of standpipes and elevated tanks is confined to the volume of water stored above the level of wanted distribution pressure. In elevated tanks, this level generally coincides with the tank bottom; in standpipes, it may lie much higher. Steel tanks are welded or riveted. Their structural design and erection have become the specialized activity of tank manufacturers.

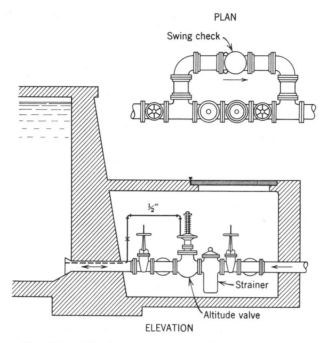

Fig. 13-14. Altitude valve on supply to distribution reservoir.

The function of elevated tanks and spheroidal tanks can be expressed to esthetic advantage in their architecture without resorting to ornamentation. Standpipes are simple cylinders. A veneer or outer shell of concrete or masonry may make them attractive.

13-14 Management, Operation, and Maintenance of Distribution Systems

For intelligent management of distribution storage, reservoir levels must be known at all times of day and night. Where levels cannot be observed directly by gages or floats, electrically operated indicators and recorders can transmit wanted information to headquarters.

Well-kept records and maps of pipes and appurtenances are essential to the efficient operation and maintenance of distribution systems. To avoid the occasional discharge of roiled water, piping should be flushed systematically, usually through hydrants. Dead ends need particular attention; a bleeder on the dead end will counteract the effects of sluggish water movements. The importance of disinfecting newly laid pipe, or pipe newly repaired, is discussed in Vol. 2; control of pipe corrosion and the cleaning and relining of water mains are mentioned in Sec. 12-8.

There is little flow through service pipes at night, and they may freeze in very cold weather. If water mains themselves are placed at reasonable depth and enough flow is maintained in the system, they should not freeze. Pipes deprived of adequate cover by the regrading of streets or subjected to protracted and exceptionally cold spells can be protected by drawing water from them through services. Pipes exposed on bridges or similar crossings should be insulated. Large and important lines may be heated where exposure is severe. In very cold climates, water and sewer pipes are often laid in a heated boxlike conduit, known as a *utilidor*.

Frozen pipes are usually thawed by electricity. A transformer connected to an electric power circuit, or a gasoline-driven generator of the electric-welding type, supplies the current: 100 to 200 amperes at 3 to 10 volts for small pipes up to several thousand amperes at 55 or 110 volts for large mains. The current applied is varied with the electrical resistance and the melting point of the pipe metals. Nonmetallic jointing and caulking compounds and asbestos-cement or plastic pipes obstruct current flow. Electric grounds on interior water piping, or the piping itself, must be disconnected during thawing operations. Grounds are needed but are an annoyance when they carry high voltages into the pipes and shock workmen. Pipes and hydrants can also be thawed with steam generated in portable boilers and introduced through flexible block-tin tubing.

Loss of water by leakage from distribution systems and connected consumer premises should be kept under control by leakage surveys (Sec. 5-8).

CHAPTER 14

Wastewater Flows

14-1 Nature of Flow

Wastewater systems and their components have been described in Chapter 3; the amounts of sewage and stormwater to be collected by them in Chapters 5 and 7. With this as a background, supporting details of design are developed in the present and the immediately following chapter.

Hydraulically, wastewater collection differs from water distribution in three essentials: (1) except in special situations, conduits do not flow under pressure; (2) flow is almost always unsteady and often nonuniform; and (3) substantial loads of floating, suspended, and soluble substances are transported by the flowing waters. For these reasons, most sewers are designed (1) to convey their burden in open-channel flow while partially filled or barely full; (2) to satisfy conditions of unsteady and nonuniform flow where required; and (3) to transport water-borne wastes or storm scourings with little or no deposition, on the one hand, and without erosion of channel surfaces, on the other hand; in other words, at self-cleansing yet nondestructive velocities.

As shown in Sec. 5-2, the design period for main collectors, intercepters, and outfalls may have to be as much as 50 years because of the inconvenience and cost of enlarging or replacing hydraulic structures of this kind in busy city streets. The sizing of needed conduits becomes complicated if they are to be self-cleansing at the beginning as well as the end of the design period. Although water-distribution systems, too, must meet changing capacity requirements, their hydraulic balance is less

14–1

delicate: the water must transport only itself, so to speak. It follows that velocities of flow in water-distribution systems are important economically rather than functionally and can be allowed to vary over a wide range of magnitudes without markedly affecting system performance. In contrast, performance of wastewater systems is tied, more or less rigidly, to inflexible hydraulic gradients and so becomes functionally as well as economically important.

14-2 Flow in Filled Sewers

In the absence of precise and conveniently applicable information on how channel roughness can be measured and introduced into theoretical formulations of flow in open channels, engineers continue to base the hydraulic design of sewers, as they do the design of water conduits (Sec. 12-2) upon empirical formulations. Equations common in North American practice are: the Kutter-Ganguillet[1] formula of 1869 and the Manning[2] formula of 1890. In principle, these formulations evaluate the velocity or discharge coefficient c in the Chezy formula of 1775 in terms of invert slope s (Kutter-Ganguillet only), hydraulic radius r, and a coefficient of roughness n. The resulting expressions for c are:

$$c_{\text{Kutter-Ganguillet}} = \frac{(41.65 + 2.81 \times 10^{-3}/s) + 1.811/n}{(41.65 + 2.81 \times 10^{-3}/s)(n/r^{1/2}) + 1} \quad (14\text{-}1)$$

$$c_{\text{Manning}} = 1.486 r^{1/6}/n \quad (14\text{-}2)$$

Of the two, Manning's equation is given preference in these pages, because it satisfies experimental findings fully as well as the mathematically clumsier Kutter-Ganguillet formula. Moreover, it lends itself more satisfactorily to algebraic manipulation, slide-rule computation, and graphical representation.

Introducing Manning's c into the Chezy formula, the complete equation[3] reads:

$$v = (1.49/n)r^{2/3}s^{1/2} \quad (14\text{-}3)$$

and is seen to resemble the Hazen-Williams formula of Sec. 12-2. Indeed, the Hazen-Williams equation could be used instead. Values of $V_0 = 1.49R^{2/3}$, $Q_0 = 1.49AR^{2/3}$, and $1/V_0$, the reciprocal of $1.49R^{2/3}$, are listed

[1] E. Ganguillet and W. R. Kutter, *Flow of Water in Rivers and Other Channels*, translated by Rudolf Hering and J. G. Trautwine, John Wiley & Sons, New York, 1888.
[2] Named after Robert Manning (1816–1897), Irish engineer who discussed the limitations of the formula $v = kr^{2/3}s^{1/2}$ and developed a dimensionally homogeneous relationship that did not find acceptance.
[3] Because the value of n is normally good to no more than two significant figures, 1.49 and, indeed, 1.5 should replace the commonly quoted numerical constant 1.486.

in Table 14-1 to speed calculations.[4] The table is based upon a generalization of Manning's formula in terms of the ratio $S^{1/2}/N$, where S/N^2 is, in a sense, the relative slope for varying conduit sizes and roughness coefficients. The ratio $S^{1/2}/N$ appears, too, in formulations for the flow of storm waters over land and into street inlets.

Table 14-1   Velocity and Discharge of Circular Sewers Flowing Full
$S^{1/2}/N = 1$ in the Manning formula*

Diameter, D, in. (1)	Area, A, sq ft (2)	Velocity, V_0, fps (3)	Discharge, Q_0, cfs (4)	$1/V_0$ (5)
6	0.1963	0.3715	0.07293	2.6922
8	0.3491	0.4500	0.1571	2.2222
10	0.5455	0.5222	0.2848	1.9158
12	0.7854	0.5897	0.4632	1.6958
15	1.2272	0.6843	0.8398	1.4613
18	1.7671	0.7728	1.366	1.2940
21	2.4053	0.8564	2.060	1.1677
24	3.1416	0.9361	2.941	1.0683
27	3.9761	1.0116	4.026	0.9885
30	4.9087	1.0863	5.332	0.9206
36	7.0686	1.2267	8.671	0.8152
42	9.6211	1.3594	13.08	0.7356
48	12.5664	1.4860	18.67	0.6729
54	15.9043	1.6074	25.56	0.6221
60	19.6350	1.7244	33.86	0.5799

* To find V or Q for given values of S and N, multiply column (3) or (4) by $S^{1/2}/N$. To find S for a given value of V or Q, multiply NV or NQ/A respectively by column (5) and square the product. This table is repeated as I-9.

Choice of a suitable roughness coefficient is of utmost importance. The following ranges in values are recommended by the Joint Committee of the American Society of Civil Engineers and the Water Pollution Control Federation:[5] (1) for vitrified-clay, concrete, asbestos-cement, and corrugated steel pipe with smooth asphaltic lining, a coefficient ranging from 0.012 for clear water to 0.015 for strong sewage, 0.013 being a common design value for sanitary sewers; (2) for dirty or tuberculated cast-iron

[4] Capital letters are chosen here to denote the hydraulic elements of conduits flowing full; lower-case letters for partially filled sections.
[5] Design and Construction of Sanitary and Storm Sewers, *Am. Soc. Civil Engrs.*, *Manuals of Engineering Practice*, No. 37, 92 (1960); *Water Poll. Control Fed.*, *Manual of Practice* No. 9, 92 (1960).

pipe, a coefficient ranging from 0.015 to 0.035; and (3) for corrugated-steel pipes often used in culverts, a coefficient of 0.021 to 0.023 for asphalt coatings and paving covering 25% of the invert section, or 0.024 to 0.026 for uncoated pipe with $\frac{1}{2}$-in. corrugations. All but corrugated pipes show little difference between values suitable for the Manning and Kutter-Ganguillet equations.

Example 14-1. 1. Given a 12-in. sewer, $N = 0.013$, laid on a grade of 4.05‰ (ft per 1000 ft), find its velocity of flow and rate of discharge.

Because $S^{\frac{1}{2}}/N = (4.05 \times 10^{-3})^{\frac{1}{2}}/1.3 \times 10^{-2} = 4.90$, $V = 4.90 \times 0.590 = 2.89$ fps, and $Q = 4.90 \times 0.463 = 2.27$ cfs.

2. Given a velocity of 3 fps for this sewer, find its (minimum) gradient for flow at full depth.

Because $NV = 3.9 \times 10^{-2}$, $S = (3.9 \times 10^{-2} \times 1.696)^2 = 4.37$‰.

Minimum grades S and capacities Q of sewers ($N = 0.013$) up to 24 in. in diameter flowing full at velocities of 2.0, 2.5, 3.0, and 5.0 fps are listed for convenience of reference in Table 14-2.

Table 14-2   Minimum Grades and Capacities of Circular Sewers Flowing Full

$N = 0.013$ in the Manning Formula

Diameter (in.)	6	8	10	12	15	18	21	24
				$V = 2.0$ fps				
S (‰)	4.89	3.33	2.48	1.94	1.44	1.13	0.923	0.775
Q (cfs)	0.393	0.698	1.09	1.57	2.45	3.53	4.81	6.28
				$V = 2.5$ fps				
S (‰)	7.64	5.20	3.88	3.06	2.25	1.74	1.44	1.21
Q (cfs)	0.491	0.873	1.36	1.96	3.07	4.42	6.01	7.85
				$V = 3.0$ fps				
S (‰)	11.0	7.50	5.58	4.37	3.24	2.54	2.08	1.74
Q (cfs)	0.589	1.05	1.64	2.36	3.68	5.30	7.22	9.42
				$V = 5.0$ fps				
S (‰)	30.5	20.8	16.1	12.2	9.00	6.96	5.76	4.84
Q (cfs)	0.982	1.75	2.73	3.93	6.14	8.84	12.0	15.7

14-3 Limiting Velocities of Flow

Wastes from bathroom, toilet, laundry, and kitchen are flushed into sanitary sewers through *house* or *building* sewers. Sand, gravel, and debris of many kinds enter storm drains through curb and yard inlets. Combined sewers carry mixtures of the two. Heavy solids are swept down sewer inverts like the *bed load* of streams. Light materials float on the water surface. When velocities fall, heavy solids are left behind as bottom deposits, while light materials strand at the water's edge. When velocities rise again, gritty substances and the flotsam of the sewer are picked up once more and carried along in heavy concentration. There may be erosion. Within reason, all of these happenings should be avoided, insofar as this can be done. Each one of them is a function of the tractive force of the carrying water which should be better known than it commonly is.

Conceptually, the drag exerted by flowing water on a channel is analogous to the friction exerted by a body sliding down an inclined plane. Because the volume of water in contact with a unit surface of channel equals the hydraulic radius of the channel,

$$\tau = \gamma rs \qquad (14\text{-}4)$$

where τ is the intensity of the tractive force, γ the specific weight of water at the prevailing temperature, r the hydraulic radius of the filled section, and s the slope of the invert or loss of head in a unit length of channel when flow is steady and uniform and the water surface parallels the invert. Substituting $rs = (v/c)^2$ in accordance with the Chezy equation (Eq. 12-3), for example,

$$\tau = \gamma(v/c)^2 \qquad (14\text{-}5)$$

and the tractive force intensity is seen to vary as the square of the velocity of flow v and inversely as the square of the Chezy coefficient, c. Moreover, v turns out to be the only manageable variable for design purposes.

Transporting Velocities. The velocity required to transport water-borne solids is derived from Eq. 14-4, with the help of Fig. 14-1, which follows on page 14-6.

For a layer of sediment of unit width and length, thickness t, and porosity ratio f', the drag force τ exerted by the water at the surface of the sediment and just causing it to slide down the inclined plane equals the frictional resistance $R = W \sin \alpha$, where $W = (\gamma_s - \gamma)t(1 - f') \sin \alpha$ is the weight of the sediment in water and α is the friction angle. Accordingly, $\tau = (\gamma_s - \gamma)t(1 - f') \sin \alpha$, and Eq. 14-4 becomes

$$\tau = (\gamma_s - \gamma)t(1 - f') \sin \alpha = k(\gamma_s - \gamma)t \qquad (14\text{-}6)$$

Here $k = (1 - f') \sin \alpha$ is an important characteristic of the sediment. For single grains, the volume per unit area t becomes a function of the diameter of the grains d as an inverse measure of the surface area of the individual grains exposed to drag or friction.

It follows from Eq. 14-4 and 14-6 that the invert slope at which sewers will be self-cleansing is

$$s = (k/r)[(\gamma_s - \gamma)/\gamma]d \tag{14-7}$$

and that, in accordance with the Chezy equation,

$$v = c[kd(\gamma_s - \gamma)/\gamma]^{\frac{1}{2}} \tag{14-8}$$

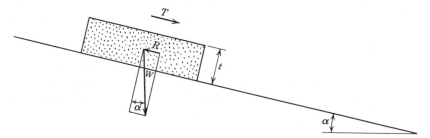

Fig. 14-1. Forces acting on sediment of unit width and length and thickness t. T is the tractive force per unit surface area. R, the resisting force, is a function of the weight of the sediment (W) and the slope of the conduit (α).

where the value of c is chosen with full recognition of the presence of deposited or depositing solids and expressed, if so desired, in accordance with any other pertinent capacity or friction factor. Examples are (a):

$$v = [(\gamma k/f)gd(\gamma_s - \gamma)/\gamma]^{\frac{1}{2}} \tag{14-9}$$

derived by Camp from studies by Shields[6] and obtainable from Eq. 14-8 by introducing the Weisbach-Darcy friction factor $f = 8g/c^2$; and (b):

$$v = (1.49/n)r^{\frac{1}{6}}[kd(\gamma_s - \gamma)/\gamma]^{\frac{1}{2}} \tag{14-10}$$

in terms of a Manning evaluation of $c = 1.49(r^{\frac{1}{6}}/n)$, where n is the Manning friction factor. When convenient, the ratio $(\gamma_s - \gamma)/\gamma$ can be replaced by the closely equal term $(s_s - 1)$, where s_s is the specific gravity of the particles (solids) composing the deposit.

Applicable magnitudes of k range from 0.04 for initiating scour of relatively clean grit to 0.8 or more for full removal of sticky grit. Their actual magnitude can be found only by experiment.

[6] A. Shields, Anwendung der Aenlichkeitsmechanik und der Turbulenzforschung an die Geschiebebewegung (Application of similitude mechanics and turbulence research to bed-load movement), *Mitt. der Preuss. Versuchsanstalt für Wasserbau und Schiffbau,* No. 26, Berlin (1936). Shields showed that particles at the sediment surface were left undisturbed so long as $v^2\alpha < gd(\gamma_s - \gamma)/\gamma$, where $\alpha = 0.10$ approximately.

Example 14-2.   1. Find the minimum velocity and gradient at which coarse quartz sand is transported without hindrance through a sewer 12 in. in diameter flowing full.

Introducing a particle diameter $d = 0.1$ cm ($10^{-1}/30.48$ ft), a specific gravity $s = 2.65$, a sediment characteristic $k = 0.04$, and a friction factor $n = 0.013$ into Eqs. 14-10 and 7

$$v = (1.49/1.3 \times 10^{-2})(\tfrac{1}{4})^{\frac{1}{6}} [4 \times 10^{-2}(10^{-1}/30.48)(2.65 - 1.00)/1.00]^{\frac{1}{2}} = 1.34 \text{ fps}$$

and

$$s = [4 \times 10^{-2}/(\tfrac{1}{4})](10^{-1}/30.48)[(2.65 - 1.00)/1.00] = 3.7 \times 10^{-3}$$

For a sediment characteristic $k = 0.8 = 20 \times 0.04$, the required velocity is $\sqrt{20} = 4.5$ times as much and the required slope 20 times as steep.

2. If, as shown in Sec. 3-6, flows in storm and combined sewers are given velocities of 3.0 and 5.0 fps respectively, find the diameter of sand or gravel moved.

In accordance with Eq. 14-10, d varies as v^2. Hence,

for $v = 3.0$ fps, $d = 10^{-1}(3.0/1.34)^2 = 0.90$ cm (medium-sized gravel), and

for $v = 5.0$ fps, $d = 10^{-1}(5.0/1.34)^2 = 1.4$ cm (large gravel)

Damaging Velocities.   Of the ceramic materials used in sewers, vitrified tile and glazed brick are very resistant to wear, building brick and concrete less so. Abrasion is greatest at the bottom of conduits, because grit, sand, and gravel are heavy and travel along the invert. Accordingly, the bottom of large concrete or brick sewers is often protected by vitrified tile liners, glazed or paving brick, or granite blocks.

Clear water can flow through hard-surfaced channels, such as good concrete conduits, at velocities higher than 40 fps without harm. Storm-water runoff, on the other hand, has to be held down to about 10 fps in concrete sewers and drains, because it usually contains abrading substances in sufficient quantity to wear away even well constructed, hard concrete surfaces. The magnitude of the associated tractive force is given by Eq. 14-5.

14-4   Flow in Partially Filled Sewers

As sewers approach their terminal manholes in the upper reaches of sanitary sewerage systems, they receive less and less sewage. Depths of flow are reduced, because minimum pipe sizes (8 in. in North America) are dictated not by flow requirements alone but also by cleaning potentials. The lower portions of the system, too, are not designed to flow full until the end of their design period is reached. Even then, they are filled only spasmodically during hours of maximum flow. Discharge ratios may vary, indeed, from as little as 4:1 at the end of the design period to as much as 20:1 at the beginning.

Hydraulic performance of the upper reaches of sanitary sewers is improved by steeper than normal grades, even though velocities of say 3.0 rather than 2.5 or 2.0 fps produce still lower depths of flow. Why this is so will appear later. Understandably, requisite capacities of storm and combined sewers are even more variable. The hydraulic performance of partially filled as well as filled sections must, therefore, be well understood, especially in reference to the maintenance of self-cleansing velocities at expected flows.

The variables encompassed by a flow formula such as Manning's, namely, Q or v, r or a/p (p = wetted perimeter), s or h/l, and n, constitute

Table 14-3   Hydraulic Elements of a Sewer of Circular Cross-Section

(Uncorrected for variations in roughness with depth)

Central angle: $\cos \frac{1}{2}\theta = 1 - 2d/D$

Area: $\dfrac{D^2}{4}\left(\dfrac{\pi\theta}{360} - \dfrac{\sin\theta}{2}\right)$

Wetted perimeter: $\pi D\theta/360$

Hydraulic radius:

$$\frac{D}{4}\left(1 - \frac{360\sin\theta}{2\pi\theta}\right)$$

Velocity: $\dfrac{1.49}{n} r^{\frac{2}{3}} s^{\frac{1}{2}}$

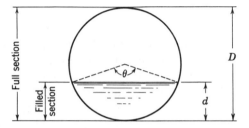

| Depth | Area | Hydraulic Radius | | | Velocity v/V | Discharge q/Q | Rough-ness |
| d/D | a/A | r/R | R/r | $(r/R)^{1/6}$ | for $N/n = 1.0$ | | N/n |
(1)	(2)	(3)	(4)	(5)	(6)	(7)	(8)
1.000	1.000	1.000	1.000	1.000	1.000	1.000	1.00
0.900	0.949	1.192	0.839	1.030	1.124	1.066	0.94
0.800	0.858	1.217	0.822	1.033	1.140	0.988	0.88
0.700	0.748	1.185	0.843	1.029	1.120	0.838	0.85
0.600	0.626	1.110	0.900	1.018	1.072	0.671	0.83
0.500	0.500	1.000	1.00	1.000	1.000	0.500	0.81
0.400	0.373	0.857	1.17	0.975	0.902	0.337	0.79
0.300	0.252	0.684	1.46	0.939	0.776	0.196	0.78
0.200	0.143	0.482	2.07	0.886	0.615	0.088	0.79
0.100	0.052	0.254	3.94	0.796	0.401	0.021	0.82
0.000	0.000	...	...	...	...	0.000	...

the *hydraulic elements* of conduits. For a given shape and a fixed coefficient of roughness and invert slope, the elements change in absolute magnitude with the depth d of the filled section. In the case of Manning's formulation, fortunately, generalization in terms of the ratio of each element of the filled section (indicated here by a lower-case letter) to the corresponding element of the full[7] section (indicated here by a capital letter) confines all ratios, including velocity and capacity ratios, to ultimate dependency on depth alone. Thus,

$$v/V = (N/n)(r/R)^{2/3} \qquad (14\text{-}11)$$

and

$$q/Q = (N/n)(a/A)(r/R)^{2/3} \qquad (14\text{-}12)$$

Of the elements normally included in diagrams or tables, area and hydraulic radius are static, or elements of shape; roughness, velocity, and discharge are dynamic, or elements of flow. Except for roughness, the basis of their computation is explained in Table 14-3. The geometric elements of circular sewers are seen to be functions of the angle θ or through it of the depth ratio d/D. The dynamic elements are observed to be functions also of roughness and, in the Kutter-Ganguillet equation but not in the Manning equation, also of slope. Variation of roughness with depth was observed by Willcox[8] on 8-in. sewer pipe, by Yarnell and Woodward[9] on clay and concrete drain tile 4 to 12 in. in diameter, and by Johnson[10] in large (Louisville, Ky.) sewers flowing at low depths. Figure 14-2 is a conventional diagram of the basic hydraulic elements of circular sewers. The two sets of curves included for v/V and q/Q mark the influence of a variable ratio of N/n upon these dynamic hydraulic elements.[11] It is important to note that velocities in partially filled, circular sections equal or exceed those in full sections whenever sewers flow more than half full and roughness is not considered to vary with depth; moreover, that where changes in roughness are taken into account, velocities equal to or greater than those in full sections are confined to the upper 20% of depth only. Nevertheless, sewers flowing between 0.5 and 0.8 full need not be placed on steeper grades to be as self-cleansing as sewers flowing full. The reason is that velocity and discharge are functions of tractive-force intensity which depends upon the friction coefficient as well as the flow velocity. Needed ratios of v_s/V, q_s/Q, and s_s/S, where the subscript s denotes cleansing equaling that obtained in the full section, can be computed with the help of Eq. 14-4 on the assumption that equality of tractive-force intensity implies equality of cleansing, or $\tau = T = \gamma r s = \gamma R S$; whence

$$s_s = (R/r)S \qquad (14\text{-}13)$$

[7] For circular sewers, half depth could be made the reference depth with good reason.
[8] E. R. Willcox, A Comparative Test of the Flow of Water in 8-Inch Concrete and Vitrified Clay Sewer Pipe, *Univ. Wash. Eng. Exp. Sta. Ser. Bull.* 27 (1924).
[9] D. L. Yarnell and S. M. Woodward, The Flow of Water in Drain Tile, *U.S. Dept. Agr. Bull.* 854 (1920).
[10] C. F. Johnson, Determination of Kutter's n for Sewers Partly Filled, *Trans. Am. Soc. Civil Engrs.*, **109**, 240 (1944).
[11] The values of N/n in Table 14-3 and Fig. 14-2 are taken from: Design and Construction of Sanitary and Storm Sewers, *Am. Soc. Civil Engrs.*, *Manuals of Engineering Practice* No. 37 (1960); *Water Pollution Control Fed.*, *Manual of Practice*, No. 9 (1960).

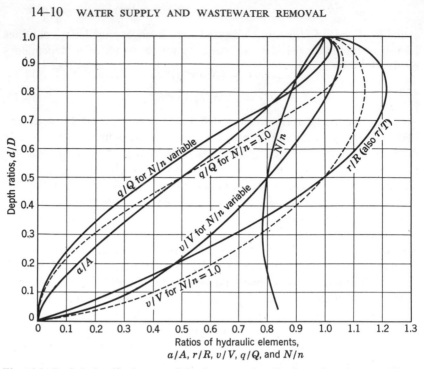

Fig. 14-2. Basic hydraulic elements of circular sewers for all values of roughness and slope.

and

$$v_s/V = (N/n)(r/R)^{\frac{2}{3}}(s_s/S)^{\frac{1}{2}} = (N/n)(r/R)^{\frac{1}{6}} \quad (14\text{-}14)$$

or

$$q_s/Q = (N/n)(a/A)(r/R)^{\frac{1}{6}} \quad (14\text{-}15)$$

What these equations imply is illustrated in Fig. 14-3 and the following example:

Example 14-3. An 8-in. sewer is to flow at 0.3 depth on a grade ensuring a degree of self-cleaning equivalent to that obtained at full depth at a velocity of 2.5 fps. Find the required grades and associated velocities and rates of discharge at full depth and 0.3 depth. Assume $N = 0.013$ at full depth.

1. From Table 14-2, find for full depth of flow and $V = 2.5$ fps, $Q = 0.873$ cfs and $S = 5.20\%_0$.

2. From Fig. 14-2 or Table 14-3, find for 0.3 depth, $a/A = 0.252$, $r/R = 0.684$ (or $R/r = 1.46$), $v/V = 0.776$, $q/Q = 0.196$, and $N/n = 0.78$; and from Table 14-3, find $(r/R)^{\frac{1}{6}} = 0.939$.

Hence at 0.3 depth and a grade of $5.20\%_0$, $v = 0.776 \times 2.5 = 1.94$ fps for $n = N$, or 1.51 fps for $N/n = 0.78$, and $q = 0.196 \times 0.873 = 0.171$ cfs for $n = N$, or 0.133 cfs for $N/n = 0.78$.

3. For self-cleaning flow, however, $s_s = 1.46 \times 5.20 = 7.6\%_0$, by Eq. 14-13; $v_s = 0.939 \times 2.5 = 2.35$ for $n = N$, or $0.78 \times 2.35 = 1.83$ fps for $N/n = 0.78$, by Eq. 14-14; and $q_s = 0.252 \times 0.939 \times 0.873 = 0.207$ cfs for $n = N$, or $0.78 \times 0.207 = 0.161$ cfs for $N/n = 0.78$, by Eq. 14-15.

Figure 14-3 confirms that minimum grades are enough so long as circular sewers flow more than half full. However when flows drop to 0.2 depth, grades must be doubled for equal self-cleansing; at 0.1 depth they must be trebled. Expressed in terms of the Weisbach-Darcy friction

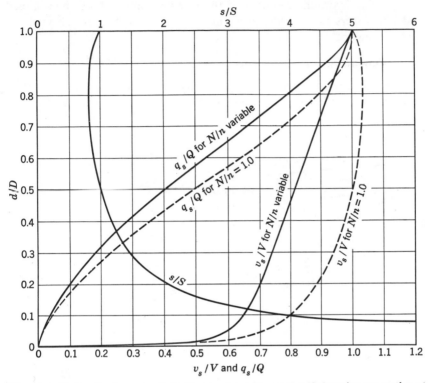

Fig. 14-3. Hydraulic elements of circular sewers with equal self-cleansing properties at all depths.

factor f, Eqs. 14-14 and 15 become, respectively,

$$v_s/V = (F/f)^{\frac{1}{2}} \qquad (14\text{-}16)$$

and

$$q_s/Q = (a/A)(F/f)^{\frac{1}{2}} \qquad (14\text{-}17)$$

Example 14-4. An 8-in. sewer is to discharge 0.161 cfs at a velocity as self-cleaning as a sewer flowing full at 2.5 fps. Find the depth and velocity of flow and the required slope.

1. From Example 14-3, $Q = 0.873$ cfs and $S = 5.20\%_0$. Hence $q_s/Q = 0.161/0.873 = 0.185$.

2. From Fig. 14-3, for $N = n$ and $q_s/Q = 0.185$, $d_s/D = 0.25$, $v_s/V = 0.91$, and $s/S = 1.70$. Hence $v_s = 0.91 \times 2.5 = 2.28$ fps, and $s_s = 1.70 \times 5.20 = 8.8\%_0$.

3. From Fig. 14-3, for N/n variable and $q_s/Q = 0.185$, $d_s/D = 0.30$, $v_s/V = 0.732$ and $s/S = 1.46$. Hence $v_s = 0.732 \times 2.5 = 1.83$ fps, and $s_s = 1.46 \times 5.20 = 7.6\%_0$.

Egg-shaped sewers and cunettes (Sec. 3-6) were introduced, principally in Europe, to provide enough velocity for dry-weather flows in combined sewers. The hydraulic elements of these sewers and of horseshoe-shaped and box sewers can be charted in the same way as they are charted for circular sewers.

14-5   Flow in Sewer Transitions

Although flow in sewers is both unsteady (changing in rate of discharge) and nonuniform (changing in velocity and depth), these factors are taken

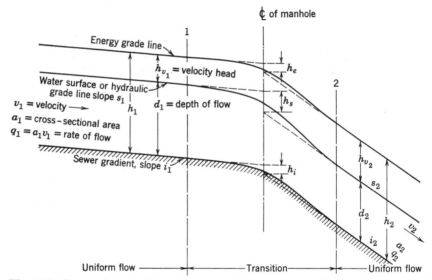

Fig. 14-4. Changes in hydraulic and energy grade lines at a transition in size or grade of sewer.

into account only at sewer transitions. This is so because it is not practicable to identify with needed accuracy the variation in flow with time in all reaches of the sewerage system and because the system is designed for maximum expected flow in any case.

Sewer transitions include (1) changes in size, grade, and volume of flow; (2) free and submerged discharge at the end of sewer lines; (3) passage through measuring and diversion devices; and (4) sewer junctions. Of these, sewer transitions at changes in size or grade are most common. How they affect the profile of the water surface and energy gradient is shown, greatly foreshortened, in Fig. 14-4. Here h_e is the loss in energy or head; h_s the drop in water surface; and h_i the required invert drop. For convenience of formulation, these changes are assumed to be concentrated at the center of the transition. The energy loss h_e is usually small. In the absence of exact information, it may be considered proportional to the difference, or change, in velocity heads, or $h_e = k(h_{v_2} - h_{v_1}) = k \Delta h_v$. According to Hinds,[12] the proportionality factor k may be as low as 0.1 for rising velocities and 0.2 for falling velocities, provided flow is in the *upper alternate stage*. For the *lower alternate stage*, k may be expected to increase approximately as the square of the velocity ratios. Camp[13] has suggested a minimum allowance of 0.02 ft for the loss of head in a transition of this kind. However, if there is a horizontal curve in the transition, more head will be lost.

The required invert drop h_i follows from the relationships demonstrated in Fig. 14-4. There $h_2 + h_e = h_1 + h_i$, or

$$h_i = (h_2 - h_1) + h_e = \Delta(d + h_v) + k \Delta h_v \qquad (14\text{-}18)$$

The calculated change h_i will be positive for increasing gradients; negative for sharply decreasing gradients. A positive value calls for a drop in the invert, a negative value for a rise. However, a rise would obstruct flow, and the invert is actually made continuous. The elevation of the water surface in the downstream sewer is thereby lowered, and the waters in the sewers entering the transition are drawn down towards it.

Rules of thumb sometimes followed by engineers in place of computations reflect average conditions encountered in practice. They may not be justified by circumstances. Common rules for drops in manholes at changes in size are:

1. Make the invert drop $h_i = \frac{1}{2}(d_2 - d_1)$ for sewers smaller than 24 in., or $h_i = \frac{3}{4}(d_2 - d_1)$ for 24-in. sewers and larger.

2. Allow a drop of 0.1 ft in a through manhole; 0.2 ft in the presence of one lateral or bend; and 0.3 ft for two laterals.

3. Keep the $0.8d$ line continuous on the principle that it is close to the line of maximum velocity.

4. Keep the crowns of sewers continuous.

5. Increase the roughness factor over that in straight runs; $N = 0.015$, for example, instead of $N = 0.013$.

Example 14-5. Two 8-in. sanitary sewers, each flowing full and carrying 0.7 cfs at a velocity of 2 fps on minimum grade, discharge into a steeper sewer that picks up 0.01 cfs in the course of its next run. The lower sewer can be laid on a grade as low as 10‰ and as high as 14‰. Find the required slope of the lower sewer and the invert drop in the transition.

[12] Julian Hinds, The Hydraulic Design of Flume and Siphon Transitions, *Trans. Am. Soc. Civil Engrs.*, **92**, 1423 (1928).
[13] T. R. Camp, Design of Sewers to Facilitate Flow, *Sewage Works J.*, **18**, 3 (1946).

1. From Table 14-1, an 8-in. sewer flowing full will carry 1.41 cfs on a slope of 13.6‰ with a velocity of 4.04 fps if $N = 0.013$. Pertinent information is, therefore, as follows:

$$d_1 = 0.67 \text{ ft, } v_1 = 2.00 \text{ fps, } h_{v_1} = 0.062 \text{ ft, } d_1 + h_{v_1} = 0.73 \text{ ft}$$
$$d_2 = 0.67 \text{ ft, } v_2 = 4.04 \text{ fps, } h_{v_2} = 0.254 \text{ ft, } d_2 + h_{v_2} = 0.92 \text{ ft}$$
$$\Delta h_v = 0.19 \text{ ft, } \Delta(d + h_v) = 0.19 \text{ ft}$$

Assuming a loss of head $h_e = 0.2\Delta h_v = 0.038$ ft, Eq. 14-18 gives the required drop in invert, $h_i = 0.19 + 0.04 = 0.23$ ft.

2. A 10-in. sewer laid on a grade of 10‰ has a capacity of 2.19 cfs and velocity of 4.02 fps when flowing full. From Fig. 14-2, for $N/n \times q/Q = 0.644$, $d/D = 0.65$, and $N/n \times v/V = 0.92$, or $d = 6.5$ in., and $v = 3.69$ fps. Hence, the upper sewers remaining unchanged,

$$d_2 = 0.542 \text{ ft, } v_2 = 3.69 \text{ fps, } h_{v_2} = 0.21 \text{ ft, } d_2 + h_{v_2} = 0.75 \text{ ft}$$
$$\Delta h_v = 0.15 \text{ ft, } \Delta(d + h_v) = 0.02 \text{ ft}$$

Assuming a loss of head $h_e = 0.2\,\Delta h_v = 0.036$ ft, Eq. 14-18 states that $h_i = 0.02 + 0.04 = 0.06$ ft.

14-6 Alternate Stages and Critical Depths

In the analysis of transitions, the designer must often find the alternate stages or depths of open-channel flow and their mergence into flow at critical depth. Referred to the sewer invert, the energy grade line shown in Fig. 14-5 is situated at a height

$$h = d + h_v = d + \frac{v^2}{2g} = d + \frac{q^2}{2ga^2} \qquad (14\text{-}19)$$

above this datum,[14] where the cross-sectional area a of the conduit is a

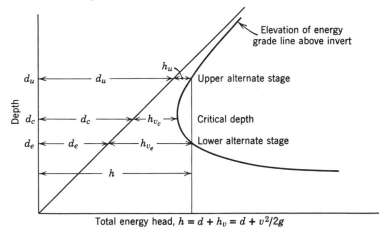

Fig. 14-5. Alternate stages of flow and total energy head at constant rate of discharge in open-channel flow.

[14] If v is the mean velocity of flow, the kinetic energy head is actually greater than $v^2/2g$ by 10 to 20%, depending upon the shape and roughness of the channel. But this fact is not ordinarily taken into account in hydraulic computations. (See footnote 13.)

function of its depth, d. Accordingly, Eq. 14-19 is a cubic equation in terms of d. Two of its roots are positive and, except at critical depth, identify the two alternate stages at which a given discharge rate q can be maintained for a given energy head h, The two stages fuse into a single *critical stage* for conditions of maximum discharge at a given total energy head, or minimum total energy head at a given discharge (Fig. 14-5 and Eq. 14-19).

For uniform flow, the water surface parallels the invert ($s = i$). At the critical stage, flow is unstable and depth of flow is uncertain and fluctuating.

Equation 14-19 can be generalized by expressing its three components as dimensionless ratios. Bringing q to one side and multiplying both sides by $(1/D)(a/A)^2$ give the following straight-line relationship:

$$(q/A\sqrt{gD})^2 = 2(a/A)^2(h/D - d/D) \qquad (14\text{-}20)$$

Again, capital letters denote the hydraulic elements of the full section, and lower-case letters those of the partially filled section. The ratios h_c/D and d_c/D are respectively the specific head and critical depth of circular sewers.

A plot of Eq. 14-20 for circular conduits is shown in Fig. 14-6. For particular values of d/D, the family of straight lines spontaneously generates a curve for the critical depth, while depths at alternate stages can be read at the intersections of ordinates and abscissas. Calculations, especially tedious for conduits of irregular cross-section, are thereby avoided.

Maximum rate of discharge obtains at critical depth d_c. The associated specific head, h_c/D, is determined analytically[15] by differentiating Eq. 14-20 with respect to d and equating the result to zero.

The following relationship is obtained for a circular cross-section:

$$h_c/D = \tfrac{1}{8}\left\{[10(d_c/D) - 1] + \frac{\tfrac{1}{4}\pi + \tfrac{1}{2}\sin^{-1}[2(d_c/D) - 1]}{\sqrt{(d_c/D)[1 - (d_c/D)]}}\right\} \qquad (14\text{-}21)$$

[15] For a circular cross-section the area a of the partially filled section is related to the depth as follows:

$$a = \frac{\tfrac{1}{2}\pi D^2}{4} + 2\int_{y=0}^{y=y} x\,dy$$

where x and y are the coordinates of a point on the circle referred to axes passing through the center of the circle. Expressed in terms of y and of D and d,

$$2\int_{y=0}^{y=y} x\,dy = 2\int_{y=0}^{y=y} \sqrt{(D^2/4 - y^2)}\,dy = 2\int_{d=D/2}^{d=d} \sqrt{d(D-d)}\,dd$$

$$= (d - \tfrac{1}{2}D)[d(D-d)]^{1/2} + \tfrac{1}{4}D^2\sin^{-1}[2(d/D) - 1]$$

Introduction of these quantities into Eq. 14-20 and differentiation yield Eq. 14-21.

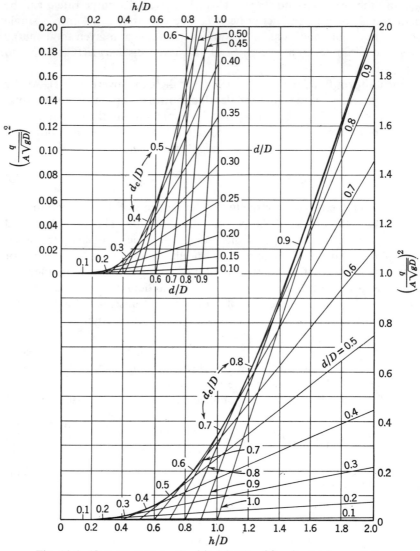

Fig. 14-6. Alternate stages and critical depths of flow in circular conduits.

Substituting values of d_c/D varying by tenths from 0.1 to 0.9 yields the numerical results[16] for h/D, $v_c/\sqrt{gD}$, and $[q/A\sqrt{gD})]^2$ shown in Table 14-4.

For a trapezoidal channel (Fig. 11-16) of bottom width b and with side slopes z (horizontal to vertical)

$$h_c/D = d_c/D + \tfrac{1}{2}(d_c/D)(b + zd_c)/(b + 2zd_c) \qquad (14\text{-}22)$$

For a rectangular channel ($z = 0$); therefore

$$h_c/D = \tfrac{3}{2}d_c/D \quad \text{or} \quad h_c = \tfrac{3}{2}d_c \qquad (14\text{-}23)$$

whence

$$v_c^2/2g = h - d_c \quad \text{or} \quad v_c = \sqrt{gd_c} \qquad (14\text{-}24)$$

Table 14-4   Values of h/D, $v_c/\sqrt{gD}$, and $[q/(A\sqrt{gD})]^2$ for Varying Values of d_c/D in a Circular Conduit

d_c/D	h/D	$v_c/\sqrt{gD}$	$[q/(A\sqrt{gD})]^2$
0.1	0.134	0.261	1.184×10^{-4}
0.2	0.270	0.378	2.86×10^{-3}
0.3	0.408	0.465	1.37×10^{-2}
0.4	0.550	0.553	4.18×10^{-2}
0.5	0.696	0.626	9.80×10^{-2}
0.6	0.851	0.709	1.97×10^{-1}
0.7	1.020	0.800	3.58×10^{-1}
0.8	1.222	0.919	6.23×10^{-1}
0.9	1.521	1.11	1.12

In a closed conduit, the critical depth line, as shown in Fig. 14-6, is asymptotic to the line $d/D = 1.0$. There is neither a critical nor an alternate stage for an enclosed conduit flowing full.

Example 14-6. The use of Fig. 14-6, construction of which is simple and straightforward, can be exemplified as follows.

Given a discharge of 60 cfs in a 4-ft sewer, find (1) the critical depth (2) the alternate stages for an energy head of 4 ft, (3) the alternate stage for an energy head of 6 ft, and (4) the lower alternate stage associated with an upper alternate stage at 0.8 depth.

1. For $q = 60$ cfs and $D = 4$ ft, $[q/(A\sqrt{gD})]^2 = [60 \times 4/(\pi \times 16\sqrt{4g})]^2 = 0.177$. From Fig. 14-6, read $d_c/D = 0.59$. Hence $d_c = 0.59 \times 4 = 2.36$ ft.

2. For $h = 4.0$, $h/D = 1.0$, and $[q/(A\sqrt{gD})]^2 = 0.177$ as in 1, read, from Fig. 14-6, $d/D = 0.42$ and 0.90, or $d_l = 0.42 \times 4 = 1.7$ ft, and $d_u = 0.90 \times 4 = 3.6$ ft.

---

[16] Within the range shown, the relationship between depth and rate of discharge is closely approximated by the equation

$$d_c/D = 0.9[q/(A\sqrt{gD})]^{0.54}$$

3. For $h = 6.0$, $h/D = 1.5$, and $[q/(A\sqrt{gD})]^2 = 0.177$ as in 1, read, from Fig. 14-6, $d/D = 0.32$, whence $d_l = 0.32 \times 4 = 1.3$ ft. There is no upper stage because the conduit flows full when h/D equals or exceeds 1.09 (at intersection of $d/D = 1.0$ and ordinate of 0.177). Hence the conduit is placed under a pressure of $1.5 - 1.09 = 0.41 \times 4 = 1.6$ ft.

4. For $[q/(A\sqrt{gD})]^2 = 0.177$ as in 1 and $d_u/D = 0.8$, or $d_u = 3.2$ ft, read, from Fig. 14-6, $d_l/D = 0.45$, or $d_l = 1.8$ ft.

14-7   Length of Transitions

Transition from one to the other alternate stage carries the flow through the critical depth. Passage from the upper alternate stage (a) to the critical depth, or (b) through it, to the lower alternate stage or to free fall produces nonuniform (accelerating) flow and a *drawdown curve* in the water surface.

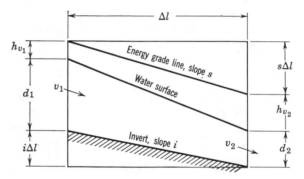

Fig. 14-7. Flow conditions changing with increasing velocity.

Passage from the lower to the upper alternate stage creates the hydraulic jump. Reduction in velocity of flow, (a) by discharge into relatively quiet water or (b) by weirs and other flow obstructions, dams up the water and induces nonuniform (decelerating) flow and a *backwater curve* in the water surface. For economy of design, size of conduit must fit conditions of flow within the range of transient depths and nonuniform flow. If initial and terminal depths of flow are known, the energy and hydraulic grade lines can be traced either by stepwise calculation or by integration (graphical[17] or analytical[18]). Both stem from the fact that the change in slope of the energy grade line must equal the sum of the changes in the slopes of (1) the invert, (2) the depth of flow, and (3) the velocity head, or $\partial h/\partial l = \partial z/\partial l + \partial d/\partial l + \partial h_v/\partial l$. Because $\partial h/\partial l$ is the slope s of the energy grade line and

[17] H. A. Thomas, *Hydraulics of Flood Movement*, Carnegie Institute of Technology, 1934.
[18] M. E. von Seggern, Integrating the Equation of Non-uniform Flow, *Trans. Am. Soc. Civil Engrs.*, **115**, 71 (1950); see also G. J. Keifer and H. H. Chu, Backwater Functions by Numerical Integration, *Trans. Am. Soc. Civil Engrs.*, **120**, 429 (1955).

$\partial z/\partial l$ is the slope i of the invert, $\partial h_v/\partial l$ being the velocity gradient,

$$s - i = \frac{\partial(d + h_v)}{\partial l} \quad \text{or} \quad \partial l = \frac{\partial(d + h_v)}{s - i} \tag{14-25}$$

For stepwise calculation of the length of conduit between cross-sections of given depth (Fig. 14-7),

$$\Delta l = \frac{\Delta(d + h_v)}{s - i} \tag{14-26}$$

Flow being steady, the rate of discharge is constant, and the velocity of flow at given depths is known. For a given invert slope i, therefore, only s needs to be calculated. This is generally done by introducing the average hydraulic elements of each conduit reach into a convenient flow formula. Averages of choice are ordinarily arithmetic means, but geometric or harmonic means will also give defendable results. Necessary calculations are shown in Example 14-7 for a backwater curve and in Example 14-8 for a drawdown curve.

Example 14-7. A 10-ft circular sewer laid on a gradient of 0.5‰ discharges 106 cfs into a pump well. The water level in this well rises, at times, 10 ft above the invert elevation of the incoming sewer. Trace the profile of the water surface in the sewer. Assume a coefficient of roughness of 0.012 for the full sewer.

1. A 10-ft sewer on a grade of 5×10^{-4} has a capacity of 400 cfs by Manning's formula. The value of q/Q, therefore, is $106/400 = 0.265$, and d/D from Fig. 14-2 is 0.40 for variable N/n. Hence the initial depth of flow is $0.40 \times 10 = 4.0$ ft, and the terminal depth 10 ft.

2. The reach in which depths change by chosen amounts is given by Eq. 14-26. Calculations are systematized in Table 14-5. The depth is seen to change from 4.0 to 10.0 ft in 14,440 ft, or slightly under 3 miles.

Calculation involves no difficulties. The values shown in the successive columns of Table 14-5 are found as shown at the top of p. 14–20.

Example 14-8. A 10-ft circular sewer laid on a gradient of 0.5‰ discharges freely into a water course. Trace the profile of the water surface in the sewer when it is flowing at maximum capacity without surcharge.

1. As shown in Example 14-7, the full capacity of this sewer is 400 cfs for $N = 0.012$.

2. To discharge in free fall, the flow must pass through the critical depth. Because $[Q/(A\sqrt{gD})]^2 = [400/(78.5\sqrt{10g})]^2 = 8.07 \times 10^{-2}$, $d_c = 0.47 \times 10 = 4.7$ ft, from Fig. 14-5 or footnote 16.

3. The reach in which the depth changes from 10 ft to 4.7 ft is calculated in Table 14-6 in accordance with Eq. 14-26 and as in Example 14-7.

The drawdown is seen to extend over a length of 23,600 ft, or over 4 miles, between the full depth of the sewer and a critical depth of 4.7 ft. There is a further short stretch of flow between the point of critical depth and the end of the sewer. As stated below, this additional distance is relatively small ($4d_c = 18.8$ ft in this example).

Table 14-5 Calculation of Backwater Curve (Example 14-7)

d (1)	d/D (2)	a/A (3)	r/R (4)	N/n (5)	a (6)	r (7)	v (8)	$h_v \times 10^2$ (9)	$d + h_v$ (10)
10.0	1.00	1.000	1.000	1.00	78.5	2.50	1.35	2.83	10.028
8.0	0.80	0.858	1.217	0.89	67.5	3.04	1.57	3.83	8.038
6.0	0.60	0.626	1.110	0.82	49.1	2.78	2.16	7.23	6.072
4.0	0.40	0.373	0.857	0.79	29.3	2.14	3.62	20.3	4.203

$n \times 10^2$ (11)	$nv \times 10^2$ (12)	Average			$s \times 10^5$ (16)	$(s-i) \times 10^5$ (17)	$\Delta(d+h_v)$ (18)	Δl (19)	$\Sigma \Delta l$ (20)
		r (13)	$r^{2/3}$ (14)	$nv \times 10^2$ (15)					
1.20	1.62								0
		2.77	1.97	1.87	4.07	−45.9	−1.990	4,330	
1.35	2.12								4330
		2.91	2.04	2.63	7.53	−42.5	−1.966	4,620	
1.46	3.15								8,950
		2.46	1.82	4.32	15.97	−34.0	−1.869	5,490	
1.52	5.50								14,440

Column 1: Depths between initial depth of 4 ft and terminal depth of 10 ft are assumed to increase by 2 ft.

Column 2: Col. 1 ÷ 10 (the diameter of the sewer).

Columns 3, 4, and 5; a/A, r/R, and N/n read from Fig. 14-2.

Column 6: Col. 3 × 78.5 (the area of the sewer).

Column 7: Col. 1 × 2.50 (the hydraulic radius of the sewer).

Column 8: 106 (the rate of flow)/Col. 6.

Column 9: $v^2/2g$ for Col. 8.

Column 10: Col. 9 + Col. 1.

Column 11: 0.012 (Manning's N for sewer)/(Col. 5).

Column 12: Col. 11 × Col. 8.

Column 13: Arithmetic mean of successive pairs of values in Col. 7.

Column 14: (Col. 13)$^{2/3}$.

Column 15: Arithmetic mean of successive pairs of values in Col. 12.

Column 16: (Col. 15/1.489 × Col. 14)^2, i.e., $s = (nv/1.49 r^{2/3})^2$.

Column 17: Col. 16 − 50.

Column 18: Difference between successive pairs of values in Col. 10.

Column 19: Col. 18/Col. 17 × 10^{-5}, i.e., $\Delta l = \Delta(d + h_v)/(s - i)$.

Column 20: Cumulative values of Col. 19.

Beyond the critical depth, the hydraulic drop terminating in free fall is a function of velocity distribution. Flow is supercritical and depth decreases. At the free outfall, pressure on the lower as well as the upper nappe is atmospheric when the nappe is ventilated. Within the conduit, calculated ratios of the terminal depth to the critical depth[19] normally range between $\frac{2}{3}$ and $\frac{3}{4}$. The critical depth itself lies upstream at a distance of about $4d_c$.

[19] For a closer definition of conditions, see B. A. Bakhmeteff, Hydraulic Drop as a Function of Velocity Distribution, *Civil Engr.*, **24**, 64 (Dec. 1954).

Table 14-6   Calculation of Drawdown Curve (Example 14-8)

d (1)	d/D (2)	a/A (3)	r/R (4)	N/n (5)	a (6)	r (7)	v (8)	h_v (9)	$d + h_v$ (10)
4.7	0.47	0.463	0.960	0.79	36.4	2.40	11.0	1.88	6.58
6.0	0.60	0.626	1.110	0.82	49.1	2.78	8.15	1.02	7.02
8.0	0.80	0.858	1.217	0.89	67.5	3.04	5.93	0.54	8.54
10.0	1.00	1.000	1.000	1.00	78.5	2.50	5.10	0.40	10.40

$n \times 10^2$ (11)	$nv \times 10^2$ (12)	Average			$s \times 10^4$ (16)	$(s - i) \times 10^4$ (17)	$\Delta(d + h_v)$ (18)	Δl (19)	$\Sigma \Delta l$ (20)
		r (13)	$r^{2/3}$ (14)	$nv \times 10^2$ (15)					
1.52	16.8								0
		2.59	1.88	14.3	26.2	21.2	0.44	210	
1.46	11.9								210
		2.91	2.04	9.9	10.65	5.65	1.52	2,690	
1.35	7.99								2,900
		2.77	1.97	7.1	5.90	0.90	1.86	20,700	
1.20	6.12								23,600

14-8   Transition by Hydraulic Jump

When a conduit steep enough to discharge at supercritical velocities and depths is followed by a relatively flat channel in which entering velocities and depths cannot be maintained, a more or less abrupt change in velocity and depth takes the form of an hydraulic jump. Whereas alternate depths are characterized by equal specific energies $(d + h_v)$, sequent depths are characterized by equal pressure plus momentum. In accordance with the momentum principle, illustrated in Fig. 14-8, the force producing momentum changes when equated to the momentum change per unit volume establishes sequent depths d_1 (lower) and d_2 (upper) such that the velocity v, associated with the depth d, is determined by the equation[20]

$$(v_1/\sqrt{gd_1})^2 = \tfrac{1}{2}(d_2/d_1)[1 + (d_2/d_1)] = \mathbf{F}^2 \qquad (14\text{-}27)$$

where $\mathbf{F}$ is the Froude number and $\sqrt{gd_1}$ is the celerity of an elementary gravity wave, or

$$d_2/d_1 = \tfrac{1}{2}[(1 + 8\mathbf{F}^2)^{1/2} - 1] \qquad (14\text{-}28)$$

As shown by Rouse,[20] depths change (1) with substantially no loss of head in a series of undulations when $2 > \mathbf{F} > 1$; and (2) with appreciable head loss and a breaking wave when $\mathbf{F} > 2$. For cross-sections other than rectangles of unit width, all terms in Eq. 14-28, have numerical coefficients that must be determined experimentally.

[20] Hunter Rouse, ed., *Engineering Hydraulics*, John Wiley & Sons, New York, 1950, p. 72. The force per unit width producing the momentum changes is $\tfrac{1}{2}(\rho g d_1{}^2 - \rho g d_2{}^2)$, where ρ is the mass density of the water and g the gravity constant. The momentum change per unit volume is $q\rho(v_2 - v_1)$, where q is the rate of flow. Equating the two and eliminating q and v_2 by the continuity equation $q = v_1 d_1 = v_2 d_2$ leads directly to Eq. 14-27.

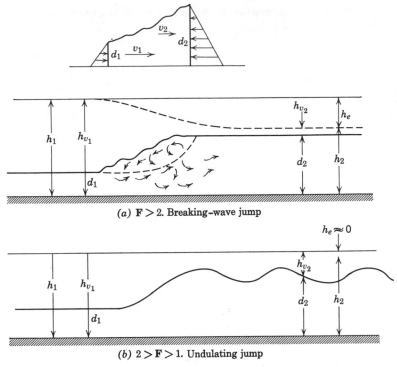

(a) $\mathbf{F} > 2$. Breaking-wave jump

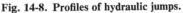

(b) $2 > \mathbf{F} > 1$. Undulating jump

Fig. 14-8. Profiles of hydraulic jumps.

14-9   Discontinuous Surge Front

As shown in Fig. 14-9, the momentum principle can be adduced to identify also the propagation of discontinuous waves in open channel flow. Waves of this kind may rush through conduits when a sudden discharge of water from a localized thunderstorm or the quick release of a large volume of industrial wastewater, for example, enters a drainage system. In cases such as these, the volume of water undergoing a change in momentum

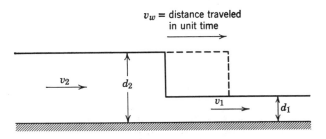

Fig. 14-9. Surge front in profile.

in unit time and unit channel width is $(v_w - v_1)d_1$. The celerity of propagation, which is the wave velocity or speed of propagation of the surge front, relative to the fluid velocity[21] being $c = v_w - v_1$,

$$(c/\sqrt{gd_1})^2 = \tfrac{1}{2}(d_2/d_1)(1 + d_2/d_1) \tag{14-29}$$

Example 14-9. Find the rate of propagation of a discontinuous surge front which raises the flow depth from 1 ft to 2 ft.

By Eq. 14-29, $c = \sqrt{g}[\tfrac{1}{2} \times \tfrac{2}{1}(1 + \tfrac{2}{1})]^{1/2} = \sqrt{3g} = 9.8$ fps. In a dry channel $c \approx \sqrt{gd}$, a matter of interest in cleansing sewers by discharge of automatic flush tanks (Fig. 3-2).

14-10 Bends and Junctions

In common with many other uncertainties of fluid behavior in hydraulic systems, head losses in bends are often approximated as functions of the velocity head $v^2/2g$. For small sewers, the radius of an optimal circular curve of the center line of the sewer is reported to be three to six times the sewer diameter.[22]

The conjoining of the flow patterns of two or more sewers normally involves curvature as well as impact effects. Generalization of resulting head losses is difficult. Where predictions of surface profiles are important, in the case of large sewers, for example, model studies are advisable. Otherwise, the usual procedure of working upstream from a known point, especially a control point, should identify the water surface profile reasonably well.

14-11 Overfalls or Side Weirs

Storm flows in excess of intercepter capacity are often diverted into natural drainage channels through overfalls or side weirs. Needed weir lengths depend upon the general dimensions and hydraulic charactcristics of the sewer and the nature and orientation of the weir itself. Understandably, side weirs paralleling the direction of flow must be longer than weirs at right angles to it.

For the conditions of flow outlined in Fig. 14-10, Bernoulli's theorem gives the following relationship when head loss is based upon Manning's formula:

$$\frac{v_1{}^2}{2g} + il + h_1 = \frac{v_2{}^2}{2g} + h_2 + l\left(\frac{nv}{1.49r^{2/3}}\right)^2$$

Hence

$$h_2 - h_1 = \frac{Q_1{}^2 - Q_2{}^2}{2ga^2} + il - l\left\{n\left[\frac{Q_1 + Q_2}{2 \times 1.49ar^{2/3}}\right]\right\}^2 \tag{14-30}$$

[21] Equating force to momentum change $\tfrac{1}{2}\rho gd_2{}^2 - \tfrac{1}{2}\rho gd_1{}^2 = \rho(v_2 - v_1)(v_w - v_1)d_1$ in a channel of unit width. Continuity of flow, moreover, requires that $v_2d_2 = v_w(d_2 - d_1) + v_1d_1$.

[22] A. G. Anderson and L. G. Straub, Hydraulics of Conduit Bends, St. Anthony Falls Hydraulic Laboratory, University of Minnesota, *Bulletin* No. 1 (1948).

The parameters a and r are based on average dimensions of the filled channel; those obtaining at the center of the weir, for example. Approximating the flow over the weir, Q, by $clh^{3/2}$,

$$Q = cl[\tfrac{1}{2}(h_1 + h_2)]^{3/2} \quad \text{and} \quad h_2 + h_1 = 2[(Q_1 - Q_2)/(cl)]^{2/3} \quad (14\text{-}31)$$

Given Q_1, Q_2, a, r, i, n, and h_2, values of l and h_1 are then determined by trial, as shown in Example 14-10. A formulation of this kind was first

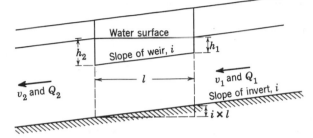

Fig. 14-10.   Flow over a side weir.

suggested by Forchheimer.[23] Other formulations have been presented by Engels[24] as follows:

For uniform channels,

$$Q = 3.32l^{0.83}h_2^{1.67} \tag{14-32}$$

and for contracted channels,

$$Q = 3.32l^{0.9}h_2^{1.6} \tag{14-33}$$

In the contracted section, the weir occupies either the contracting side of the channel or the straight side in juxtaposition to the contracting side. In terms of Engels' equations, therefore, the lengths of side weir that will discharge at the same rate as a sharp-crested, transverse weir of unit length and head h_2 are closely equal to $(l/h_2)^{0.17}$ and $(l/h_2)^{0.1}$ unit lengths respectively. Because the order of magnitude of l/h_2 is generally between 10^2 and 10^3, the length of a side weir must be 1.7 to 2.1 (contracted section) or 2.2 to 3.2 (uniform section) times that of a cross weir. Forchheimer's analysis produces somewhat lower ratios.

Example 14-10.   Given $Q_1 = 30$ cfs; $Q_2 = 16$ cfs; $a = 32$ sq ft; $r = 1.6$ ft; $i = 10^{-4}$; $n = 1.25 \times 10^{-2}$; and $h_2 = 0.50$ ft.
  Find l and h, by Forchheimer's method; assume $c = 3.33$.
  By Eq. 14-30: $h_1 = 0.49022 - 8.04 \times 10^{-5}l$.
  By Eq. 14-31: $h_1 = 5.20l^{-2/3} - 0.5$. Hence

$$(0.99022 - 8.04 \times 10^{-5}l)l^{2/3} = 5.20 \quad \text{or} \quad (12{,}320 - l)l^{2/3} = 64{,}700.$$

[23] Philip Forchheimer, *Hydraulik*, B. Teubner, Leipzig, p. 406, 1930.
[24] Hubert Engels, *Handbuch des Wasserbaues* (Manual of Hydraulic Engineering), W. Engelmann, Leipzig, Vol. 1, p. 501, 1921.

By trial

$$l = 12 \text{ ft} \quad \text{and} \quad h_1 = 0.49 \text{ ft} \qquad \textit{Answer.}$$

or

$$l = 12{,}248 \text{ ft} \quad \text{and} \quad h_1 = -0.49 \text{ ft}$$

14-12 Street Inlets

As stated in Sec. 3-6, street inlets admitting storm waters to drainage systems are so placed and designed as to concentrate and remove the flow in gutters at minimum cost with minimum interference to both pedestrian and vehicular traffic. Some features of design improve hydraulic

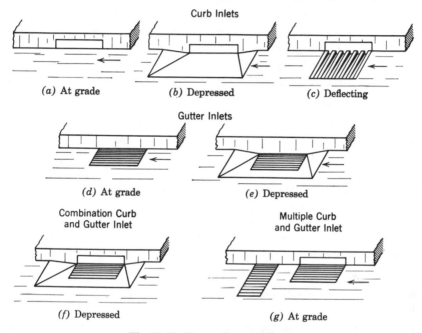

Curb Inlets

(a) At grade   *(b)* Depressed   *(c)* Deflecting

Gutter Inlets

(d) At grade   *(e)* Depressed

Combination Curb and Gutter Inlet   Multiple Curb and Gutter Inlet

(f) Depressed   *(g)* At grade

Fig. 14-11. Types of street inlets.[5]

capacity but are costly; other features interfere with traffic. Compromises produce a wide variety of designs (Fig. 14-11). Inlets are of three general types: curb inlets, gutter inlets, and combination inlets, the last-named combining curb openings with gutter openings. Only where traffic is forced to move relatively slowly may gutter surfaces and gutter inlets be depressed to increase intake capacity. Gutter capacity can be expressed by formulations such as Manning's, the coefficient of roughness being suitably increased to 0.015 or more.

The intake capacity of inlets, particularly curb inlets, increases with decreasing street grade and increasing crown slope. However, curb inlets with diagonal deflectors in the gutter along the opening become more efficient as grades become steeper. Gutter inlets are more efficient than curb inlets in capturing gutter flow, but clogging by debris is a problem. Combination inlets are better still, especially if gratings are placed downstream from curb openings. Debris accumulating on the gratings will then deflect water into the curb inlets. Gratings for gutter inlets are most efficient when their bars parallel the curb. If cross-bars are added for structural reasons, they should be kept near the bottom of the longitudinal bars. Depression of inlets, especially curb inlets, enhances their capacity. Long shallow depressions are as effective as short deep ones. If a small flow is allowed to outrun the inlet, the relative intake of water is greatly magnified. Significant economies are effected, therefore, by small carry-over flows and their acceptance by down-grade inlets.

Model studies and street tests have produced empirical formulas for flow into gutter inlets and curb inlets with and without depressions.[25] A relationship for curb openings without depressions is

$$Q/l = 4.82 \times 10^{-3} \, d\sqrt{gd} \qquad (14\text{-}34)$$

or

$$d = (35.1/g^{1/3})(Q/l)^{2/3} \qquad (14\text{-}35)$$

Here Q is the discharge into the inlet in cubic feet per second, l the length of the opening in feet, g the gravitational acceleration in feet per second squared, and d the depth of gutter flow at the curb in inches. As previously stated, the value of d can be calculated by Manning's formula. The equation for a gutter of wedge-shaped cross-section is

$$d = 0.1105 \frac{(1 + \sec\theta)^{1/4}}{\tan^{5/8}\theta} \left(\frac{Q_0}{\sqrt{s}/n}\right)^{3/8} \qquad (14\text{-}36)$$

where Q_0 is the flow in the gutter in cubic feet per second, θ the angle between the vertical curb and the mean crosswise slope of the gutter within the width of flow, n the coefficient of roughness of the gutter, and s the hydraulic gradient of the gutter which is assumed to parallel the longitudinal slope of the street surface.

Combining Eqs. 14-36 and 14-35 and solving for Q/l,

$$\frac{Q}{l} = 1.74 \frac{(1 + \sec\theta)^{3/8}}{\tan^{15/16}\theta} \left(\frac{Q_0}{\sqrt{s}/n}\right)^{9/16} \qquad (14\text{-}37)$$

[25] W. H. Li, J. C. Geyer, G. S. Benton, and K. K. Sorteberg, Hydraulic Behavior of Storm-Water Inlets—Parts I and II, *Sewage and Ind. Wastes*, 23, 34, 722 (1951); also see *The Design of Storm-Water Inlets*, Storm Drainage Research Committee, Johns Hopkins University, Baltimore, Md., 1956.

For cross-sectional street slopes of 10^{-3} to 10^{-1}, Eq. 14-36 is closely approximated by

$$\frac{Q}{l} = 1.87 i^{0.579} \left(\frac{Q_0}{\sqrt{s/n}} \right)^{0.563} \tag{14-38}$$

Here i is the mean crosswise slope of the gutter within the width of flow.

Example 14-11. For a flow of 1.0 cfs, a longitudinal street grade of 2.0%, a mean crosswise street grade of 5.6%, and a Kutter coefficient of roughness of 0.015, find (1) the length of an undepressed curb inlet required to capture 90% of the flow, and (2) the maximum depth of flow in the gutter.

1. By Eq. 14-38: $Q/l = 1.87(5.6 \times 10^{-2})^{0.579}[1.0/(\sqrt{2 \times 10^{-2}}/1.5 \times 10^{-2})]^{0.563} = 0.10$, or $l = 10$ $Q = 10 \times 0.9 \times Q_0 = 10 \times 0.9 \times 1.0 = 9$ ft.

2. By Eq. 14-35: $d = 3.48g^{1/3} \times 0.10^{2/3} = 2.4$ in.

14-13   Depressed Sewers and Appurtenant Structures

The purpose and performance of depressed sewers, inverted siphons, or sag pipes have been discussed in Sec. 2-6. The design of required siphon pipes presents no special problems. They flow full, and the velocity of flow varies directly with the rate of discharge. In order to prevent deposition of solids in pipes when flows fluctuate, relatively high velocities are employed: 3 fps for pipes carrying sanitary sewage and 5 fps for pipes conveying storm or combined sewage. The smallest pipe diameter is 6 in., and the choice of pipe material is adjusted to the hydrostatic head under which it must operate.

Inlet chambers, as suggested in Fig. 3-5, generally contain lateral weirs which eventually become submerged. Head losses are approximated by assuming that a velocity head must be created to effect each change in direction. Outlet chambers are streamlined to reduce hydraulic losses and keep eddy currents from sweeping grit and other solids back into idle pipes within the sag system. A by-pass over the obstruction circumvented by the system, or a relief outlet to a receiving water course, will prevent street inundations when individual pipes clog or system capacity is exceeded.

CHAPTER 15

Wastewater Collection

15-1 Local Information

The amount and detail of local information required for the design of sewers and drains are large. Special surveys are generally made to produce needed maps and tables as follows: (1) detailed plans and profiles of streets to be sewered; (2) plans and contour lines of properties to be drained; (3) sill or cellar elevations of buildings to be connected; (4) location and elevation of existing or projected building drains; (5) location of existing or planned surface and subsurface utilities; (6) kind and location of soils and rock through which sewers and drains must be laid; (7) depth of groundwater table; (8) location of drainage-area divides; (9) nature of street paving; (10) projected changes in street grades; (11) location and availability of sites for pumping stations, treatment works, and outfalls, and (12) nature of receiving bodies of water and other disposal facilities.

Much of the topographic information needed is assembled for illustrative purposes in Fig. 15-1 for a single sanitary sewer in a street containing also a storm drain. Aerial maps are useful.

15-2 Expected Flows

Variations in flow to be handled by *sanitary sewers* are determined (1) by anticipated population growth and water use during a chosen design period; (2) by fluctuations in flow springing from normal water use (Chap. 5). Choice of the design period itself will depend on anticipated population increases and interest rates (Sec. 5-2). By contrast, the design period for *storm drains* and *combined sewers* is important principally in connection

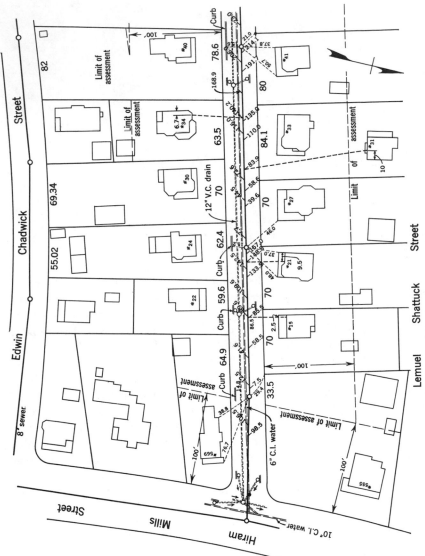

Fig. 15-1a. Plan of sanitary sewer shown in profile in Fig. 15-1b.

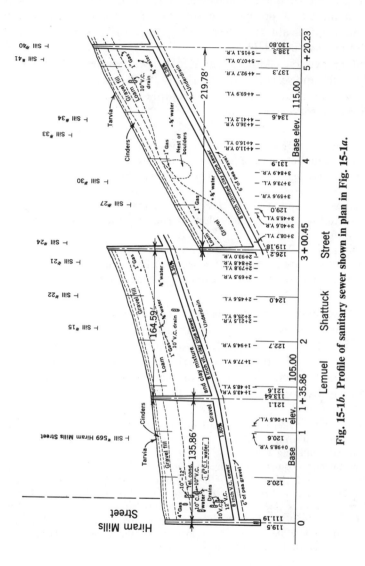

Fig. 15-1b. Profile of sanitary sewer shown in plan in Fig. 15-1a.

with expected effects of drainage-area development on runoff coefficients and magnitude of flood damage. Required storm-drain capacity is primarily a matter of probable runoff patterns. Because storms occur at random, adopted values may be reached or exceeded as soon as storm sewers and drains have been laid.

Sanitary Sewers. Although anticipated wastewater volumes and their hourly, daily, and seasonal variations (Sec. 5-12) determine design capacity, the system must function properly from the start. Comparative flows are shown in the following schedule.

Beginning of Design Period. (a) Extreme minimum flow $= \frac{1}{2}$ minimum daily flow. Critical for velocities of flow and cleanliness of sewers. (b) Minimum daily flow $= \frac{2}{3}$ of average daily flow. Critical for subdivision of units in treatment works.

Beginning and End of Design Period. (c) Average daily flow at beginning of design period $= \frac{1}{2}$ average daily flow at end of period. Critical for velocities of flow in force mains.

End of Design Period. (d) Maximum daily flow $= 2 \times$ average daily flow. Critical for capacity of treatment works. (e) Extreme maximum flow $= 1\frac{1}{2} \times$ maximum daily flow. Critical for capacity of sewers and pumps.

The flow ratios in this outline are suggestive of small sewers and relatively rapidly growing areas, the over-all ratio of the extremes being $(2 \times 1.5 \times 2 \times 2 \times 1.5 = 18):1$. For large sewers and stationary populations the over-all ratio is more nearly $4:1$. The influence of this variation on depth and velocity of flow and on the self-cleaning force of the system is shown in Example 15-1.

Example 15-1. What are the depth ratios and velocities of flow in sewers transporting (1) one-fourth their full flow and (2) one-eighteenth their full flow, the velocity of the full section being 2 fps?

The pertinent ratios read from Fig. 14-1 are:

1. For $q/Q = 0.25$, $d/D = 0.34$, $r/R = 0.76$, $v/V = 0.83$, and $N/n = 0.78$; and for $N/n \times q/Q = 0.25$, $d/D = 0.39$, $r/R = 0.84$, and $N/n \times v/V = 0.70$. For $N = n$, therefore, $v = 0.83 \times 2 = 1.66$ fps, and for $N = 0.78n$, $v = 0.70 \times 2 = 1.40$ fps.

In accordance with Eq. 14-1, the intensity of tractive force in the filled section for constant s is r/R times the intensity of tractive force in the full section. Hence the relative intensities of tractive force in the filled section are 76% for $N = n$ and 84% for $N = 0.78n$.

2. For $q/Q = 0.056$, $d/D = 0.16$, $v/V = 0.53$, and $N/n = 0.80$; and for $N/n \times q/Q = 0.056$, $d/D = 0.18$, and $N/n \times v/V = 0.46$. For $N = n$, therefore, $v = 0.53 \times 2 = 1.06$ fps; and for $N = 0.80n$, $v = 0.46 \times 2 = 0.92$ fps. Hence the relative intensities of tractive force are 39% for $N = n$ and 44% for $N = 0.80n$.

The apparent paradox of higher cleaning action at lower velocity is explained by the increase in the friction factor n.

Important unknowns in necessary calculations are the entering volumes of groundwater and stormwater. Their magnitude depends upon construction practices, especially on private property (house or building sewers).[1]

Storm Drains and Combined Sewers. Storm drains are dry much of the time. When rains are gentle, the runoff is relatively clear, and low flows present no serious problem. Flooding runoffs, however, may wash a heavy load of silt into the system. But most of the drains then flow full or nearly full and so tend to keep themselves clean. In terms of Fuller's flood frequency parameter (Sec. 7-10), for example, a drainage system designed to handle the 10-year storm may be expected to carry $(1 + 0.8 \log T_1)/(1 + 0.8 \log T_{10}) = 1/1.8 = 55\%$ of the 10-year storm at least once a year. Similarly, in accordance with Eq. 7-3 and for $m = 0.3$, the proportion of the 10-year storm flow that would be produced once a year on an average would be $(T_1/T_{10})^m = 0.1^{0.3} = 50\%$.

The situation is not so favorable when storm and sanitary flows are combined. A combined sewer designed for a runoff of 1 in. an hour, for example, will receive a storm flow of 1 cfs or 646,000 gpd from a single acre of drainage area against an average daily dry-weather contribution of about 10,000 gpd from a very densely populated acre. The resulting ratio, $q/Q = 0.016$, places the depth ratio d/D at only 0.07 and the velocity ratio v/V at only 0.3. This supports the choice of a high design velocity, such as 5.0 fps at full depth, for combined sewers. Putrescible solids accumulating in combined systems during dry weather not only create septic conditions and offensive odors; they also increase the escape of sewage solids into receiving waters through storm overflows.

15-3   Common Elements of Sewer Profiles

For specified conditions of minimum velocity, minimum sewer depth, and maximum distance between manholes, a number of situations repeat themselves in general schemes of sewerage wherein street gradient, sewer gradient, size of sewer, and depth of sewer become interrelated elements of design. Some of these recurrent situations are illustrated in Fig. 15-2. Beside a flow formulation such as Manning's, they involve the following simple equational relationship:

$$h_1 - h_2 = l(g - s) \qquad (15\text{-}1)$$

where h_1 and h_2 are sewer depths *in excess of minimum requirements*, l is the distance between manholes, and g and s are respectively the street and sewer grades. Conditions of flow are stated below Fig. 15-2.

[1] J. C. Geyer and J. J. Lentz, *An Evaluation of the Problems of Sanitary Sewer System Design*, Final Report of the Residential Sewerage Research Project of the Federal Housing Administration, Technical Studies Program, 1964.

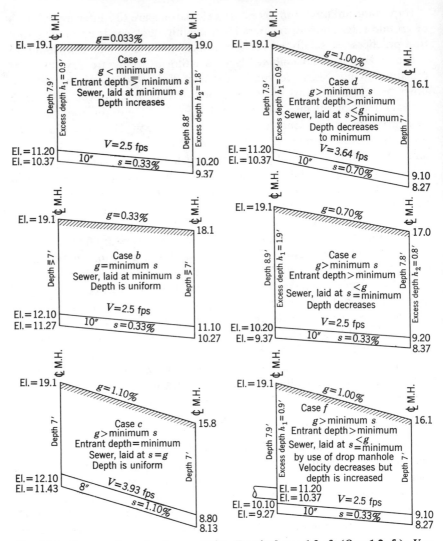

Fig. 15-2. Common elements of sewer design. Required $q = 1.2$ cfs ($Q = 1.2$ cfs); $V = 2.5$ fps; $N = 0.012$; $l = 300$ ft. Minimum depth to crown $= 7.0$ ft; 8-in. sewer $Q = 1.2$ cfs; $S = 0.84\%$; $V = 3.4$ fps; 10-in. sewer $V = 2.5$ fps; $S = 0.33\%$; $Q = 1.36$ cfs.

Case a is encountered whenever the required sewer grade is greater than the street grade. Arriving at a depth equal to or greater than the minimum, 7.0 ft in this instance, the sewer becomes deeper and deeper until it is more economical to lift the sewage by placing a pumping station in the line. Specifically for Case *a* in Fig. 15-2, the sewer grade is held at minimum (0.33%), and $h_2 = h_1 - l(g - s) = 0.9 - 3(0.033 - 0.33) = 1.8$ ft, the depth increasing by $(1.8 - 0.9) = 0.9$ ft.

Case b is unusual in that the required sewer grade is the same as the street grade. Therefore, the depth of the sewer remains unchanged.

Case c introduces a street grade steep enough to provide the required capacity in an 8-in. rather than a 10-in. parallel conduit. Arriving at minimum depth, there is no possibility of utilizing the available fall in part or as a whole to recover minimum depth as in Cases *d* and *e*. The reduced pipe size becomes the sole profit from the steep street grade, provided usually that the upstream sewer is also no greater than 8 in.

Case d aims at maximum reduction of excess depth by replacing a 10-in. sewer on minimum grade, or, in accordance with Eq. 15-1, $s = g - (h_1 - h_2)/l$. For $h_2 = 0$, $s = 1.00 - (0.9 - 0.0)/3 = 0.70\%$, which is more than the required minimum of 0.33%. Hence the sewer can be brought back to minimum depth, or $h_2 = 0$.

Case e is like Case *d*, but full reduction to minimum depth is not attainable, because $s = 0.70 - (1.9 - 0)/3 = 0.07\%$. This is less than the required minimum of 0.33%. Hence the minimum grade must be used, and $h_2 = 1.9 - 3(0.70 - 0.33) = 0.8$ ft.

Case f illustrates how high velocities can be avoided by introducing drop manholes on steep slopes. Case *f* parallels Case *d* but provides a drop of 1.1 ft to place the sewer on minimum grade and give it minimum velocity. Such action is normal only when grades are extraordinarily steep. Excessive drops and resulting excessive sewer depths can then be avoided by breaking the drops into two or more steps through insertion of intermediate drop manholes.

Because the sewers flow nearly full, no attention needed to be paid to actual velocities and depths of flow in these illustrative cases. Consideration of actual depths and velocities of flow is generally restricted to the upper reaches of sewers flowing less than half full. There, the designer may have to forgo self-cleaning grades for lateral sewers. Otherwise, they might reach the main sewer at an elevation below that of the main itself, and the main would have to be lowered to intercept them. Normally this would be expensive.

Generally speaking, the designer should try for the fullest possible exploitation of the capacity of minimum-sized sewers before joining them to larger sewers. The implications are demonstrated in Fig. 15-3. There Scheme *a* keeps lateral flows from joining the main conductor until as many as 10 units of flow have accumulated, whereas no lateral carries more than 3 units in Scheme *b*. Moreover, Scheme *b* exceeds 10 units in two sections for which the required capacities in Scheme *a* are still only 6 and 8 units.

15-4 Capacity Design in Sanitary Sewerage

Systems of sanitary sewers receive the water-borne wastes from households, mercantile and industrial establishments, and public buildings and institutions. In addition, groundwater enters by infiltration from the soil and, too often, illicit storm drains and leaking manhole covers increase the flow. Accordingly, their requisite capacity is determined by the tributary domestic and institutional population, commercial water use, industrial activity, height of groundwater table, tightness of construction, and enforcement of rainwater separation. To translate these matters into

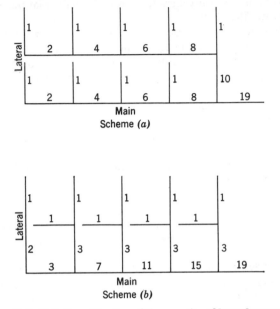

Fig. 15-3. Relative utilization of the capacity of lateral sewers.

working figures for individual runs and the complex of sewers is a responsibility that cannot be taken lightly.

It is generally convenient to arrive at unit values of domestic flows on the basis of population density and area served; but it would also be possible to develop figures for the number of people per front foot in districts of varying occupancy and make *sewer length* rather than *area served* the criterion of capacity design. Length (sometimes coupled with diameter) of sewer, indeed, offers a perhaps more rational basis for the estimation of groundwater infiltration. Unit values for flows from commercial districts are generally expressed in terms of the area served. The quantities of wastewaters produced by industrial operations are more logically evaluated in terms of the units of daily production, e.g., gallons per barrel of beer, 100 cases of canned goods, 1000 bushels of grain mashed, 100 lb of live weight of animals slaughtered, or 1000 lb of raw milk processed. Common values are suggested in Vol. 2.

Peak domestic and commercial flows originate at about the same hour of the day but travel varying distances before they reach a given point in the system. Hence a reduction in, or damping of, the peak of the cumulative flows must generally be assumed. In a fashion similar to the reduction in flood flows with time of concentration (as represented by the size and shape of drainage area), the lowering of peak flows in sanitary sewers is conveniently related to the volume of flow or to the number of people served, and unit values of design are generally not accumulated in direct proportion to the rate of discharge (Eq. 5-9) or to the tributary population (Eqs. 5-11, 12, 13).

15-5 Layout and Hydraulic Design in Sanitary Sewerage

Before entering upon the design of individual sewer runs, a preliminary layout is made of the entire system. Sanitary sewers are placed in streets or alleys in proper reference to the buildings served, and terminal manholes of lateral sewers generally lie within the service frontage of the last lot sewered.

Sewers should slope with the ground surface and follow as direct a route to the point of discharge as topography and street layout permit. To this purpose, flow in a well-designed system will normally take the path of surface runoff. Stormwater infiltration through manhole covers is kept down by placing sanitary sewers under the crown of the street.

In communities with alleys, choice of location will depend upon relative advantages of alleys and streets. Alley location is often preferable in business as well as residential districts.

Instructions for preliminary layouts are as follows: (1) show all sewers as single lines; (2) insert arrows to indicate flow direction; (3) show manholes as circles at all changes in directions or grade, at all sewer junctions, and at intermediate points that will keep manhole spacing below the allowable maximum; and (4) number manholes for identification. Alternate layouts will determine the final design.

The hydraulic design of a system of sanitary sewers is straightforward and is readily carried to completion in a series of systematic computations, as in Example 15-2.[2]

Example 15-2. Determine the required capacity and find the slope, size, and hydraulic characteristics of the system of sanitary sewers shown in the accompanying tabulation (Table 15-1) of their location, areas and population served, and expected sewage flows.

[2] The numerical values shown in this example are taken from computations for the sewerage system of R. I. Cranston, by the firm of Fay, Spofford, and Thorndike as reported in *Eng. News-Rec.*, **123**, 419 (1939). Some of the values there given do not agree in detail with values suggested in this book.

Table 15-1 Illustrative Computations for a System of Sanitary Sewers* (Example 15-2)

Section (1)	Location of Sewer			Adjacent Area						Total Tributary Area				
	Street (2)	Stations or limits		Total acres (5)	Industrial acres (6)	Commercial acres (7)	Domestic acres (8)	Population		Industrial acres (11)	Commercial acres (12)	Domestic acres (13)	Population	
		From (3)	To (4)					Per acre (9)	Total (10)				Per acre (14)	Total (15)
a	A Ave.	B Ave.	C St.	49	5	4	40	27	1,080	5	4	40	27.0	1,080
b	D Ave.	C St.	E St.	37	3	7	27	19	513	8	11	67	23.8	1,593
c	F St.	G St.	H St.	29	8	1	20	25	500	16	12	87	24.1	2,093
d	I St.	J St.	K St.	63	...	10	53	21	1,113	16	22	140	22.9	3,206

Design Profile

Section (1)	Maximum Volume of Sewage, cfs					Size, in. (21)	Slopes, % (22)	Capacity, cfs (23)	Velocity, fps		Depth of flow, in. (26)	Length, ft (27)	Invert elevation		Cut		
	Industrial (16)	Commercial (17)	Domestic (18)	Infiltration (19)	Total (20)				Full (24)	Actual (25)			Upper end (28)	Lower end (29)	Upper end (30)	Lower end (31)	Average (32)
a	.156	.155	.440	.044	0.795	8	0.8	0.82	2.35	2.72	6.37	850	120.00	113.20	7.50	11.50	9.50
b	.248	.429	.650	.086	1.413	10	0.7	1.42	2.22	3.02	8.1	1,260	113.03	104.21	11.67	8.50	10.08
c	.496	.468	.852	.115	1.931	12	0.45	2.23	2.45	2.84	9.7	1,880	104.04	95.58	8.67	12.00	10.33
d	.496	.858	1.300	.178	2.832	15	0.3	3.35	2.35	2.72	12.0	1,760	95.33	90.05	12.25	11.00	11.63

* Note: Sections of sewers rather than individual runs between manholes are shown in this example in order to include major changes in required capacity and consequent size.

1. Capacity requirements are based upon the following assumptions:

(a) Water consumption: Average day, 95 gpcd; maximum day, 175% of average; maximum hour, 140% of maximum day.

(b) Domestic sewage: 70% of water consumption; maximum is 285 gpcd for 5 acres decreasing to 245 gpcd for 100 acres or more.

(c) Groundwater: 30,000 to 50,000 gpd per mile of sewer for low land and 20,000 to 35,000 gpd per mile of sewer for high land; 0.14 to 0.15 cfs per 100 acres for 8-in. to 15-in. sewers in low land and 0.09 to 0.11 cfs per 100 acres in high land. These figures would be lowered by using preformed joints.

(d) Commercial sewage: 25,000 gpd per acre = 3.88 cfs per 100 acres.

(e) Industrial sewage: Flow in accordance with industry.

2. Hydraulic requirements are as follows:

(a) Minimum velocity in sewers: 2.5 fps (actual).

(b) Kutter's coefficient of roughness $N = 0.015$ includes allowances for change in direction and related losses in manholes except for (c) below.

(c) Crown of sewers is made continuous to prevent surcharge of upstream sewer.

3. Design procedures are as follows:

Columns 1–4 identify the location of the sewer run. The sections are continuous.
Columns 5–8 list the acreage immediately adjacent to the sewer.
Column 9 gives the density of the population per domestic acre.
Column 10 = Col. 9 × Col. 8.
Columns 11–13 list the accumulated acreage drained by the sewer. For example, in Sec. b, Col. 13 is the sum of Col. 8 in Secs. a and b, or (40 + 27) = 67.
Column 14 gives the average population density for the total tributary area. For example, in Sec. b, Col. 14 = (40 × 27 + 27 × 19)/(40 + 27) = 23.8.
Column 15 = Col. 14 × Col. 13.
Column 16 lists values obtained in a survey of industries in the areas served.
Column 17 = Col. 12 × 0.0388.
Column 18 = Col. 15 × (245 to 285) × (1.547 × 10⁻⁶). For example, in Sec. a, 1080 × 264 × (1.547 × 10⁻⁶) = 0.440 cfs.
Column 19 = Sum of Col. 5 times rate of infiltration. For example, in Sec. a, 49 × 0.09/100 = 0.044 cfs.
Column 20 = Sum of Cols. 16–19.
Columns 21–29 record the size of sewer for required capacity and available, or required, grade together with depth and velocity of flow. For example, in Sec. a, an 8-in. sewer laid on a grade of 6.8/850 = 0.008 or 0.8% will discharge $Q = 0.82$ cfs at a velocity of 2.35 cfs when it flows full. Hence for $q/Q = 0.795/0.82 = 0.971$, $d/D = 0.796$, $v/V = 1.16$, or $d = 8 \times 0.796 = 6.37$ in. and $v = 2.35 \times 1.16 = 2.72$ fps.
Columns 28–31 are taken from profiles of streets and sewers.
Column 28, Sec. b, shows a drop in the manhole of (113.20 − 113.03) = 0.17 ft compared with Col. 28, Sec. a. This allows for a full drop of 0.17 × 12 = 2 in. to offset the increase in the diameter of the sewer from 8 in. to 10 in.
Column 32 = arithmetic mean of Cols. 30 and 31.

15-6 Capacity Design in Storm Drainage

As shown in Sec. 7-9, the rational method of estimating runoff from rainfall provides a common hydrological basis for the capacity design of storm-drainage systems. The axiom of design is $Q = cia$ (Eq. 7-9). Accordingly, the designer must arrive at the best possible estimates of c, the runoff-rainfall ratio, and i, the rainfall intensity, the area a being determined by measuring tributary areas. As stated in Sec. 7-9, both c and i are variable in time. Because of this, storm flows reaching a given point in the drainage system are compounded of waters falling within the time of concentration, and peak runoff is normally built up when the entire tributary area has come into action.

Time of Concentration.   The time of concentration is composed of two parts: (1) the inlet time, or time required for runoff to gain entrance to a sewer, and (2) the time of flow in the sewerage system.

The inlet time is a function of (1) surface roughness offering resistance to flow; (2) depression storage delaying runoff and often reducing its total; (3) steepness of areal slope, governing speed of overland flow; (4) size of block or distance from the areal divide to the sewer inlet determining time of travel; (5) degree of direct roof and surface drainage reducing losses and shortening inlet time; and (6) spacing of street inlets affecting elapsed time of flow. In large communities, in which roofs shed water directly to sewers, and runoff from paved yards and streets enters the drainage system through closely spaced street inlets, the time of overland flow is usually less than 5 min. In commercial districts with relatively flat slopes and greater inlet spacing, the time lengthens to 10 to 15 min. In relatively flat residential areas in which street inlets are minimal, 20 to 30 min elapse. With steeper slopes, inlet times are naturally reduced.

Time of concentration for overland flow has been formulated by Kerby:[3]

$$t = [\tfrac{2}{3}l(n/\sqrt{s})]^{0.467} \tag{15-2}$$

where t is the inlet time in minutes, $l \leq 1200$ ft, is the distance to the farthest tributary point, s is the slope, and n is a retardance coefficient analogous to the coefficient of roughness. Suggested values of n are:

Type of Surface	n
Impervious surfaces	0.02
Bare packed soil, smooth	0.10
Bare surfaces, moderately rough	0.20
Poor grass and cultivated row crops	0.20
Pasture or average grass	0.40
Timberland, deciduous trees	0.60
Timberland, deciduous trees, deep litter	0.80
Timberland, conifers	0.80
Dense grass	0.80

[3] W. S. Kerby, *Civil Engineering*, **29**, 174 (1959). Equation 15-2 can be approximated by the dimensionally consistent expression: $t = 4.3[(l/g)(n/\sqrt{s})]^{1/2}$ Also see Eq. 15-3.

For $l = 500$ ft, $s = 1.0\%_0$, and $n = 0.1$, for example, $t = 1000^{0.467} =$ 29 min.

As a matter of arithmetic, the time of flow in the system equals the sum of the quotients of the length of constituent sewers and their velocity when flowing full. Ordinarily, neither time increase, as sewers are filled, nor time decrease, as flood waves are generated by rapid discharge of lateral sewers is taken into account.

Runoff Coefficients. Runoff from storm rainfall is reduced by evaporation, depression storage, surface wetting, and percolation. Losses decrease with rainfall duration; runoff-rainfall ratios, or shedding characteristics,

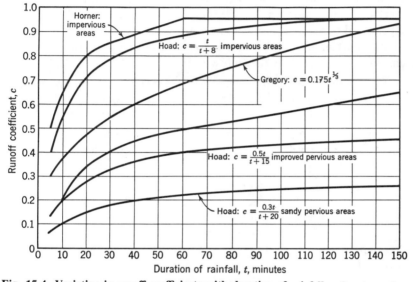

Fig. 15-4. Variation in runoff coefficients with duration of rainfall and nature of area drained.

rise proportionately. As stated in Sec. 7-9, the coefficient c may exceed unity; for example, when ice and snow accumulations are melted by sun, rain, or fog. Ordinarily, however, c is less than 1.0 and climbs toward unity only when drainage areas are impervious and storms last long enough. Choice of meaningful runoff coefficients is difficult. It may be made a complex decision. The runoff coefficient for a particular time of concentration should logically be an average weighted in accordance with the geometric configuration of the area drained, but fundamental evaluations of c and i are generally not sufficiently exact to warrant this refinement.

Choice of a suitable runoff coefficient is complicated not only by existing conditions, but also by the uncertainties of change in evolving urban complexes. Difficult to account for are the variations in runoff-rainfall relations to be expected in given drainage areas along with variations in rainfall intensities in the course of major storms. Fundamental runoff efficiency is least at storm onset and improves as storms progress. Graphic and equational relationships proposed by different authorities are shown in Fig. 15-4. However, they are not actually very helpful. Weighted average coefficients are calculated for drainage areas composed of districts with different runoff efficiencies.

Least arduous is acceptance of the fact that the degree of imperviousness of a given area is a rough measure of its shedding efficiency. Streets, alleys, side and yard walks, together with house and shed roofs, as the principal impervious components, produce high coefficients; lawns and gardens, as the principal pervious components, produce low coefficients. To arrive at a composite runoff-rainfall ratio, a weighted average is often computed from information such as the following:[4]

Areal Component	Runoff Coefficient, %
Streets: asphalt	70 to 95
concrete	80 to 95
brick	70 to 85
Drives and walks	75 to 85
Roofs	75 to 95
Lawns: sandy soil, flat (2%)	5 to 10
steep (7%)	15 to 20
heavy soil, flat (2%)	13 to 17
steep (7%)	25 to 35

Resulting overall values for North American communities range between limits not far from the following:

Areas	Overall Runoff Coefficient, %
Business blocks: high-value district	70 to 95
neighborhood district	50 to 70
Residential blocks: single-family dwellings	30 to 50
multiple-family, detached	40 to 60
multiple-family, attached	60 to 75
suburban	25 to 40
apartment dwellings	50 to 70
Industrial blocks: light	50 to 80
heavy	60 to 90
Parks and cemeteries	10 to 25
Playgrounds	20 to 35
Unimproved land	10 to 30

[4] *Am. Soc. Civil Engrs. Manuals of Engineering Practice*, No. 37, p. 48 (1960).

Intensity of Rainfall. If the time-intensity-frequency analysis of storm rainfalls elaborated in Sec. 7-3 to 7-6 is followed, the important engineering decision is not alone the selection of a suitable storm but also the pairing of significant values of the runoff coefficient c with the varying rainfall intensities i. Even though c is known to be time and rainfall dependent, engineers frequently seek shelter under the umbrella of the mean by selecting an average value of c that will combine reasonably well with varying values of t and i. However, it is possible to avoid poor pairing of c and i values by deriving a runoff hydrograph from the hyetograph of a *design* storm. How this is done is shown in Sec. 15-7.

15-7 Storm Pattern Analysis

Different from the averaging procedures associated in practice with the rational method of runoff analysis is the development of a generalized chronological storm pattern or hyetograph and its translation into a

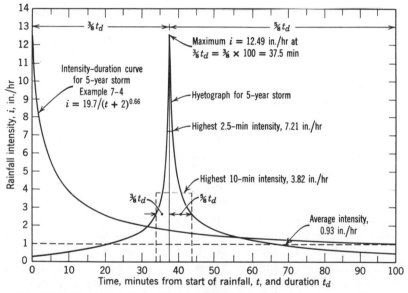

Fig. 15-5. Hyetograph derived from rainfall intensity-duration frequency curve.

design runoff pattern by subtracting rates of (1) surface infiltration, (2) depression storage, and (3) surface detention during overland flow. The runoff hydrograph obtained is routed through overland flow, gutter flow, and flow in building drains, catch basins, and component sewers.[5] Generalization of rainfall information by converting an intensity-duration-frequency curve into a hyetograph is illustrated in Fig. 15-5. An advanced

[5] A. L. Tholin and C. J. Keifer, The Hydrology of Urban Runoff, *Trans. Am. Soc. Civil Engrs.*, **125**, 1308 (1960).

peak in rainfall intensity is assumed in this case at three-eighths the time distance or storm duration from the beginning of appreciable precipitation, selection of a suitable fraction being based upon specific rainfall experiences.[6]

Figure 15-5 illustrates results obtained in the application of conversion and routing procedures developed by Tholin and Keifer[5] for the city of Chicago. Necessary calculations are based on (1) infiltration-capacity curves shown in Fig. 15-5; (2) depth of depression storage assumed at $\frac{1}{4}$ and $\frac{1}{2}$ inch, for example, and normally distributed about this mean depth, 50% of the area covered by depressions lying within 20% of the mean depth ($\sigma = \pm 14\%$); and (3) surface detention computed by Izzard's equation.[7]

$$D = 0.342[(7 \times 10^{-4}i + c_r)/s^{1/3}](lQ)^{1/3} \qquad (15\text{-}3)$$

where D is the surface detention in inches of depth, s is the slope of the ground, l is the distance of overland flow in feet, Q is the overland supply in inches per hour (cfs per acre), i is the intensity of rainfall in inches per hour, and c_r is a coefficient of roughness varying downward from 6.0×10^{-2} for pervious areas of turf, through 3.2×10^{-2} for bare, packed pervious areas and 1.2×10^{-2} for pavements, to 1.7×10^{-2} for flat, gravel roofs.

15-8   Empirical Formulations

Variations of c and i with time (time being a function of watershed area a and of other factors such as surface slope s) can be incorporated into overall runoff formulations developed empirically for given localities (Sec. 7-10). An example is McMath's formula $Q = cia^{4/5}s^{1/5}$ for St. Louis, Mo. If rainfall intensity i and resulting runoff ci are properly determined, over-all formulas should yield results comparable with the rational method.

As storm drains are actually constructed in a given community, it becomes possible to design stormwater systems for adjacent unsewered areas on the basis of (1) actual runoff measurements conducted in times of heavy rainfall or (2) surcharge experience with recorded storm intensities. In necessary calculations, it is important to identify possible downstream effects upon surcharge.

15-9   Layout and Hydraulic Design in Storm Drainage

The layout of storm drains and sanitary sewers follows much the same procedure. Street inlets must be served as well as roof and other property

[6] In Example 7-2, the maximum rainfall was clocked between the 30th and 35th minute from the beginning of a 120-minute storm: 32.5/120 = 2.2/8.
[7] C. F. Izzard, Hydraulics of Runoff from Developed Surfaces, *Proc. Highway Research Bd.*, **26**, 129 (1946).

drains connected directly to the storm sewers. How inlets are placed at street intersections to keep pedestrian crossings passable is indicated in Fig. 3-6. To prevent the flooding of gutters or to keep flows within inlet capacities, street inlets may be constructed also between the corners of long blocks. Required inlet capacity (Sec. 14-12) is a function of tributary area and its pertinent runoff coefficient and rainfall intensity.

Separate storm drains should proceed by the most direct route to outlets emptying into natural drainage channels. Easements or rights of way across private property may shorten their path. Manholes are included in much the same way and for much the same reasons as for sanitary sewers.

Surface topography determines the area tributary to each inlet. However, it is often assumed that lots drain to adjacent street gutters and thence to the sewers themselves. Direct drainage of roofs and areaways reduces the inlet time and places a greater load intensity upon the drainage system. Necessary computations are illustrated in Table 15-2 which accompanies Example 15-3.

Example 15-3. Determine the required capacity and find the slope, size, and hydraulic characteristics of the system of storm drains shown in the accompanying tabulation of location, tributary area, and expected storm runoff.

Capacity requirements are based upon the rainfall curves included in Fig. 15-5. The area is assumed to be an improved pervious one, and the inlet time is assumed to be 20 min. Hydraulic requirements include a value of $N = 0.012$ in Manning's formula and drops in manholes equal to $\Delta(d + h_v) + 0.2\Delta h_v$ (Eq. 14-18) for the sewers flowing full.

Columns 1–4 identify the location of the drains. The runs are continuous.

Column 5 records the area tributary to the street inlets discharging into the manhole at the upper end of the line.

Column 6 gives cumulative area tributary to a line. For example, in Line 2, Col. 6 is the sum of Col. 6, Line 1, and Col. 5, Line 2, or $(2.19 + 1.97) = 4.16$.

Columns 7 and 8 record the times of flow to the upper end of the drain and in the drain. For example, the inlet time to Manhole 1 is estimated to be 20 min, and the time of flow in Line 1 is calculated to be $340/(60 \times 3.94) = 1.5$ min from Col. 15/(60 × Col. 14). Hence the time of flow to the upper end of Line 2 is $(20 + 1.5) = 21.5$ min.

Column 9 is the mean intensity of rainfall during the inlet time (time of flow to the upper end) read from Fig. 15-5.

Column 10 is the weighted mean runoff coefficient for the tributary area.

Column 11 is Col. (9) × Col. (10). For example, for Line 1, $2.56 \times 0.508 = 1.30$.

Column 12 = Col. 11 × Col. 6. For example, the runoff entering Line 1 is $1.30 \times 2.19 = 2.85$ cfs.

Columns 13–16 record the chosen size and resulting capacity and flow velocity of the drains for the tributary runoff and available or required grade. For example, in Line 1, a grade of 6.42‰ and a flow of 2.85 cfs call for a 12-in. drain. This drain will have a capacity of 3.09 cfs and flow at a velocity of 3.94 fps.

Columns 17–21 identify the profile of the drain. Col. 17 is taken from the plan or profile of the street; Col. 18 = Col. 17 × Col. 14; Col. 19 is obtained from Eq. 14-18,

Table 15-2   Illustrative Computations for a Storm Drainage System (Example 15-3)

Line number (1)	Location of drain			Tributary area, acres, a		Time of flow min		Mean rainfall intensity, i in./hr (9)	Weighted mean runoff coefficient, c (10)
	Street (2)	Manhole Number		Increment (5)	Total (6)	To upper end (7)	In drain (8)		
		from (3)	to (4)						
1	A	1	2	2.19	2.19	20.0	1.5	2.56	0.508
2	A	2	3	1.97	4.16	21.5	1.9	2.45	0.518
3	B	3	4	3.05	7.21	23.4	1.3	2.35	0.532

Design

Profile

Line number (1)	Runoff, cfs, Q		Diameter, in. (13)	Slope, ‰ (14)	Capacity, cfs (15)	Velocity, fps (16)	Length, ft (17)	Fall, ft (18)	Drop in M.H., ft (19)	Invert elevation	
	Per acre ci (11)	Total (12)								Upper end (20)	Lower end (21)
1	1.30	2.85	12	6.42	3.09	3.94	340	2.18	0.00	86.46	84.28
2	1.27	5.28	18	2.71	5.93	3.35	340	0.92	0.42	83.86	82.94
3	1.25	9.02	24	1.50	9.48	3.02	440	0.66	0.46	82.48	81.82

the required drop in Manhole 2 being $\Delta(d + h_v) + 0.2\Delta h_v = [(1.5 + 0.17) - (1.0 + 0.24)] + 0.2(0.17 - 0.24) = 0.42$ ft; and Col. 21 = Col. 20 − Col. 19, Col. 20 furthermore being Col. 21 for the entrant line − Col. 19. For example, for Line 2, (84.28 − 0.42) = 83.86 and subsequently (83.86 − 0.92) = 82.94.

15-10 Hydraulic Design of Combined Sewers

The capacity design of combined sewers allows for maximum rate of sewage flow in addition to stormwater runoff. If entering rainwater is confined to roof water, the sanitary sewage flows are considerable items in required sewer capacities. The resulting system is sometimes called a roof-water system rather than a combined system. If the full runoff from storms of unusual intensity is carried away by the system, sanitary sewage flows become relatively insignificant items in required sewer capacity.

The hydraulic design of truly combined-sewerage systems and storm-sewerage systems is essentially the same. However, combined systems often include structures not ordinarily associated with separate systems. Some of these, namely, intercepters, inverted siphons, overflows, regulators, and stormwater stand-by tanks are discussed in Secs. 3-6, 8-8, and 14-11.

15-11 Operation and Maintenance of Drainage Systems

The principal problem in the operation and maintenance of sewers is the prevention and relief of stoppages.[1] Tree roots and debris accumulation are the main causes. Important, too, in areas of cohesionless soil is the entrance of sand and gravel through leaky joints and pipe breaks. Cement, mortar, and lime-mortar joints will not keep out roots as effectively as bitumastic hot-poured or factory-installed rubber joints. The plastic and other newer jointing materials are promising, but their long-time performance is still to be evaluated. Understandably, debris is more likely to accumulate in the upper reaches of sewers where flows are low and unsteady. Sharp changes in grade and junctions at grade are danger points. Grease from eating places and mud from construction sites, often discharged intermittently and in high concentration, are leading offenders. Well-scheduled sewer flushing is an obvious answer when system design cannot be altered.

In arctic (permafrost) regions, sewers as well as water pipes may have to be placed in *utilidors*. Combined sewers are no longer built in the United States.

15-12 Outfalls into Receiving Waters

Hydraulically and hydrographically, wastewater outfalls have much in common with water intakes from surface sources (Sec. 11-12). Studies of their location and design call for much the same hydrographic information and the application of essentially the same hydraulic principles. Involved in effective water-quality management is not merely the collection of clean water in the one instance and the dispersal of pollutional wastewater in the other, but the useful conservation of natural bodies of water as a whole whether they are rivers and lakes or the estuarine and coastal waters of seas and oceans.

Freshwater Streams. Shoreline release of wastewaters and treatment-plant effluents into rivers is rarely satisfactory. Nuisances often extend over many stream miles below the outfall. The wastes are poorly dispersed and hug one bank or the other without much mixing with river flows. In accordance with Falk's observations,[8] the distance of travel before a wanted dilution has been reached is

$$l = 7.7S^{1.32} \tag{15-4}$$

where l is the distance in feet below the point of discharge, and $S = Q/Q_w = c_w/c$ identifies the degree of dispersal of wastewaters along the axis of the pollutional plume (Fig. 15-6) in terms of the relative dilution or concentration of waste matters in the shoreline release (Q_w and c_w) and the mixture of river water with wastewater (c and Q) respectively. Dilution, for example, is not 100-fold until the wastes have traveled 3400 ft downstream.

How outlet orientation affects wastewater dispersal from single-jet releases into streams is sketched in Fig. 15-6 a, b, c, d. Because sewage is warm, it is relatively lighter than most receiving waters. Consequently, the sewage rises while it is being swept along by dominant river currents.[9] Understandably, countercurrent discharge produces better dispersion than cocurrent discharge, provided the energy of waste discharge is great enough to force the plume upstream in adequate dimension. In each instance, the pattern of dispersal is constructed from the vector sums of effective mean velocities. The concentration of waste substances within the plume cross-section can be visualized as a distribution curve or distribution surface (Fig. 15-6a). The area or volume beneath the curve or surface is then a measure of the total weight of waste substances in a given cross-section at right angles to the discharge axis. The weights of dissolved substances will stay substantially constant, because chemical diffusion is slow.

Freshwater Lakes. The release of wastewater into lakes creates problems of its own; among them, the more crucial relationship between water supply and wastewater disposal when lakes, as they often do, serve both purposes. Wind and thermal currents along with entrant and effluent

[8] L. L. Falk, Some Modes of Waste Dilution in Receiving Waters, *Proc. Sixteenth Purdue Ind. Wastes Conf.*, 126 (1962).
[9] T. R. Camp, *Water and Its Impurities*, Reinhold Publishing Corp., New York, 1963.

flows as well as Coriolis effects[10] establish more complex flow patterns in lakes than are encountered in streams (Vol. 2). Moreover, water masses are in delicate vertical and horizontal balance, and their response to

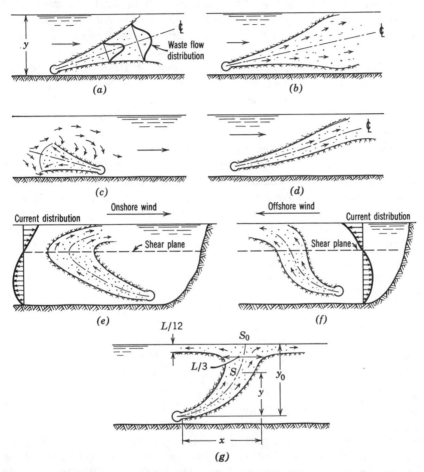

Fig. 15-6. Dispersion of wastewater jets. (After *Camp.*[9]) (*a*) Dispersion in stream, showing distribution. (*b*) Cocurrent dispersion in slow stream. (*c*) Countercurrent dispersion in slow stream. (*d*) Cocurrent dispersion in swift stream. (*e*) Dispersion in lake, onshore wind, summer stratification. (*f*) Dispersion in lake, offshore wind, summer stratification. (*g*) Dispersion in calm sea water.

external forces is consequently more sensitive and variable. The relative effects of onshore and offshore winds on wastewater outlets in deep water, sketched in Fig. 15-6*e* and *f*, are examples. Facing the prevailing currents,

[10] Named after Gaspard Gustave de Coriolis (1792–1843), French physicist, and concerned with the dynamic effects of the earth's rotation upon air and water currents.

but not necessarily the prevailing winds, recommends itself.[11] Fortunately, this does not require a change in the direction of outlets and their jets when wind directions are reversed. Perhaps most difficult to deal with is the reduction of dispersal when currents remain weak for protracted periods of time and stagnation swells the volume of heavily polluted water. Ice cover and winter stratification, too, intensify wastewater accumulation.

Marine Outfalls. Although the dispersal of fresh water into salt water is counter to the doctrine of freshwater conservation, marine outfalls have remained in common use (Fig. 15-8).[12] Dispersal and dilution for shore protection are optimized by subsurface horizontal discharge (Fig. 15-6g) and the use of multiple outlet ports with low head loss and wide enough spacing of staggered ports to avoid interference between rising wastewater columns. Flows through individual ports are equalized, within reason, in ways discussed and exemplified for manifolds (Vol. 2). However, the slope of the ocean bottom enters into necessary calculations. Proceeding stepwise from the most distant port, changing elevations, flows, and velocities and accompanying energy losses and gains are identified until the main outfall is reached. To reduce deposition of solids, peak-rate velocities should be 2 to 3 fps. If movable bulkheads are introduced at the terminus of diffuser branches, a recoverable cleaning device, such as a ball, can be driven through the outfall system. For ease of recovery, the device may be so constructed that it will float to the surface after passing through a diffuser.

Rawn, Bowerman, and Brooks[12] have shown that, in addition to the dimensionless ratios $S_0 = Q_0/Q$ and y_0/d (Fig. 15-6g), the hydraulic behavior of discharge jets near their ports is governed only by the Froude number $\mathbf{F} = v/\sqrt{gd}$, even though the Pi theorem suggests the formation of $6 - 2 = 4$ dimensionless numbers for the six variables, S_0, y_0, d, v or q, g', and ν. Here S_0 is the dilution at the head of the rising column, y_0 the depth of seawater above a port of diameter d, v the jet velocity, q being the rate of orifice flow and $g' = g(\rho_s - \rho)/\rho$, the apparent acceleration of the jet as a function of the buoyant force. The kinematic viscosity, ν, would be included as the sixth variable if observations and calculations did not show that the Reynolds number $\mathbf{R} = vd/\nu$ need not, in fact, be introduced as the fourth dimensionless number, because jet flow is usually turbulent

[11] G. C. Whipple, Effect of the Sewage of Rochester, N.Y., on the Genesee River and Lake Ontario under Recent Conditions, *Appendix 5, Report on the Sewage Disposal System of Rochester, N.Y.*, by Edwin A. Fisher, 1913.
[12] A. M. Rawn and H. K. Palmer, Predetermining the Extent of a Sewage Field in Sea Water, *Trans. Am. Soc. Civil Engrs.*, **94**, 1036 (1930); and A. M. Rawn, F. R. Bowerman, and N. H. Brooks, Diffusers for Disposal of Sewage in Sea Water, *Trans. Am. Soc. Civil Engrs.*, **126**, III, 344 (1961).

and the Reynolds number commensurately high. Circular ports with rounded entrances can be expected to flow full when $\mathbf{F} \geq 1.0$.

Among other phenomena of interest are: (1) horizontal jets follow a longer path, L, and achieve greater dilution, S_0, than vertical jets issuing from otherwise identical ports into the same depth of water; (2) the rising,

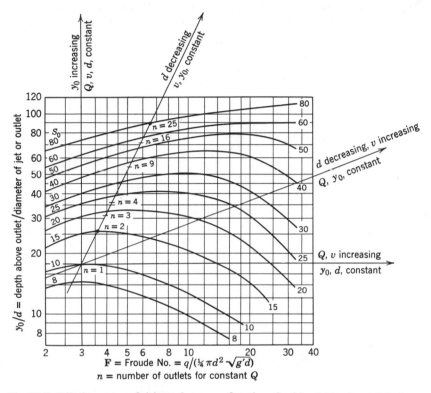

Fig. 15-7. Dilution at top of rising column as a function of y_0/d and F horizontal discharge (based on Rawn-Palmer data). Radial lines indicate ways for increasing dilutions S_0. (After *Rawn, Bowerman, and Brooks.*[12])

wastewater plume is the mirrored image of an initially horizontal jet of water falling through the air; (3) the outward diversion of the rising column is as much as a foot in 5 ft of travel; (4) the deeper the terminal port relative to the first port of the diffuser, the smaller, relatively, is the pressure differential at the terminal opening; and (5) the diameter of the rising column approaching the surface is about $\frac{1}{3}L$ and the thickness of the out-spreading pollutional field about $\frac{1}{12}L$. As is true for manifold flows of significant magnitude, the rate of discharge, q, through an orifice of area, a, supplied from a pipe of relatively considerable size is affected by the pipe velocity, or

$$q = c_d a[2g(h + v_p^2/2g)]^{1/2} = c_d a(2gh + v_p^2) \qquad (15\text{-}5)$$

Here g is the gravity constant, h the head differential and $v_p^2/2g$ the pipe-flow velocity-head at the port. The discharge coefficient c_d of the ports approaches 0.9 for well-rounded openings and 0.6 for sharp-edged openings when the ratio of $(v_p^2/2g)$ to $(h + v_p^2/2g)$ is small (about 1%). The magnitude of c_d decreases thence by 10% when the ratio increases to about 10%. After that, it drops rapidly to about half its highest value when the velocity head is as large as 50% of $(h + v_p^2/2g)$. An explanation for this discharge response to flow within the diffuser pipe is that the orifice becomes analogous to a side weir as v_p becomes large.[13]

The dilution S_0 at the top of a rising column is charted in Fig. 15-7. Ways of increasing S_0 suggested by Rawn, Bowerman, and Brooks are incorporated in this diagram.

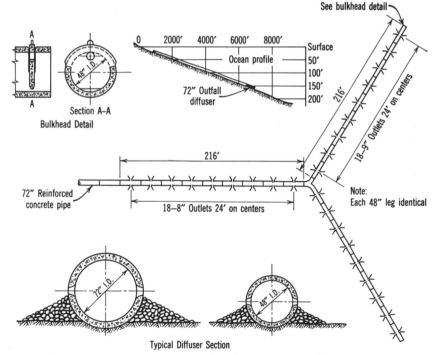

Fig. 15-8. Ocean outfall with branching diffusers, Los Angeles County Sanitation Districts, California. (After *Rawn, Bowerman, and Brooks*.[12])

[13] W. E. Howland, *Hydraulic Elements in Design of Perforated Filter Laterals*, Doctoral Thesis, Harvard University, 1939; see also J. S. McNown and E. Y. Hus, Application of Conformal Mapping to Divided Flow, *Proc. First Midwestern Conf. on Fluid Dynamics*, J. W. Edwards, Ann Arbor, Mich., 1951.

Example 15-4.   An outfall 42 in. in diameter discharges at a maximum rate of 45 mgd through thirteen 9-in. and nine 8.4-in. circular, sharp-edged ports at an average depth of 60 ft below mean sea level. Estimate the dilution at the top of the column for a discrete jet issuing from a 9-in. port near the end of the diffuser pipe.

1. The combined area of 9-in. ports is $13 \times 63.6 = 827$ sq in.
   The combined area of 8.4-in. ports is $9 \times 55.4 = 499$ sq in.
   The total port area is $(827 + 499) = 1326$ sq in. $= 9.21$ sq ft.
2. 45 mgd $= 45 \times 1.547 = 69.6$ cfs, and $v = 69.5/9.21 = 7.55$ fps.
3. $g' = g(1.025 - 1.00)/1.00 = 0.025 \times 32.2 = 0.805$ ft/sec^2, and
   $F = 7.55/\sqrt{0.805 \times 9/12} = 9.69$.
4. $y_0/d = 60/0.75 = 80$.
5. From Fig. 15-7, $S_0 = 56$.

Large outfalls are quite commonly reinforced concrete pipes, smaller ones are constructed of cast iron or steel pipe. Corrugated iron, wrought iron, wood stave, and vitrified-tile pipes have also been used. Simple circular ports have stood up well; more complicated outlets seeking greater dispersal have given some trouble.

The effects of wastewater discharge on the quality of receiving waters are discussed in Vol. 2; only the most immediate hydrographic and hydraulic aspects of outfall structures have been considered here. Resulting sewage fields and their extent can be defined only in terms of water quality.

CHAPTER 16

Machinery and Equipment

16-1 Scope of Enquiry

Pumps and blowers are important components of water supply and wastewater collection systems. They are much used, too, in water and wastewater treatment works. So are racks, screens, and flow meters. Ancillary equipment for air compressors and vacuum pumps includes air filters and air piping.

Because of their shared use, these essentially mechanical devices are discussed by themselves, rather than being considered in separate chapters. Yet, the reader will be made aware, through cross-reference to other chapters and sections, and to illustrations accompanying them, that other machines and equipment are assigned, by preference, to other parts of this book.

Many more pieces of equipment might be considered. However, the multiplication of descriptive matter would not be in keeping with the general purpose of this chapter, which is primarily concerned with significant principles that find expression in the hydraulic and process design of water and wastewater works.

16-2 Water and Wastewater Pumps

Pumps and pumping machinery serve the following purposes in water and wastewater systems:

1. *In water supply systems.*
    (a) Lifting water from its source (surface or ground), either immediately to the community through high-lift installations, or after low-lift to purification works (Sec. 2-11, Figs. 12-2, 4, 13, 15, 16).

(b) Boosting water from low-service to high-service areas, to separate, fire supplies, and to the upper floors of many-storied buildings (Secs. 2-9, 13-1 and Fig. 2-9).

(c) Transporting water through treatment works, draining component settling tanks and other treatment units, withdrawing deposited solids, supplying water (especially pressure water) to operating equipment and pumping chemical solutions to treatment units (Sec. 2-7 and Vol. 2).

2. *In wastewater systems.*

(a) Lifting wastewater from low-lying basements or low-lying secondary drainage areas into the main drainage system, and from uneconomically deep runs in collecting or intercepting systems into high-lying continuations of the runs or into outfalls (Fig. 3-1).

(b) Pumping out stormwater detention tanks in combined systems (Sec. 3-6).

(c) Lifting wastewater to and through treatment works, draining component settling tanks and other treatment units, withdrawing wastewater sludges and transporting them within the works to treatment units, supplying water to treatment units, discharging wastewater and wastewater sludge through outfalls, and pumping chemicals to treatment units (Sec. 3-8 and Vol. 2).

In addition to centrifugal and propeller pumps (Sec. 16-3), water and wastewater systems may include (1) displacement pumps, ranging in size from hand-operated pitcher pumps to the huge pumping engines of the last century built as steam-driven units; (2) rotary pumps equipped with two or more rotors (varying in shape from meshing lobes to gears and often used as small fire pumps); (3) hydraulic rams utilizing the impulse of large masses of low-pressure water to drive much smaller masses of water (one-half to one-sixth of the driving water) through the delivery pipe to higher elevations, in synchronism with the pressure waves and sequences induced by water hammer;[1] (4) jet pumps or jet ejectors, used in wells and dewatering operations, introducing a high-speed jet of air through a nozzle into a constricted section of pipe; (5) air lifts in which air bubbles, released from an upward-directed air pipe, lift water from a well or sump through an eductor pipe; and (6) displacement ejectors housed in a pressure vessel in which water (especially wastewater) accumulates and from which it is displaced through an eductor pipe when a float-operated valve is tripped by the rising water and admits compressed air to the vessel.

16-3   Centrifugal and Propeller Pumps

Today most water and wastewater pumping is done either by centrifugal pumps or by propeller pumps. These are usually driven by electric motors,

---

[1] The driving water may or may not be derived from the same source as the driven water. Where it is not, a dangerous cross-connection may be established.

less often by steam turbines, internal combustion engines, or hydraulic turbines. How the water is directed through the impeller determines the type of pump. There is (1) *radial flow* in open- or closed-*impeller pumps*, with volute or turbine casings, and single or double suction through the eye of the impeller, (2) *axial flow* in *propeller pumps*, and (3) *diagonal flow* in *mixed-flow, open-impeller pumps*. Propeller pumps are not centrifugal pumps. Both can be referred to as *rotodynamic* pumps.

Open-impeller pumps are less efficient than closed-impeller pumps, but they can pass relatively large debris without being clogged. Accordingly, they are useful in pumping wastewaters and sludges. *Single-stage pumps* have but *one impeller, multistage pumps* have *two or more*, each feeding into the next higher stage. Multistage turbine pumps and their motors may be submerged in deep wells (Fig. 10-3), or they may be driven by a shaft suspended from the prime mover situated on the floor of the pumping station (Fig. 10-5).

16-4 Pump Characteristics

Pumping units are chosen in accordance with *system heads* and *pump characteristics*. As shown in Fig. 16-1, the system head is the sum of the static and dynamic heads against the pump. As such, it varies with required flows and with changes in storage and suction levels. When a distribution system lies between pump and distribution reservoir, the system head responds also to fluctuations in demand. Pump characteristics depend on pump size, speed, and design. For a given speed N in revolutions per minute, they are determined by the relationships between the rate of discharge Q, usually in gallons per minute, and the head H in feet, the efficiency E in per cent, and the power input P in horsepower. For purposes of comparison, pumps of given geometrical design are characterized also by their specific speed N_s, the hypothetical speed of an homologous (geometrically similar) pump with an impeller diameter D such that it will discharge 1 gpm against a 1-ft head. Because discharge varies as the product of area and velocity, and velocity varies as $H^{1/2}$, Q varies as $D^2 H^{1/2}$. But velocity varies also as $\pi DN/60$. Hence $H^{1/2}$ varies as DN, or N varies as $H^{3/4}Q^{1/2}$, and the specific speed becomes

$$N_s = NQ^{1/2}/H^{3/4} \tag{16-1}$$

Generally speaking, pump efficiencies increase with pump size and capacity. Below specific speeds of 1000 units, efficiencies drop off rapidly. Radial-flow pumps perform well between specific speeds of 1000 and 3500 units; mixed-flow pumps in the range of 3500 to 7500 units; axial-flow pumps after that up to 12,000 units. As shown in Eq. 16-1, specific speeds at constant N increase more slowly with rising discharge than with falling head. This explains why axial-flow pumps are preferred in drainage and irrigation works and radial-flow pumps in municipal water works. For double-suction pumps, the specific speed is computed for half the capacity.

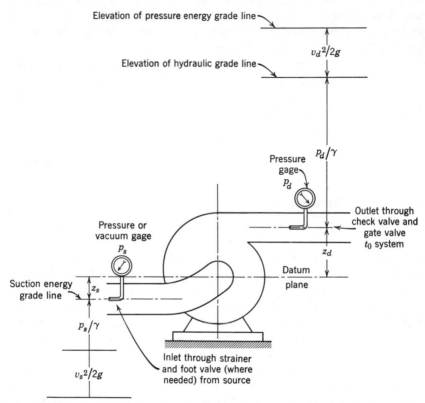

Fig. 16-1. Head relationships in pumping systems. System head $H = (z_d - z_s) + (p_d/\gamma - p_s/\gamma) + (v_d^2/2g - v_s^2/2g)$. For suction lift, p_s/γ and z_s are negative, and $v_s^2/2g$ is positive. For suction pressure, p_s/γ and $v_s^2/2g$ are positive, and z_s is negative.

For multistage pumps, the head is distributed between the stages. In accordance with Eq. 16-1, this keeps the specific speed high and with it, also, the efficiency.

16-5   Cavitation

Specific speed is an important criterion, too, of safety against cavitation, a phenomenon accompanied by vibration, noise, and rapid destruction of pump impellers. Cavitation occurs when enough potential energy is converted to kinetic energy to reduce the absolute pressure at the impeller surface below the vapor pressure of water at the ambient temperature.

Water then vaporizes and forms pockets of vapor that collapse suddenly as they are swept into regions of higher pressure. There is cavitation when inlet pressures are too low or pump capacity or speed of rotation is increased without a compensating rise in inlet pressure. Lowering a pump in relation to its water source, therefore, reduces cavitation. If we replace the head H in Eq. 16-1 by H_{sv}, the net positive inlet or suction head, namely, the difference between the total inlet head (the absolute head plus the velocity head in the inlet pipe) and the head corresponding to the vapor pressure of the water pumped (Table I-4), we obtain the *suction specific speed*[2]

$$S = NQ^{1/2}/H_{sv}{}^{3/4} \qquad (16\text{-}2)$$

for which certain general safe limits have been established by experiment.[3] The following are examples:

Single-suction pumps with overhung impellers $\qquad S \le 8,000\text{--}12,000$
Single-stage pumps with shaft through eye of impeller $\qquad S \le 7,000\text{--}11,000$
High-pressure, multistage pumps (single suction) $\qquad S \le 5,500\text{--}7,500$
High-pressure, multistage pumps with special
first-stage impeller (single suction) $\qquad S \le 7,500\text{--}10,000$

16-6 Performance Characteristics

Common performance characteristics of a centrifugal pump operating at constant speed are illustrated in Fig. 16-2. Note that the shut-off head is a fixed limit and that power consumption is minimum at shut-off. For this reason, centrifugal pumps, after being *primed* or filled with water, are often started with the pump discharge valve closed. As the head falls past the point of maximum efficiency, normal discharge, or rated capacity of the pump (point 1 in Fig. 16-2), the power continues to rise. If a centrifugal pump is operated against too low a head, a motor selected to operate the pump in the head range around maximum efficiency may be overloaded. Pump delivery can be regulated (1) by a valve on the discharge line, (2) by varying the pump speed mechanically or electrically, or (3) by throwing two or more pumps in and out of service to best advantage.

---

[2] $H_{sv} = p_s/\gamma + v_s^2/2g - p_w/\gamma$, where p_s/γ is the absolute pressure, v_s the velocity of the water in the inlet pipe, and p_w the vapor pressure of the water pumped, γ being the specific weight of water and g the gravity constant. The energy grade line is at a distance $h_s = p_a/\gamma - (p_s/\gamma + v_s^2/2g)$ from the eye of the impeller to the head delivered by the pump where p_a is the atmospheric pressure. The ratio H_{sv}/h_s where $h = p_a/\gamma - h_s$, is called the cavitation parameter.

[3] G. F. Wislicensus, R. M. Watson, and I. J. Karassik, Cavitation Characteristics of Centrifugal Pumps Described by Similarity Considerations, *Trans. Am. Soc. Mech. Engrs.*, **61**, 170 (1939); also G. F. Wislicensus, section on centrifugal pumps, *Mechanical Engineers' Handbook*, L. S. Marks, Editor, McGraw-Hill Book Co., New York, 1951.

What happens when more than one pumping unit is placed in service is shown in Fig. 16-2 with the help of a curve for the system head. Obviously, pumping units can operate only at the point of intersection of their own

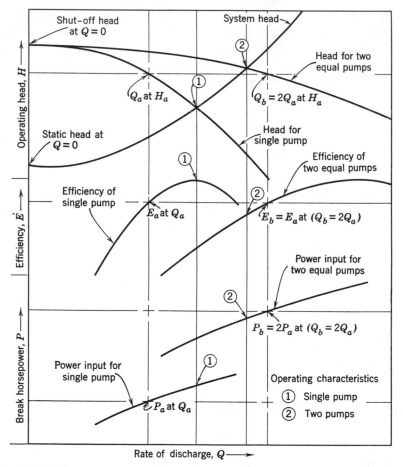

Fig. 16-2. Performance characteristics of single and twin centrifugal pumps operating at constant speed.

head curves with this head curve. In practice, the system head varies over a considerable range at a given discharge (Fig. 16-3). For example, where a distributing reservoir is part of a system and both the reservoir and the source of water fluctuate in elevation, (1) a *lower* curve identifies head requirements when the reservoir is empty and the water surface of the source is high, and (2) an *upper* curve establishes the system head for a full reservoir and a low water level at the source. How the characteristic curves for twin-unit operation are developed is indicated in Fig. 16-2. It should be noted that the two identical pumping units have not been selected with an eye to highest efficiency of operation in parallel. Character-istic curves for other multiple units are developed in the same way from the known curves of individual units.

Where most of the operating head is static lift, when the water is pumped through relatively short lengths of suction and discharge piping,

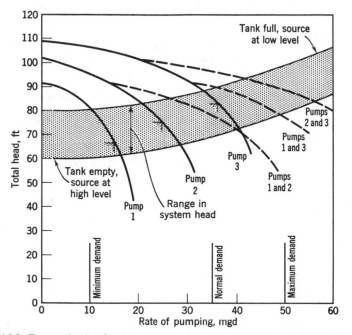

Fig. 16-3. Pump selection for the water supply described in Example 16-1. (After *Richard Hazen.*)

for example, there is little change in the system head at different rates of flow. In these circumstances, the head curve is nearly horizontal, and the discharge of parallel pumps is substantially additive. This is common in wastewater pumping stations in which the flow is lifted from a lower to an immediately adjacent higher level. Examples are pumping stations along intercepters or at outfalls.

By contrast, friction may control the head on pumps discharging through long force mains, and it may not be feasible to subdivide flows between pumping units with reasonable efficiency. Multispeed motors or different combinations of pumps and motors may then be required.

Because flows from a number of pumps may have to be fed through a different piping system than flows from any single unit, it may be necessary to develop characteristic curves for the different combinations of piping.

Example 16-1. A mill supply drawing relatively large quantities of water from a river is to deliver them at a fairly low head.[4] The minimum demand is 10 mgd, the normal 35 mgd, and the maximum 50 mgd. The river fluctuates in level by 5 ft, and the working range of a balancing tank is 15 ft. The vertical distance between the bottom of the tank and the surface of the river at high stage is 60 ft. The friction head in the pumping station and a 54-in. force main rises from a minimum of 1 ft at the 10-mgd rate to a maximum of nearly 20 ft at the 50-mgd rate. Make a study of suitable pumping units.

Hazen's solution of this problem is shown in Fig. 16-3. Three pumps are provided: No. 1 with a capacity of 15 mgd at 66-ft head; No. 2 with 25 mgd at 78-ft head; and No. 3 with 37 mgd at 84-ft head. Each pump has an efficiency of 89% at the design point.

The efficiencies at the top and bottom of the working range are listed in Table 16-1.

Table 16-1   Pumping Characteristics of System in Example 16-1

Pumps in service, No.	1	2	3	1 & 2	1 & 3	2 & 3
Rate of pumping, mgd	10	21	33.5	27	36	42
Head, ft	81	83	88	85	90	93
Efficiency, %	80	88˙	88	71, 86	35, 87	68, 84
Rate of pumping, mgd	15	25	37	34	43.5	49.5
Head, ft	66	78	84	80	85	89
Efficiency, %	89	89	89	82, 88	71, 89	79, 87
Rate of pumping, mgd	16.5	28.5	40.5	40	49.5	56.5
Head, ft	62	66	73	73	79	84
Efficiency, %	88	84	86	88, 88	83, 88	79, 89

Centrifugal pumps are normally operated with discharge velocities of 5 to 15 fps. The resulting average outlet diameter (in inches) of the pump, called the pump size, is $0.2\sqrt{Q}$, where Q is the capacity of the pump in gallons per minute.

16-7   Air Compressors and Vacuum Pumps

In addition to its role in ejectors and air lifts (Sec. 16-2), and in the operation of gates and valves, *compressed air* performs a number of other useful functions, among them the following:

1. *In water treatment systems* (Vol. 2).
   (*a*) Cleaning rapid filters by air scour.
   (*b*) Flushing out odors and gases.
   (*c*) Oxygenation and agitation in deferrization and demanganization units.
   (*d*) Agitation in coagulation and chemical-precipitation units.
   (*e*) Flotation of fine precipitates or light suspended solids.

[4] Richard Hazen, Pumps and Pumping Stations, *J. New England Water Works Assoc.*, **67**, 121 (1953).

2. *In wastewater treatment systems* (Vol. 2).
   (a) Agitation and oxygenation in activated-sludge units.
   (b) Selective resuspension of organic matter in grit chambers.
   (c) Separation of solids by flotation.
   (d) Suspension of solids in channels connecting treatment units.
   (e) Reaeration of receiving bodies of water.

16-8   Air Compression

In reference to air compression by a piston in a cylinder, the work done in compressing a unit volume of free air from atmospheric pressure to pressure p and volume v includes (1) the work of compression $\int p \, dv$, plus (2) the work of expulsion pv, minus (3) the work done on the piston by the incoming air $p_0 v_0$. In isothermal compression $pv = $ constant; in adiabatic compression $pv^n = pv^{1.40} = $ constant. Here $pv = RT$, R being the gas constant and $n = 1.40$ being the ratio of the specific heats of the air at constant pressure and constant volume.

Most air compressors employed in water and wastewater treatment works operate adiabatically. The work of compression can therefore be formulated as $\int p \, dv = \int_{v_0}^{v} \text{constant} \times v^{-n} \, dv = -\text{constant}(v_0^{1-n} - v^{1-n})/$ $(1 - n) = (pv - p_0 v_0)/(n - 1)$, because the constant equals both pv^n and $p_0 v_0^n$. It follows that the work done by the compressor is $[(pv - p_0 v_0)/(n - 1)] + pv - p_0 v_0$. Expressing v in terms of v_0 and substituting Q cfm of free air for v_0, the theoretical horsepower requirement P of the compressor is

$$P = \frac{144}{33,000} \frac{n}{n-1} p_0 Q \left[\left(\frac{p}{p_0}\right)^{(n-1)/n} - 1 \right] \qquad (16\text{-}3)$$

or

$$P = 0.22 Q [(p/14.7)^{0.283} - 1] \qquad (16\text{-}4)$$

for an atmospheric pressure of 14.7 psia and for $n = 1.40$. Because compressor efficiencies lie in the vicinity of 80%, the power requirement of a compressor handling 10^6 cu ft of free air per day (694 cfm) against a pressure of 7 psig is $P = 18.4$ hp theoretical and 23 hp actual. The corresponding energy requirement is 24 times as great, or 440 hp-hr theoretical and 550 hp-hr actual, or 330 kw-hr theoretical and 410 kw-hr actual. Understandably, the energy requirements of mechanical stirring devices are of the same order of magnitude for identical rates of flow.

Rotary and centrifugal blowers are commonly employed to deliver air at the pressures normally called for in water-treatment processes

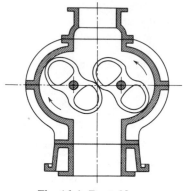

Fig. 16-4. Roots blower.

(Fig. 16-4). Reciprocal compressors feeding into storage tanks are used when higher pressures are needed in other operations.

16-9 Vacuum Pumps

In a sense a vacuum pump is a compressor taking suction from an enclosed vessel or chamber and generally discharging to the atmosphere. In this way the pressure within the chamber is lowered and ultimately held at a designated low absolute pressure by intermittent or continuous operation of the pump. Water and water condensates in the chamber are withdrawn from it through a barometric leg or tail pipe at least 34 ft tall and terminating in a trap or well open to the atmosphere. Thence the released water can be removed by gravity or pumping.

Vacuum pumps are essential to (1) the operation of vacuum filters in sludge dewatering; (2) the degasification of groundwater supplies; (3) the deactivation of corrosive waters, especially in hot-water systems; (4) the maintenance of high-suction lifts; (5) the operation of pipelines that rise above the hydraulic grade line; and (6) the functioning of specialized equipment serving gages or meters (rate-of-flow and pressure) and vacuum chlorination. Pressures above and below atmospheric are combined sequentially in seawater distillation plants and can add much to their economy (Vol. 2).

16-10 Air Filters

Air filters keep diffusers from being clogged and reduce wear and tear on compressors.[5] Two types are in general use: (1) viscous filters consisting of a mat of noncorrosive metal, glass wool, or hair covered with oil and (2) cloth filters. Viscous filters come in unit frames (20 in. square and about $4\frac{1}{2}$ in. thick) and are suspended in large rectangular frames. At face velocities as high as 300 fpm, their pressure loss is only $\frac{1}{8}$ to $\frac{3}{8}$ in. of water. Metallic filters are reconditioned by immersion in a cleansing bath and recoating with oil. Glass-wool and hair filters are discarded when they become clogged. Cloth filters are given face velocities of about 200 fpm and are cleansed by air backflow or by vacuum-cleaning devices. The probable dust loading of filters is 1 to 3 mg per 100 cu ft of air when the air intake is placed so as to avoid dusty areas such as driveways.

[5] *Handbook of Air Cleaning*, U.S. Atomic Energy Commission, Government Printing Office, Washington, D.C., 1952.

16-11   Air Piping

A satisfactory relation for the resistance of air piping can be derived from the Weisbach-Darcy equation for the flow of incompressible fluids: $h_f = f(l/d)(v^2/2g)$. A useful transformation to the flow of air as a compressible fluid includes the following substitutions.

1. $\Delta p = h_f \gamma/144$, where Δp is the pressure difference in psi and γ is the weight density of the air, 0.076 lb per cu ft at atmospheric pressure ($p_0 = 14.7$ psia) and an absolute temperature $T_0 = (60 + 459.6) = 520$ F, and varying directly with the absolute pressure p and inversely with the absolute temperature T, or $\gamma = 0.076\,(p/p_0)(T_0/T) = 2.71\,p/T$.

2. Because the weight of air transported is constant but varies in volume with its density, the rate of air flow in the pipe is $0.076Q/(2.71p/T) = 0.0282(T/p)Q$, where Q is the rate of flow of free air in cubic feet per minute. Furthermore, $Q = v \times 60 \times \pi D^2/(4 \times 144)$, where D is the diameter of the pipe in inches; and $T = 519.6(p/14.7)^{0.283}$ for adiabatic compression of the air.

The resulting equation is

$$\Delta p = \frac{flTQ^2}{38 \times 10^3 pD^5} .$$ (16-5)

Here f varies for new piping from 2.5×10^{-2} for 3-in. pipe to 1.6×10^{-2} for 18-in. pipe; for old piping from 4.9×10^{-2} for 3-in. pipe to 2.8×10^{-2} for 18-in. pipe.

As observed by Fritsche,

$$f = 4.8 \times 10^{-2} D^{0.027}/Q^{0.148}$$ (16-6)

for pipes less than 10 in. in diameter.

Example 16-2.   Find the pressure drop in 500 ft of 6-in. pipe transporting 500 cfm of free air under a pressure of 7 psig:

1. The absolute pressure of the air, $p = 7 + 14.7 = 21.7$ psia.
2. The absolute temperature of the air $T = 520(21.7/14.7)^{0.283} = 581$ F.
3. By Eq. 16-6, $f = 0.048 \times 6^{0.027}/(500)^{0.148} = 0.020$.
4. By Eq. 16-5, therefore, $\Delta p = 20 \times 10^{-3} \times 500 \times 581(500)^2/(38 \times 10^3 \times 21.7 \times 6^5) = 0.23$ psi.

The length of pipe that will produce the same loss of head as elbows and tees is approximated by the observational relationship:

$$l = 7.6D/(1 + 3.6D)$$ (16-7)

Similarly for globe valves commonly employed because of their tightness:

$$l = 11.4D/(1 + 3.6D)$$ (16-8)

16-12   Racks and Screens

Racks and screens are installed (1) in water intakes, to keep out leaves and the flotsam of lakes and streams, (2) in advance of water and waste-water pumps, to protect them against trash and other clogging substances, (3) ahead of wastewater treatment units or works and outfalls for untreated wastewater, to remove coarse, floating solids that make receiving waters unsightly and, because of their size, reduce the efficiency of chlorination.

16-13   Racks and Screens on Water Intakes

Trash *racks* are often included in dams and other intake structures. To facilitate cleaning, they are placed on a slope of 3 to 6 vertical to 1 horizontal below a working platform from which long-tined rakes can engage the bars to pull up the rakings. Three intake structures equipped with more or less self-cleaning *screens* are illustrated in Fig. 16-5: (1) a vertical screen constructed either of wire mesh or solely of vertical wires or bars in order to deprive leaves and other debris of purchase against horizontal elements, (2) an upward-flow screen that can be lifted into a vertical position for cleaning, and (3) a surface-wash screen.[6] A common arrangement of a different kind is to slide a pair of removable screens into vertical grooves in the walls and bottom of an inlet channel and to leave one in place while the other is being lifted out to flush off the collected debris with high-velocity water jets. Intake screens are normally constructed of 2- to 4-mesh screening, more rarely of screening with 6 meshes to the inch. An exception is a fine-mesh, rotating drum screen, called a

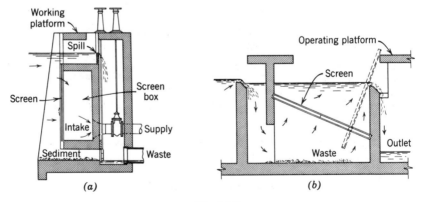

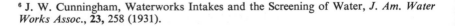

Fig. 16-5

[6] J. W. Cunningham, Waterworks Intakes and the Screening of Water, *J. Am. Water Works Assoc.*, **23,** 258 (1931).

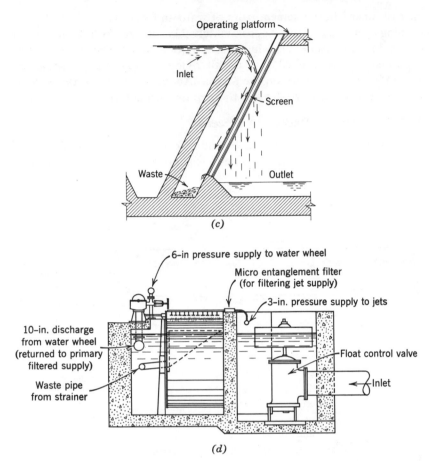

(c)

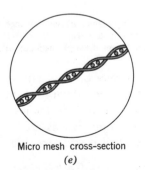

Micro mesh cross-section
(e)

Fig. 16-5. Racks and Screens on Water Intakes. (a) **Vertical rack cleaned by hand-operated long-tined rake;** (b) **inclined screen with upward flow (screen can be tilted for cleaning);** (c) **self-flushing inclined screen;** (d) **microstrainer;** (e) **cross-section of twinned mesh fabric for microstrainer.** [(a) to (c) after *J. W. Cunningham*; (d) and (e) after *P. L. Boucher*.]

microstrainer.[7] In this screen, pairs of warp and weft wires create 160,000 openings per square inch, approximately 23 μ in size. In tests at Denver, Colorado, lake water flowing radially outward through the screen deposited in excess of 90% of its filter-clogging microscopic organisms and 25% of its turbidity on the screen. About 3% of the water strained had to be recycled as washwater to keep the strainer in service.[8]

16-14 Wastewater Racks and Screens

A number of wastewater racks and screens are shown in Fig. 16-6. Coarse racks of steel bars are given clear openings $1\frac{1}{2}$ to $2\frac{1}{2}$ in. wide or

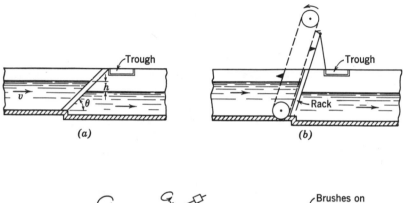

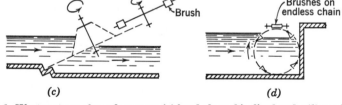

Fig. 16-6. Wastewater racks and screens: (a) hand-cleaned inclined rack; (b) mechanically cleaned rack; (c) brush-cleaned disk screen (*Riensch-Wurl*); (d) brush-cleaned drum screen (*Link-Belt Co.*), sewage leaves through open end of drum.

wider. Fine-rack openings may be as small as $\frac{1}{2}$ in. Screens are usually expected to collect waste matters down to $\frac{1}{16}$ in. in size, but some screens have openings as small as $\frac{1}{32}$ in. in their smallest, or controlling, dimension. They may be many inches long. Racks are cleared by hand with long-handled rakes, or by mechanical scrapers (Fig. 16-6a and b). To expand

[7] P. L. Boucher, Microstraining, *J. Inst. Water Engineers*, **5**, 561 (1951); Richard Hazen, Application of the Microstrainer to Water Treatment in Great Britain, *J. Am. Water Works Assoc.*, **45**, 723 (1953).
[8] G. W. Turre, Use of Microstrainer Unit at Denver, *J. Am. Water Works Assoc.*, **51**, 354 (1959).

the rack area, the bars are placed on a slope of 1 vertical to 1, 2, or 3 horizontal. Cage racks are arranged in pairs (in series) and lifted from the wastewater channel for clearing. Screens are rotated through the water as endless bands, disks, or drums and are cleaned by brushes, jets of water, or blasts of air (Fig. 16-6c and d). Hydraulic requirements are (1) that the approach velocity in the raking or screening channel shall not fall below a self-cleaning value (1.25 fps) or rise so high as to dislodge rakings or screenings (2.5 fps); and (2) that the loss of head through the rack or screen shall not back up the flow and place the entrant sewer under pressure.

The loss of head through racks and screens can be formulated as an orifice loss. As such, it is a function of the velocity head. Kirschmer[9] has suggested the following empirical relationship and coefficients for racks with differently shaped bars:

$$h = \beta(w/b)^{4/3} h_v \sin \theta \qquad (16-9)$$

Here h is the loss of head in feet, w the maximum width of the bars facing the flow, b the minimum width of the clear openings between pairs of bars, h_v the velocity head (in feet) of the water approaching the rack (face velocity), θ the angle of the rack with the horizontal, and β a bar shape factor (Fig. 16-6a). The coefficient β is 2.42 for sharp-edged rectangular bars, 1.83 for rectangular bars with semicircular upstream face, 1.79 for circular rods, 1.67 for rectangular bars with semicircular upstream and downstream faces, and 0.76 for bars with semicircular upstream face and tapering symmetrically to a small, semicircular, downstream face (teardrop). The geometric mean of the horizontal, longitudinal, approach velocity v and the component of the velocity at right angles to the rack ($v \sin \theta$), i.e., $v\sqrt{\sin \theta}$, is considered the effective velocity.

A rack of $\frac{3}{8}$-in. rectangular bars placed at an angle of 60 deg (sin θ = 0.866) to the horizontal and possessing clear openings of $\frac{3}{4}$ in., for example, produces a loss of head $h = 2.42(\frac{1}{2})^{4/3} h_v \times 0.866 = 0.83 h_v$ when the rack is clean.

The maximum head loss through clogged racks and screens is generally kept below 2.5 ft. The annual per capita rakings from racks with clear openings of 0.5, 1, and 2 in. are normally about 0.2, 0.1, and 0.02 cu ft respectively. Fine screens will remove 0.2 to 1.0 cu ft of screenings (2 to 20% of the suspended solids), depending upon the size of their openings. Peak collections of rakings and screenings may rise as high as five times the average quantity.

Rakings and screenings are unsightly and are made putrescible by much moisture and organic matter. Presses and centrifuges cannot reduce their

[9] O. Kirschmer, Untersuchungen über den Gefällsverlust an Rechen (Investigations of head loss in racks), *Trans. Hydraulic Inst.*, Munich, R. Oldenbourg, **21**, (1926).

water content much below 65%. Although they can be digested with other wastewater solids (Sec. 3-8), burial or incineration are more common. Their removal and separate disposal are avoided by comminuting them in the flowing sewage. A *cutting screen* or *comminuter* used for this purpose consists of a revolving, slotted drum equipped with knives that shear the coarse materials collected on the drum against a comb (Fig. 16-7a). The solids are chopped down until the wastewater carries them through the

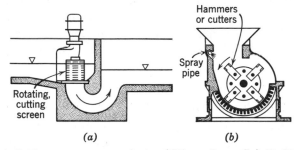

(a)   (b)

Fig. 16-7. (*a*) Cutting screen or comminuter. (*Chicago Pump Co.*) (*b*) Shredder or disintegrator. (*Jeffrey Co.*)

$\frac{3}{16}$-in. to $\frac{3}{8}$-in. slots of the drum and into the effluent channel. The returned solids are too small to clog pumps or to float at the water surface. Grinding rakings and screenings after they have been removed from the wastewater and returning them to the flowing sewage are also common practices. (Fig. 16-7*b*).

16-15 Flow Meters and Regulators

Hydraulic meters and regulators are installed in water and wastewater systems either as fixed units built into conduits and other components of existing works or as devices employed here and there in studies of system performance. Examples of fixed units in water systems are venturi meters, flow nozzles, and orifice plates installed in pipe lines, and mechanical meters inserted in service lines. Examples of devices employed in testing system performance are (1) hydrant pitometers (Sec. 13-5) in connection with fire-flow studies, (2) pitot static tubes or pitometers for velocity traverses in large pipes in leakage or water-waste surveys, (3) built-in, by-pass meters around controlling valves, and (4) mechanical meters inserted in hose lines connecting pairs of hydrants to record flows around a closed valve into isolated portions of a distribution system under test.

Venturi meters operate without much difficulty in force mains carrying wastewaters. So do magnetic flow meters.[10] In the measurement of

[10] R. H. Babcock, The Magnetic Flow Meter, *Water and Sewage Works*, **104**, 380 (1957).

open-channel flow, flumes, such as the Parshall[11] and Palmer-Bowlus[12] flumes, take the place of venturi meters; weirs of many kinds including proportional-flow weirs (Vol. 2) are substitutes for orifices; and nozzles, such as the Kennison nozzle,[13] share the characteristics of flow nozzles.

For all but mechanical and magnetic flow meters, velocity and discharge formulations emanate from Bernoulli's theorem and the equation of continuity of flow. A coefficient converts theoretical relationships into practical formulas. Magnetic flow meters register the voltage generated when waters or wastewaters contain enough salt to become conductors moving at right angles to a magnetic field. Their performance is based upon Faraday's law of electromagnetic induction. Head losses are understandably small.

Mechanical meters usually contain moving parts such as nutating disks, that displace known amounts of water as the part is revolved by the flowing water. Turbine or propeller units may be substituted and are instruments of choice in the large channel of compound meters, a parallel channel for small flows being gaged by a displacement or a turbine meter until the pressure drop becomes large enough to open a bypass into the large channel. Mechanical meters operate with relatively high head losses because much energy is required to rotate the displacement device or turbine and to drive the gear train operating the clocklike register. Pressure drops through disk meters are approximated by the following equation:

$$\Delta p = 0.01 Q^2/d^{3.33} \qquad (16\text{-}10)$$

where Δp is the pressure drop through the meter in psi, Q the flow in gpm, and d the nominal size of the meter inlet in inches. Normal test and operating flows run from 1 to 20 gpm for a $\frac{5}{8}$-in. meter (minimum test flow $\frac{1}{4}$ gpm) up to 48 to 100 gpm for a 6-in. meter (minimum test flow 12 gpm). Mechanical meters are generally expected to register $100 \pm 2\%$ of the water passing through them under normal operating conditions and at least 90% under minimum test-flow conditions. In accordance with Eq. 16-10, the pressure drop is about 7 psi at average operating flows. At the upper limits of normal flow, the pressure drop is generally required to be no more than 25 psi. Compound meters cover a wide range of flows.

[11] R. L. Parshall, The Parshall Measuring Flume, *Colorado Agr. Exp. Sta. Bull.* 423 (1936).
[12] H. K. Palmer and F. D. Bowlus, Adaptation of Venturi Flumes to Flow Measurement in Conduits, *Trans. Am. Soc. Civil Engrs.*, **101**, 1195 (1936).
[13] K. R. Kennison, New Type Open-Nozzle for Measurement of Sewage Flow, *J. Boston Soc. Civil Engrs.*, **21**, 1 (1934).

CHAPTER 17

Optimization Techniques

17-1 Objectives of Optimization

Instead of concentrating on hydrologic and hydraulic equipment, constructions, and systems, the present chapter gives way to a consideration of sets of functional relationships, or models, for examining and optimizing the degree to which a prototype system, if constructed, will serve the community. However, service to the community is difficult to measure, for the same reasons that it is difficult to educe with rigorous and unambiguous mathematical precision the aim of an engineering project within a given economy. Although simple engineering systems may pose no serious problems of economic evaluation, multivariate systems, exemplified by multipurpose, multistructured, water-resources schemes, normally introduce a complex of questions to which there is no easy answer. Composing this complex are questions of the following kind: Should national or merely regional interests be served? Should budgetary constraints be imposed? Should income redistribution be a component of the objective? At what rate of interest and for what time horizon should the project be evaluated? What benefits should be included in the project formulation? And, of central importance, should system performance be measured by monetary profit, a benefit-cost ratio, or more intricately related parameters, such as the reduction of hunger, disease, and poverty? A final question might be: How should the effects of hydrologic and economic uncertainty be treated?

For reasons of space, the specification of project rationale will be bypassed in favor of proceeding directly to a consideration of techniques that are useful for sorting out sets of design alternatives and selecting one that, by meeting imposed constraints, will define a feasible solution and satisfy the objective of the system to a greater extent than any other alternative. Briefly, therefore, the techniques to be discussed must identify the optimal, or near-optimal system.

System components in which money can be invested to change the response of the system are *decision variables*. Typical variables in the development of surface water resource systems, for example, are dam size, operating rules for the release of reservoir waters, storage allocation for flood control, treatment plant capacity, conduit routes and sizes, and target levels for community water supply. The decision variables can be physical entities, parameters of a rule curve, or economic constraint levels. They can be continuously variable or, like the diameter of a cast-iron pipe, limited to discrete (commercially available) increments. The process of *systems design* is equivalent to assigning a set of numerical values to each element of the set of decision variables. For many systems, an index of performance can be written, exactly or approximately, as an explicit function of the decision variables, so that

$$y = f[x_1, x_2, \ldots, x_n] \qquad (17\text{-}1)$$

where y is the performance index and the individual components of the function, x_i, are the decision variables. If the function has continuous first and second partial derivatives, it is a straightforward problem in the calculus to write the first-order condition for an optimum, namely,

$$\partial f/\partial x_i = \partial f/\partial x_1 = \partial f/\partial x_2 = \cdots = \partial f/\partial x_n = 0 \qquad (17\text{-}2)$$

and to investigate the determinant of second partial derivatives

$$\begin{vmatrix} \partial^2 f/\partial x_1{}^2 & \partial^2 f/\partial x_1\,\partial x_2 & \cdots & \partial^2 f/\partial x_1\,\partial x_n \\ \partial^2 f/\partial x_1\,\partial x_2 & \partial^2 f/\partial x_2{}^2 & \cdots & \partial^2 f/\partial x_2\,\partial x_n \\ \partial^2 f/\partial x_1\,\partial x_n & \cdots & \cdots & \partial^2 f/\partial x_n{}^2 \end{vmatrix}$$

to confirm a maximum or minimum.[1] In this model the decision variables, x_i, are unconstrained and can assume any values.

17-2   Production Functions and Technologic Efficiency

Economists often call the production function the technological function, because it represents the component of the analysis provided by the engineer for the guidance of the economic planner. The development of such a function is illustrated in Fig. 17-1 *a, b, c*, for a single-purpose

[1] For the 2-variable case, $y = f(x)$; d^2f/dx^2 is negative at a maximum, positive at a minimum, and zero at a point of inflection. See J. M. Henderson and Richard Quandt, *Microeconomic Theory*, McGraw-Hill Book Co., New York, 1958, p. 272.

reservoir. As there shown, the *input vector* X is the dam size, reservoir capacity, or construction cost. In more general terms, the components of X are manpower, capital, raw materials, or any other constituent of the production process. As a consequence of the production process, the vector components generate a large number of alternative output vectors; in our example, possibly, community water supplies, water power, flood

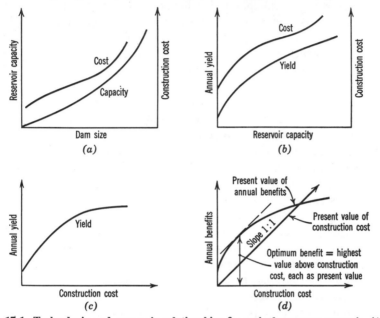

Fig. 17-1. Technologic and economic relationships for a single-purpose reservoir. (After Dorfman.[2]) (a) Reservoir capacity and construction cost as a function of dam size. (b) Annual water yield and construction cost as a function of reservoir capacity. (c) Annual yield as a function of construction cost. This is the production function. (d) Annual benefits as a function of construction cost, both on a present-value basis. *Not to scale.*

control, or recreational waters. If two alternative output vectors are to be considered, such as community water supply Y and flood control Z, the vectors are compared, element by element. If all the elements of one vector, Y for instance, equal or exceed the corresponding elements of Z, then Y is said to be efficient, Z wasteful. If more than two output vectors can be generated, all but one vector are more or less wasteful. If any components of the output vector represent undesirable elements, such as pollutants, they will rank lower (i.e., have smaller magnitudes) in the efficient vector than in the wasteful vectors.[2]

[2] A. A. Maass, M. M. Hufschmidt, Robert Dorfman, H. A. Thomas, Jr., S. A. Marglin, and G. M. Fair, *The Design of Water Resource Systems*, Harvard University Press, Cambridge, Mass., 1962, p. 90.

For every input vector X, there exists an efficient output vector Y; the components x_i and y_j define a locus of efficient points, namely, the technological function. The function expresses the productive capacity of the system for each array of input quantities X (Fig. 17-1c). That is why it is also called the production function.

Another approach to a study of production is to consider a fixed output vector, say Z (electrical energy, for instance), the input vectors X (water power) and Y (steam power) being candidates for producing Z. If the elements of X and Y are obtained at non-negative costs, that input vector is efficient for which each element is less than or equal to the corresponding element of the other, or more generally, all the others.

There are many shortcomings in this simple functional formulation. Most damaging is the fact that a production function cannot be written for an overwhelming number of real production processes. Even if the general form of the function were known, random or stochastic influences in the production process would generally require the inclusion of statistical measures or components in the function. In the simplest case, in putting stream flow to use, for example, each of the input and output components could be described by a pertinent statistical distribution, say the Gaussian or normal distribution (Sec. 4-6) for which each of the several input and output components would require a mean and variance. To compare input or output vectors in these circumstances, it becomes necessary to specify a desirable *direction* of inequality for the statistical moments, i.e., an increase in the mean of one vector over the others, or a decrease in the variance of one vector over the others. For the normal distribution, it might be proposed that expectation of output is desirable; whereas uncertainty, measured by the output variance, is undesirable. Understandably, the vector with maximum expected output is not necessarily the most desirable vector, because maximum expectation may be associated with a large variance or band of uncertainty. This leads to a further criticism of the production function, namely, its inability to distinguish between output vectors when their inequalities are not all in the desirable direction.

Even with these shortcomings, sanitary engineers traditionally deal with technological functions, a typical one being the storage-yield relationship for a reservoir. From a mass curve analysis of the hydrologic record (Sec. 8-3), the engineer derives a function giving the storage required for different levels of yield or, conversely, the yields assured by different levels of storage. Traditionally, storage, or input, is recorded in volume units; it could just as well be stated in dollars because there exists a *mapping* (i.e., the existence of a direct functional dependence without uncertainty) between dollars and units of storage for any reservoir site.

17-3   The Utility Function

The utility, objective, or ranking function (Fig. 17-1*d*) contains, explicitly or implicitly, all the information required for a rational *decision maker* to rank or select among the alternatives. The political, social, economic, environmental, and technologic features of a project are blended into a single quantifiable objective by the utility function. The ranking permits a comparison of two output vectors when the inequalities between their several components do not go in the same or desirable direction. If the utility ascribed to each of two vectors is identical, the decision maker is said to be indifferent between them. Nevertheless, the alternatives are not incomparable. A typical objective for a water resource development is to maximize utility; utility, in turn, is a scalar or numerical quantity derived, for instance, from net benefits (gross benefits less cost) discounted to present value over the economic time horizon for the enterprise (Fig. 17-1*d*). In some formulations, optimization of a linear combination of the mean and standard deviation of benefits might be the objective.[3]

It is reasonable to require that the first derivative of the utility function for money be everywhere positive. The behavior of the second derivative is more erratic, because *aversion to risk* (or *propensity to insure*) varies markedly from person to person or, for one person, as a function of the money in hand. This is reflected by the local convexity or concavity of the utility function, i.e., by its second derivative. Constructing a utility function for a large engineering enterprise is difficult, but the difficulty must be surmounted if rational design decisions are to be made.

17-4   The Meaning of Optimization

Optimal design can be defined as arriving at the set of decisions that are constrained to lie on the production function and that confer the maximal (or minimal) value on the utility or objective function (Fig. 17-1*d*). The optimal design is so constrained, because only efficient input and output vectors are considered. In this sense, optimization is a superposition of the objective and technologic functions. All design decisions satisfying the technologic function are candidates for further examination and ranking by means of the objective or utility function.

Specification of the objective function in water resource development is not wholly within the province of the design engineer or economic planner. Instead it lies, more generally, within the purview of legislative

[3] Such analytical simplicity does not obtain in all utility functions. As a homely illustration, the utility of an individual for money is different for his last dollar than for his hundredth dollar, and both are different from the utility of his millionth dollar.

or administrative agencies of government. The objectives of such agencies may differ at different levels of government. Typically, the legislative authorization and agency policy set forth the design criteria; in the terminology of operations research, these are tantamount to constraints on the input and output vectors and specification of the utility or objective functions. The objective might be to maximize one of the following: (1) the benefit-cost ratio; (2) the expected value of net benefits; (3) income redistribution in favor of some segment of the population; or (4) the expected value of gross benefits. If constraints on performance (output) or cost (input) are incorporated, the objective might be selected, furthermore, from the following possibilities: (1) maximization of expected value of net benefits subject to an input or budgetary constraint; (2) minimization of cost subject to an output constraint; or (3) maximization of a benefit-cost ratio subject to budgetary constraints, or output constraints, or both.

A measure of risk aversion might be introduced by considering combinations of the moments or other statistical parameters of system performance. For normally distributed net benefits, for instance, Thomas[4] has devised a model in which an insurance or balancing fund is augmented by output accruals from surpluses during profitable periods and depleted by penalties for output shortages during unprofitable periods. The initial contribution to the balancing fund, imposed at the outset of the economic life of the project, combines technologic, economic, and sociologic parameters, and depends on the performance characteristics of the system, the discount rate, the economic time horizon for the project, and a measure of risk aversion or similar purpose. Pratt[5] has developed a model for a known analytical utility function, continuous in its first and second derivatives, in which a measure of risk aversion is based on the concavity of the utility function. These, or other, indices of risk aversion can be incorporated into suitably written objective functions and make it possible to maximize a combination of the mean, standard deviation, and higher statistical moments of the benefits. Generally, the coefficient of the standard deviation is negative when it appears in an objective function, because the performance of the system is penalized by variability; variability, in turn, is measured by the output standard deviation.

17-5 Present Value

The two economic parameters to which explicit reference has been made, namely, interest rate and economic time horizon, find expression

[4] Harold A. Thomas, Jr., A Method of Accounting for Benefit and Cost Uncertainties in Water Resource Project Design, *Memorandum*, Harvard University, 1958.
[5] John W. Pratt, Risk Aversion in the Small and in the Large, *Econometrics*, **32,** 122 (1964).

in the present value PV. If the value of a given project or investment worth $y(t) = A$ dollars at some remote time t is discounted at a rate $k = r/100$, its value at any time $t_i < t$ is reduced at a rate $dy/dt = ky$. Accordingly, integration between the limits $y(0) = PV$ and $y(t) = A$ establishes the present value of the project from the relationship

$$\ln y - \ln A = -kt.$$

Hence,

$$PV = A \exp\left[-(r/100)t\right] \tag{17-3}$$

Because interest is not compounded continuously in actual practice, Eq. 17-3 is only a convenient and approximate representation of the exact computation of present value when interest (or discount) is compounded at frequent intervals. For values based upon annual interest payments, tables of present values or a simple computer program will provide the required information. If the economic life of an engineering project is T years, each year's receipts or their equivalent in benefits are discounted to zero time and summed. The total is called the present value of gross benefits. To evaluate net benefits, the costs of the project are subtracted. Capital cost is incurred at time zero so that it is not discounted. By contrast, annual or periodic operation, maintenance, and replacement (OMR) costs are discounted. Thus, for the T intervals with an expected gross benefit B_i, an OMR charge C_i, and a capital cost K incurred at zero time, the discounted or present value, PV, of net benefits is

$$PV = (B_1 - C_1)\exp\left(-r/100\right) + (B_2 - C_2)\exp\left(-2r/100\right) + \cdots$$
$$+ (B_T - C_T)\exp\left(-T/100\right) - K,$$

or

$$PV = \sum_{j=1}^{T}(B_j - C_j)\exp\left(-jr/100\right) - K \tag{17-4}$$

It follows that the *average* or *expected* value of the present value PV is $\overline{PV} = (1/T)\left[\sum_{j=1}^{T}(B_j - C_j)\exp\left(-jr/100\right) - K\right]$ which becomes $\overline{PV} = (1/T)\left[\sum_{j=1}^{T}[(B_j - C_j)/(1 + r/100)^j] - K\right]$ when interest is compounded annually. Writing $\mu_B = (1/T)\sum_{j}^{T}(B_j - C_j)$ for the mean annual net benefit,

$$PV(\mu_B) = \frac{\mu_B[1 - (1 + r/100)]^{-T}}{r/100} = \mu_B\beta(r, T) \tag{17-5}$$

Here, $\beta(r, T)$ is a function of the economic parameters r and T, increasing as T increases and decreasing as r increases.

Typical values for the economic time horizon, T, range from 25 to 100 years for engineering projects (Sec. 5-2). Selecting a suitable discount rate is rarely an easy economic decision. With large expenditures, financed by government funds or bond issues, consideration of long-term repayments, including the fact that later generations will continue to enjoy the benefits of the project, establishes a social rate of discount normally lower than the commercial market rate. Many design analyses are made at several rates. The interest rate is considered a parameter of the economic analysis, typical lower and upper boundaries being $2\frac{1}{2}$ and 6% per annum.[6]

17-6   Further Implications of Risk and Uncertainty

The indifference-to-risk level imputes a measure of risk aversion to the decision maker, indicating that expectation of performance need not, indeed cannot, be the sole measure of system design. For alternatives designated 1, 2, and 3, and returns or benefits normally distributed with mean μ_i and standard deviation σ_i, such that $\mu_1 < \mu_2 < \mu_3$ and $\sigma_1 = 0 < \sigma_2 < \sigma_3$ (the standard deviation σ_1 being set to zero), the question to be answered is which of the three alternatives should be chosen. Based on expectation alone, the return from the third alternative (largest μ and σ) is greatest, and would become the choice if the objective is maximization of the expected return. However, if the larger variability is to be taken into account, a risk factor must be introduced to devaluate alternative 3. One way to do this is to define a new measure of *worth*, v, such that $v_1 = \mu_1 - \lambda\sigma_1$; $v_2 = \mu_2 - \lambda\sigma_2$; and $v_3 = \mu_3 - \lambda\sigma_3$; wherein λ is a measure of risk aversion. For $\lambda = 0$, there is indifference to risk, the worth of the investment being given by its expectation alone. For $\lambda < 0$ or negative, there is averseness to insurance; and for $\lambda > 0$ or positive, there is averseness to risk. For more complicated outcome distributions than the normal, statistical moments higher than the second might be required if a *worth function* is to be written for ranking the alternatives.

A large literature in classical, and modern economics is concerned with the development and manipulation of utility functions.[7] The assumption of nineteenth-century economists that the consumer possesses a *cardinal* measure of utility, making him capable of assigning to every commodity a *cardinal number* (1, 2.7, 3, etc.), representing the associated utility, led to unacceptable conclusions. Among them was not only the conclusion that traditionally incomparable utilities, but also differences between them,

[6] S. A. Marglin, The Social Rate of Discount and the Optimal Rate of Investment, *Quart. J. Econ.*, **77**, (1963); also Footnote 2, p. 48.
[7] R. D. Luce and Howard Raiffa, *Games and Decisions*, John Wiley & Sons, New York, 1957.

could be compared.[8] Such virtues as inhere in the theory of cardinal utility can acquire useful meaning, however, on the basis of the much weaker assumptions attaching to a scheme of *ordinal utilities*. An *ordinal scheme* (1st, 2nd, 3rd, etc.) only requires that the consumer be able to rank commodities in a transitive mode, i.e., to list standard quantities of available commodities in decreasing order of desirability. With this ranking, the consumer's behavior can be predicted as accurately as though he possessed an acceptable cardinal measure of utility.

Ordinal scales of measurement are familiar from other disciplines. Moh's scale for the scratch hardness of minerals is an example.[9] Based on the theory of ordinal utility is the fact that for an ordinal utility function

$$U = U(x_1, x_2, \ldots, x_n) \tag{17-6}$$

where the x_i components are decision variables, the set of decisions that optimizes the utility

$$U^* = U^*(x_1{}^*, x_2{}^*, \ldots, x_n{}^*) \tag{17-7}$$

is invariant under a monotonic (nonmodal) transform of the original utility function. Useful, too, is the *pseudo-ordinal* utility function proposed by von Neumann[10] for situations characterized by uncertainty. Starting from the proposition that two outcomes, A and B, assigned arbitrary utilities U_A and U_B, respectively, such that $U_A > U_B$, because the outcome A is preferred to the outcome B, von Neumann has shown (1) that this illustrates an important feature of utility functions, namely, that the assignment of utility follows the determination of preference and not conversely, and (2) that a third utility U_C is strictly determined by the other utilities, although they are arbitrary, and by the level of the probability of indifference.[11] Thus U_C is constrained to lie between U_A and U_B, or $U_A \leq U_C \leq U_B$, U_C being called the *certainty equivalent* of the uncertain outcomes A and B. Once determined, the certainty equivalent can be manipulated in the same fashion as the original arbitrary utilities.

[8] In this sense, it became feasible not only to compare incomparables, apples and oranges for instance, but also to assign numerical differences to comparisons, stating, for example, that apples are preferred to oranges twice as much as pears are preferred to peaches.

[9] Proposed by the German mineralogist Friedrich Moh (1773–1839).

[10] John von Neumann and Oskar Morgenstern, *Theory of Games and Economic Behavior*, Princeton University Press, Princeton, 1944. John von Neumann (1903–1957), Hungarian-American mathematician, was a leader in the theory of operations research, high-speed computers, and many other branches of mathematics.

[11] The reasoning behind the conclusion can be illustrated as follows. If A is a successful investment, B an unsuccessful investment, and C no investment, and if an investment is made, either A or B obtains. If the probability of a successful investment is p, then every investor has a characteristic value of p such that he is indifferent between not investing and participating in the investment or lottery, i.e., $U_c = pU_A + (1 - p)U_B$. For a conservative investor, p approaches unity; for a gambler, p lies close to zero.

For example, if U_F is the certainty equivalent corresponding to uncertain outcomes D and E, the two certainty equivalents U_C and U_F can be compared in the usual fashion. For certainty equivalents, preference follows utility, thereby differing from the construction of the transitive ranking of the underlying ordinal utility scale. However, von Neumann showed that the induced utilities can be operated upon in the usual way and can lead to meaningful and important results in decision making. Subsequent sections of this chapter will consider the formalisms whereby the optimal design decisions, given by the starred variables in the optimal utility function U^* (Eq. 17-7), can be determined exactly or approximately.

17-7   Models and Economic Decision Points

A model is a convenient representation of the relevant factors characterizing a process or entity. For simple prototype systems, involving few components and relationships between components, it is often possible to intuit those features of the prototype that should be preserved in the model. For sophisticated systems, in which the components are highly interdependent, prior determination of the model's relevant characteristics is often impossible, whence the model implies a sequence of trial-and-error and frequent adjustment until it is satisfactorily validated. Models are frequently used as aids to elucidation in the engineering sciences (Vol. 2). In operations research and engineering, models are aids in evaluating system performance. Churchman, Ackoff, and Arnoff[12] have discussed three types of models:

1. An *iconic*[13] model that looks like the prototype is the simplest type. It is exemplified by the familiar representations of atoms and crystals, and by a blueprint or scale model of an engineering structure.

2. An *analog* model replaces prototype properties with quantities bearing the same relations to each other as do those of the prototype, but they are easier to measure or visualize. Examples are an organization chart showing the relative position of each employee in a firm, and the slide rule with logarithmic scales that transform additions into multiplications.

3. A *symbolic* model neither resembles nor imitates prototype systems, but replaces the relevant features of a system by a set of mathematical relationships. In studying mechanics, for example, a free body is isolated by excising a segment of the system and considering all the forces acting upon it. The forces are represented by vectors or, symbolically, by their algebraic equivalents. The set of equations identifying equilibrium and conservation of energy and momentum defines this symbolic model. In

[12] C. W. Churchman, Russell Ackoff, and E. L. Arnoff, *Introduction to Operations Research*, John Wiley & Sons, New York, 1957.
[13] From the Greek *eikonikos*, image; i.e., looking like the prototype.

operations research and engineering, symbolic models can be further subdivided into *simulation, iterative,* or *analytic* formulations.

Models chosen are generally those that evaluate rather than elucidate the performance of engineering systems. In dealing with rainfall, for instance, the engineering hydrologist is more concerned with an adequate statistical representation of precipitation than with the basic details of the underlying hydrologic and meteorologic phenomena. However, he should remain aware of the fact that the work of descriptive hydrologists is essential to statistical as well as scientific progress.

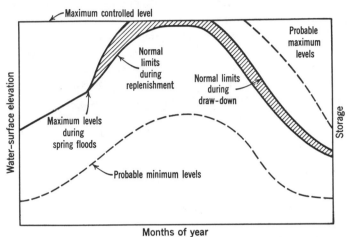

Fig. 17-2. Rule curve for reservoir operation.

The present chapter is concerned only with symbolic models derived for use in operations research and engineering. A symbolic model consists of (1) *components,* (2) *relations,* and (3) *variables.*

1. The *system components* are members of the set of decision variables and represent structures or physical entities in the prototype. For example, a reservoir, a pipeline, a hydroelectric generating structure, and a waste-water treatment plant might be components of a multipurpose water resource system.[14]

2. The *system relations* are formalisms that monitor or govern the operation of the model and are frequently displayed by a *rule curve* (Fig. 17-2). For a water resource system, typical parameters of the rule curves are target output levels, flood storage allocations, dead storage levels, and a strategy for making releases when faced with an output shortage. These variables are subject to adjustment in the optimization

[14] Footnote 2, Chapters 13 and 14 by Dorfman and by Thomas and Watermeyer respectively.

procedure, because it is evident that for the one *optimal* set of structures there must be an associated optimal operating policy. Traditional design techniques may overlook the fact that the parameters of the operating policy or rule curve must be optimized along with the components of the system. It is regrettable that only in a few instances are our analytical techniques equal to the task of isolating the optimal components and parameters simultaneously. A simple relationship is continuity. This assures that the quantity (of water, for instance) entering a system minus the quantity leaving the system equals the change in storage within the system. More complicated relationships enter into the computation of energy, flood routing, oxygen sag, or in any of the relevant characteristics of the model. The relationships may be deterministic, purely stochastic, or a combination of the two. For example, under given conditions of head and flow, and for a particular turbine, the hydroelectric energy can be reliably computed using a deterministic formulation. On the other hand, the evaporation loss from impounded water, being a function of temperature, wind, humidity, and other meteorological parameters, might be estimated as a function of meteorological data and include a random component accounting for imperfect knowledge of the exact functional dependence of evaporation on the several independent variables. Such a stochastic component decreases in importance as estimation procedures improve.

3. The *system variables* in a typical decision model are of four groups. Unlike the parameters of the rule curves, they are not subjected to adjustment in the optimization procedure. The condition of each component in the model is characterized by at least one *state variable*. Thus the storage behind a reservoir dam and the resulting power generation capacity are elements of the *state* of the associated components. When a component requires several variables for its specification one speaks of its *state vector*, recognizing that each element of a state vector is another state variable. The second group of variables comprises the *exogenous variables* (variables generated outside the system) upon which the system acts. For example, in a water resource system, the representative flows at several gaging sites constitute an array of *exogenous* variables.

A symbolic model produces a third group of variables (the *endogenous* variables or variables generated within the system) from the state variables, the exogenous variables, and the system parameters. They display the technological capabilities of the system and represent its output, ultimately being mapped into an index of performance. Hydroelectric energy, irrigation water, BOD removal, and municipal water supply are examples of endogenous variables that can be evaluated in dollars and ranked by the system objective function. Because the endogenous variables are calculated in accordance with the technologic function and evaluated by means of the utility function, they play a singularly important role in operations research. It follows that the central thrust of the theory of utility revolves around these endogenous variables. The fourth and last group of variables is composed of the miscellaneous indices, counters, intermediate results, and general debris of the mathematics involved in operations research.

The problem of optimization can now be stated in terms of the concepts just defined. Given the exogenous variables or the statistical distributions of which they are thought to be samples, and given the relations that determine the physical capabilities of the system, it is the task of optimization to select those components and those system-operation parameters that confer on the objective function its maximal or minimal value, subject to budgetary or output constraints.

17-8 Analytic Solutions

Optimization problems are classified according to objective and constraints in Table 17-1. Although stochastic, deterministic, and sequential

Table 17-1 Classification of Optimization Problems

| Objective | Constraints Present | | Constraints Absent |
	Equality	Inequality	
Linear (analytic)	Lagrange multipliers	Linear program	Calculus
Nonlinear	Lagrange multipliers	Quadratic program Calculus of variations	Calculus
Mixed (complicated structure)		Simulation analysis	

decision problems are not included in the classification the suggested scheme is helpful because it shows where some of the standard techniques fit into the current pattern of available solutions.

17-9 Solution by the Calculus

The strategy for solving problems without constraints is straightforward. The utility function is the sole measure of system performance. Accordingly, its first partial derivatives with respect to the several decision variables are set equal to zero; the resulting system of equations is solved, exactly or approximately; and the principal minors of the determinant of second partial derivatives are investigated to ascertain whether a maximum or a minimum is involved.

Example 17-1. Find the optimum pipe diameter for a pumped supply, assuming the cost, C, per linear foot of pipe equals the sum of the following component costs, also per linear foot.

1. Cost of pipe per pound and inch diameter, including appurtenances, c_1, the rate of interest and depreciation being r and the cost varying directly as the pipe diameter d to the mth power, which is normally between 1 and 2.

2. Cost of laying the pipe in the trench per inch diameter, c_2, the rate of interest and depreciation being r and the cost varying directly as the pipe diameter, d.

3. Cost of lifting a unit volume of water against unit frictional resistance, c_3, the cost varying inversely as the nth power of the pipe diameter, d, which is established by the flow (Q)-diameter (d)-friction (h_f) relationship.

In the Hazen-Williams formulation, for example, $h_f = kQ^{1.85}/d^{4.87}$ and $c_3Qh_f/d^n = c_3kQ^{2.15}/d^{4.87}$ or $n = 4.87$. Accordingly, $C = c_1rd^m + c_2rd + c_3kQh_f/d^n$.

Setting the first derivative with respect to d equal to zero: $dC/dd = mc_1rd^{m-1} + c_2r - nc_3kQh_f/d^{n+1} = 0$, or $mc_1rd^{m+n} + c_2rd^{n+1} - nc_3kQh_f = 0$. This equation can be solved for d by trial, the values of m and n being known. Because the second derivative $d^2C/dd^2 = m(m-1)c_1rd^{m-2} + n(n+1)c_3kQh_f/d^{n+2}$ is positive, the cost is, by inference, a minimum.

17-10   Lagrange Multipliers

Where equality constraints are present, the method of Lagrange multipliers is widely useful. This method can be illustrated for a given utility function $U = U(x_1, x_2, \ldots, x_n)$ of Eq. 17-6 or any monotonic transforms of the utility such as $U^* = g[U]$ on the assumption that U is to be maximized, subject to some constraint $\phi = 0$. For example, if r_i is the unit price for input commodity x_i, the amount expended being B, the constraint can be written

$$\phi = B - \sum_{i=1}^{n} r_i x_i = 0 \tag{17-8}$$

For the linear combination

$$V = U + \lambda\phi \tag{17-9}$$

in which λ is an undetermined scalar or multiplier, optimizing V is equivalent to optimizing U when the constraint is obeyed. This is so because along the constraint the quantity $\lambda\phi$ is zero, reducing the relationship to $V = U$. Employing the usual maximization technique, the n first partial derivatives of V with respect to x_i and the partial derivative with respect to the undetermined multiplier are set to zero. This results in the set of $n + 1$ simultaneous equations

$$\frac{\partial V}{\partial x_1} = \frac{\partial U}{\partial x_1} - \lambda r_1 = 0, \ldots \frac{\partial V}{\partial x_n} = \frac{\partial U}{\partial x_n} - \lambda r_n = 0 \cdots \text{and} \ \frac{\partial V}{\partial \lambda} = \phi = 0 \tag{17-10}$$

which, theoretically, can be solved for x_1, x_2, ..., x_n, and λ. To verify whether a maximum or minimum has been found, it is necessary to investigate the principal minors of the matrix of second partial derivatives

$$\frac{\partial^2 V}{\partial x_1^2}, \frac{\partial^2 V}{\partial x_1 \partial x_2} \cdots \frac{\partial^2 V}{\partial x_1 \partial \lambda} \cdots \frac{\partial^2 V}{\partial x_n \partial x_1} \cdots \frac{\partial^2 V}{\partial x_n \partial \lambda} \qquad (17\text{-}11)$$

and to note whether the matrix is *positive definite* or *negative definite*.[15]

Example 17-2. A graphical solution of an optimization problem based upon Lagrange's method is included in Sec. 12-3. The problem is to minimize the cost of a conduit by optimizing the distribution of the available head between three component portions: (1) a low-pressure pipe, (2) a pressure tunnel, and (3) a river crossing. The cost, c, of each portion is a function of the pressure drop within it (the higher the drop, the smaller the conduit, and the lower the cost), or $c = \sum_1^3 c_i = \Sigma f(h)$. This function must be minimized subject to the constraint $h_a = \sum_1^3 h_i$, where h_a is the total available head loss. In accordance with Lagrange's method, the imposed conditions are satisfied by the relationship $\partial c_i/\partial h + \lambda \ \partial h_a/\partial h_i = 0$ for each of the component portions. Because $\partial h_a/\partial h_i = 1$, the construction-cost head-loss relationship yields $\partial c_i/\partial h + \lambda \ \partial h_a/\partial h_i = \partial c_i/\partial h + \lambda$, and it follows that $\partial c_i/\partial h = \partial c_2/\partial h = \partial c_3/\partial h$. This result leads to the conclusion that the imposed conditions are satisfied when the tangents to the three construction cost-head loss curves (Fig. 12-2) are parallel (i.e., possess the same slope $\lambda = \partial c/\partial h$). Accordingly, the Lagrange method for compound pipes of this kind is also known specifically as the method of parallel tangents.

17-11   Linear Programming

If the constraints and objective function are linear, an efficient algorithm[16] for proceeding to the optimal decision vector is encompassed in the technique of *linear programming*. The problem is detailed in the following inequalities and equations:

$$a_{11}x_1 + a_{12}x_2 + \cdots + a_{1n}x_n = b_1;$$

$$\cdots \qquad \cdots \qquad \cdots \qquad \cdots \qquad \cdots$$

$$a_{m1}x_1 + a_{m2}x_2 + \cdots + a_{mn}x_n = b_m \qquad (17\text{-}12)$$

$$x_j \geq 0; \ n > m \qquad (17\text{-}13)$$

$$C = \sum_{j=1}^{n} c_j x_j \quad \text{a minimum} \qquad (17\text{-}14)$$

[15] The reader is referred to the standard literature on matrix analysis for details of the computation, e.g., Henderson and Quandt, Reference 1, p. 257, or R. G. D. Allen, *Mathematical Analysis for Economists*, Macmillan Co., London, 1960, Chapters 18 and 19.

[16] Algorithm or Algorism, a word derived from the name of al-Khowarizmi, ninth-century Arabian arithmetician, and implying the art of calculation with any species of positional notation.

The strategy for locating the optimal solution is simple. Select a set of m variables from among the n. The number of sets of m simultaneous linear equations which can be so derived from Eqs. 17-12 is

$$\binom{n}{m} = \frac{n!}{(n - m)!\, m!} \qquad (17\text{-}15)$$

Some, or all, of these sets of equations might lead to infeasible solutions for which one or more of the x_j is negative, whence the first inequality (Eq. 17-13) is violated. If a feasible solution exists, it implies that there is an optimal combination of m variables, all of which are positive, complemented by $n\text{-}m$ variables which are set to zero. This optimal feasible solution imparts a minimum value to the objective function of Eq. 17-14. With sufficient patience, one could solve all $\binom{n}{m}$ sets of simultaneous linear equations, m variables at a time, and evaluate the linear objective for each feasible solution. The optimal solution is that feasible set of x_j which minimizes Eq. 17-14. This algorithm is clearly inefficient if the number of variables is large, but we have a suitable alternative. An algorithm called the *Simplex Algorithm* assures the analyst that, at worst, each subsequent solution is at least as good as the current solution. Accordingly, if there is a feasible solution as a starting point, the Simplex Algorithm will guide the computation in such manner that each new set of m simultaneous equations imparts an equal or smaller value to the objective function. Finally, when the objective function can be made no smaller, the solution terminates at the optimum. The mechanism by which this remarkable algorithm converges to a solution, and the details of the degeneracies that may be encountered in practice, are not properly the subject for this chapter.[17] However, it is not essential to know the details of the algorithm in order to use the method. Almost every computing installation has a linear program available, and in accordance with a specified format, the user provides the coefficients a_{ij}, b_i, and c_j; he also indicates whether his is a problem in minimization or maximization, and he includes any other control or system information required by the program. The computer then takes charge, finds an initial feasible solution, and improves it until an optimum is reached or some degeneracy or inconsistency is identified. At that point, appropriate information is printed, and the solution terminates.

[17] The interested reader should consult references such as Robert Dorfman, Paul Samuelson, and Robert Solow, *Linear Programming and Economic Analysis*, McGraw-Hill Book Co., New York, 1958; and Saul I. Gass, *Linear Programming*, McGraw-Hill Book Co., New York, 1958.

Example 17-3. As an example of linear programming, let it be required to optimize the management of the two-reservoir system shown in Fig. 17-3 for which the flows and storages are expressed in some consistent set of units. Neglecting inflows between the dams and the use points, the economic benefit, B, in dollars, is a linear function of the releases, x_i, or $B = \Sigma\, a_i x_i = 2x_1 + 3x_2$ in this example. A_i is the amount of water available for release during the period of interest, Δt, and equals the storage S_i^* at the

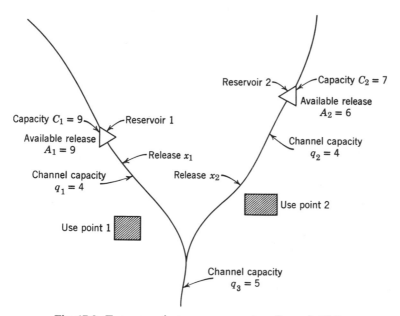

Fig. 17-3. Two-reservoir, two-purpose system, Example 17-3.

start of Δt plus the inflow Q_i during Δt. Continuity requires that $(A_i - x_i) \le$ capacity C_i. If $A_1 = 9$, $A_2 = 6$, $C_1 = 9$, $C_2 = 7$, and the channel capacities $q_1 = 4$, $q_2 = 4$, and and $q_3 = 5$ are not to be violated, the following constraints can be written:

$$
\begin{aligned}
x_1 + x_2 &\le q_3 = 5 \\
x_1 &\le q_1 = 4 \\
x_2 &\le q_2 = 4 \\
9 - x_1 &\le C_1 = 9 \\
6 - x_2 &\le C_2 = 7
\end{aligned}
$$

and the objective function is $B = 2x_1 + 3x_2$ which is to be maximized. The solution consists of the values $[x_1, x_2]$ and the maximal value of B.

Solution. Convert the inequalities into equalities by adding five variables $x_3, x_4, \ldots, x_7 \ge 0$ so that

$$
\begin{aligned}
x_1 + x_2 + x_3 &= 5 \\
x_1 \qquad\quad + x_4 &= 4 \\
x_2 \quad\;\; + x_5 &= 4 \\
-x_1 \qquad\quad + x_6 &= 0 \\
-x_2 \qquad\quad + x_7 &= 1
\end{aligned}
$$

This gives 5 equations in 7 variables, which clearly cannot define a unique solution unless the objective function is imposed, i.e., there are $\binom{7}{5}$ or 21 sets of 5 equations in 5 unknowns, some of which are infeasible in that one or more of the x_i is negative, but one of which confers the maximal value on the objective function $B(x)$. The Simplex Algorithm gives the solution vector [1, 4, 0, 3, 0, 1, 5] for the variables [x_i], and the maximal value of B is $2(1) + 3(4) = 14$. In this simple example, the solution is obvious by inspection, but in more complicated cases, involving hundreds of variables and perhaps thousands of constraints, the Simplex Algorithm converges directly to a solution (if a solution exists).

Discussion. This example could be complicated by including hydroelectric energy as a benefit, i.e., instead of ascribing benefits only to the releases x_i, one might adjust the objective function to include a benefit for storage because power depends on head, which in turn depends on the storage in the reservoir. Whereas the system is prompted to release water to the use points and to increase the flow past the turbines, therefore, there is a counteracting tendency to retain water and build up the head on the turbines to generate more energy with less discharge. The decision ultimately depends on the importance of each use, namely, the production or technological function, and on the degree of complementarity between uses.

Linear programming has many sophisticated relatives. *Integer programming* requires that the elements x_j of the solution vector be integers. Surprisingly, the optimal integer solution may be quite different from the optimal general solution, primarily because the optimal integer solution is not merely a rounded version of the optimal general solution. *Quadratic programming* is a technique for converging to an optimal decision vector when the objective function is quadratic. Unlike linear programming, which converges to an exact solution or terminates in degeneracy, the solution to a quadratic program cannot always be guaranteed. *Dynamic programming* is an optimization technique based on a sequential decision model. Virtually all attempts at solving practical problems in water resources with dynamic programming run afoul of the computer's storage capacity.[18]

17-12   Particular Solutions and Systems Simulation

The optimization models and techniques of Sec. 17-11 are general. Having once devised an algorithm for solving a linear program, all users merely provide their coefficients and allow the computer to produce an optimal solution. The algorithm is independent of the intended application or the size of the matrix of coefficients. However, when the objective and the constraints are each neither linear nor quadratic, when stochastic influences abound, and when the geometry of the system is complicated, all hopes of isolating an exact analytical or iterative solution vanish. In

[18] Richard Bellman and Stuart Dreyfus, *Applied Dynamic Programming*, Princeton University Press, Princeton, 1962.

these circumstances, frequently the best that can be done is to devise a solution by simulation, a technique that retains the essence of the prototype without itself attaining reality.[19]

In digital simulation analysis, the strategy is: Numerical values are assigned to the set of decision variables; exogenous variables are made available or generated; and the system operates on these inputs to produce endogenous variables that are evaluated by means of the utility function. Typically, a long sequence of endogenous variables is utilized so that the performance characteristics of the system can be thoroughly tested.[20] After a run of desired length has been completed, the output or utility is tabulated, and the method moves on to consider another combination of design variables. When a large number of combinations have been run, the designer selects the combination conferring the best value on the objective function. It will be noted that the word *optimal* is conspicuously absent from the description of the technique. For all but the most trivial problems, the total number of designs or combinations that can be investigated is but a small fraction of the number of possible combinations. Consequently, strict optimality is not obtained. The vast portion of the *response surface* remains unexplored. Instead, we must settle for the best observed combination, which will or, more likely, will not coincide with the true optimum. In its simplest sense the concept of developing a response surface is like the construction of a relief map on which elevations are shown as functions of longitude and latitude (Fig. 17-4).

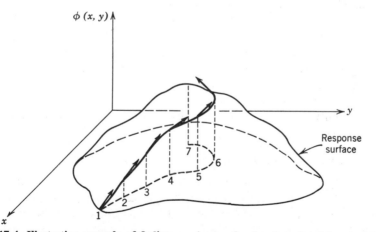

Fig. 17-4. Illustrative example of finding maximum of a function, ϕ, of two variables, x and y by a discrete step, steepest-ascent technique. (After *Hufschmidt, Footnote 2, Fig. 10-3*.)

[19] Footnote 2, Chapters 9–11.
[20] Footnote 2, Chapter 12.

A water resource problem can easily include ten decision variables. If only three possible values are assigned to each (for instance, small, medium, and large), the total number of alternate combinations is 3^{10}. Experience shows that a typical computer can test and evaluate each combination in a minimum time of about twenty seconds; the entire set of alternatives would still require 3^9 minutes or approximately 12 days of running time; and this is too long to be of practical value. Accordingly, a sampling technique is indicated, refuge being taken in a suitable theorem that helps to evaluate a random sampling scheme. If n independent combinations are attempted and if p_a is the probability that a single outcome drawn at random is less than or equal to some arbitrary value a, the probability that none of the n samples drawn exceeds a is $p_a{}^n$, and the probability that at least one outcome exceeds a is $1 - p_a{}^n$. If a is the 90-percentile net benefit, for instance, the probability (Sec. 4-2) that the best of $n = 30$ samples lies in the upper 10-percentile ($p = 0.1$) of the total population of outcomes is $q = 1 - (1 - p)^n = 0.958$.

If the response surface is subject to abrupt changes of slope and elevation, the results obtained might not be satisfactory, because the uppermost members of the population might lie very far from the bulk of the points. However, if the response surface is characterized by a gentle slope, this level of confidence might be sufficiently accurate for the purpose at hand. Ultimately, the designer's intuition, experience, and judgment, combined with sample results and the cost of uncertainty, must determine whether additional points should be investigated.

The role of system simulation is to provide the information ordinarily contained in the technologic function. Simulation alone does not optimize; it must be used together with an optimum-seeking technique. For complicated systems, for which no single production function can be written, system simulation provides the output corresponding to a given array of input elements. The best of all possible outcomes can rarely be reached with certainty, and virtually all replies must be couched in statistical terminology.

17-13   Search Techniques and Steepest Ascent

If a sample of size n is drawn and the response in each case is based on m decision variables, the next step in approaching more closely to the optimal solution, after isolating the best of n outcomes, may be described as follows.

The partial derivative of the outcome is evaluated in each of the m directions. For example, the utility may be given by the equation $U = U(x_1, x_2, \ldots, x_m)$ and its total differential by $dU = (\partial U/\partial x_1)\, dx_1 + \ldots + (\partial U/\partial x_m)\, dx_m$, while the benefit from the initial decision vector, $x_i{}^0$, is

$B^0 = B(x_1^0, x_2^0, \ldots, x_m^0)$. It is desired to progress to a second vector, x_i^1, with benefit given by $B^1 = B(x_1^1, x_2^1, \ldots, x_m^1)$ such that $dB = B^1 - B^0$ is a maximum. If the distance moved, Δ, is constrained by

$$\Delta^2 = dx_1^2 + \ldots + dx_m^2 \qquad (17\text{-}16)$$

the maximal value of dB subject to the constraint contained in Eq. 17-16 can be found. To do this it is convenient to use Lagrange's method of undetermined multipliers, which gives the solution

$$dx_i = -(\partial U/\partial x_i)/(2\lambda) \qquad (17\text{-}17)$$

$$\lambda = (1/2\Delta)\sqrt{\sum_{i=1}^{m} (\partial U/\partial x_i)^2} \qquad (17\text{-}18)$$

By assuring progress of the analysis along the gradient, this *method of steepest ascent* indicates the most advantageous design change that can serve as the basis for further ascending moves (Fig. 17-4). It is necessary only to specify the magnitude of step size, Δ, and to evaluate the several partial derivatives numerically. With large steps, convergence to the optimum is possible, but the peak may be overstepped. How to optimize step size is a difficult problem in nonlinear mathematics, for which the use of polynomial extrapolation rules offers some interesting prospects.

Other search techniques are well documented in the operations-research literature.[21] Efficient techniques, Fibonacci[22] search methods, for instance, are available for unimodal (single peak) response surfaces. However, comprehensive water-resource projects are characterized by response surfaces so complicated that analysis should not be based on the assumption of unimodality in the absence of suitable evidence.

17-14 Machines, Models, and Men

Operations research offers much promise. Its components are machines, models, and men. The availability of high-speed digital and analog computing machines has opened new approaches to engineering economics and project evaluation. Useful mathematical models are based on statistics, econometrics, objective functions, and other elements that are touched upon briefly in this chapter. The wider study of operations research by engineers is essential to progress in practice as well as research.

[21] Douglass Wilde, *Optimum Seeking Methods*, Prentice-Hall, Englewood Cliffs, N.J., 1964.
[22] Named for Leonardo Fibonacci (Leonardo of Pisa), thirteenth-century Italian mathematician, author of *Liber Abaci* (*The Abacus or Counting Board Book*), a treatise on the art of computing.

CHAPTER 18

Engineering Projects

18-1 Role of Engineers

The planning, design, and construction of water and wastewater systems for metropolitan areas usually bring together a sizable and varied group of engineering practitioners and their consultants, not for months but for years, in bold and busy venture. As their work is completed, elements of their most important and powerful membership move on to new enterprises; older men drop out; younger men move in; and offshoots accept parallel, usually smaller, but nevertheless important, assignments. Under proper leadership, task forces perpetuate themselves to attack new problems or deal with old ones in new ways. The science and practice of water supply and wastewater disposal are preserved and promoted in this way.

Because the systems are generally in public ownership in the United States, studies, plans, specifications, and contracts for the construction of water and wastewater works are prepared by engineers normally engaged by the cities and towns or the water or wastewater districts to be served. Private water companies are not increasing in number; private sewerage corporations are rare institutions. The engineers may belong to the professional staff of municipal or metropolitan governmental agencies responsible for designing and managing public works, or they may be members of a firm of consulting engineers. For very large undertakings, governmental and consulting staffs may be expanded for the duration of the enterprise, as suggested in the first paragraph of this chapter. For smaller undertakings, this is seldom true. Consultant groups are given most and possibly all of the responsibility. Engineers for manufacturers of

18–1

water and wastewater equipment also have a part. The engineers of contractors or construction companies bring the design into being.

18-2 Steps in Project Development

Community action leading to the study, design, construction, and operation of new or enlarged water or wastewater systems and the engineering response elicited by community action are conveniently listed in sequence, in special reference to projects for which engineering consultants are engaged.

Community Action

1. Invitation to consulting engineers to submit proposals for preparing an engineering report or appointment of a consultant to the regular or expanded engineering staff of the community.

2. Engagement of a consultant on evidence of his qualifications and not by competitive bidding.[1]

3. Examination of the consulting engineering report and its acceptance or rejection. If the report is not accepted, step 1 may have to be taken again.

4. Authorization of the preparation of plans and specifications. The consultant responsible for the report, and other engineers, too, may be asked to submit proposals for doing the work under the stipulations of step 2.

5. Advertisement for construction contracts after the plans and specifications have been accepted. Local newpapers and national engineering journals are used for this purpose.

6. Selection of the contractor, generally on the basis of the lowest bid received from a technically qualified and financially responsible construction company.

7. Construction under supervision of a *resident engineer*, employed by the owner (the municipality or district) or the consulting engineer.

8. Acceptance of the completed works upon the recommendation of the engineer. The consultant may be retained to advise and assist in putting the system into operation.

9. Examination and adoption of project financing. This is done at a suitable stage of project development, often with the assistance of the engineering consultant or a financial consultant.

Engineering Response[2]

1. Collection and evaluation of available and required basic information—demographic, hydrologic, geologic, topographic, and industrial. The advice of local engineering practitioners who know the community and region may be useful.

[1] A guide for engaging engineering services has been prepared by the American Society of Civil Engineers as *Manual of Engineering Practice*, No. 45, April 1, 1964.
[2] For the role of the consulting engineer and the organization of a consulting office, see C. M. Stanley, *The Consulting Engineer*, John Wiley & Sons, New York, 1961.

2. Preparation of a preliminary or feasibility report, or of a final engineering report (Sec. 18-3).

3. Preparation of plans and specifications, if the report is accepted and the detailed design authorized. Basing his decision upon needed and available materials, the engineer will normally discuss his ideas with qualified manufacturers and suppliers.

4. Preparation of contract documents, including an estimate of construction costs after the plans and specifications have been accepted.

5. Assistance in advertising for bids and selecting the successful bidder.

6. Supervision of construction to make sure that the contractor performs his work in accordance with the plans and specifications. Approval of necessary shop drawings supplied by the contractor.

7. Authorization of payment when the work has been completed and preparation of *as-built* plans in record of the construction work.

8. Preparation of an operating manual for the system and supervision of its operation during its early years, most often when the community does not have experienced operating personnel of its own.

9. Assistance in setting up accounting procedures and establishing appropriate rates for service.

18-3   The Engineering Report

Engineers are known by the quality of their reports. They are judged by the performance of completed designs. Good reports have opened up new channels of learning. Good designs and constructions have created new technologies. Of the many outstanding examples, some are allied to consultants, others to special commissions, and others to governmental agencies at all levels. The references cited in this book are a measure of their importance and variety.

No matter whether the community does its own engineering work or engages a consultant to do it, its water and wastewater schemes should receive the benefit of well-documented studies of feasible projects before detailed designs are authorized. This maxim of sound engineering practice and good governmental procedure should be honored.

Engineering reports commissioned for the purpose of identifying the need for new or expanded water and wastewater constructions and offering acceptable proposals for their development are expected to state their mission clearly, analyze and summarize available and needed data, assess the technical, economic, legal, and political feasibility of projected works, offer alternative answers to the questions asked, and point out the one or two most suitable replies, estimate costs, investigate methods of financing, and, by these studies, lay a firm base for the recommendations made and the execution of a feasible scheme.

If the report is well written, its purpose will be understood by lay boards as well as by fellow engineers. If its findings, conclusions, and recommendations are carefully worded, they can be quoted verbatim in news releases and give the public the information to which it is entitled. Bonds funding the proposed works can then receive justifiable support. If the report is imaginative and exhaustive, it should become the document of reference in re-studies and further planning and development of the water resource. If the report is accepted, it should allow the orderly and economic acquisition of needed rights and properties, the preparation and enactment of required legislation, and the exploration of obtainable financial support.

Most reports are scheduled to contain the information itemized in the form of a table of contents in the following paragraphs.

A Table of Contents for an Engineering Report

Letter of transmittal, addressed to the responsible agency of government.
Letter of authorization, from the agency to the engineer.
Summary of findings, conclusions, and recommendations.
Detailed report:
1. Purpose and scope of the report.
2. The community, its geography and people, its history and expectations.
3. Existing water or wastewater works and their historical development.
4. Population: past, present, and probable future population and population density.
5. (a) Report on water supply:
   i. Water use—domestic, fire, mercantile, and industrial, by area served and expected total.
   ii. Available water sources, source development, pumping, transmission, treatment, distribution, and service storage.
   iii. Project comparisons, including construction and operating costs.
   iv. Recommended project.
5. (b) Report on wastewater disposal:
   i. For sanitary sewerage: wastewater production—domestic, infiltration, mercantile, and industrial by kind of area served and expected total.
   ii. For stormwater drainage: rainfall and runoff—design storm and its recurrence interval by area served.
   iii. Proposals for disposal, including interception of sewage from combined systems; stormwater holding tanks, sewage treatment works, and outfalls.
   iv. Effect of effluent on receiving bodies of water.
   v. Project comparisons, including capital and operating costs.
   vi. Recommended project.
6. Financing.
7. Rates.
Appendix:
   Charts and tables of basic data.

18-4   Feasibility Studies

Engineering feasibility implies both technical and economic practicability. Technical practicability is readily demonstrated in engineering studies such as those described in earlier chapters of this book. Although economic practicability can find expression in optimization procedures of benefits in relation to costs, either as ratios or as differences, it may not be possible to do so in full measure and in all circumstances (Chap. 17). Resource developments competing for funds in developing countries and the national, regional, or basin-wide comprehensive planning of industrially advanced societies, for example, may create so many constraints or introduce so many decision variables that true optimization is left in suspense (Sec. 17-12). Moreover, it is difficult to attach monetary values to intangible benefits. Recreation is a notable example.

Engineering feasibility may be encumbered also by legal and political restrictions. The fact that surface waters are common bounds between states or provinces and that large rivers may cross national and international boundaries in their course towards the sea may add political as well as legal constraints of much significance.[3] The Congress of the United States may be asked to lift some of them through interstate and international compacts. However, legal contests between states are not unknown. The Federal courts, in which interstate cases are tried, have handed down far-reaching decisions. In the United States, the *common law* or *riparian doctrine* governing water use in the eastern portion of the country and the *doctrine of prior use* or *prior appropriation* prevailing in the western portion may add legal constraints. They, too, may require interpretation by the courts.

18-5   Alternatives

There is no single solution to a given water-resource problem, and development of the best solution is not a matter of objective optimization alone. Community and regional wants and wishes must be taken into account. To be meaningful, decisions must identify comparative advantages and disadvantages of promising alternative schemes. The community is then free to make its own choice (but see Sec. 18-15). The most immediately economical system may not be the most acceptable system. A recurrent example is the common preference for naturally clean water rather than water made clean by treatment. In many instances, upland supplies

[3] Examples are the taking of water from Lake Michigan by Chicago for water supply and effluent dilution purposes, the diversion of needed additions to its water supply from the Delaware River by the City of New York, the sharing of the waters of the Colorado River by the State of California, and the disposition of Mexican and Canadian boundary waters between these countries and the United States.

reaching the city by gravity meet the specification of naturally clean waters; supplies pumped from polluted rivers coursing past the city and purified in treatment works before delivery to its distribution system are descriptive of the second. Of the two, upland water supplies are usually more costly to develop, but their cost of operation, maintenance, and repair may be smaller because of differences in power and treatment requirements. Esthetic imponderables become decision variables in cases such as this.[4] Quite different is the example of large industrial users who must make their choice between tying into a public supply and developing one of their own. Entering into their decisions are the economy of lower interest rates available to public bodies, the economy of scale, and possible advantages of more useful water temperatures where surface and groundwater temperatures are in competition.

18-6 Plans and Specifications

More expensive and time-consuming than an engineering report, but proportionately more remunerative to the engineer, are the detailed planning and specification of works to be built. To assure a meeting of the minds of the owner, the designer, and the contractor, plans and specifications must be comprehensive as well as precise. Vague and conflicting documents create confusion and increase bids as well as actual costs. Indeed, they may be responsible for unsatisfactory constructions.

In the course of their careers, most engineers develop specific interests and capacities. If these are given recognition in design offices—and it is generally of advantage to do so—design assignments can be based on competencies in basic elements of engineering, structural, mechanical, and electrical, for instance, or on competencies in specific system components such as pipelines, pumps, filters, and other treatment units. For major projects, a team leader carries the responsibility and should be given the discretion of work assignments and the proper timing and coordination of effort by members of his team. Specifications may be compiled from individual statements, or they may be written by a separate group.

Preliminary reports, by contrast, are usually tasks performed by one or two senior men who generally tackle the essential subjects in sequence.

18-7 Sources of Information

A busy office must be supported by a good library. A sizable engineering organization may employ a professional librarian. Professional organizations develop standards.

---

[4] An example is the election of New York City to seek clean upland waters in the Delaware River Basin rather than drawing upon the Hudson River even though that was recommended in a report of an engineering panel on water supply. *Future Water Sources of the City of New York*, New York, July, 1951.

The shelflist of a working library usually includes the following:

1. Engineering manuals, texts, and serial publications. The bibliography at the end of this book gives a reasonably complete list of useful works and journals.

2. Standards and specifications of professional organizations. Standards published by the American Water Works Association and by the American Society for Testing and Materials are examples. They may be referred to in specifications in lieu of the presentation of details.

3. Manuals of engineering practice and design, among them those of the American Society of Civil Engineers, the American Water Works Association, and the Water Pollution Control Federation.

4. National, state, and local building and electrical codes.[5]

5. Handbooks of associations of manufacturers: the Cast Iron Pipe Research Association; the American Concrete Pipe Association; the Clay Sewer Pipe Association; the Hydraulic Institute; and the Portland Cement Association.

6. Catalogs of equipment manufacturers.

7. Reference annuals published by trade magazines, some of which are listed in the bibliography of the present volume.

18-8   Standards

Undoubtedly, standards have done much to improve the performance of water and wastewater works, but the underlying philosophy continues to be questioned. Standardization of pipes and other equipment for water and wastewater systems normally reduces the cost of the *standard* items. Together with standardization of materials of construction it simplifies not only design but also construction and the procurement of materials that meet minimum criteria and assure compatibility. Standards of water quality set a goal to be reached in the protection of waters for the many purposes they serve (Vol. 2). Design standards of regulatory agencies are generally written for the protection of small communities. Their aim is to promote the successful construction of small works. To this purpose, they may specify minimum sizes and strengths of water and wastewater pipes and minimum velocities of flow in sewers, for example. Standards of this kind should not be applied to works of all sizes. Otherwise they may impede the development and adoption of new processes and fruitful introduction of new ideas. The engineering profession should see to it that new enterprise is not obstructed because it happens to be in conflict with existing standards. Opportunities for large-scale experimentation should be kept open. Examples of obsolescent requirements are (1) rules and regulations against curved sewers of small diameter in residential developments and (2) rules and regulations governing the maximum allowable spacing of manholes in sanitary sewers (Sec. 3-4).

[5] Abbott's *National Electrical Code Handbook*, McGraw-Hill Book Co., New York, 1963, is an example.

An institutional approach to water supply and wastewater disposal which reduces the need for regulatory control is offered in some of the river basins of Germany. The Ruhr and Emscher basins are examples. There, ownership in the total water resource is vested in the population of the basin through an elective and appointive basin authority. Charges are levied against municipalities and industries in proportion to the waste discharge and to the cost of works necessary to keep the regional water economy in balance.[6]

There can be no quarrel with the importance of health and safety standards. Standards of this kind protect water from gathering ground to points of use, maintain adequate capacity and pressures, and introduce standby power and water reserves for use in emergencies. In similar fashion, standards of this kind introduce safe guards into wastewater systems from points of collection to their disposal grounds, prevent surcharge of sewers and resulting flooding of basements and low-lying areas, and protect receiving waters.

18-9   Design Specifications

Two extremes for specifying the work to be performed by a contractor are exemplified by: (1) the *turn-key project* or *performance specification* and (2) the *descriptive specification*. Where performance is specified, the contractor becomes responsible for both design and construction. This is common practice in industry and in many developing countries. Where descriptive specifications underlie design, the owner's engineer specifies what the work is to be, and constructions are expected to perform properly if the specifications are met. As equipment becomes more complex, there is a tendency to shift to performance specifications. The engineer then becomes a coordinator of devices and relinquishes some of his responsibility in design.

Performance specification has a place when mass production is of benefit to the purchaser of the product. It is justified, too, when performance can be pretested, or when it is possible to test equipment after installation and to replace it if it does not meet specified performance. Pumps are examples of equipment that is generally selected on the basis of performance specifications. However, pump performance specifications are usually supplemented by descriptive specifications that provide protection against overload and ensure compatibility with other elements of the system. Performance specifications for a pumping station rather than for pumps only, and for an entire treatment plant or even for individual units of a treatment plant are rarely appropriate. The claim that performance specifications

[6] Allen Kneese, *The Economics of Regional Water Quality Management*, Johns Hopkins Press, Baltimore, Maryland, 1964.

save money because the engineer need not prepare detailed designs is valid only when standardized *shelf items* can be incorporated in the projected system. When this is not so, the owner, in fact, bears not only the direct cost of design but also the hidden cost of *turn-key* or other projects prepared for bids that were not successful.

When a descriptive specification interferes with competitive bidding by suppliers of material or equipment that will serve the design purpose equally well, the engineers normally prepare two or more alternative designs and invite bids on them.

18-10   Project Construction

Public construction projects are generally required by law to go to the low bidder. Award can be withheld only on evidence that a contractor does not possess the qualifications and financial backing to undertake and complete the project successfully.

Documents formulated by the engineer and used by the contractor in preparing his bids are:[7]

1. **Notice to Bidders.** This notice advertises the project and tells where copies of plans and specifications can be inspected and how they can be obtained.

2. **General Conditions.** This is a statement of the conditions under which the contract is to be performed. Normally, it includes information on the following matters:

(*a*) *Proposal requirements and conditions.* These specify the conditions under which proposals will be received, requirements for bond, necessary qualifications of bidders, the basis for disqualifying bidders, and conditions for the employment of subcontractors.

(*b*) *Award of contract.* In the case of public agencies a statement says that if the contract is awarded, it will go to the lowest responsible bidder.

(*c*) *Contract terms.* To assure a meeting of the minds of the contracting parties, the terms used in the contract document are defined, and the authority of the resident engineer, management of extra work orders, and general rules for interpreting plans and specifications are stated.

(*d*) *Bonds and insurance.* Bonding requirements and guarantees against defective workmanship are specified together with types of insurance demanded of the contractor.

(*e*) *Responsibilities and rights of the contractor.* The specific responsibilities of the contractor on the project are stipulated. As a rule the contractor must give assurance to the owner that he does not become liable for patent infringement when patented equipment is installed.

(*f*) *Responsibilities and rights of the owner.* The owner furnishes property surveys and, through his engineers, necessary base lines and bench marks for

[7] The American Public Works Association and the Associated General Contractors of America have prepared jointly a *Uniform Public Works Engineering Construction Form Manual* which provides a model for such documents.

the work to be done. He specifies the conditions under which he or his engineers have the right to inspect the operation and the mechanics of issuing changes in work. Although the engineer is employed by the owner, he is made the final judge in disputes between owner and contractor. However, the contractor is given a right of appeal for arbitration.

(g) *Workmanship and materials.* The general basis for controlling the quality of materials and equipment is stated. The contractor must submit shop drawings, lists of materials, and other required information in ample time for review by the engineer prior to their incorporation into the construction. The contractor is generally required to field-test equipment after its installation and to assure its proper operation. In turn, the contractor may require the equipment supplier to direct the installation of specialized equipment and to supervise its initial operation.

(h) *Prosecution of work.* Conditions governing the time for completion of the work are covered. Except in unusual cases there is no penalty for late compliance with the contract. However, associated costs of engineering and inspection may have to be reimbursed by the contractor. Specification of damages for delay generally raises the bid prices for contracts.

(i) *Payments.* The contractor is paid periodically for work actually performed and materials brought to the construction site. A small share of the total, normally 10%, is held against project completion and final acceptance. Methods of payment for extra work and work omitted are stipulated.

3. **Special Provisions.** To apply to a particular project, these may include requirements for the continuation of existing services while construction is under way, for particular methods of construction the engineers believe should be followed in executing the work, and for the specific scope of work.

4. **Detailed Specifications.** These comprise the bulk and most-used section of the document. Although some specifications are not changed significantly from project to project (for example, specifications for concrete, steel, and certain kinds of pipe), most of the detailed specifications have reference only to the project for which they have been written. They are essential companions of the plans. Neither plans nor detailed specifications are self-sufficient.[8]

The detailed specifications include such items as site preparation, demolition of existing structures, earth excavation, fill and backfill, rock excavation, preparation of foundations, embankments, paving, concrete, reinforcing steel, piping, drain piping, gates, valves, meters, specific items of equipment, metal work, painting, plumbing, heating and ventilating, electrical work, fencing, and final grading and surfacing or seeding, and planting.

5. **The Proposal.** The contractor's proposal, accompanied by a certain percentage of the total bid price, constitutes his bid. Ordinarily he quotes a price for each category of materials or equipment detailed in the specifications. Some of them are unit prices, for example, dollars per acre for clearing and grubbing; per cubic yard for concrete, excavation, and fill; per linear foot for piping;

[8] Plans may be incorporated into the volume of contract documents and detailed specifications, a practice made possible by modern methods of reproduction. In the case of small projects, it may be useful to print the specifications on the plans.

per square foot for paving; and *lump sum* for items of equipment. Where unit prices are asked for, the engineer lists his estimated quantities. In a conflict between actual quantities and quantities listed in the proposal, the actual quantity is paid for. The more precise the engineer can make his estimates and the more extensively he uses unit prices, the lower is the total bid likely to be.

In arriving at cost estimates, both engineer and contractor spend much time in measuring and calculating quantities—the engineer to make sure that the bid is compatible with the budget of his client; the contractor to decide on his bids. Itemized estimates cover bulk and finished concrete, brick, painting, steel, pipe, paving, trim, planting, and many others in seemingly endless flow. Bid prices normally reflect the local situation of construction and employment.

Written too tightly, specifications may lose the advantages of competitive bidding among equipment suppliers. Written too loosely, they may allow unsatisfactory equipment to be installed. To protect the owner, the engineer may either require the bidder to identify the equipment upon which his bid is based, or exclude equipment from price competition. This lets the successful bidder and the engineer select the equipment after the contract has been awarded.

With his proposal, the bidder is asked to supply information on his experience, equipment available for constructing the project, names and qualifications of persons who will have responsible charge of the work, and his own financial resources.

6. **The contract** is the agreement signed by representatives of owner and contractor. A contract bond serves as a guarantee of performance, quality of materials, and workmanship. Normally it remains in force for twelve months beyond final acceptance of the project.

18-11 Project Financing

Funds for the construction of major water or wastewater systems are usually borrowed. Loans normally stipulate how funds will be obtained for their repayment and for meeting other continuing obligations of the enterprise. Interest payments and operation, maintenance, and replacement (OMR) costs are examples.

1. **Capital costs** are the costs of the project from its beginning to the time the works are placed in operation. Included are (1) the purchase of property and rights-of-way; (2) payments for equipment and construction and for engineering and legal services; and (3) interest charges during construction. For this phase of the undertaking money must be borrowed on short-term bond anticipation notes.

2. **Fixed charges** are the annual charges made to repay capital costs, both interest and principal, together with applicable taxes.

3. **Amortization** is the serial repayment of principal.

4. **Principal** (P) is the amount borrowed. Repayment (R) of principal is a part of the fixed charges.

5. **Interest** (i) is the cost of borrowing money. It is a function of the unrepaid principal and is expressed as a per cent per year. Like repayment, it is part of the fixed charges.

6. **OMR costs** include the expenditures for operation of the works, their maintenance and repair, the replacement of equipment in the normal course of operation, and minor normal extensions.

7. **Annual charges** comprehend the sum of fixed charges and OMR costs. Two or more dissimilar alternative projects are often compared on the basis of annual charges because each one must be paid for from taxes, special assessments, service charges, or commodity rates.

8. **Future value** is a function of P, i, and n. Calling FV the value of a *single* payment after n years, $FV = P(1 + i)^n$. A payment or loan of $1000 accumulating interest at 4% annually, for instance, has a future value or repayment requirement of $1480 after 10 years.

9. **Annuity or uniform series future worth** is a function of R, i, and n. If A is the value of the annuity or *series* of n annual end-of-the-year investments, $A = (R/i)[(1 + i)^n - 1]$. For example, $1000 invested each year for 10 years at an interest rate of 4% compounded annually has a future value of $12,000.

10. **Sinking fund** is a fund established to retire a debt in a *series* of equal payments R to provide an amount A in n years. It is a function of A, i, and n, namely, $R = Ai/[(1 + i)^n - 1]$. For example, a sinking fund of $12,000 after a 10-year period at 4% interest compounded annually is built up by an annual investment of $1000.

11. **Discounting** describes the practice of reducing future costs of benefits to an equivalent present value PV (Sec. 17-5). As a function of A, i, and n, it provides common ground for estimating alternative projects by bringing them to a common present date, i.e., $PV = A/(1 + i)^n$. The present worth of $1480 paid at the end of 10 years is $1000, for instance, if the interest rate is 4% compounded annually.

12. **Discounted series payment** determines the present value, or discounts the value of a *series* of equal annual future payments in terms of R, i, and n, or $PV = (R/i)[(1 + i)^n - 1]/(1 + i)^n$. Thus the present worth of $1000 to be repaid each year for 10 years with interest at 4% is $8111, i.e., this amount invested at 4% interest compounded annually over a 10-year period would produce an income or payments of $1000 a year for each of the 10 years.

13. **Capital recovery factor** is the annual payment, including both principal and interest, necessary to amortize debt A in n years at an interest rate of i, i.e., $R = Ai(1 + i)^n/[(1 + i)^n - 1]$. To repay a loan of $8111 by a *series* of payments each year over a period of 10 years, for example, requires equal payments of $1000.

Tables of these factors for various periods of time and different rates of interest are found in most engineering handbooks.[9]

[9] See also E. L. Grant and W. G. Ireson, *Principles of Engineering Economy*, Ronald Press, New York, 1960.

18-12   Methods of Borrowing

For relatively simple and straight-forward projects, the engineer advises on the most suitable methods of borrowing needed funds. Where funds are to be derived from several sources or for large projects, special financial advice may be sought. The methods of borrowing depend upon the resources of the borrower, the sources from which funds can be borrowed, regulations of appropriate government agencies, and the nature of repayment arrangements. Borrowing is arranged through the sale of bonds. In the United States, the income from municipal bonds is not taxable. Bonds are of three general types:

1. **General obligation bonds** that generally carry the lowest interest rates because they are backed by the *full faith and credit* of the community with income generally derived from *ad valorem* taxes on property. When the bonds are to be repaid over a period of years, they are called serial bonds.

2. **Revenue bonds** that are based on repayments earned from the sale of water or from sewer service charges (sometimes called sewer rentals). The revenue bonds of an enterprise with a history of good management may carry as low an interest rate as general obligation bonds. New projects or projects for which the quality of management is uncertain may have to pay high interest rates.

3. **Special assessment bonds,** like general obligation bonds, are backed by the value of the property they serve. They are generally short-term bonds that are normally designed to permit borrowing for a specific project serving only part of the community. Examples are lateral sewers or booster pumping-stations.

Only rarely are two or three types of bonds issued in combination. Reasons for combining bonds may be the allocation of charges for service in some relation to benefits received or, more pragmatically, the avoidance of legal limits on bonded indebtedness.

18-13   Rate Making

The principle adopted as a guide in financing and rate-making schemes has been stated usefully as follows:[10] "The needed total annual revenue of a water or sewage works shall be contributed by users and non-users (or by users and properties) for whose use, need and benefit the facilities of the work are provided, approximately in proportion to the cost of providing the use and the benefits of the works."

On the one hand, payments for water supply and wastewater removal obtained solely through general taxation would be inequitable, because property owners would be assessed for these goods and services in full and

[10] *Fundamental Consideration in Rates and Rate Structure for Water and Sewage Works,* Am. Soc. Civil Engrs., Bulletin No. 2, reprinted from *Ohio Law J.,* Spring, 1951.

irrespective of use. On the other hand, payments derived solely from the sale of water and through it from sewer-use charges would also be inequitable because properties benefiting from the availability of water or drainage facilities would not contribute to any part of system costs. Even if the cost of delivering water or collecting wastewater could be ascertained exactly for each water consumer or owner of property, it would be impractical to base a rate structure on such changeable information. Instead, the rate maker generally resorts to the mean, i.e., he arrives at an approximation by averaging costs within categories of users of the same general kind. Should inequity be proved for one or more of the categories, imbalance can be righted when rates are next adjusted.

Understandably, rates must bring in sufficient income to cover fixed charges, normal OMR costs, and the cost of reasonable improvements. In some instances they may be designed to provide also a modest reserve for normal expansion of the system. Too large a reserve would place an unfair burden on current users; too small a reserve would entail frequent and expensive bond issues.

Water Rates.   Water rates are normally structured to accord with the classes of consumers served and their water uses (Sec. 5-7). Common classifications point to manufacturing or wholesale, commercial, or intermediate, and residential or domestic users, each category being subdivided according to rate of draft. A first or *minimum block* of charges covers the cost of metering and meter-reading, and of billing and collecting; it is independent of the quantity of water drawn. A second or *wholesale block* of charges assesses them in direct proportion to the cost of supplying water. Rates are obtained by dividing the system costs by the volume of water delivered. Water furnished a neighboring community that resells it to its residents is usually charged for in this way. A third block of charges allows for the addition of incremental costs to the wholesale cost; it is divided into subclasses with individual rates.

In terms of cost alone, unit prices generally decrease for large users. However, where water is in short supply and each incremental use adds higher costs, it is not unreasonable to increase unit prices for larger users.

Fire Protection.   Water service for fire protection bears no relationship to the amount of water used. For this reason, charges for fire service should be subtracted from the total cost of water. Fire service is charged for in various ways. If revenue is to be proportioned to use and benefits, for example, the cost of each element of the system must be isolated and apportioned in relation to its contribution to fire protection and to general water service. Costs of a transmission main sized to carry water for fire protection plus the coincident draft, for instance, would then be divided in proportion to these flows. By contrast, no charges for water purification would be allocated to fire protection, because a negligible quantity of water is actually consumed in fire fighting.

If the primary purpose of a water system is to be water-supply service, only the incremental costs necessary to equip the system for fire protection would be so assessed. To find the cost, a hypothetical system not providing fire protection would be laid out and its cost estimated. Fire-protection charges would then be based on the difference in cost between the hypothetical system (without fire service) and the actual system (with fire service).[11]

When the cost of fire service is met from general tax funds, as it usually is, the benefits of fire protection are assumed to be proportional to property values. Actually, costs of fire service range from 10% of the total cost of water for large communities to as much as 30% for small communities.

Peak-flow Demands. Peak-flow costs are exemplified by larger capacities of pipelines furnishing seasonal peak flow demands for lawn sprinkling. There is no easy way of adjusting income received to these flows. Charges are normally the same as for other water uses. In the electrical industry, by contrast, peak costs are based on demand-meter readings, and charges per unit of electricity are related to the consumer's peak-demand rate or to his demand during peak periods. Although it would probably not pay to install demand meters on residential water services, their use may be justified for wholesale customers—neighboring communities, for instance. An incidental advantage would be the resulting encouragement of wholesale customers to put in service storage and equalize the system demand.

Sewer Service Charges. For historical reasons, sewerage systems were paid for from general taxation (Sec. 1-3). However, as communities have turned to easier, although sometimes more costly, revenue financing, and as wastewater treatment has become more common, sewer service charges have been introduced with the example of water rates in mind. Inasmuch as the wastewater released to the system is a more or less uniform fraction of the water used, the service charge is often made a fixed percentage of the water bill.

However, it can be argued that well-balanced financing of a sewerage system should actually be composed of special assessments for lateral sewers, general taxation for storm sewers, or the stormwater portion of combined sewers, as well as service charges based on water-meter readings for domestic wastewater collection and disposal.

Although metering the wastewater from households may be neither practical nor necessary where the water is metered, it may be both practical and equitable to meter industrial wastewaters. Basic charges may be determined in much the same way as for water. Surcharges may be

[11] *Water Rates Manual*, American Water Works Association, New York, 1960.

imposed when admission of the wastewater is damaging to sewers or increases the cost of treatment out of proportion to their quantity.[12] An incidental advantage to be gained from surcharges is the possible inducement of industries to reduce and alter their waste discharges by recirculation of process water and modification of manufacturing processes. Pretreatment of wastewaters before their discharge to the sewer is another possibility.

18-14   Systems Management

A good system is a flexible system. However, if ways of taking advantage of built-in flexibility are not clearly understood and put to use by operating personnel, the advantages of flexibility are lost. Only if it is operated effectively and efficiently does an otherwise well-conceived, well-designed, and well constructed system become a credit to the community and to the participants in the project. To meet their responsibility to society in full measure, engineers should see to it that the systems they have designed accomplish their mission. Accordingly, they must be prepared to assist the community in the operation of projects as effectively as they did in their design and construction. To this purpose, consultants may be engaged by communities for introductory or continuing surveillance of systems operations and management. A manual describing the purpose and operations of each unit and the required sequence of operations for the works as a whole may be useful. So may schematic diagrams that outline available methods of control, as well as record forms, data-collection sheets, and equipment and maintenance cards.

State regulatory agencies, professional organizations, and educational institutions often assist in training plant personnel and other officials in the management of water and wastewater facilities. Both technical and fiscal operations may be covered to advantage.

18-15   A Closing Example

As the growing cities of nineteenth century North America were becoming aware of their destiny, towns on the eastern shores of the continent were the first to recognize a need of more and better water. Among them was Boston, Massachusetts. Loammi Baldwin, foremost American engineer of his day, had recommended that Boston acquire a great pond, later named Lake Cochituate, as the source of a gravity supply. However, a dozen years passed by before construction was authorized. It was impossible to muster general agreement on the source to be tapped. During the resulting period of uncertainty, a veritable barrage of pamphlets descended

---

[12] *Industrial Waste Disposal Charges in Cities over* 5000 *Population*, Special Report No. 18-5, American Public Works Association, Chicago, January, 1955.

upon the town. Even Walter Channing, the Professor of Obstetrics and Medical Jurisprudence who was serving as Dean of the Harvard Medical School, joined in the debate. He argued "that an abundant supply of pure and fresh water directly promotes health and longevity, and as surely tends to diminish and prevent pauperism." Possibly, indeed probably, this opinion of the learned doctor helped the authorities to make up their minds, for not much later the source recommended by Baldwin was acquired and construction of an aqueduct was authorized. Eventually the supply was ready to be turned on and contemporary records (1848) tell how it was done.[13]

The weather was propitious and at the break of day, a salute of one hundred guns, accompanied by the ringing of the bells, opened the ceremonies. At an early hour the streets were filled with people, attracted by the decorations, mottoes and devices, by which the principal avenues through which the procession was to pass, were embellished. These were very numerous, well arranged and in good taste, and some of them extremely beautiful.

The SERVICES on the COMMON were brief, on account of the lateness of the hour at which the procession reached the spot; they were as follows:

FIRST, Hymn by George Russell, Esq., which was sung by the Handel and Haydn Society and the audience.

SECOND, Prayer by Rev. Daniel Sharp, D.D.

THIRD, Ode by James Russell Lowell, Esq., which was sung by the School children.[14]

FOURTH, ADDRESS by the HON. NATHAN HALE, one of the WATER COMMISSIONERS.

FIFTH, ADDRESS by the HON. JOSIAH QUINCY, JR., MAYOR OF BOSTON.

At the conclusion of the Mayor's address, he asked the Assembly if it were their pleasure that the water should now be introduced. An immense number of voices responded, "Aye!" Whereupon the gate was gradually opened and the water began to rise in a strong column, six inches in diameter, increasing rapidly in height, until it reached an elevation of eighty feet.

After a moment of silence, shouts rent the air, the bells began to ring, cannon were fired, and rockets streamed across the sky. The scene was one of intense excitement, which it is impossible to describe, but which no one can forget. In the evening, there was a grand display of fireworks, and all the public buildings and many of the private houses were brilliantly illuminated.

So ended a day of welcome to water in the service of cities.

[13] These are extracts taken from the account of the proceedings in N. J. Bradlee's *History of the Introduction of Pure Water into the City of Boston.*
[14] See Section 1-9.

Appendix

Table I-1   Abbreviations

The abbreviations common to this volume are shown in the following schedule. Unless noted, there is no differentiation between the singular and plural.

AC	alternating current	F	Froude number
AM	before noon	Fig.	figure
atm	atmosphere	Figs.	figures
ave	average	fpm	foot per minute
Btu	British thermal unit	fps	foot per second
C	Centigrade degrees	ft	foot
cc	cubic centimeter	FV	future value
cfm	cubic foot/minute	gal	gallon
cfs	cubic foot/second	gpad	gallon per acre daily
cgs	centimeter-gram-second	gpcd	gallon per capita daily
Chap.	chapter	gpd	gallon per day
Chaps.	chapters	gpm	gallon per minute
cm	centimeter	hp	horsepower
Col.	column	hr	hour
Cols.	columns	in.	inch
csm	cubic foot/(second)	kw	kilowatt
	(square mile)	l	liter
cu	cubic	lb	pound
deg	degree	MAF	mean annual flow
DC	direct current	m	meter
DWF	dry-weather flow	mg	million gallons
Eq.	equation		also milligram
Eqs.	equations	mgad	million gallons daily/acre
F	Fahrenheit degree	mgd	million gallons daily

1

min	minute	psi	pound/square inch
ml	milliliter	psia	pound/square inch,
mm	millimeter		absolute
mph	mile per hour	psig	pound/square inch, gage
No.	number	R	Reynolds number
OMR	operation, maintenance,	rpm	revolution per minute
	and replacement	sec	second
p.	page	Sec.	section
pp.	pages	Secs.	sections
PE	polyethylene	sq	square
PM	after noon	UK	United Kingdom (Britain)
PV	present value	US	United States
PVC	polyvinyl chloride	Vol.	volume
ppm	part per million	wt	weight
psf	pound/square foot	yd	yard

Table I-2   Weights and Measures

The American and English weights and measures referred to in this book are alike except for the gallon. The United States gallon is employed. The United States billion, which equals 1000 million, is also employed.

		Length		
Miles	Yards	Feet	Inches	Centimeters
1	1760	5280	. . .	. . .
. . .	1	3	36	91.44
. . .	. . .	1	12	30.48
. . .	. . .	. . .	1	2.540

1 m = 100 cm = 3.281 ft = 39.37 in.

		Area		
Square Miles	Acres	Square Feet	Square Inches	Square Centimeters
1	640	. . .	. . .	. . .
. . .	1	43,560	. . .	. . .
. . .	. . .	1	144	929.0
. . .	. . .	. . .	1	6.452

1 sq m = 10.76 sq ft

Table I-2. (continued)

Volume

Cubic Feet	Imperial Gallons	U.S Gallons	Cubic Inches	Liters
1	6.23	7.481	1728	28.32
...	1	1.2	277.4	4.536
...	...	1	231	3.785
...	...	...	57.75	0.946
...	...	...	61.02	1

1 cu m = 35.31 cu ft = 264.2 gal
1 Imperial (UK) gal weighs 10 lb   1 US gal weighs 8.34 lb
1 cu ft of water weighs 62.43 lb   1 cu m weighs 2283 lb
1 cu m = 10^3 l and weighs 1000 kg

Velocity

Miles per Hour	Feet per Second	Inches per Minute	Centimeters Second	Kilometers per Hour
1	1.467	1056	...	1.609
...	1	720	30.48	...
...	...	1	0.423	...

Time

Days	Hours	Minutes	Seconds
1	24	1440	86,400
...	1	60	3,600
...	...	1	60

Weight

Tons	Pounds	Grams	Grains	Metric Tons
1	2000	...	...	0.9078
...	1	454	7000	...
...	...	1	15.43	...

1 long ton = 2240 lb
1 ppm = 1 mg/1 = 8.34 lb per mg

Table I-2. (Continued)

Discharge

Cubic Feet per Second	Million Gallons Daily	Gallons per Minute
1	0.6463	448.8
1.547	1	694.4

1 in. per hour per acre = 1.008 cfs
1 cu m/sec = 22.83 mgd = 35.32 cfs

Pressure

Pounds per Square Inch	Feet of Water	Inches of Mercury
1	2.307	2.036
0.4335	1	0.8825
0.4912	1.133	1

1 atm = 14.70 psia = 29.92 in. Hg = 33.93 ft water = 76.0 cm Hg

Power

Kilowatts	Horsepower	Foot-Pounds per Second	Kilogram-Meters per Second
1	1.341	737.6	102.0
0.7457	1	550	76.04

Work and Energy

Kilowatt-Hours	Horsepower-Hours	British Thermal Units
1	1.341	3412
0.7457	1	2544

Temperature

$$\text{Degree Fahrenheit} = 32 + \frac{9}{5} \times \text{degrees Centigrade}$$

0	5	10	15	20	25	30	35	40	45	50	55	60	C
32	41	50	59	68	77	86	95	104	113	122	131	140	F

Table I-3   Viscosity and Density of Water

Calculated from *International Critical Tables*, 1928 and 1929

Tempera-ture, C	Density ρ, γ (grams/cm³), also s	Absolute Viscosity μ, centipoises*	Kinematic Viscosity ν, centistokes†	Tempera-ture, F
0	0.99987	1.7921	1.7923	32.0
2	0.99997	1.6740	1.6741	35.6
4	1.00000	1.5676	1.5676	39.2
6	0.99997	1.4726	1.4726	42.8
8	0.99988	1.3872	1.3874	46.4
10	0.99973	1.3097	1.3101	50.0
12	0.99952	1.2390	1.2396	53.6
14	0.99927	1.1748	1.1756	57.2
16	0.99897	1.1156	1.1168	60.8
18	0.99862	1.0603	1.0618	64.4
20	0.99823	1.0087	1.0105	68.0
22	0.99780	0.9608	0.9629	71.6
24	0.99733	0.9161	0.9186	75.2
26	0.99681	0.8746	0.8774	78.8
28	0.99626	0.8363	0.8394	82.4
30	0.99568	0.8004	0.8039	86.0

* 1 centipoise $= 10^{-2}$ (gram mass)/(cm)(sec). To convert to (lb force) (sec)/(sq ft) multiply centipoise by 2.088×10^{-5}.

† 1 centistoke $= 10^{-2}$ cm²/sec. To convert to (sq ft)/(sec) multiply centistoke by 1.075×10^{-5}.

1 gram/cm³ $= 62.43$ lb/cu ft.

Table I-4   Vapor Pressure of Water and Surface Tension of Water in Contact with Air

Temperature, C	0	5	10	15	20	25	30
Vapor pressure (p_w), mm Hg*	4.58	6.54	9.21	12.8	17.5	23.8	31.8
Surface tension (σ), dyne/cm†	75.6	74.9	74.2	73.5	72.8	72.0	71.2

* To convert to in. Hg divide by 25.4.

† To convert to (lb force)/ft divide by 14.9.

Table I-5   Values of the Exponential e^{-x} for x Ranging from 0.00 to 10.00

x	0	1	2	3	4	5	6	7	8	9
0.0	1.000	0.990	0.980	0.970	0.961	0.951	0.942	0.932	0.932	0.914
0.1	0.905	.896	.887	.878	.869	.861	.852	.844	.835	.827
0.2	.819	.811	.803	.794	.787	.779	.771	.763	.756	.748
0.3	.741	.733	.726	.719	.712	.705	.698	.691	.684	.677
0.4	.670	.664	.657	.651	.644	.638	.631	.625	.619	.613
0.5	.607	.600	.595	.589	.583	.577	.571	.566	.560	.554
0.6	.549	.543	.538	.533	.527	.522	.517	.512	.507	.502
0.7	.497	.492	.487	.482	.477	.472	.468	.463	.458	.454
0.8	.449	.445	.440	.436	.432	.427	.423	.419	.415	.411
0.9	.407	.403	.399	.395	.391	.387	.383	.379	.375	.372
1.0	.368	.364	.361	.357	.353	.350	.347	.343	.340	.336
1.1	.333	.330	.326	.323	.320	.317	.313	.310	.307	.304
1.2	.301	.298	.295	.292	.289	.287	.284	.281	.278	.275
1.3	.273	.270	.267	.264	.262	.259	.257	.254	.252	.249
1.4	.247	.244	.242	.239	.237	.235	.232	.230	.228	.225
1.5	.223	.221	.219	.217	.214	.212	.210	.208	.206	.204
1.6	.202	.200	.198	.196	.194	.192	.190	.188	.186	.185
1.7	.183	.181	.179	.177	.176	.173	.172	.170	.169	.167
1.8	.165	.164	.162	.160	.159	.157	.156	.154	.153	.151
1.9	.150	.148	.147	.145	.144	.142	.141	.139	.138	.137

x	e^{-x}	x	e^{-x}	x	e^{-x}	x	e^{-x}	x	e^{-x}
2.00	0.135	3.00	0.0498	4.00	0.0183	5.00	0.00674	6.0	0.00248
2.05	.129	3.05	.0474	4.05	.0174	5.05	.00641	6.2	.00203
2.10	.122	3.10	.0450	4.10	.0166	5.10	.00610	6.4	.00166
2.15	.116	3.15	.0429	4.15	.0158	5.15	.00580	6.6	.00136
2.20	.111	3.20	.0408	4.20	.0150	5.20	.00552	6.8	.00111
2.25	.105	3.25	.0388	4.25	.0143	5.25	.00525	7.0	.000912
2.30	.100	3.30	.0369	4.30	.0136	5.30	.00499	7.2	.000747
2.35	.0954	3.35	.0351	4.35	.0129	5.35	.00475	7.4	.000611
2.40	.0907	3.40	.0334	4.40	.0123	5.40	.00452	7.6	.000500
2.45	.0863	3.45	.0317	4.45	.0117	5.45	.00430	7.8	.000410
2.50	.0821	3.50	.0302	4.50	.0111	5.50	.00409	8.0	.000335
2.55	.0781	3.55	.0287	4.55	.0106	5.55	.00389	8.2	.000275
2.60	.0743	3.60	.0273	4.60	.0101	5.60	.00370	8.4	.000225
2.65	.0707	3.65	.0260	4.65	.00956	5.65	.00352	8.6	.000184
2.70	.0672	3.70	.0247	4.70	.00910	5.70	.00335	8.8	.000151
2.75	.0639	3.75	.0235	4.75	.00865	5.75	.00319	9.0	.000123
2.80	.0608	3.80	.0224	4.80	.00823	5.80	.00303	9.2	.000101
2.85	.0578	3.85	.0213	4.85	.00783	5.85	.00288	9.4	.000083
2.90	.0550	3.90	.0202	4.90	.00745	5.90	.00274	9.6	.000068
2.95	.0523	3.95	.0193	4.95	.00708	5.95	.00261	9.8	.000055
3.00	.0498	4.00	.0183	5.00	.00674	6.00	.00248	10.0	.000045

$e = 2.7183$; $\log e = 0.43429$; $\ln 10 = 2.30258$.
$\pi = 3.1415$; $\sqrt{\pi} = 1.7724$; $\sqrt{2\pi} = 2.5066$.

Table I-6 Areas under Normal Probability Curve

Fractional parts of the total area (1.0000) corresponding to distances between the mean (μ) and given values (x) in terms of the standard deviation (σ), i.e., $(x - \mu)/\sigma = t$

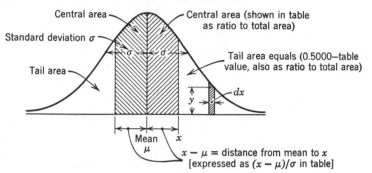

t	.00	.01	.02	.03	.04	.05	.06	.07	.08	.09
0.0	.0000	.0040	.0080	.0120	.0160	.0199	.0239	.0279	.0319	.0359
0.1	.0398	.0438	.0478	.0517	.0557	.0596	.0636	.0675	.0714	.0753
0.2	.0793	.0832	.0871	.0910	.0948	.0987	.1026	.1064	.1103	.1141
0.3	.1179	.1217	.1255	.1293	.1331	.1368	.1406	.1443	.1480	.1517
0.4	.1554	.1591	.1628	.1664	.1700	.1736	.1772	.1808	.1844	.1879
0.5	.1915	.1950	.1985	.2019	.2054	.2088	.2123	.2157	.2190	.2224
0.6	.2257	.2291	.2324	.2357	.2389	.2422	.2454	.2486	.2517	.2549
0.7	.2580	.2611	.2642	.2673	.2704	.2734	.2764	.2794	.2823	.2852
0.8	.2881	.2910	.2939	.2967	.2995	.3023	.3051	.3078	.3106	.3133
0.9	.3159	.3186	.3212	.3238	.3264	.3289	.3315	.3340	.3365	.3389
1.0	.3413	.3438	.3461	.3485	.3508	.3531	.3554	.3577	.3599	.3621
1.1	.3643	.3665	.3686	.3708	.3729	.3749	.3770	.3790	.3810	.3830
1.2	.3849	.3869	.3888	.3907	.3925	.3944	.3962	.3980	.3997	.4015
1.3	.4032	.4049	.4066	.4083	.4099	.4115	.4131	.4147	.4162	.4177
1.4	.4192	.4207	.4222	.4236	.4251	.4265	.4279	.4292	.4306	.4319
1.5	.4332	.4345	.4357	.4370	.4382	.4394	.4406	.4418	.4429	.4441
1.6	.4452	.4463	.4474	.4484	.4495	.4505	.4515	.4525	.4535	.4545
1.7	.4554	.4564	.4573	.4582	.4591	.4599	.4608	.4616	.4625	.4633
1.8	.4641	.4649	.4656	.4664	.4671	.4678	.4686	.4693	.4699	.4706
1.9	.4713	.4719	.4726	.4732	.4738	.4744	.4750	.4758	.4761	.4767
2.0	.4772	.4778	.4783	.4788	.4793	.4798	.4803	.4808	.4812	.4817
2.1	.4821	.4826	.4830	.4834	.4838	.4842	.4846	.4850	.4854	.4857
2.2	.4861	.4864	.4868	.4871	.4875	.4878	.4881	.4884	.4887	.4890
2.3	.4893	.4896	.4898	.4901	.4904	.4906	.4909	.4911	.4913	.4916
2.4	.4918	.4920	.4922	.4925	.4927	.4929	.4931	.4932	.4934	.4936
2.5	.4938	.4940	.4941	.4943	.4945	.4946	.4948	.4949	.4951	.4952
2.6	.4953	.4955	.4956	.4957	.4959	.4960	.4961	.4962	.4963	.4964
2.7	.4965	.4966	.4967	.4968	.4969	.4970	.4971	.4972	.4973	.4974
2.8	.4974	.4975	.4976	.4977	.4977	.4978	.4979	.4979	.4980	.4981
2.9	.4981	.4982	.4982	.4983	.4984	.4984	.4985	.4985	.4986	.4986
3.0	.4987	.4987	.4987	.4988	.4988	.4989	.4989	.4989	.4990	.4990
3.5	.499367			4.0 .499968		4.5 .499997			5.0 .4999997	

Example: For $x = 10.8$, $\mu = 9.0$, and $\sigma = 2.0$, $(x - \mu)/\sigma = 0.90$, and $0.3159 = 31.59\%$ of the area is included between $x = 10.8$ and $\mu = 9.0$.

Table I-7　Values of the Well Function $W(u)$ for Various Values of u
From U.S. Geological Survey Water Supply Paper 887

					u			
N	$N \times 10^{-15}$	$N \times 10^{-14}$	$N \times 10^{-13}$	$N \times 10^{-12}$	$N \times 10^{-11}$	$N \times 10^{-10}$	$N \times 10^{-9}$	$N \times 10^{-8}$
1.0	33.96	31.66	29.36	27.05	24.75	22.45	20.15	17.84
1.5	33.56	31.25	28.95	26.65	24.35	22.04	19.74	17.44
2.0	33.27	30.97	28.66	26.36	24.06	21.76	19.45	17.15
2.5	33.05	30.74	28.44	26.14	28.83	21.53	19.23	16.93
3.0	32.86	30.56	28.26	25.96	23.65	21.35	19.05	16.75
3.5	32.71	30.41	28.10	25.80	23.50	21.20	18.89	16.59
4.0	32.57	30.27	27.97	25.67	23.36	21.06	18.76	16.46
4.5	32.46	30.15	27.85	25.55	23.25	20.94	18.64	16.34
5.0	32.35	30.05	27.75	25.44	23.14	20.84	18.54	16.23
5.5	32.26	29.95	27.65	25.35	23.05	20.74	18.44	16.14
6.0	32.17	29.87	27.56	25.26	22.96	20.66	18.35	16.05
6.5	32.09	29.79	27.48	25.18	22.88	20.58	18.27	15.97
7.0	32.02	29.71	27.41	25.11	22.81	20.50	18.20	15.90
7.5	31.95	29.64	27.34	25.04	22.74	20.43	18.13	15.83
8.0	31.88	29.58	27.28	24.97	22.67	20.37	18.07	15.76
8.5	31.82	29.52	27.22	24.91	22.61	20.31	18.01	15.70
9.0	31.76	29.46	27.16	24.86	22.55	20.25	17.95	15.65
9.5	31.71	29.41	27.11	24.80	22.50	20.20	17.89	15.59

					u			
N	$N \times 10^{-7}$	$N \times 10^{-6}$	$N \times 10^{-5}$	$N \times 10^{-4}$	$N \times 10^{-3}$	$N \times 10^{-2}$	$N \times 10^{-1}$	N
1.0	15.54	13.24	10.94	8.633	6.332	4.038	1.823	2.194×10^{-1}
1.5	15.14	12.83	10.53	8.228	5.927	3.637	1.465	1.000×10^{-1}
2.0	14.85	12.55	10.24	7.940	5.639	3.355	1.223	4.890×10^{-2}
2.5	14.62	12.32	10.02	7.717	5.417	3.137	1.044	2.491×10^{-2}
3.0	14.44	12.14	9.837	7.535	5.235	2.959	0.9057	1.305×10^{-2}
3.5	14.29	11.99	9.683	7.381	5.081	2.810	0.7942	6.970×10^{-3}
4.0	14.15	11.85	9.550	7.247	4.948	2.681	0.7024	3.779×10^{-3}
4.5	14.04	11.73	9.432	7.130	4.831	2.568	0.6253	2.073×10^{-3}
5.0	13.93	11.63	9.326	7.024	4.726	2,468	0.5598	1.148×10^{-3}
5.5	13.84	11.53	9.231	6.929	4.631	2.378	0.5034	6.409×10^{-4}
6.0	13.75	11.45	9.144	6.842	4.545	2.295	0.4544	3.601×10^{-4}
6.5	13.67	11.37	9.064	6.762	4.465	2.220	0.4115	2.034×10^{-4}
7.0	13.60	11.29	8.990	6.688	4.392	2.151	0.3738	1.155×10^{-4}
7.5	13.53	11.22	8.921	6.619	4.323	2.087	0.3403	6.583×10^{-5}
8.0	13.46	11.16	8.856	6.555	4.259	2.027	0.3106	3.767×10^{-5}
8.5	13.40	11.10	8.796	6.494	4.199	1.971	0.2840	2.162×10^{-5}
9.0	13.34	11.04	8.739	6.437	4.142	1.919	0.2602	1.245×10^{-5}
9.5	13.29	10.99	8.685	6.383	4.089	1.870	0.2387	7.185×10^{-6}

Table I-8 Velocity and Discharge of Pipes When Frictional Resistance is 2 ft per 1000 (2‰)

$C = 100$ in Hazen-Williams Formula

Diameter, d, in.	Area, A, sq ft	Velocity, v, fps	Discharge Q, 1000 gpd
(1)	(2)	(3)	(4)
4	0.0873	0.96	54.3
5	0.137	1.11	97.5
6	0.196	1.24	157
8	0.349	1.49	336
10	0.546	1.71	602
12	0.785	1.92	971
14	1.07	2.12	1,380
16	1.40	2.29	2,080
18	1.77	2.48	2,830
20	2.18	2.64	3,760
24	3.14	2.97	6,060
30	4.91	3.42	10,800
36	7.07	3.83	17,500
42	9.62	4.32	26,200
48	12.57	4.60	37,300
54	15.90	4.93	50,900
60	19.64	5.29	67,200

Table I-9   Velocity and Rate of Discharge of Pipes Flowing Full for $\sqrt{S}/N = 1$ in Manning's Formula*

Diameter, D, in.	Area, A, sq ft	Velocity, V_0, fps	Discharge, Q_0, cfs	Reciprocal of Velocity, $1/V_0$
(1)	(2)	(3)	(4)	(5)
6	0.1963	0.3715	0.07293	2.6921
8	0.3491	0.4500	0.1571	2.2222
10	0.5455	0.5222	0.2848	1.9158
12	0.7852	0.5897	0.4632	1.6958
15	1.2272	0.6843	0.8398	1.4613
18	1.7671	0.7728	1.366	1.2940
21	2.4053	0.8564	2.060	1.1677
24	3.1416	0.9361	2.941	1.0683
27	3.9761	1.0116	4.026	0.9885
30	4.9087	1.0863	5.332	0.9206
36	7.0686	1.2267	8.671	0.8152
42	9.6211	1.3594	13.08	0.7356
48	12.5664	1.4860	18.67	0.6729
54	15.9043	1.6074	25.56	0.6221
60	19.6350	1.7244	33.86	0.5799

* To find V or Q for given values of S and N, multiply column (3) or (4) by $\sqrt{S}/N$.

To find S for given values of V or Q and N, multiply NV or NQ/A respectively by column (5) and square the product.

Bibliography

REFERENCE WORKS

Introductory

American Society of Civil Engineers, *Location of underground utilities*, Manual of Engineering Practice No. 14, New York, 1937.

Baker, M. N., *The quest for pure water*, American Water Works Association, New York, 1948.

Blake, N. M., *Water for the cities*, Syracuse University, Syracuse, N.Y., 1956.

Camp, T. R., *Water and its impurities*, Reinhold, New York, 1964.

Daley, Robert, *The world beneath the city*, J. B. Lippincott, Philadelphia, 1959.

Dieterich, B. H., and J. M. Henderson, *Urban water supply conditions and needs in seventy-five developing countries*, World Health Organization, Geneva, Switzerland, Public Health Papers No. 23, 1963.

Dunno, E. S., *Sir John Harrington's a new discourse of a stale subject, called the metamorphosis of Ajax*, Routledge & Kegan Paul, London, 1962.

Durfor, C. N., and Edith Becker, *Public water supplies of the hundred largest cities in the United States*, 1962. U.S. Geological Service, Water Supply Paper 1812, 1964.

Escritt, L. B., and S. F. Rich, *The work of the Sanitary engineer*, Macdonald & Evans, London, 1949.

Henderson, L. J., *The fitness of the environment*, Macmillan, New York, 1913; Paperback, Beacon, Boston, 1958.

Isaac, P. C. G., *Public health engineering*, E. & F. N. Spon, London, 1953.

Miller, A. P., *Water and man's health*, Agency for International Development, Washington, D.C., 1962.

Reynolds, Reginald, *Cleanliness and godliness*, George Allen & Unwin, London, 1943.

Sartwell, P. E., Maxcy-Rosenau, *Preventive medicine and public health*, 9th ed., Appleton-Century-Crofts, New York, 1965.

Whipple, G. C., *State sanitation*, 2 vols., Harvard University Press, Cambridge, Mass., 1917.

Wright, Lawrence, *Clean and decent*, Viking, New York, 1962.

Water Supply and Wastewater Removal

Fair, G. M., and J. C. Geyer, *Elements of water supply and wastewater disposal*, Wiley, New York, 1958.

Hardenbergh, W. A., and E. R. Rodie, *Water supply and waste disposal*, International Textbook, Scranton, Pa., 1961.

Phelps, E. B. (in collaboration with C. J. Velz), *Public health engineering*, Vol. 1, Part 2, Wiley, New York, 1948.

Steel, E. W., *Water Supply and sewerage*, 4th ed., McGraw-Hill, New York, 1960.

Water Supply

Babbitt, H. E., J. J. Doland, and J. C. Cleasby, *Water supply engineering*, 6th ed., McGraw-Hill, New York, 1962.

Skeat, W. O., ed., *Manual of British water engineering practice*, 3rd ed., Institution of Water Engineers, Heffer & Sons, Cambridge, England, 1961.

Turneaure, F. E., and H. L. Russell, *Public water supplies*, 4th ed., Wiley, New York, 1940.

Wastewater Removal

American Society of Civil Engineers and Water Pollution Control Federation, *Design and construction of sanitary and storm sewers*, Manual of Engineering Practice (ASCE) No. 37, New York, Manual of Practice (WPCF) No. 9, Washington, D.C. 1960.

Babbitt, H. E., and E. R. Baumann, *Sewerage and sewage treatment*, 8th ed., Wiley, New York, 1958.

Escritt, L. B., *Sewerage and sewage disposal*, Contractor's Record, London, 1956.

Metcalf, Leonard, and H. P. Eddy, *American sewerage practice*, Vol. I, *Design of sewers*, 2nd ed., McGraw-Hill, New York, 1928.

Pearson, E. A., ed. *Waste disposal in the marine environment*. Pergamon, New York, 1960.

Water Supply and Drainage of Buildings

American Society of Mechanical Engineers, *American standard plumbing code*, American Public Health Association and American Society of Mechanical Engineers, New York, 1955.

Babbitt, H. E., *Plumbing*, 2nd ed., McGraw-Hill, New York, 1950.

Day, L. J., *Standard plumbing details*, Wiley, New York, 1938.

Department of Commerce, *Uniform plumbing code*, Government Printing Office, Washington, D.C., 1949.

Hunter, R. B., *Methods for estimating loads in plumbing systems*, Government Printing Office, Washington, D.C., 1940; also *Water distribution systems for buildings*, 1951.

Manas, V. T., *National plumbing code, illustrated*, Manas, Washington, D.C., 1952.

McGuinness, W. J., Benjamin Stein, C. M. Gay, and Charles De van Fawcett, *Mechanical and electrical equipment for buildings*, 4th ed., Wiley, New York, 1964.

Plum, Svend, *Plumbing practice and design*, Wiley, New York, 1943.

Rural Water Supply and Wastewater Disposal

Ehlers, V. M., and E. W. Steel, *Municipal and rural sanitation*, 5th ed., McGraw-Hill, New York, 1958.

Salvato, J. A., Jr., *Enviromental sanitation*, Wiley, New York, 1958.

Wagner, E. G., and J. N. Lanoix, *Water Supply in rural areas and small communities*, World Health Organization, Geneva, Switzerland, 1958; also *Excreta disposal in rural areas and small communities*, World Health Organization, Geneva, Switzerland, 1959.

Wright, F. B., *Rural water supply and sanitation*, 2nd ed., Wiley, New York, 1956.

Water-Resource Management

Ackerman, E. A., and G. O. G. Löf, *Technology in American water development*, Johns Hopkins Press, Baltimore, 1959.

American Society of Civil Engineers, *Manual on groundwater basin management*, Manual of Engineering Practice No. 40, New York, 1961.

Bullinger, C. E., *Engineering economic analysis*, 3rd ed., McGraw-Hill, New York, 1958.

Eckstein, Otto, *Water resources development*, Harvard University Press, Cambridge, Mass., 1958.

Grant, E. L., and W. G. Ireson, *Principles of engineering economy*, 4th ed., Ronald, New York, 1960.

Hirshleifer, J. J., J. C. De Haven, and J. W. Millman, *Water supply—economics, technology*, and *policy*, University of Chicago Press, Chicago, 1960.

Kneese, A. V., *Water resource development and use*, Federal Reserve Bank of Kansas City, Mo., 1959.

Kneese, A. V., *The economics of regional water quality management*, Johns Hopkins Press, Baltimore, 1964.

Krutilla, J. V., and Otto Eckstein, *Multiple purpose river development*, Johns Hopkins Press, Baltimore, 1958.

Linsley R. K., and J. B. Franzini, *Water resource engineering*, McGraw-Hill, New York, 1964.

Maass, Arthur, M. M. Hufschmidt, Robert Dorfman, H. A. Thomas, Jr., S. A. Marglin, and G. M. Fair, *Design of water resource systems*, Harvard University Press, Cambridge, Mass., 1962.

McKean, R. N., *Efficiency in government through systems analysis: with emphasis on water resource development*, Wiley, New York, 1958.

University of Michigan Law School, *Water resources and the law*, Ann Arbor, Mich., 1958.

Woods, B. M., and E. P. DeGarmo, *Introduction to engineering economy*, 2nd ed., Macmillan, New York, 1953.

Information Analysis

Arden, Bruce, *An Introduction to digital computing*, Addison-Wesley, Reading, Mass., 1963.

Dixon, W. J., and F. J. Massey, Jr., *Introduction to statistical probability*, McGraw-Hill, New York, 1951.

Gale, David, *The theory of linear economic models*, McGraw-Hill, New York, 1960.

Gass, S. I., *Linear programming*, 2nd ed., McGraw-Hill, New York, 1964.

Goddard, L. S., *Mathematical techniques of operational research*, Pergamon, New York, 1963.

Hadley, G., *Linear programming*, Addison-Wesley, Reading, Mass., 1962; also *Nonlinear and dynamic programming*, 1964.

Hammig, R. W., *Numerical methods for scientists and engineers*, McGraw-Hill, New York, 1962.

Hoel, P. G., *Introduction to mathematical statistics*, 3rd ed., Wiley, New York, 1962.

Llewellyn, R. W., *Linear programming*, Rinehart & Winston, New York, 1964.

Machol, R. E., and Paul Gray, eds., *Recent developments in information and decision processes*, Macmillan, New York, 1960.

Ralston, Anthony, and H. S. Wiff, eds., *Mathematical methods for digital computers*, Wiley, New York, 1960.

Saaty, T. L., *Mathematical methods of operations research*, McGraw-Hill, New York, 1959.

Singer, James, *Elements of numerical analysis*, Academic Press, New York, 1964.

von Neumann, John, and Oskar Morgenstern, *Theory of games and economic behavior*, Princeton University Press, Princeton, N.J., 1953.

Hydrology

American Society of Civil Engineers, *Hydrology handbook*, Manual of Engineering Practice No. 28, New York, 1949.

Blair, T. A., *Weather elements*, Prentice-Hall, New York, 1946.

Butler, S. S., *Engineering hydrology*, Prentice-Hall, Englewood Cliffs, N.J., 1957.

Collins, R. E., *Flow of fluids through porous media*, Reinhold, New York, 1961.

Foster, E. E., *Rainfall and runoff*, Macmillan, New York, 1948.

Grover, N. C., and A. W. Harrington, *Stream flow*, Wiley, New York, 1943.

Harr, M. E., *Ground water and seepage*, McGraw-Hill, New York, 1962.

Hoyt, W. G., and W. B. Langbein, *Floods*, Princeton University Press, Princeton, N.J., 1955.

Johnstone, Don, and W. P. Cross, *Elements of applied hydrology*, Ronald, New York, 1949.

Langbein, W. B., and W. G. Hoyt, *Water facts for the nation's future*, Ronald, New York, 1959.

Linsley, R. K., M. A. Kohler, and J. L. H. Paulhus, *Applied hydrology*, McGraw-Hill, New York, 1949; also *Hydrology for engineers*, 1955.

Mead, D. W., *Hydrology*, 2nd ed., McGraw-Hill, New York, 1950.

Meinzer, O. E., *Hydrology*, McGraw-Hill, New York, 1942.

Moran, P. A. P., *The theory of storage*, Methuen, London, 1959.

Muskat, Morris, *Flow of homogeneous fluids through porous media*, McGraw-Hill, New York, 1937.

Thomas, H. E., *The conservation of ground water*, McGraw-Hill, New York, 1951.

Todd, D. K., *Ground water hydrology*, Wiley, New York, 1959.

Tolman, C. F., *Ground water*, McGraw-Hill, New York, 1937.

Trask, P. D., *Applied sedimentation*, Wiley, New York, 1950.

Wisler, C. O., and E. F. Brater, *Hydrology*, 2nd ed., Wiley, New York, 1959.

Hydraulics

Abbett, R. W., ed., *American civil engineering practice*, Vol. II, Wiley, New York, 1956.

American Society of Civil Engineers, *Nomenclature for hydraulics*, Manual and Report on Engineering Practice, No. 43, New York, 1962.

Chow, V. T., *Open channel hydraulics*, McGraw-Hill, New York, 1959.

Daugherty, R. L., and A. C. Ingersoll, *Fluid mechanics*, 5th ed., McGraw-Hill, New York, 1954.

Davis, C. V., ed., *Handbook of applied hydraulics*, 2nd ed., McGraw-Hill, New York, 1952.

King, H. W., and E. F. Brater, *Handbook of hydraulics*, 4th ed., McGraw-Hill, New York, 1954.

Pamakian, John, *Waterhammer analysis*, Prentice-Hall, Englewood Cliffs, N.J., 1955.

Rouse, Hunter, ed., *Engineering hydraulics*, Wiley, New York, 1950.

Rouse, Hunter, and Simon Ince, *History of hydraulics*, Iowa Institute of Hydraulic Research, Iowa City, Iowa, 1957.

Troskolanski, Adam T., *Hydrometry*, Pergamon, New York, 1960.

Vennard, J. K., *Elementary fluid mechanics*, 4th ed., Wiley, New York, 1961.

Woodard, S. M., and C. J. Posey, *Hydraulics of steady flow in open channels*, Wiley, New York, 1941.

Dams

Baver, L. D., *Soil physics*, 3rd ed., Wiley, New York, 1956.

British Standard Code Practice, *Site investigations*, British Standards Institution, London, 1957.

Bureau of Reclamation, *Design of small dams*, Government Printing Office, Washington, D.C., 1960.

Creager, W. P., J. D. Justin, and Julian Hinds, *Engineering for dams*, Wiley, New York, 1945.

Longwell, C. R., Adolph Knopf, and R. F. Flint, *Physical geology*, 3rd ed., Wiley, New York, 1960.

National Resources Committee, *Low dams*, Government Printing Office, Washington, D.C., 1939.

Sherard, J. L., R. J. Woodward, S. G. Gizienski, and W. A. Clevenger, *Earth and earth-rock dams*, Wiley, New York, 1963.

Terzaghi, Karl, and R. B. Peck, *Soil mechanics in engineering practice*, Wiley, New York, 1948.

Wegmann, Edward, *Design and construction of dams*, 8th ed., Wiley, New York, 1927.

Machinery

Addison, Herbert, *Centrifugal and other rotodynamic pumps*, Chapman & Hall, London, 1948.

Karassik, Igor, and Roy Carter, *Centrifugal pumps*, F. W. Dodge, New York, 1960.
Kristal, F. A., and F. A. Annett, *Pumps*, 2nd ed., McGraw-Hill, New York, 1953.
Stepanoff, A. J., *Centrifugal and axial flow pumps*, 2nd ed., Wiley, New York, 1957.

SERIAL PUBLICATIONS

Professional Societies
American Geophysical Union: *Transactions*, quarterly; *Water Resources Research*, quarterly; *Journal of Geophysical Research*, monthly.
American Society of Civil Engineers: *Transactions*, annual; *Proceedings*, quarterly, printed as Journals of the Divisions of the Society, e.g., *Sanitary Engineering, Hydraulics, Pipeline, Waterways and Harbors*, formerly monthly and as separates; *Civil Engineering*, monthly; *Manuals of Engineering Practice*.
American Water Works Association: *Journal*, monthly; *Manuals*; *Standards*.
American Water Resources Association: *Hydata, International Review of Periodical Contents*, monthly.
British Waterworks Association, London: *Journal*, several times a year.
Institution of Civil Engineers, London: *Proceedings*, monthly.
Institution of Public Health Engineers, London: *Journal*, several times a year.
Institution of Water Engineers, London: *Journal*, 6 to 8 times a year.
New England Water Works Association: *Journal*, quarterly.
Water Pollution Control Federation: *Journal* (formerly *Sewage and Industrial Wastes* and *Sewage Works Journal*), monthly; *Manuals of Practice*.

Governmental Agencies
U.S. Geological Survey: *Water Supply Papers*.
U.S. Public Health Service: *Public Health Engineering Abstracts*, monthly; *Bulletins*.
U.S. Weather Bureau: *Climatological Data*, monthly; *Monthly Weather Review*.

Magazines
Case-Sheppard-Mann Publishing Co., New York, *Wastes Engineering*, monthly; *Water Works Engineering*, monthly.
McGraw-Hill Publishing Co., New York: *Engineering News-Record*, weekly.
Public Works Journal Corp., Ridgewood N.J.: *Public Works*, monthly.
Scranton Publishing Co., Chicago: *Water and Sewage Works*, monthly.

Index

1